LEVINE'S GUIDE TO KNIVES AND THEIR VALUES

By Bernard Levine

DBI BOOKS, INC.

Editorial Staff

Managing Editor & Publisher
Sheldon L. Factor

Associate Editor
Harold A. Murtz

Editorial Assistant
Julia Roane

Cover Photography
John Hanusin

The Cover Knives

Illustrated on our cover is a representative sampling of collector knives. Clockwise from the left: Folding bowie knife with half-horse/half-alligator pommel, made by George Wostenholm & Sons before 1848 (Roger Baker collection); Randall Model 5 Camp and Trail with stag handle (Courtesy San Francisco Gun Exchange); California Highway Patrol limited edition Buck Model 110 Folding Hunter (Vern Taylor collection); Engraved Walker's Locker by Michael and Patricia Walker (Courtesy San Francisco Gun Exchange); Remington R1123 large trapper with bullet shield and non-standard (Rogers) bone stag handle (Roger Baker collection); and Ulster Knife Company swell-center hunting knife with picture handles showing Buffalo Bill Cody (Roger Baker collection).

Illustration Acknowledgements

Most of the line illustrations in this book are reproduced from old hardware and cutlery catalogs. A few of these catalogs are my own, but most of them were either loaned to me or reproduced by other writers, collectors, publishers, and knife dealers. Most old catalogs were never copyrighted, and for the few that were, the copyrights have expired. Therefore, all of these catalog illustrations are in the public domain. Other line illustrations are from old books and magazines, also now in the public domain. The author would like to express his gratitude to those individuals and organizations who made these line illustrations available for use in this book.

Bill Adams, Roger Baker, M. H. Cole, Robert Crandall, Dennis Ellingsen, Jim Emerson, Mrs. Dewey Ferguson, Theo Fisher, John Goins, Hugh Hayes, Tom Heitzman, N. H. Kamb, Bill Lung, Ernie Modlin, Gary Patterson, Harvey Platts, Houston Price, Cindy Rabb, A. G. Russell, Jim Sargent, George Sarris, John P. Schroll, Tom Sewell, Robert Soares, Rhett Stidham, Tracy Tudor, and Bruce Voyles. American Reprints, Baker Library (Harvard Business School), California Historical Society, Collector Books, Dover Books, Early American Industries Association, and J. B. Enterprises. Also, of course, the hardware and cutlery firms that originally published the catalogs.

PREFACE

This book will help you to identify just about every knife of any type that you have or may find. Equally important, this book will show you how to estimate the knife's current value in the collector market-place, step by step, just the way an appraiser would. The information is all here between these covers. All you need is the knife.

This book is designed to be as useful to the complete beginner as it will be to the experienced collector and dealer. It contains more information than any other knife book ever published, yet the information is easy to find and use. To use it you do not need to know a thing about pattern numbering codes or knife terminology. However, if you are interested, every cutlery name and term is explained.

This book has three sections. The first section, **Collecting Knives**, is a detailed introduction to knives and knife collecting. This is followed by the two main sections, **Folding Knives** and **Fixed Blade Knives**. The introduction to each of these sections includes simple instructions for its use. At the end of the book is a list of knife dealers who cater to collectors, and a handy recap of the method of estimating the value of a factory-made pocketknife.

I hope that you will enjoy reading this book, but even more I hope that you will *use* it. If I see you at a knife show and you have this book with you, and it is dog-eared and scuffed and full of notes and underlining, then I will be truly gratified.

Bernard Levine

EXPLANATION OF PRICES

All the prices of older knives listed in this book are ESTIMATES of fair market value at the time of publication. These estimates are based on my nearly 15 years of experience with collectible knives, supplemented by information from dealers and collectors around the country.

The prices of new knives shown here are retail prices suggested by the makers and manufacturers in their most recent catalogs and lists.

Please read the chapter on buying and selling knives for more information on price and value.

NONE OF THE PRICES IN THIS BOOK ARE OFFERS TO BUY OR TO SELL BY MYSELF OR BY ANYONE ELSE.

TABLE OF CONTENTS

III: FIXED BLADE KNIVES

IV: APPENDIX

I: COLLECTING KNIVES

Buying and Selling Knives

THE "TRUE" VALUE of a knife, if such a thing exists, is the actual amount of money paid for it by a knowledgeable buyer to a knowledgeable seller in an unpressured transaction. In the real world, these conditions are not always met, so knives often sell for either less or more than they are "worth."

Uninformed sellers often undervalue their knives, furnishing real bargains to the lucky collector. Just as often, of course, an uninformed (or misinformed) seller will overvalue his knives, perhaps tempting some unlucky beginning collector into a costly and discouraging error.

Sometimes a seller "needs the money," and must take less for a knife than he knows it is worth. Other times a buyer "has to have *that* knife," and will grudgingly pay more for it than he believes it is really worth. Then too, all or part of many knife transactions are trade or barter, allowing both parties greatly to overvalue their knives.

If you have a knife to sell or there is one that you are seeking to buy, how much it is "really" worth is *your* opinion. The prices in this book will help you to form your opinions, to become more knowledgeable as a buyer or seller. However, in the marketplace as in the voting booth, the final decisions are yours and yours alone.

For example, if I estimate that a knife is worth $100 and it is only worth $50 to you, then don't pay more than $50 for it. On the other hand, if you would happily pay $200 for it, then by all means do so, and don't worry about what I say. Just don't be surprised if no one is willing to pay you $250 (or even $150) for it later on.

Evaluating Factory-Made Folding Knives

In this book, the prices of most factory folding knives are presented in charts. The use of these charts is explained in the *Introduction to Standard American Folding Knife Patterns*. All fixed blade knives are priced individually.

The folding knife price charts present a great deal of information in a very compact and easy to use form. Just as important, they cover the widest possible variety of knives. Even if you should find a knife so odd that no one has seen one like it in a hundred years, the charts will give you an accurate idea of what it is worth. Also, if you find a popular brand knife such as a Case, a Remington, or a Winchester, you do not need to figure out its pattern number in order to look up its value, as you would with other knife books.

Evaluating Hand-Made and Custom Knives

The prices of hand-made and custom knives often fluctuate, usually upward. Most of the hand-made knives that are illustrated in this book were selected by the makers themselves to represent the types of work they prefer to do. The prices shown are usually the makers' current list prices.

Most knifemakers have waiting periods ranging from months to years. Knives the same as or similar to the ones shown can often be purchased without a wait, though at a higher price, from custom knife dealers such as those listed at the end of the book. Since the dealers themselves often pay list price to the makers for their knives, they must sell them for more to cover their overhead and make a profit. Many collectors are happy to pay a premium to get immediate delivery on hand-made knives that they want.

In addition to stocking current hand-made knives for immediate sale, dealers are almost the only source for hand-made knives by retired or deceased custom knifemakers. Dealers can also supply early or discontinued knives by currently active makers. They do this by buying knives or accepting consignments from collectors and estates. I have relied on recent dealer lists, and on the expertise of several collectors, to evaluate older custom knives of these types.

Buying Wisely

To buy wisely, you need only remember two principles:

First, select your knives based on your own taste and judgement, and buy only types or brands of knives that you really like. When you like a certain type of knife, you will develop a sense of its good and bad features. For example, if you collect timber scribers, you will soon learn what makes a good timber scriber, what brands are rare, and what are the signs of wear or poor construction. Unless you are willing to spend the time and take the financial risk of becoming a knife dealer, don't try to second-guess other collectors' tastes; stick to your own.

The second principle of buying wisely is to base the prices you pay on both condition and market. Don't pay high for knives in poor condition. On the other hand, do occasionally stretch your budget for a fine rare knife in pristine condition. Study ads, sale lists, knives for sale at shows, and the values in this book until you have a feel for current market prices. Refuse to pay much more than going prices. Also be wary of a knife for sale well below current market. Is it genuine or counterfeit? Is it original or reworked? What is the reputation of the seller?

Knife Show Etiquette

Knife shows and combined knife and gun shows are held all over the country throughout the year. Some are sponsored by commercial show promotion companies. A growing number is sponsored by local, regional, and national knife collecting organizations. For current listings, consult the show calendar section in *Knife World* magazine.

Knife shows are a lot of fun. They are best, however, when visitors follow a few basic rules of courtesy. These are:

- Do not handle knives without permission.
- Never touch the blade or the edge of any knife offered or displayed as a collector's item.
- Never open more than one blade of a folding knife at a time.
- Do not block a sale table if you are only "window shopping."
- If you have brought knives to trade or sell, obtain permission before displaying them at or in front of someone's table.
- Do not interrupt or comment on any transaction.

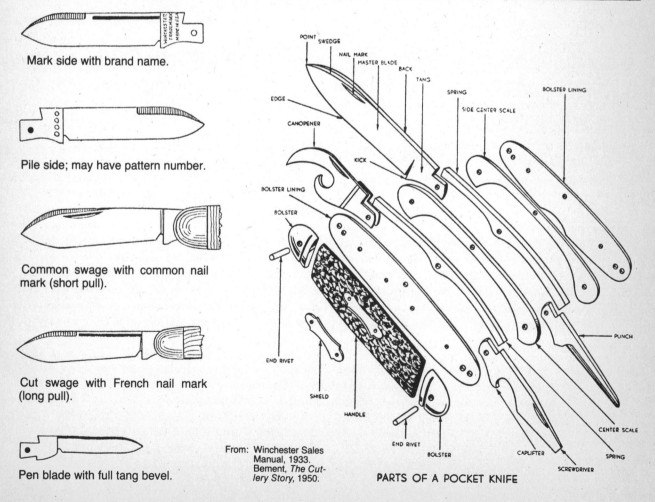

Mark side with brand name.

Pile side; may have pattern number.

Common swage with common nail mark (short pull).

Cut swage with French nail mark (long pull).

Pen blade with full tang bevel.

From: Winchester Sales Manual, 1933. Bement, *The Cutlery Story*, 1950.

PARTS OF A POCKET KNIFE

What Should You Collect?

AS I WAS compiling the chapters and tables for this book, I was struck by the incredible variety of interesting and potentially rewarding collecting specialties that knives offer. What's more, the whole field of knife collecting is still new enough that some of these specialties have not even been explored yet. In all but a few specialties, there is still relatively little competition. Therefore, there is no better time than the present for a collector to start.

In this chapter, I would like to give you a few suggestions about what sorts of knives you might consider collecting. Some people collect every knife that comes along. Many start this way until they discover which knives they really like.

However, this approach is both frustrating and, after a while, a real waste of money. I strongly recommend specializing early (while continuing to *look* at other knives). When and if your tastes change, it is much easier to sell or trade out of a relatively coherent collection (often all at once) than out of a helter-skelter accumulation.

Factory Knives: Areas to Collect

Specialties

Years ago, knife collectors chose their collecting specialties from among three basic areas: *brand, handle material,* and *pattern.* As collecting has developed, other areas have been opened up. These include: *function, geographical region, time period* (usually combined with a city, state, or region), *brand types* (such as wholesale and hardware brands), and knives by *one contract manufacturer,* regardless of brand.

All of these areas have potential for enjoyment, education, and eventual profit. Which area and specialty you select is up to you. No matter which you choose, and I cannot repeat this too often, always go for quality, condition, and authenticity. If there is any chance at all that you (or your children) will want to display or sell your collection, then the extra trouble and expense that got you the best in your field will be amply rewarded.

I will take each of the areas of knife collecting and list some of the possible fields within them. Let these ideas inspire you, but don't be limited by them. Trust your own taste and interests, but remember: stay with quality and condition.

Brands

The possibilities of collecting knives by brand are nearly unlimited. I list well over a thousand brands in this book, and I encounter new ones (new to me) nearly every week.

The reasons collectors chose to focus on particular brands are almost as varied as the brands themselves. The most common reason is that other collectors already collect that brand. Thus the popularity of Case, Remington, Winchester, Russell, Henckels, Keen Kutter, and a few others continues to grow. Collecting popular brands is fine if you don't mind lots of competition, high prices, and constant danger of counterfeits and re-worked knives.

Two other good (better, in my opinion) reasons for picking a brand are personal association and history. History is discussed in detail below. Personal association can mean something as simple as choosing a brand name the same as your own. In a few instances that I know of, the names are the same because granddad or great-granddad owned the knife company. Most of the time it is only coincidence, but it is still fun to find your name on a tang stamp.

Personal association can also mean picking a brand or brands made or marketed in your own town or state. If there aren't any, or any that appeal to you, how about your old home town, or a town that you like to visit?

Of course a little judgement is in order when making choices by name. Are knives with the ''right'' name of decent quality? Are they available, or are they scarce as hen's teeth? Do they already command big prices because of historical or other associations?

Personal association can even mean choosing knives of the same brand or the same pattern as your first very own knife. I used to be amazed at how many major collections got started just this way. Now I have almost come to expect it.

Types of Brand

In my brand listings there is a column headed "Type of Firm." If you are considering collecting knives by brand, pay attention to this column. There are several different types of brand, and the type often has an important influence on the value and desirability of a knife. Under "Type of Firm," here are the basic possibilities to be aware of:

Manufacturers' Brands

First, of course, is manufacturers' brands. These range from giant firms such as Henckels or Landers Frary & Clark that had thousands of employees, down to one-man operations such as Ostwald or Dooley. Knives from one-man shops are a lot rarer than knives from the big firms. In fact they are so rare that there is not much demand for them, so most are not especially valuable. They are interesting curiosities, however.

Some of the big cutlery manufacturers, besides selling knives under their own name and making contract knives for other companies, also marketed knives under alternate or secondary brands. These knives were usually of lesser quality than the firm's first line "name" brand.

Let me emphasize that most secondary brands were *not* manufacturing "seconds." They were just made plainer and simpler to sell at a lower price. Camillus would probably win the prize for the largest number of secondary brands (in the 1930s and 1940s), and no Camillus collection would be complete without examples of each of them.

Contract Brands

I have seen more than one collector disappointed after collecting a brand for a while, and then learning that the company in question never made a single knife. All their knives were "contract knives," made by a variety of big manufacturers.

There is nothing actually *wrong* with contract knives. Still, if you are interested in knives *made* in a certain place, specializing in a contract brand is not for you. Also, except in a few cases, a knife with a private or contract brand is worth less than an identical knife with the manufacturer's own brand.

On the other hand, if you are interested in a firm such as Schrade or Camillus that has done a lot of contract manufacturing (Camillus still does a lot), then it is fun to try and identify contract knives that "your" manufacturer made. The question of "who made what for whom?" intrigues many collectors, and can lead to endless debates and *tours de force* of detective work.

There is plenty still to be learned in this area. I had believed for years that Winchester was a contract brand. I now know that Winchester made most of their own knives, moving the equipment from Napanoch and Eagle (1919) and Walden Knife Co. (1923) to the Winchester plant in New Haven. I still wonder about their cheap "assortment knives" from the 1930s, though.

Here are the different types of contract brands:

Wholesalers' Brands

Wholesalers' contract brands break down naturally into two groups. First there are the cutlery wholesale brands. Cutlery wholesalers and importers, most based in New York City, distributed knives nationwide, sometimes even continent- or worldwide. They sold knives to retail stores, to advertisers, and even to regional hardware wholesalers.

The second group is regional hardware wholesale brands.

 J. A. HENCKELS TWIN BRAND CUTLERY

CORPORATE NEVA AND EXPRESS MARKS.

JOHN CLARKE & SON, LTD.,
SHEFFIELD, :: ENGLAND.
—— Incorporating the firms of ——
WILLIAM RODGERS AND JOHN HOLMES & CO.

Corporate Mark.
I CUT MY WAY
WILLIAM RODGERS
SHEFFIELD.

CATTARAUGUS CUTLERY CO. LITTLE VALLEY. N.Y. U.S.A.

These brands usually show a highly local flavor, both in trade names and in choice of patterns.

Wholesale hardware firms, up until less than a generation ago, mostly covered limited areas of a hundred miles radius or less. Competition between them was intense, as was competition among manufacturers to make their private branded knives. A few hardware firms covered broader regions, or even went nationwide.

Just a handful of these wholesale hardware firms still survives. None of them, to the best of my knowledge, still sells privately branded knives.

Retailers' Brands

Next we come to retailer brands. Not too many retailers are now big enough to come up with the minimum orders for privately branded knives.

In the old days, when 10 dozen of a pattern was sufficient, many cutlery and sporting goods stores carried private branded knives. Today, when 10,000 is a more typical minimum, only the big catalog outfits can stay in the game.

Some retailer brands such as Will & Finck (who made bowies and carvers but no pocketknives) and Abercrombie & Fitch have as much collector appeal as any maker's mark. I have yet to see a collection of knives marked for famous sporting goods houses, but this would certainly be an interesting area to pursue.

WILL & FINCK,
769 Market,
Have the Largest
CUTLERY MANUFACTORY
On the Pacific Coast.

English, French, German and American Cutlery always on hand. Razors and Shears ground, and Cutlery of every description made to order at short notice.

Advertiser's Brands

The final type of knife branding has already attracted a lot of collector interest, though information on this area is in short supply. This is privately branded advertising knives.

These knives were made for advertisers who did not care to have their message diluted by someone else's brand name stamped on the tang of their giveaway knives. Most advertising knives are tang-stamped with the name of the manufacturer or wholesaler (or ad specialty house) from which they were ordered. These others, with such tang stampings as Coca Cola or Anheuser Busch, are rare and command good prices. Many have also been counterfeited, so do be careful.

Handle Material

The possibilities of specializing in particular handle materials are so self-evident, that I do not need to discuss them in detail. The current favorites are mother-of-pearl and genuine stag. Almost as popular are ''bone stag'' (jigged and dyed bone) and fancy colored celluloid.

One interesting area that seems to have been neglected is decorated metal handles, and you might want to look into this. Both the Swedes and the Germans did some remarkable things with selective etching, electroplating, and enameling.

No. 7192—Swedish Etching on Nickel Silver Handle, Full Crocus Polished Blades.

Advertising knives might be considered a handle specialty, though in a sense they have a special ''function''— advertising. In any case, advertising knives are very popular, particularly fancy ones whose handles were made with special dies, and also knives advertising well-known national brands.

Knives carrying advertising for local or regional firms do not generally command high prices. They can nonetheless form an interesting collection.

Patterns

The variety of knife patterns made over the years sometimes can seem endless. Every pattern can be a collecting specialty, and quite a few of them already are. Throughout the pattern chapters, I mention those patterns which are currently popular.

Of course there is no rule that says you must collect just one pattern. It can make a lot of sense to collect functionally related patterns, such as cattle knives and premium stock knives, or boys' knives and barlows. It also can make sense to collect physically related patterns, such as the crown, the congress, and the swayback. The relationships among patterns are made clear in the text.

It can even make sense to collect several unrelated patterns, such as gunstocks, canoes, and eurekas. You could do this simply because you like them all, or because each of them is so rare that examples of any one of them do not turn up often enough to satisfy your acquisitive urge.

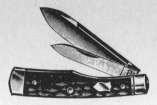

No. 2693
Gunstock pattern, 3 inches long; 2 blades;
brass lined; nickel silver bolsters, caps and
shield; cleaned inside; large blade crocus
polished on one side; Bone Stag handle.

Don't forget that you are free to combine specialties any way you like. You could, for example, assemble four collections: Schrades, multi-colored celluloid handles, swell-end jacks, and harness knives. Then again, you could limit yourself to Schrade swell-end jack harness knives with multi-colored handles, and hardly ever have occasion to buy a knife.

There is another way to approach pattern collecting. Instead of specializing in one or a few patterns, it might be interesting to collect one knife of every standard pattern. To be even more diverse, each of these knives might be of a different brand and, of course, every handle material should be represented. Needless to say, all of these knives should be in excellent-to-mint condition.

I have yet to see a collection organized this way, though I would like to. If you have a lot of money and not much time, you could just about complete such a collection in one visit to a major knife show. Building a display for it, with each knife identified, would, of course, take a little bit longer.

History

Collecting knives as history is closest to my own heart. There are two basic ways to go about this.

The most popular (and the most risky) is collecting knives that reflect the "big picture," as it used to be called. Thus the popularity of bowie knives, military knives, Indian trade knives, and presentation knives. The Chinese have a curse: "May you live in interesting times!" These are the knives made and used in "interesting" times.

Historical knives are popular and expensive, just as all fine historical artifacts are. They are risky because, being valuable, they are often counterfeited. If you want to get involved with these sorts of knives, you had better have deep pockets and a lot of time to study and develop your judgment.

The other historical approach, and my own favorite, is to collect knives that reflect the history of knives. Huh? Don't all knives reflect the history of knives? Sure, but some do more than others.

You can focus on company history, such as by collecting knives by the earliest American manufacturers. You can limit yourself to pocketknives, or choose other types as well, or instead.

You can focus on technical history by collecting "firsts": the first picture-handled knives, the first all-steel dinner knives, the first closed-back pocketknives. Choose whatever appeals to you.

Instead of technical history, you can focus on cultural history by collecting brands and styles known to have been used in particular places and times. Not just the "interesting" places and times, either, and not just weapons. An 1840s American bowie knife will cost as much as a car, but a carving set or a pen knife from that period will not cost much more than a new knife.

These historical specialties require more study and patience than most of the others. However, because they generally lead you into little-known areas, areas that are not (yet) widely collected, they tend to be easy on the pocketbook.

Let me add that once you are willing to consider the "little picture," you need not limit yourself to the history just of knives. You can collect knives that reflect the history of a trade or profession: medical or veterinary knives, office knives, trapper's knives, farmer's or rancher's knives, automobilist's knives, or anything else you can think of. Believe me, once you get into the spirit of the hobby, the hard part is not deciding what to collect, it is deciding what *not* to collect.

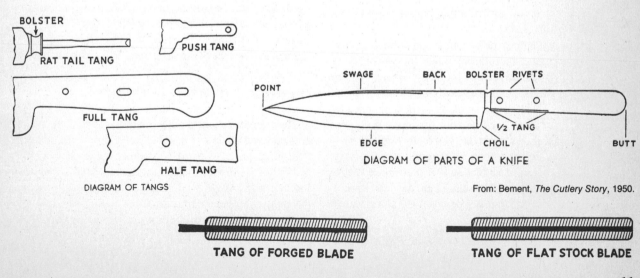

BOLSTER

RAT TAIL TANG

PUSH TANG

FULL TANG

HALF TANG

DIAGRAM OF TANGS

POINT

SWAGE   BACK   BOLSTER RIVETS

EDGE   CHOIL   ½ TANG   BUTT

DIAGRAM OF PARTS OF A KNIFE

From: Bement, *The Cutlery Story*, 1950.

TANG OF FORGED BLADE

TANG OF FLAT STOCK BLADE

New Factory Knives

Don't let all this talk about history put you off if what interests you is new knives. I have a lot of new factory knives around the house, mainly because I know so many people in the knife business. Most of these new knives are very nice indeed.

I wrote an article for *Knives '83* in which I compared the motives for collecting old versus new knives. Here is part of what I said:

"With new knives, just about the only limiting factor on a collection is budget. Almost any new knife, except the most limited or exotic, can be had by anyone any time he comes up with the going price.

"If you collect new knives and you have a budget and you have a collecting goal such as 'all of a current brand' . . . you can predict down to day and date just when your collection will be complete. . . . If you like to go out every payday and buy a knife for your collection, old knives are not for you. . . . ."

Another critical factor is time. Collecting old knives can require a lot of time spent scrounging and visiting shows. With new knives, one cooperative local retailer who accepts special orders, or else a handful of mail order catalogs [see the list of dealers at the back of the book], can let you do an awful lot of collecting in just an hour or two per month.

Let me offer one warning about collecting new factory knives. The manufacturers and dealers may hate me for saying this, but I doubt that any of them will stand up and argue the point. In my opinion, at the present time, there is little potential for profit in collecting new regular production factory-made knives.

Of course, there is no *guarantee* of profit in any branch of knife collecting, or any other type of collecting for that matter. However, antique factory knives, modern hand-made knives, and better quality limited edition knives, if collected intelligently, do offer a good *chance* of eventual profit. I have more to say below on collecting both hand-made and limited edition knives.

Of course, collecting new regular production factory knives is not nearly as unpromising financially as collecting, say, new postage stamps, where you are guaranteed to lose money every time the postage rates go up. However, if you buy single knives at retail, the *resale* value of your collection probably will not even keep up with inflation. If you buy cartons of knives at wholesale, are you really a collector?

Of course people will continue to collect new postage stamps and continue to collect new regular issue factory knives. As long as they enjoy themselves, they are certainly getting their money's worth. Besides, you might just want to bet that my crystal ball is wrong.

Hand-Made and Custom Knives: Areas to Collect

To many collectors, modern hand-made knives are the most exciting area of knife collecting. There are now hundreds of makers across the country and around the world. Each of them tries each day to exact something new and special from his tools, his materials, his hands, and his mind.

In the realm of the art knife, a small but growing band of artists and craftsmen is pushing back the limits of the possible to create some of the most beautiful knives the world has ever seen. Collectors scramble to acquire these knives, sometimes ordering them years in advance, other times bidding staggering sums to acquire rare or unique masterpieces.

In collecting hand-made knives, the advantages of specializing are as great as in factory knives. Most collectors of hand-made knives still favor fixed blades, but more collectors and more makers are turning to folders. Many collectors favor one or a select handful of makers. A few like knives made in one state. Others prefer to collect by pattern or style.

Custom-Made Knives

Hand-made knives can have a special appeal, as well. In this area alone can you get *exactly* what you want in the way of a knife.

Would you like a folding knife that is custom fitted to your hand, one with, say, a drop-point hollow ground stellite blade, a concealed lock that works with one hand, checkered rosewood handles, and a picture of your favorite dog engraved on the front bolster? Quite a few of the makers whose work is shown in this book will undertake to make something this special for you. It won't be cheap, but it will be as near to perfect as a knife can be.

For the addresses of the makers, check the latest *Knives* annual, edited by Ken Warner for DBI Books, or the Knifemakers Guild Directory, edited by Bruce Voyles for *Blade* magazine. Also check the ads in the current knife magazines.

On the Cutting Edge: Fixed Blades

There are three outstanding trends to watch in the realm of custom fixed blade knives. One is modern interpretations of traditional designs, such as left-hand daggers, bowie knives, and tantos. A few of the damascus bladesmiths are making Indo-Persian and Oriental-style knives that rival the work of the greatest masters of the past. Some of the finest knifemaking being done today is in this area.

The second area is fantasy knives and swords. Fantasy knives are as fantastic as the maker or customer wants them to be. If you can imagine it, chances are there is a maker who can build it for you.

The third area is combat and survival knives. Some fine work is being done in this area, though most of it simply rings the changes on a few very solid designs.

On the Cutting Edge: Folders

In the realm of custom folders, I see two "hot" areas. There is a lot less physical variety of shape and size in custom folders than there is in fixed blades. The areas here to watch are locking mechanisms and damascus.

At every knife show I visit, I see new locking mechanisms for folders. Some are a little silly, and others are very slick indeed. I know one collector who has made a specialty of the slick ones.

Because folders are relatively small, they pose a nifty challenge for the damascus bladesmith to keep the texture of his metal in scale with his knife. Also, because a folder has lots of metal parts besides the blade—spring, liners, bolsters, shield, pins—there are a lot of chances for the makers to combine different colors and textures of metal.

Miniatures

Miniature knives can be fixed blade or folding. Most hand-made miniatures are fixed blades. Some custom makers can be persuaded to make miniatures of their regular knives and a few makers specialize in miniature versions of other people's designs.

Miniatures as a rule are modestly priced, at least in comparison to full-sized knives of the same quality. They also don't take up much space. I think they are a lot of fun.

Brochures

Most knifemakers offer a printed brochure. Those who belong to the Knifemakers Guild are required to do so. Some collectors who do not have a whole lot of money to spend on knives also (or instead) collect these brochures. In fact, so many people who never buy knives now collect brochures that makers have been compelled to charge up to several dollars a copy, especially for the costly full-color productions some makers now favor. I believe that makers are entirely justified in charging enough for their brochures to make a profit on them.

Brochures are nonetheless a very inexpensive way to get to look at a lot of fine knives. The better quality brochures might even increase in value as the years go by.

Commemorative and Limited Edition Knives

Commemorative Knives

Commemorative knives were inspired by the popularity of commemorative stamps and coins. They are knives with inscriptions on handle or blade that commemorate a birth or an event. Most were made in the last 15 years, but I have seen a few older ones, such as the Henckels 200th anniversary knife from 1931.

Unlike souvenir knives [see the *Advertising Knives* chapter], commemorative knives are usually dated and made for a limited time in a limited quantity. Sometimes they are even serial numbered. Often, commemorative knives are standard patterns that are dressed up with non-standard handle materials, shields, or blade etching. Rarely they are specially designed patterns.

Limited Edition Knives

Limited edition knives are, in effect, commemorative knives that do not commemorate anything in particular. I guess you could say that they commemorate the fact that someone wanted to make a special knife in limited numbers. Some brands of limited edition knives are bench-made, but most are factory-made.

An increasingly popular class of limited edition knives is annual club knives issued by local and national knife collecting organizations. Most local club knives are very limited in quantity. Often they are sold only to club members, though all clubs allow you to join and purchase knives by mail. An up-to-date list of knife clubs is published every month in *Knife World* magazine.

Why There Are Limited Edition Knives

Because of their special features and limited numbers, commemorative and limited edition knives when new sell for more money than similar plain knives. To be precise, commemorative and limited edition knives are given special features *in order that* they may be sold for a higher price.

While occasionally an element of sentiment may help to inspire the issuing of a commemorative knife, the main reason they and limited edition knives are made is for profit. Even club knives are made to help improve the clubs' treasuries, though they also allow club members to have "something special."

Similarly, though some collectors buy these knives simply because they like them, most who purchase them do so in hope of future profit. With the supply of each issue fixed and the hobby of knife collecting growing, increased demand should, in theory, lead to increasing prices. Often this has indeed proved true.

Making a Profit

There is no direct route to profit in buying and selling commemorative and limited edition knives. However, there are a few rules you can follow that should improve your chances of making money. Most of these rules apply equally well to buying any type of knife as an "investment."

The first rule is so obvious that most people forget it. This is that the profit, if any, comes in *selling*. A knife is not a productive asset like a machine or a share in a business. It yields no return except capital gain, and that gain cannot be realized except by selling the knife.

Let's say the "value" of your knife has doubled in 3 years. So what? Where do you propose to sell it to realize this increase? At a show? Through an ad? Have you figured how much these *cost*?

Perhaps you can sell it to a dealer. Of course, he will want some or all of the increase for himself.

Obviously, it is possible to sell collectible knives at a profit, but you had better plan your method and figure in your overhead before you start spending money.

One good way to limit your selling overhead is to spread it out over many knives. If you are buying for future profit and you think you have picked a winner, why buy just one? Buy all you can get your hands on (if you can only *afford* just one, put your money in the bank). Talk to the issuer and see if you can buy a quantity at a discount. (Catch 22: If he says yes, it may mean the issue is a dud. You have to use your judgement.)

Another important rule is to look at the knife, not just the advertising. Is it made by a well-known firm? Is it at least as well finished as a comparably priced plain knife? Are the inscriptions and serial numbers neatly and *permanently* affixed to the knife, not just printed on the box or on a slip of paper?

Is there a box, and is it of appropriate quality? I would rather have no box than a flimsy box that will not stand up to any handling. A knife that was issued with a box is always worth much less if the box is missing or damaged.

Besides looking at the knife, look at the edition as a whole. Just how limited is it? You would be surprised how many are "limited" to as many as the issuer can sell.

Be skeptical of any quantity much over 2,500. When you go to sell your knives, you want to be fairly confident that there will not be lots of others on the market at the same time.

"Collectible" Knives

In the last decade or so, a lot of pocketknives have come on the market which, though in "unlimited" editions, are nonetheless aimed mainly at the collector market. Such "collectible" knives most often have impressive "list" prices, but if you check mail order catalogs and ads you will find them offered regularly at a 50 per cent or greater discount in "wholesale" quantities of three, or sometimes even one.

These collectible knives are sometimes favored by the good-old-boy courthouse traders. Those are the fellows who used to entertain themselves by swapping old pocketknives back and forth, until us covetous collectors bought up all their good ones at suitably inflated prices. Rather than trading old junkers (they save those to sell to gullible new collectors), the courthouse traders now swap new knives.

Knife manufacturers and importers today are highly conscious both of the popularity of knife collecting and also of their own history. They vie with each other to create new and different (and sometimes absurd) patterns. Most of these are aimed at the collector and trader markets. The makers also ring endless (and again sometimes absurd) changes on the more popular traditional patterns.

> " *a few of the innovations are genuine improvements* "

The marketplace consigns many of these innovations to the obscurity they deserve. This has ever been the fate of odd innovations in the cutlery field. Still, a few of the innovations are genuine improvements and will be with us for a long time.

I have found that the only sure way to keep up with the latest twists in folding knives is to obtain or look at each manufacturer's or importer's catalog as soon as it is published. If something new appeals to you, buy it right away. Chances are that it will no longer be available 6 months or a year from now. In any case, current catalogs are the surest guide to the current prices of regular issue current knives.

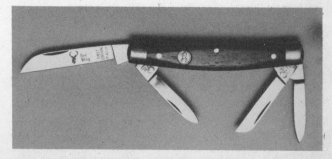

Red Stag limited edition congress knife with red bone handles. **$27.50–40,** according to serial number.

Collecting Knives to Use

Here are two similar questions with two very different answers. How many knife collectors are there in this country? How many people in this country collect knives?

A reasonable estimate of how many knife collectors there are in the United States right now would be around 50,000 to 100,000. As to how many Americans collect knives, a reasonable estimate would be about 200 million—in other words just about every adult man and woman in the nation, with a fair number of kids thrown in for good measure.

Of course, most of these 200-million Americans collect knives only to use. At least that is what they say. The fact is that many of them also have a few knives that they bought because the knives looked neat, and maybe some day they would use them.

I travel a lot. When I sit next to someone on an airplane, I usually introduce myself. As soon as I say that I write about knives, I brace myself. For the next 5 minutes, at least, my neighbor is sure to tell me all about his or her knives. I wonder what happens to people who write about sex? Maybe that's how they get their material.

The first serious knife collectors that I met, and by serious I mean that they spent a fair amount of their leisure time looking for knives to add to their collections, were people who collect knives to use. The majority of these people are cooks, amateur and professional, men and women; many are whittlers and wood carvers; others are hunters, fishermen, butchers, or gardeners.

These collectors are so diverse in background and interests that it is risky to generalize about them. Most are interested first and foremost in quality, but a few of them have picked up some truly odd notions of how to recognize it. I learned early on not to argue about this. Most knives work adequately, and people defend their ideas about knives just as fervently as they do their ideas about guns, cars, love, and religion.

Next to quality, these practical collectors are concerned with functional design. They have learned what types of knives work best for them, but they always have an eye out for something a little better.

Most of these collectors have one or a few favorite brands. Some are curious and try any brand that looks good. A hard-headed minority steadfastly ignores any writing on their blades.

Ten or 15 years ago, few of these collectors had any sense of the history of their knives. More recently, as more knife books and magazines have come on the market, this has begun to change.

If you collect knives to use, you probably do not need much advice from me. However, since advice is my job, I will offer some anyway.

When you buy an old knife that appears unused, look up its value in this book *before* you sharpen it and use it. If it proves to be relatively valuable, you must decide if you want

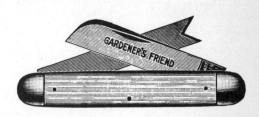

to destroy up to half of that value by sharpening it. Perhaps having this knife to use will be worth it to you, but at least you will find out before it is too late. See the chapter on *Grading the Condition of a Knife* for information on how to tell if an old knife is really unused.

MARBLE'S EXPERT KNIFE

These knives were particularly designed to meet the requirements of the professional hunter, trapper and guide who requires a thin keen edge for dressing skins and furs. The back of the blade is designed for scraping skins while on the forms. Has leather handle, aluminum tip. Length of blade 5 inches, weight 3½ ounces.

If you are one of the noble fellowship of knife fanciers, you are in good company. People aware of the myriad possibilities in the world of knives are most often also aware of the countless other wonders the world has to offer. I believe with Socrates that "the unexamined life is not worth living." The knife is the most basic of our tools. If you do not know your knives, you cannot claim to know your world.

of-a-kind handmade knives. Another is advertising value, such as when a visitor to your display says, ''I've got a knife sort of like that one at home, only the handle is a different color. Would you like to have it?''

Planning Ahead

A well planned and well displayed collection offers immediate personal satisfaction and, if you ever decide to sell it, a good chance of eventual profit. Just as important to many individuals, a noteworthy collection can be a direct source of personal prestige.

Knife journalists and other collectors often mention outstanding collections in conversation and in print. Much of my knife education has come from studying people's collections. If you have ever wanted to ''make a name for yourself,'' building an interesting and informative knife collection would be a practical way to go about it.

A collector who builds an organized and well documented collection may eventually find a permanent home for it in a museum. There the collection will bear his name for generations to come. Of course, museums rarely *buy* collections, so you may have to choose between prestige and profit. Gifts to most museums are tax deductible, though, and this fact may prove advantageous to you.

Building and Displaying Your Collection

DO YOU have tens of thousands of dollars to play with? Are you willing to go head to head with some very competitive and long-established collectors? If you do, you can enter absolutely any area of knife collecting you choose.

However, no matter how deep your pockets and aggressive your fighting instincts, if you want to put together an outstanding collection of such popular items as American bowie knives, Remington pocketknives, or Warenski or Frank art knives, you would still need a lot of time and patience. Not only have the established big-league collectors scooped up the best examples on the market, they have earned the first shot at most of the new ones that are found or made.

If you do have the money and the drive, don't let my warning discourage you. Decide what you want and show the dealers or makers that you are serious (and appreciative). Courtesy, sincerity, and prompt payment without haggling will soon confirm your place in the big league, and your name will move up quickly on their lists.

At the other extreme, a collecting budget of as little as $10 or $20 a week can in a few years be parlayed into a pre-eminent collection of any of several hundred less popular types or brands of good quality or historically interesting knives. What it takes instead of a lot of money is a lot of time, patience, study, and effort. A little bit of advantageous trading and resale do not hurt, either, though this can involve extra time and risk.

Big league or little, as your collection grows, your knowledge of your chosen area or areas will grow, too. You should start to seek ''go-withs'' for your knives: ads, catalogs, original packaging and store displays, photos of knives being made or in use. Before long, you will have enough knives and related material to put together a display that you can set up in your home, exhibit at knife shows, or loan to local banks or museums.

A good display is not cheap to build, but it can pay for itself in the satisfaction of enjoying your collection as a complete entity. There are also some nifty fringe benefits to displaying your collection at shows. One is the chance of winning awards, such as trophies, expense-paid trips, or one-

Don Peters and his collection of Remington Scout knives. Courtesy *Knife World*.

Display

It is a fact much bemoaned, but a fact nonetheless, that the flashiest displays at knife shows are the displays that win the awards. Your collection may be the most interesting or the most valuable at the show, but if it does not attract attention by its presentation and then hold attention by its organization, hardly anyone will ever know.

Think about the theme of your collection. That theme should be evident half way across the room. One prize-winning collection of custom knives made in California is displayed on a large wooden map of the state. Another collection of barbershop cutlery is displayed in a replica old-time barber shop. A large magnificent wood carving would make a fine centerpiece for a collection of whittlers.

Think also about the organization of your collection. Your display should be arranged to make that organization clear to the viewer. A recent first-prize display of custom knives relied on clearly labeled and dramatically lit thematic groupings to enchant visitors and judges alike. If you collect a single brand, try to show its evolution and diversity.

Just as there is no "right" kind of knife to collect, there is no "right" way to display your collection. Here are some good rules to follow, no matter what kind of display you are planning.

Make sure your knives are securely affixed to the display, but be careful not to damage them when mounting or removing them. Display valuable or fragile knives behind glass. Thieves are a problem, and so are fingerprints, which can leave permanent stains. Do not expose your display to direct sunlight. Do not store or display your knives in leather sheaths—acid in the leather can corrode the blade and fittings.

Design your display in interchangeable modules. This has two benefits. First, it makes it easy to set up, take down, ship, and store your display, without having to take it completely apart. Second, as your collection grows and changes, you can add or modify one or several modules without having to redesign and rebuild the entire display. Be sure the leave room in your display for "go-withs" and for brief legible labels.

Safety

If you plan to display your collection, take some elementary precautions ahead of time. In fact, every collector should take these precautions:

● Do not leave your collection unattended in a parked vehicle, even in the trunk. Consider installing a safe and a burglar alarm in your home. Your safe or storage place should be in a climate-controlled part of the house to minimize the danger of rust.

● Don't give out your home address. Do all your collecting business through a Post Office box.

● Make sure your home address is not shown in the telephone directory. Most telephone companies will omit your address or substitute your Post Office box number at no charge.

Using a box number means that you cannot ship via United Parcel Service. This is no handicap, however, since U.P.S. states that it will not accept or insure antiques or one-of-a-kind items such as art knives. If you sneak one by them and it gets lost or damaged, they can refuse to honor your claim. I have found that the most satisfactory way to ship valuable knives is by Registered Priority Mail insured for full value.

Grading the Condition of a Knife

THE National Knife Collectors Association (NKCA), with headquarters and museum in Chattanooga, Tennessee, has published a set of standards for grading old knives, especially pocketknives. These NKCA standards are widely used by collectors and dealers. They are virtually universal in mail order knife lists. With the permission of the NKCA, I list these standards here. For clarity, I have expanded their definitions.

If you are building a serious collection, one that you one day hope to display or to sell, you should limit yourself to knives in Mint (unused) or Near Mint (excellent unsharpened) condition. Mint knives are preferable to Near Mint, of course, but mint knives from before about 1915 are extremely rare, while mint knives from before about 1870 are virtually unknown.

A Mint or Near Mint knife has the same shape it had when new. It looks exactly the way its maker intended it to look. That is why it is most suitable for a collection.

An Excellent or lesser condition knife is still an example of its type and of its maker's work. However, it is not an entirely accurate example, since its shape has been modified by wear, use, and sharpening.

Knives grading Fair or Poor are suitable for a serious collection only as examples of exceedingly rare or early patterns, brands, or types of construction. To merit consideration, such a knife should be all original.

Some collectors and dealers insist on taking a Near Mint or even a Mint knife and buffing or polishing it up. *THIS IS AN UNFORGIVABLE MISTAKE!* Over-eager polishing destroys any remaining original finish on a knife (see below). It softens all contours and edges. It eliminates all traces of honest age, which may leave the very authenticity of the knife open to doubt. *IT SUBSTANTIALLY REDUCES ITS VALUE TO A SERIOUS AND KNOWLEDGEABLE COLLECTOR.*

N.K.C.A. GRADES

MINT: Absolutely new, exactly as shipped from the factory. A mint knife has no blemishes. It was never carried, never sharpened, and never used. A Mint knife may be lightly oiled and wiped with a soft rag. Any harsher cleaning will turn it into a Near Mint knife, with a ⅓ to ½ reduction in value.

NEAR MINT: An unused knife with a few minor blemishes. It may show slight carry wear or age checking on the handles. The blades may have been lightly honed or show slight discoloration, even a tiny rust spot or two. Any original blade etch must be present and clear. Most of the original finish (see below) must be present. I prefer to call this condition **"Excellent Unsharpened."** *The base prices in this book are for knives in this condition.*

EXCELLENT: Up to 10% blade wear. All blades "walk and talk" (to "walk" is to operate smoothly under tension from the backspring. To "talk" is to snap crisply when opened or shut. A blade that does not walk and talk is said to be "lazy"). Blades or handles may be discolored or cleaned. Sophisticated collectors prefer discoloration to heavy cleaning, but most collectors are not sophisticated. A heavily cleaned or buffed knife cannot grade higher than Excellent. *An Excellent knife is worth 10–25% less than a Near Mint (excellent unsharpened) knife.*

VERY GOOD or GOOD: Up to 25% blade wear. Slight cracks or chips in the handles. May have one lazy blade. All stampings clear. No replaced parts. *In this book, Good or Very Good knives are described as "Worn."*

FAIR: Up to 50% blade wear. Blades may be lazy. Large cracks or chips in the handles. Handles or blades may have been replaced with original parts (some dealers and repairmen have stocks of unused old parts; they and others also cannibalize broken knives for good parts). Stampings faint but legible.

POOR: Blades heavily worn. Handles broken or missing. Obviously replaced blade(s). Stampings faint or illegible.

Blade Finishes

To avoid being fooled by a reworked knife, it is essential to understand that no commercial knife factory has ever used rag buffing wheels. A knife blade or handle that shows the softened edges and slightly wavy surface produced by rag wheel buffing has certainly been reworked. Even worse, a knife that shows signs of such buffing over the whole tang or on the inner surfaces of liners or springs has probably been taken apart, most likely for blade or handle replacement.

For polishing their knives, old time cutlers used hard wheels. These wheels were either wood covered with leather (usually walrus hide) or else they were hard felt. The surface of the wheel was covered with a mixture of glue and the proper abrasive. This coating had to be painstakingly renewed at least once a day.

Even modern mass-produced knife blades, which are gang-polished on special machines, are polished on hard wheels so that the edges and lines look clean. Inexpensive blades are polished by drum tumbling, which produces a very respectable looking finish that is almost impossible to fake.

Two different finishes were used on older knife blades: glaze and crocus. For a glaze finish, the abrasive glued on to the final polishing wheel was a very fine powdered emery. A true glaze finish (sometimes called ''blue glaze'') looks like a series of very fine even parallel lines at right angles to the main cutting edge of the blade. There are collectors and dealers who fail to recognize this as an original finish, and insist on buffing it out.

For a crocus finish, the abrasive on the final wheel was crocus of iron, an extremely fine powdered iron oxide. A crocus polish is, in effect, a mirror finish. It is smooth and shiny. It shows undistorted reflections. By contrast, a rag wheel polish yields a wavy surface and distorted reflections.

The glaze finish was standard on all low priced knives including most plain jack knives. Crocus polish was sometimes used all around on the very finest pearl handled dress knives.

Standard American practice on all but both the cheapest and costliest knives was to crocus polish the mark side of the master blade. This polished surface would then usually receive a trademark etch. The back of the master blade, and both sides of the other blade or blades would be glazed.

If you are or hope to be a serious collector willing to pay a premium for mint condition knives, it is essential that you learn to recognize authentic crocus and glaze finishes. Get an experienced dealer or collector to show you what they look like.

Proper Cleaning

What is the proper way to clean an old knife? The most important rule is to work slowly and patiently. If you clean too little now, you can always clean more later. If you clean too much, however, you may hurt the knife, or at least reduce its value.

The first step is to remove any loose dirt, grease, and lint. Your basic tools for this are soft clean rags, wooden toothpicks, and cotton swabs such as Q-Tips.

Use these tools in conjunction with a light non-drying non-staining oil such as Norton sharpening stone oil or Japanese sword oil. (Japanese sword oil is made from camellia flowers. It smells good and is good for your knives. It is available for $5 postpaid for 4 ounces from Morty the Knife Man, P.O. Box 7, Little Neck, NY 11363.)

Put a drop of oil in each joint of the knife. Wipe down the handles and the blades with a soft rag. Use a drop or two of oil on the rag. Clean inside the knife with swabs and toothpicks. Use a toothpick to clean old grease out of jigged bone.

If there is a sticky residue on the handles from old self-adhesive labels, try removing this with oily nail-polish remover on a rag. The active ingredient in this stuff is acetone, so work by an open window and do not breathe the fumes.

If there are spots of rust on the knife, oil them well and let the knife sit for several days. Then carefully scrape away the actual rust with the tip of a sharp stiff knife.

Some collectors use non-abrasive Nevr-Dull to clean tarnished knives. Another good product is called Flitz.

By scraping away only the actual rust, you leave intact any of the original finish that remains. Of course, if no original finish remains, then it can do no harm carefully to refinish the entire knife. For best appearance, and to keep from grinding into the tang, re-establish the choil (the notch in front of the tang) with a small triangular file.

Little high-speed bench grinders are not meant for use on knives. If you plan to do much refinishing, invest in a small high quality belt sander from one of the dealers in knifemaking supplies listed in Ken Warner's *Knives* annuals published by DBI Books.

Learning to Recognize Fakes

THE BANE of the collector's existence is fakes. Hardly a week goes by that I do not get a letter from an anxious collector who, in the cold light of the morning after his big find, realizes that he might have been had. All too often, when he thinks he's been had, he's been had.

There are countless ways to be had. Even if you could count them, fellows are out there right now dreaming up new ones. However, all the various ways can be divided into three groups. These are counterfeits, reworks, and fantasies.

Counterfeits

A counterfeit is a careful copy or imitation of a genuine item that was intentionally made to deceive the buyer. An honest reproduction, one that is *permanently* marked as a reproduction, is not a counterfeit. See *American Military Fixed Blade Knives* for more about reproductions.

So far, knife collecting has largely been spared the gambits of high-powered counterfeiters. In theory, there may exist counterfeit knives so exact that no one can spot them. In practice, this is very unlikely. The raw materials and the tools that were standard even as recently as the 1930s are simply not available anywhere any more.

The main reason there aren't many high quality counterfeit knives now is that prices are not yet so very high as to call forth the requisite skill. Besides, given the strength of the custom knife market, a guy with the skill to fake a 19th century American bowie well enough to fool an experienced collector could get even more money for the same knife with his own name on it.

A potential danger, of course, as modern hand-made knives grow ever more popular, is that someone may start to counterfeit them. Indeed, I have heard rumors of this already happening, but I have yet to see the evidence. Do think about this, though, if you are offered some suspicious "bargains."

There are, of course, lots of low quality counterfeit knives around. The favorite brand to fake seems to be Remington, followed closely by Winchester. The markings, finish, and handle materials on these counterfeits are so poor and inappropriate that they are embarrassing, yet they sell briskly to inexperienced collectors and greedy antiques dealers and swap-meet merchants.

Another favorite brand among low-class counterfeiters is Will & Finck. Some of the fakes that are glorified with this famous old name are incredibly bad, but they will still catch those with the will to believe just about every time. Remember, a crummy knife with a quality name is probably a fake.

Reworks

A rework is a knife that has been "improved." It can be a knife that was repaired with old or borrowed parts, or even entirely assembled from parts. It can be a knife that had an undesirable brand removed and a desirable name cobbled into its place. It can simply be a knife that was so heavily cleaned and polished that it is impossible to tell what has or has not been done to it.

Unlike believable counterfeits, which are rare, reworks are epidemic in knife collecting. An awful lot of guys think they are competent knife repairmen. Almost all of them are wrong.

To start with, a competent and honest repairman uses correct original parts. Most repairmen neither know, nor care which parts are correct or original, and would not know where to get good parts if they did.

Strange as it may seem, a knife that is obviously made up from mismatched parts may well be an authentic old knife. There are many documented instances of cutlery firms buying up the parts inventory of defunct competitors, of using up the inventories of firms they took over, and of re-stamping knives made for contracts that were cancelled. In the *Pocketknife Brand Listings,* I mention several of these cases.

As far as I know, not even the most competent of today's repairmen have either the skill or the equipment to do a good crocus or glaze polish. Therefore, if he is smart, when he reassembles a knife, a repairman leaves the blade and inside patina strictly as he found it.

Most guys who take apart an old knife to rework it can't resist the impulse to polish the inside before putting it back together. If the tang of a pocketknife has been buffed in places a buffing wheel can't reach, you can be reasonably sure that the knife has been apart.

As far as fake markings go, a strong light and a good magnifier will show up just about all of them. Any mark struck one letter at a time is immediate bad news; so is a ragged-edged engraved mark or any "cold-stamped" mark.

When a mark is struck cold into steel, it remains clean inside. (Note: deep-etched marks on fixed blades are also clean inside. This type of mark was not used on folding knives.) An authentic hot-stamped mark (or a mark stamped prior to heat-treating) is black inside. Some fakers put black ink in their cold-stamped marks, but this is easily wiped away.

A cold-stamped mark has raised edges you can feel. If these edges have been ground away, you can usually see where this was done. Sometimes a fake mark shows through on the back of the blade. A real one never does.

If an original mark was ground off of a tang, the tang will appear too thin when viewed edge-on. Also, if a blade and its spring are not the same thickness and also the same color (or a blade and its tang are not exactly the same color), then something is almost certainly wrong—there are some very skillful welders out there. There are also some sloppy ones, and bubbles in the steel are a dead giveaway of a welded blade.

Another certain giveaway on a reworked knife is glue. Glues were simply not used in knife assembly until quite recently. In particular, epoxy and cyanoacrylate (''Super'' glue), both recent inventions, were not used in assembling factory-made knives. If a shield or handle is glued on (they should be pinned on), something is definitely amiss.

The only exception to the glue rule is that most older narrow-tanged fixed blade knives had their handles attached with ''cutler's cement.'' Cutler's cement is made of rosin, beeswax, and brick dust. It is dark brown and crumbly, it smells bad, and it melts in boiling water.

The best way to immunize yourself against reworks is to learn what correct knives look like. Study the colors of old steel and other metals. Study the textures of old handle materials. Study blade shapes and tapers, markings and finishes.

By observation, learn what was standard practice in these areas for the makers you are interested in, and also learn what was not. Study catalog illustrations and study knives you know to be authentic. Doing this will also help to protect you from the third class of fakes: fantasies

Fantasies

A fantasy item is a fake that is made to look old and historically interesting, but that is in fact based on no real prototype. The remarkable thing about virtually every fantasy knife I have seen is that they are impossible. There is just no way that they could have been made in the time they pretend to be from.

If you know your knife history, your cultural history, and your technological history, you will recognize at first glance when a knife you are looking at is a fantasy. Of course the people who fall for fantasy knives don't know any history, or they know just enough to get themselves into trouble.

The favorite marking on fantasy knives is WELLS FARGO. Trust me: *any* knife that says WELLS FARGO on it is a fake. Write this on the blackboard 100 times.

Any knife that has the maker's name spelled wrong on it is a fake. I have seen a few contract knives that had the distributor's name spelled wrong, but these were tiny knives worth just a few dollars.

Any knife with the word Gambler or Gambling on it is a fake. An awful lot of nice old oyster knives have gotten themselves etched GAMBLER'S PUSH DAGGER or some such nonsense. They are in the same league as coins dated 69 B.C.

In the realm of the technological, you should learn the difference between old celluloid and new plastic [see the *Picture Handle Knives* chapter]. You should learn the difference between a forged blade with its tapers in every direction, and a blanked blade with only one taper (toward the edge). Study the next chapter called *Some Clues For Dating and Identifying Knives*. It will help you to spot most of the anachronisms that the makers and purveyors of fantasy knives can't be bothered to avoid.

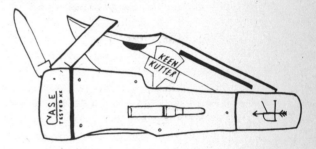

My favorite fantasy knife. (courtesy *Knife World*)

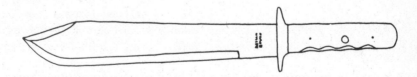

No matter what it is marked, if a knife looks like this, it is a fantasy. (courtesy *Knife World*)

Self Defense

To sum up, if a knife SEEMS too good to be true, chances are that it *is*. Put it down and walk away. Don't get into an argument with the seller. If the knife is a fake, he probably knows it, and is not about to admit it. If it isn't a fake, won't you look silly?

If there is a knowledgeable dealer or collector (or writer) at the show, ask him or her to take a look. We may not be able to give you a definite "yes" when it *seems* all right, but we can sure give you a definite "no" when it's not.

Most reputable dealers will, on request, guarantee to refund your money if a knife is shown to be a fake or substantially not as represented. (If the knife is sold to you *as a rework,* don't ask for your money back when someone else confirms that it is. Yes, I *have* seen people try that.) Such a refund guarantee is usually valid for from 3 to 10 days. However, I once saw a prominent dealer refund the price of a knife after 3 *years,* when the knife was found to have been a very clever re-stamping (not done by him).

There are a few dealers out there who are famous for selling reworks. Libel law forbids my mentioning their names, but if you keep your eyes and ears open, you will learn soon enough who they are.

What should you do if you get stuck with a fake and the seller either can't be found or refuses to make good. You might be tempted to sell it to another collector and recover some of your money. DON'T! Even if you sell it as a fake, what will be remembered and passed on is that YOU sold it, not what you said about it at the time.

Your most valuable possession is your reputation. If you lose it, you will find that is is a very lonely world out there. Either keep the fake as a reminder to be more careful in the future, destroy it, or donate it to the counterfeit study collection of the National Knife Museum in Chattanooga.

A Cautionary Tale

In one of the museum knife collections that I catalogued, after I had sorted all the knives by area of origin and by age, I was left with about a drawerful of strange knives that had me baffled. None of them fit into any category that I had encountered before.

My first idea was to card them all as "unidentified primitive," and in fact that is what I ended up doing with several of them. However, most of these mystery knives lacked the design integrity one expects in primitive artifacts. Therefore, I was not satisfied with this explanation.

After several days, a little clue on one of the knife blades (the remains of an early 20th century trademark which had not been fully ground away) jogged my mental processes so that I realized what I was up against. Most of these mysterious knives had been made up from a hodge-podge of old (and not so old) parts, probably by an unethical European antiques dealer. They had then been crudely shaped and aged to look "primitive." No doubt the dealer had sold them as genuine primitives to the unsuspecting American collector who had originally assembled the collection.

In the same collection were some table knives and forks with green dyed ivory handles. Green dyed ivory was in vogue in the early 19th century. It was popular among knife collectors in the early to mid-20th century, when this collection was put together.

These green handled knives and forks were quite heavily worn. Their handles had been octagonal, but the edges were worn nearly round. However, the green dye on them was uniform and as bright as a new leaf.

I had learned (the hard way) that original green ivory dye is very unstable. It would penetrate only the surface of the ivory. You can almost but not quite rub it off. Boiling water causes it to fade.

Well, Sherlock, what would you conclude about the Case of the Green Handles? I concluded there had been another (or the same) greedy dealer at work.

Historical Fakes

Knife collecting has been around for a long time. I have seen medieval inventories that list in detail the family's precious knives. Some had jeweled or inlaid and engraved hilts. Others had been presented by or to monarchs, ambassadors, or distinguished clergymen. Some were wedding knives that commemorated important marital alliances. Even then there were famous knifemakers, and even then there were fakes.

I once saw a little Japanese dagger of inferior quality. It was signed Muramassa, one of the most famous Japanese swordsmiths. Fake Muramassas are not unusual, but this one was because it appeared old enough to have been made in Muramassa's own lifetime, about 6 centuries ago. Swordsmith Michael Bell told me that Japanese sword collectors have a saying that for every ten signed samurai swords, 11 of the signatures are fake.

Another time, I saw a 16th century European knife with a "matching" fork. The fork had been made in the late 19th century to enhance the value of the knife to an unsophisticated collector at that time, a collector who did not know that eating forks had not yet been invented in the 16th century. Today, the 19th century fake fork is an antique in its own right.

Some Clues for Dating and Identifying Knives

MATERIALS

CAST STEEL: also called crucible steel, *acier fondu, guss stahl (G. S.)*: invented 1740 for clock springs. First used for blades and pocketknife springs within about 30 years. In general use on better knives c1840–1920. Last made commercially about 1940.

SHEAR STEEL: invented in the Middle Ages, but blades so marked are middle to late 19th Century.
[For more about cast steel and shear steel, see *Kitchen and Butcher Knives*.]

CHROME STEEL: invented 1865, occasional use in blades circa 1870s, but it rusts badly; not widely used in knives until the invention of . . .
CHROMIUM PLATING: invented and first used 1924.

STELLITE: cobalt tungsten alloy, invented 1907, first used in knives 1910. Last commercial use in pocketknives, April, 1920. Now used by custom makers.

STAINLESS STEEL: invented 1914; first commercial use in knives circa 1921.

American change from **COIN** to **STERLING** standard for silver knives: 1868 [see *Silver Fruit Knives*].

NICKEL SILVER: invented circa 1810.

CAST IN PLACE TIN ALLOY BOLSTERS: first used circa 1867.

HARD RUBBER: patented 1844, first used for knife handles circa 1856.

CELLULOID: invented 1869, first commercial use 1872.

CLEAR CELLULOID HANDLES: invented and first used 1879 [see *Picture Handle Pocketknives* chapter].

MECHANISMS

Integral iron bolsters and liners on pocketknives: Sheffield manufacture before circa 1860.

Long narrow square kicks on pocketknife blades, to facilitate hand fitting: usually before circa 1860.

This William Greaves regular jack with smooth bone handles has integral iron bolster-liners and a narrow square kick. The marking dates the knife 1780–1816.

Wrought iron bolsters on steel-bladed table and kitchen knives: Sheffield manufacture before circa 1880.

Fixed blades blanked on punch presses (tangs have uniform thickness, or else taper only toward the edge), first used circa late 1860s. Forged blades almost always have tangs that taper toward the end. (Many modern custom knives have tangs tapered by grinding.)

Sheffield 'Press the small blade' switchblade: patented 1850.

Harrison patent punch blade dated June 10, 1902, or numbered 701,878: made by New York Knife Company, probably before 1920.

Liner lock (e.g. on electrician's knives): patented 1906 for Cattaraugus, in general use after about 1930.

Hollow sheet steel handles secured by folded tabs: made after 1936.

MARKING TECHNOLOGY

Deep stamped brand markings were universal on all types of knives up until the 1880s. They are still universal on pocketknife tangs.

The stamping dies for these markings were hand cut and appear relatively rough and simple up through about the 1820s. After this time, the use of mechanical reduction techniques (the reducing lathe) permitted the making of precise and complex stamping dies.

In the mid-1880s, deep etching was introduced as a substitute for stamping the trademark on fixed blade knives. Under a glass, a deep etched mark has slightly ragged edges and is clean inside. A stamped mark is black inside.

In the 1940s, the electro-etch supplanted the deep etch. It was also used on pocketknife blades, though not on their tangs. This etch has a fuzzy frosty look. It has no depth, and is readily worn away.

Decorative and trademark blade etching with masks was used from at least c1800 through the 1930s. Such an etch was done on a crocus polished surface [see *Blade Finishes* in the *Grading* chapter]. It is sharp edged and bright, unlike electro-etch. It has barely perceptible depth. The etching on current fakes is more deep and less crisp and bright than the real thing.

BRITISH MONARCHS (inclusion of the Royal Cypher in a stamp indicates a member of the Royal Household purchased cutlery from the firm).

G (crown) **R** (hand cut stamp) [George II, III, and IV] = before 1830

W (crown) **R** [William IV] = 1830–1837 (but evidently used as a trademark for some time afterwards)

V (crown) **R** [Victoria] = 1837–1901

E (crown) **R** [Edward VII] = 1901–1910

G (crown) **R** (modern style stamp) [George V and VI] = 1910–1952

HELPFUL MARKINGS

COUNTRY NAME: The U. S. Tariff Act of 1890 required manufactured goods imported to the United States in or after 1891 to be permanently marked with the name of the country of origin. Therefore, almost every knife marked with the name of a country was made after 1890.

Here are some geographic and other markings whose meanings are not obvious.

PRUSSIA: dominant kingdom of the German Empire, name sometimes used on Solingen export goods between 1891 and 1915.

AUSTRIA: before 1918 was shorthand for the Austro-Hungarian Empire. Knives so marked were made both in Austria and in Bohemia (now part of Czechoslovakia) between 1891 and about 1915.

MADE IN U.S.A.: first used by a few firms in the late 1910s or early 1920s. Uncommon until the mid-1960s when it was required on American-made knives exported to Canada. Nearly universal on American factory-made knives today.

SHEFFIELD (*NOT* used with "ENGLAND", i.e. pre–1891): seems to indicate goods made for export to the United States after about 1830. Known post–1830s Sheffield names without "SHEFFIELD" made for sale in England.

LONDON = made in London.

London street address *without* LONDON = made in Sheffield for a London cutler.

CELEBRATED, WARRANTED, CAST STEEL, ENGLISH STEEL, etc., without *English* place name (such as "Sheffield"): made in Germany or Austria-Hungary for export, usually to the United States, before 1891.

STEEL (on shank of fork): Sheffield made, 19th Century.

FOREIGN or FOREIGN MADE: made, usually in Germany, for export to England, after about 1924.

Numerals as part of a French-sounding trademark: made in Thiers, France, usually before about 1920.

Handle Materials

PEARL (mother-of-pearl): The inner lining of certain mollusk shells from the Orient and Australia.

ABALONE SHELL: The inner lining of a gastropod shell found in California and Mexico.

GENUINE IVORY: Elephant tusks, usually from West Africa. Distinguished by extreme hardness and a delicate wood-like grain.

WALRUS IVORY: Obtained from Alaska and the Russian Arctic. It has no grain, but each tusk has an obvious crystalline-appearing core. Not used on factory-made pocketknives.

TORTOISE SHELL: Mottled brownish yellow shell of such sea turtles as the hawksbill, sometimes backed with gold foil or orange paper to enhance its color. At one time, translucent cow horn was spotted to resemble tortoise shell.

BLACK BUFFALO HORN: Rich glossy black horn obtained from the water buffaloes of Asia.

GRAY or GREEN BUFFALO HORN: Smooth horn often streaked with white, it is in fact usually cow horn.

GENUINE STAG: Outside cut ("bark") of deer antler, obtained originally from Hungary, Bohemia, Ceylon, and China, but now mainly from India (Sambar stag). Its color is almost always enhanced with dye.

SMOOTH WHITE BONE: The shin bone of beef cattle, distinguished from ivory by its many tiny pores and its lack of grain.

JIGGED BONE or BONE STAG (called STAG in most knife catalogs): mechanically scored and gouged bone or, rarely, second-cut stag, that is dyed to resemble genuine stag. With experience one can often identify a knife's maker by the pattern and color of jigged bone.

EBONY: A hard very fine-grained black wood from East Africa and Madagascar.

COCOBOLO: A hard fine-grained reddish brown wood from Central America.

HARD RUBBER: Relatively soft material in black, reddish brown, or white. When rubbed briskly, it *smells* like burning rubber.

CELLULOID: The first moldable synthetic plastic, made of cellulose nitrate treated with camphor and alcohol. It can be made in every color of the rainbow, or any combination of colors arranged in swirled or geometric patterns. It can be fabricated to simulate most natural materials, including

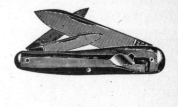

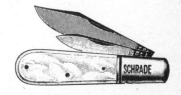

Celluloids

ivory, horn, stag, pearl, amber, agate, tortoise-shell, and wood. It can also be made transparent and used to cover printed pictures. [For more information, see *Picture Handle Knives*.]

"DELRIN": A modern moldable plastic material, not as versatile as celluloid, but much more durable.

"MICARTA": A nearly indestructible laminated plastic material that can be machined and engraved.

BRONZE (copper and tin) and **BRASS** (copper and zinc): sometimes used for the handles of jack knives intended to be used around salt water.

NICKEL SILVER: An alloy of copper and nickel used often for bolsters and sometimes for liners. Used for the handles of veterinary knives and of inexpensive knives with embossed advertisements and designs. [For more on metal handles see *Pen Knives*, and also *Boy's Knives*.]

Embossed, Color Etched, and Enamelled Handles (Add 25—60%)

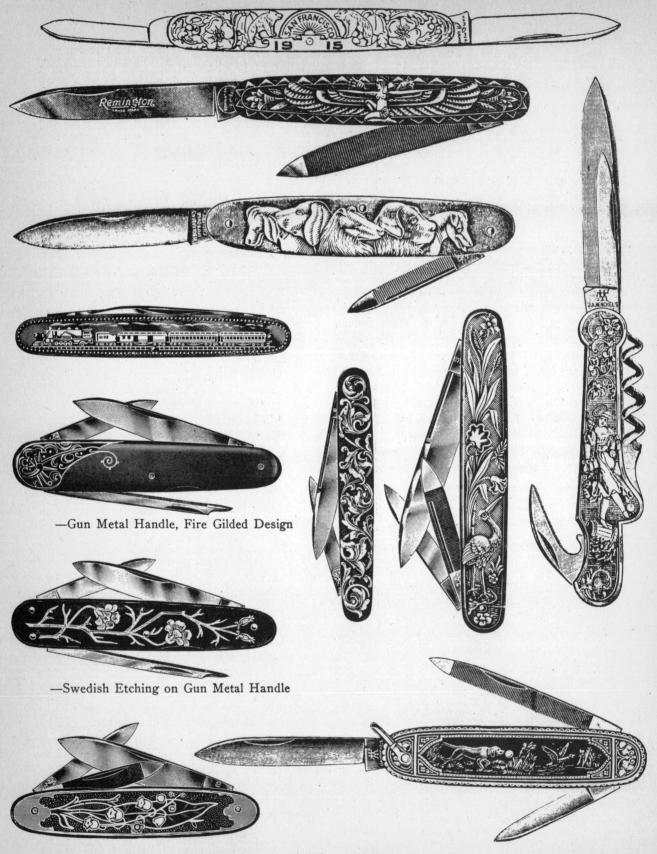

—Gun Metal Handle, Fire Gilded Design

—Swedish Etching on Gun Metal Handle

—Gold, Green, Red and White, Designed
Enameled Handle, Brass Lined

Toledo scales
(black iron with design in gold and silver wire).

II: FOLDING KNIVES

INTRODUCTION TO FOLDING KNIVES

THIS PART of the book is divided into three sections:

1: Standard American Folding Knife Patterns.

This section includes all of the shapes and styles of pocketknives commerically made for the American market since about the middle of the last century.

At the end of this section is a special appendix on recent commemorative and limited edition folding knives made primarily for sale to knife collectors. Most of these knives are factory-made, though some are bench-made. For convenience, a few limited edition fixed blade knives are included in this appendix.

2: Foreign, Exotic, Primitive, and Historical Folding Knives.

This section includes standard folding knife styles made before the middle of the last century, and also a selection of more recent pocketknife styles made in foreign countries for foreign markets. As there is wide variation among these knives, each type is described and priced individually.

3: Contemporary Custom and Hand-Made Folding Knives.

These are modern knives crafted one at a time by individual knifemakers. These folders are also extremely varied, so they, too, are priced individually.

Many Pocket Knives are not drawn full size, but length of Haft (or Handle) is stated. To get a good idea of the actual size, place your old knife on the sketch of six-inch rule shown below.

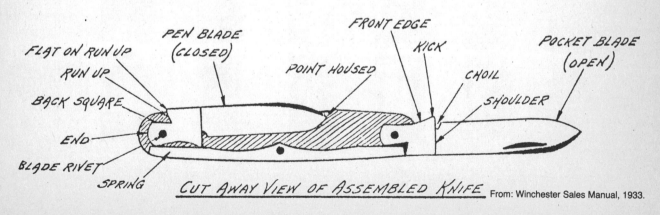

1 2 W. JNO. BAKER 3 HUNTER ST SYDNEY 3 4 5 6

NOTE: THE SIZE OF A FOLDING KNIFE IS ITS LENGTH CLOSED.

CUT AWAY VIEW OF ASSEMBLED KNIFE From: Winchester Sales Manual, 1933.

Remington Cutlery
Remington Pocket Knife Blades

Pen
blade

Cut-off
pen blade

Curved
pen blade

Coping
blade

Sheep-
foot blade

Spey
blade

Long clip
blade

"B" clip
blade

"A" clip
blade

Turkish
clip blade

Long sabre
clip blade

Sabre clip
blade

Remington Cutlery

Remington Pocket Knife Blades

Corn blade

Surgical pen blade

Curved manicure blade

Lawton manicure blade

Grooved manicure blade

Manicure blade

Long curved spey blade

Long spey blade

Spear blade

Sabre spear blade

Long sheep foot blade

Texas Tickler clip blade

Remington Cutlery
Remington Pocket Knife Blades

Budding blade

Wharncliffe blade

Razor blade

Long spear or physician's blade

Cotton sampler's blade

Pruning blade

Long screw driver cap lifter

Punch blade

Electrician's screw-driver and wire-scraper

Screw-driver

Screw-driver cap-lifter

Can-opener

Spatula

Schrade Cutlery Company Pocketknife Blades, 1926

E.C. Simmons Blades, 1930

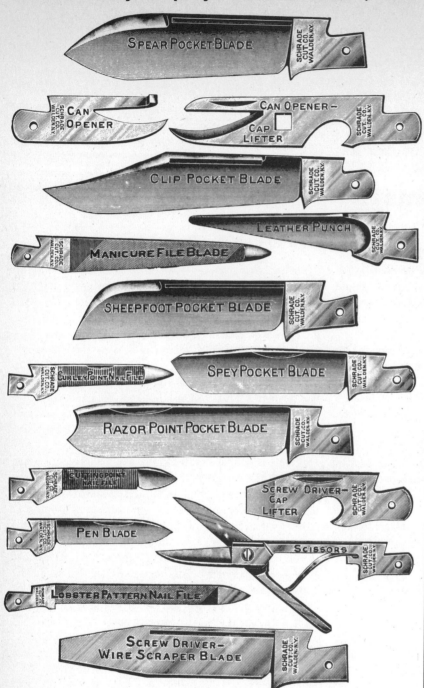

SPEAR POCKET BLADE

CAN OPENER

CAN OPENER — CAP LIFTER

CLIP POCKET BLADE

LEATHER PUNCH

MANICURE FILE BLADE

SHEEPFOOT POCKET BLADE

CURLEY POINT NAIL FILE

SPEY POCKET BLADE

RAZOR POINT POCKET BLADE

CUTTING POINT NAIL FILE

SCREW DRIVER — CAP LIFTER

PEN BLADE

SCISSORS

LOBSTER PATTERN NAIL FILE

SCREW DRIVER — WIRE SCRAPER BLADE

Spear.

Combination Electricians' Contact Point, File and Wire Scraper.

Saber.

Screw Driver.

Clip.

Corn.

Saber Clip.

Flexible Nail File.

Spey.

Pen.

Sheep Foot or Tobacco.

File.

Wharncliffe.

Patent Leather Punch Blade.

Eraser.

Cuticle Pusher.

Razor.

Flesh Blade.

Florist Square Point Grafting Knife.

Combination Blade, with Cap Lifter and Screw Driver.

Budding.

Can Opener.

Pruning.

Combination Blade, with Cap Lifter, Tack Puller and Screw Driver.

Cotton.

Combination Blade, with Cap Lifter, Prest-O-Lite Tank Key and Screw Driver.

NOTES:

Pocket blade means master blade, the principal blade in a pocketknife.

A **saber ground** blade is beveled for only part of its width, making it stouter than an ordinary blade.

The **cut-off pen blade** was also called a "coping blade."

The **long curved spey blade** was later called the **Great Western spey blade.**

The **Curley point** file was patented by J. Curley of New York in the 1880s.

Remington two piece patented can opener

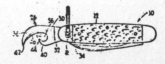

Previous pages: REMINGTON BLADES, 1920

The square hole in some opener blades is a Prest-O-Lite tank key, for the fuel tanks of a popular early brand of automobile headlight.

Remington replaced the one-piece can opener with the stronger Tillmanns two-piece can opener in 1926. It was patented in 1927.

In 1945, Imperial introduced the modern style of hooked "safety can opener" blade.

Introduction to Standard American Folding Knife Patterns

THE FOLDING KNIVES covered in this section of the book are the types and patterns that have been made for commercial sale in the United States from about the middle of the last century up to the present day. Included here are knives made in this country, and also those made abroad for export to the United States.

Knives made for American customers in this period fit into a definite range of shapes and patterns. In the chapters that follow, each of these patterns is described, illustrated, and priced in great detail, along with all of its variations. Instructions for use of the price charts in these chapters begin in the next column.

Some of these American pocketknife styles span the entire period of nearly a century and a half. Others went out of favor after a while, and quite a few were introduced more recently. The history of each pattern, as far as it is known, is included in its chapter.

Except for some rare early knives and occasional foreign knives brought here by individual immigrants or travelers, virtually every factory-made pocketknife one can find in this country is covered in this section.

The American pocketknife pattern section is divided into three parts. They are **Jack Knives, Pen Knives,** and **Multi-Blades** [see the *Pictorial Key*].

Jack knives are relatively plain sturdy knives. Standard jack knives are single-ended: they have their blade or blades hinged at one end. There are also a few stout double-ended jack knife patterns.

Standard pen knives are small light-weight double-ended knives. They have blades hinged in both ends. However, some of the smallest pen knives, now called quill knives, are single-ended, much like tiny jack knives.

Multi-blades, as the name implies, have a multitude of blades. The multitude can be as small as three and as great as a hundred or more.

At least one of the multitude of blades in a multi-blade is either a special purpose blade, such as a spey blade, or else it is a special implement (other than a cutting blade, a nail file, or a leather punch). It can be a can opener, a scissors, a champagne wire cutter, a hoof pick, a wrench, or even a dinner fork.

Multi-blades are usually large and sturdy, like standard jack knives. They are almost always double-ended, like standard pen knives. The two most common modern multi-blades, the scout knife and the ''Swiss Army'' knife, should be familiar to everyone.

How to Use The Price Charts

First open your knife. Open only one blade at a time, so that you don't cut yourself or break the springs. Look for a brand on one of the blades, down near where it joins the handle. Find that brand in the alphabetical brand listing. If there is only a picture on the blade, look up the name of the pictured object or check the pictorial trademark charts just after the brand listings.

The brand listing will tell you where and when that brand was made or sold. It will also tell you which price category that brand falls into: Very High (**V**), High (**H**), Medium (**M**), or Low (**L**). Detailed histories of some of the more important brands can be found in subsequent chapters.

If there is no brand on the knife, assume it belongs in the Low (**L**) price category. If it is clearly a high quality knife, add to it accordingly, but an unmarked knife's value is at least one category lower than an identical marked example's.

Next you need to know the shape or pattern name of your knife. If you already know, turn to the appropriate chapter. If you are not sure, turn to the *Pictorial Key to American Folding Knives* which begins on page 34 and find the picture that looks most like it. Then turn to the indicated chapter. The pictures and text will tell you if you have come to the right place, and if not, where to turn next.

In the chapters, you will find that each folding knife shape or pattern has four base prices, one for each price category. Find the base price for the price category of your knife's brand. For example, if the brand is rated **M**, find the ''Medium'' base price. This base price is the estimated value of a typical knife of that type (as shown and described) in *excellent unsharpened condition*.

Does your knife fit this ''typical'' description? If it does, then you are all set.

If your knife has different features from the typical example, look at the list of variations. Also, and this is *very* important, if its condition is other than ''excellent unsharpened'' (N.K.C.A. Near Mint), look at the last part of the variations list. ''Mint'' means new, just as the knife came from the factory.

Pictures in each chapter show what many of the listed variations look like. Their captions describe the key features and indicate the value of that particular knife, computed using the charts. Unusual terms are defined when they are first used. Also see the exploded drawings in the front of the book.

The Method

To estimate the value of your knife, start with the correct base price (**V**, **H**, **M**, or **L**). Take the first variation which applies and follow the direction to add or subtract a percentage.

Take *THE RESULT* and go to the next *relevant* variation (ignore ones that do not apply). Follow its direction, adding or subtracting a percentage to or from the previous result.

Now take the *NEW* result and go to the *next* relevant variation. . . . Get the picture? If your knife has more than one or two of the listed variations, you might want to use a piece of scratch paper or a pocket calculator to do your figuring. I use a $7 calculator.

Remember, when you are figuring, always to apply the variations *IN ORDER*. Handle material is always next to last, and condition is always last. If your final result is something silly like $92.47, round it off, in this case to $92 or $93 (or to $90 or $95, as you like).

The knives illustrated in the shape and pattern chapters have had their values computed using this method. You might want to turn to one of these chapters right now and estimate the values of a few of the knives. When your results agree with the values in the captions (within $2 or $3 due to rounding), then you have gotten the hang of the method.

For example, turn to the page headed "BAREHEAD REGULAR JACKS" in the *Jack Knives* section (page 105). The first knife on this page is an Ulster Knife Co. This is a fine old American brand and is rated High (**H**).

The "High" base price for a regular jack is $65. This knife has only one blade, while the base price is for a knife with two blades. Therefore subtract 20%. With a calculator, enter 65 X .80 (100% − 20% = 80% = 0.80). Then press "=". You should get 52 or $52.

Then note that this knife is a lockback. This increases its value by 50%. With "52" still showing in the display, press "X 1.50 =". You will see 78 or $78.

Also note that this knife is a "barehead;" it has no cap bolsters. This decreases its value by 20%. All jack knife base prices are for knives *with* cap bolsters. Press "X .8 = ", and you should see 62.4 or $62.40.

Finally, note that this knife has wooden handles. Jack knife prices are for knives with jigged bone handles. The wood handles decrease this knife's value by 25%. Press "X .75 =". You will see 46.8 ($46.80) or roughly $47.

Forty-seven dollars is the approximate value of this knife in excellent unsharpened condition. If it were mint it would be worth 50% more, about $70. If it were heavily worn it would be worth 50% less, about $23. If it were only moderately worn, its value would lie somewhere between $23 and $47, depending on the degree of wear.

Let's try a simpler example. Turn to the following page headed "REGULAR JACKS (cont.)." The first knife on this page is a Remington. Remington is one of the most popular brands among collectors so it is rated Very High (**V**). The Very High base price for a regular jack is $100.

This particular Remington has all the features in the base price description, no more and no less. It is a typical jack knife. Therefore, if it is in excellent unsharpened condition, no calculations are necessary. Its value is the base price, $100. If it were mint, it would be worth 50% more, $150. If one of its blades were broken, it would be worth 90% less, $10. Broken knives are not very valuable.

The Generalization Factor

The values you will get by using this book are reasonably accurate, but remember that they are only *ESTIMATES*. You must allow for two important factors when applying them.

First is the "generalization" factor. The base prices and variations are based on large numbers of knives. As with any generalization, they will not apply equally well to all knives in all situations in all places. If you need to sell *this* knife *this* weekend at *this* show, expect to get less than "book value" for it, probably a lot less.

If you need to buy *this* knife for your collection, and there is suddenly a lot of competition for its type, do not hesitate to pay somewhat more than book price. There is a fine line between "increased demand" and extortion, so you have to use your judgement.

The "N" Factor

The second important factor in adjusting the estimated values in this book is the "N" factor. I am sure that you have used the "N" factor yourself, probably without realizing it.

After you have calculated the approximate value of a knife using the tables in the correct chapter, give the knife an overall look. All that counts is your opinion, your gut feeling.

If the knife looks **Neat** to *you*, then the "N" factor is positive, and you might want to raise the estimated value. If it is **Not Neat**, then the "N" factor is negative and you should probably reduce the estimate somewhat.

Of course, if you don't *like* knives, the "N" factor will always be negative. This is reasonable, because if you don't like them, you should be happy to sell them at a discount. However, if you are a person all of whose ugly ducklings are potential swans, to whom *all* knives are **Neat**, regardless, then you had better leave the "N" factor strictly alone.

PICTORIAL KEY TO AMERICAN FOLDING KNIVES
Standard Jack Knife Shapes

EQUAL-END JACK

REGULAR JACK

JACK WITH EASY-OPEN NOTCH

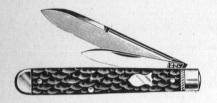

SLIM JACK

SLEEVEBOARD JACK

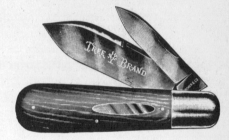

JUMBO JACK

CURVED REGULAR JACK

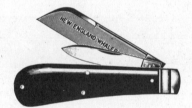

CURVED JACK

CONGRESS JACK

SWELL-END JACK

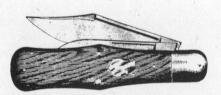

SWELL-CENTER JACK

BALLOON JACK

SWELL-CENTER REGULAR JACK

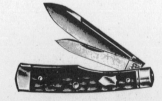

GUNSTOCK JACK

PREMIUM JACK

Standard Jack Knife Shapes (cont.)

SERPENTINE JACK

SLIM SERPENTINE JACK

EUREKA JACK

FISHTAIL JACK

FISH JACK

SURVEYOR JACK

Named Jack Knife Patterns

BARLOW KNIFE

BOY'S KNIFE

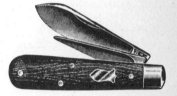

HARNESS KNIFE

ELECTRICIAN'S KNIFE

PRUNING KNIFE

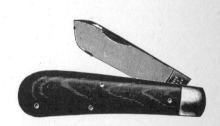

MAIZE KNIFE

COTTON SAMPLER

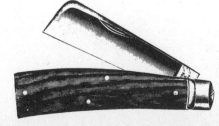

SAILOR'S (ROPE) KNIFE

SAILOR'S (RIGGING) KNIFE

PICTORIAL KEY TO AMERICAN FOLDING KNIVES
Named Jack Knife Patterns (cont.)

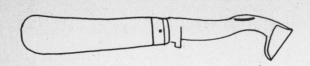

RASE KNIFE (TIMBER SCRIBER)

PHYSICIAN'S KNIFE

CORN KNIFE

SPEY KNIFE

SPEY KNIFE

FLEAM

BUDDING KNIFE

FLORIST'S KNIFE

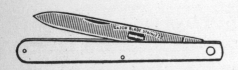

MELON TESTER

SILVER FRUIT KNIFE

DOUBLE-END JACKS:

MOOSE (TEXAS JACK)

FARMER'S JACK

SUNFISH

LIGHT TRAPPER

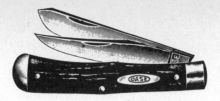

HEAVY TRAPPER

LARGE TRAPPER

MUSKRAT

TICKLER

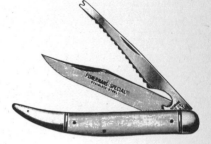

FISH KNIFE

FOLDING HUNTERS: AT LEAST 4½ INCHES LONG

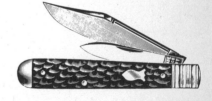

CLASP-TYPE FOLDING HUNTERS

ENGLISH JACK

PICTORIAL KEY TO AMERICAN FOLDING KNIVES

Standard Pen Knife Shapes

SENATOR OR EQUAL-END PEN KNIVES

SLEEVEBOARD PEN

OVAL PEN

CROWN PEN

CONGRESS KNIFE

SWELL-CENTER CONGRESS

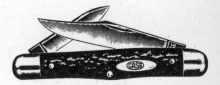

SWELL-CENTER SERPENTINE

SERPENTINE PEN

WHARNCLIFFE KNIFE

SWELL-CENTER PEN

Pen Knives—Special Types

QUILL KNIFE

  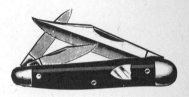

WHITTLERS (LARGE BLADE ON TWO SPRINGS; EACH SMALL BLADE ON ONE SPRING)

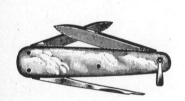 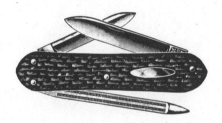 

LOBSTERS (BLADES TOP AND BOTTOM; OFF-CENTER HINGE PINS)

OFFICE KNIFE

LETTER OPENER KNIFE

ADVERTISING KNIFE

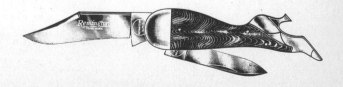

FIGURAL KNIFE (JACK OR PEN)

PICTORIAL KEY TO AMERICAN FOLDING KNIVES
Multi-Blades

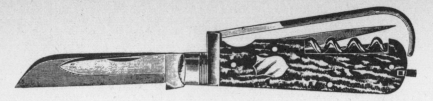

HORSEMAN'S KNIFE

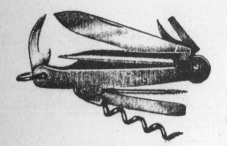

SPORTSMAN'S KNIFE

CHAMPAGNE PATTERN

OPENER KNIFE

KNIFE-FORK-SPOON COMBO.

SCOUT-UTILITY KNIFE

UTILITY KNIFE

CATTLE KNIFE

CATTLE KNIFE

CATTLE KNIFE

PREMIUM STOCK KNIFE

PLIERS KNIFE

TOOL KIT KNIFE

Pocketknife Brand List

Introduction

THIS LIST includes the brand markings on about 98% of the pocketknives one is likely to encounter in the United States. The list has two purposes.

The first purpose is to provide you with a capsule history of each brand. This history includes:

Who distributed the brand,

Trademarks associated with the brand,

What cutlery firm made the brand, when known,

Where the distributor was located,

What country or countries the brand was made in,

What business the distributor was in,

What years it was in business.

The second purpose of this list is to help you to estimate the value of almost any pocketknife that you are interested in. For this purpose, refer to the last column in the list, the one headed "$."

In this "$" column, each brand is rated either **V** (Very High), **H** (High), **M** (Medium), or **L** (Low).

These ratings are used, together with the price charts in the pocketknife shape and pattern chapters, to determine the values of pocketknives. The method is explained in the *Introduction to Standard American Folding Knife Patterns*. For brands and patterns not listed, consult either *Foreign Exotic, Primitive and Historical Folding Knives*, or else *Contemporary Custom and Hand-Made Folding Knives*.

Acknowledgements

In compiling this list, I received the help of several books and many individuals. The books I found most helpful were:

Pocketknives, Markings of Manufacturers and Dealers
    by John Goins,
Collector Knives
    by James Parker and Bruce Voyles,
Romance of Knife Collecting
    by Dewey and Lavona Ferguson,
Sheffield Bowie and Pocket-knife Makers
    by Richard Washer,
Sword and Bayonet Makers of Imperial Germany
    by John Walter,
Cutlery Made in Germany 1953 and 1983 Editions.

Dozens of collectors and dealers around the world helped me in my search for brands and for information about them. Special contributions were made by Siegfried Rosenkaimer of Solingen, Nilo Miori of Camillus, Cindy Rabb, Tom Heitzman, Charlie Dorton, Adrian Van Dyk, Bill Lung, Oscar Hauenstein, Larry Angell, and Charles Ochs.

If you have a knife with a brand not listed here, please send me a copy of the marking, along with a picture (tracing, photo, or photocopy) and description of the knife: Bernard Levine, Box 40336-D, San Francisco CA 94140.

POCKETKNIFE BRAND	TRADEMARK (or Reference)	LOCATION	MADE IN:	TYPE OF FIRM	DATES	$
A. & F. Co.	see Abercrombie & Fitch					
A. A. A. 1	see A. J. Jordan					
A. C. S.	see Alex. Coppel					
A. Co.	see Albertson Co.	Kane PA				
Abercrombie & Fitch Co.	A. & F. Co.	New York NY	US/Ger/Eng	Retail	1892–c1978	H
Acier Fondu = Cast Steel (French)	(also on old Sheffield blades)					
Adolphus Cutlery Co.	by A. J. Jordan	St. Louis MO	Ger./Eng.	Import brand	c1882–90s	M
Aerial Cutlery Co.	Jaeger Bros.	Duluth MN	USA	Mfr.	1909–1912	H
Aerial Cutlery Co.	Jaeger Bros.	Marinette WI	USA	Mfr.	1912–1944	M
Ahrens, Ernst G.		Solingen	Germany	Mfr. ?	c1910 ?	M
Ainslie-Martin Co.		Lynchburg VA		Hdw. Whol.	1900–1922	M
Akron Cutlery Works		Akron OH			1911–1928	M
Alamo			Japan	Import brand	recent	L
Albacete	(place name)		Spain			
Albertson Co. (A. Co.)	formerly Hollingsworth	Kane PA	USA	Mfr.	c1930–1938	M
Alcoso	see Alex. Coppel	Solingen	Germany	Mfr.	c1933–pres.	L
Alexander		Sheffield	England	Mfr.?	c1860s	H

POCKETKNIFE BRAND	TRADEMARK (or Reference)	LOCATION	MADE IN:	TYPE OF FIRM	DATES	$
Allen Cutlery Co.		Newburgh NY	USA	Mfr.	1917–1925	M
Allen, E. T.	The Club	San Francisco CA	England(?)	Whol. Importer	1878–1899	H
Allen, Edgar	Imperial Steel Works	Sheffield	England	Mfr.	c1870–1927	M
Allen, Joseph & Sons	NON-XLL	Sheffield	England	Mfr.	1886–1947	M
Alpha	see Harrison Brothers & Howson					
Altenbach, Peter, & Sohne	Swanwerk	Solingen	Germany	Mfr.	c1920–pres.	L
Altman, B., & Co.		New York NY	Germany	Retail	c1900?	M
Ambacher, J.		Sandusky OH	USA	Mfr. & Ret.	c1869–1891	M
Ambassador	see Colonial Knife Co.	Providence RI	USA	Mfr.	1951–pres.	L
American Ace	see N. J. Cutlery Co.					
American Blade Cutlery Co.	see Parker Cutlery Co.	Chattanooga TN	Japan	Whol. Importer	1981–pres.	M
American Cutlery Co.	pocketknives pre-1900	Chicago IL	USA	Mfr.	1879–c1923	M
American Hardware & Supply Co.	American Beauty	Pittsburgh PA		Hdw. Whol.	c1911–1935	M
American Knife Co.		Thomaston CT (called Plymouth Hollow to 1875)	USA	Mfr.	1849–1911	H
American Knife Co.		Winsted CT	USA	Mfr.	1919–1955	H
American Shear & Knife Co.	first pocketknives 1870	Hotchkissville CT	USA	Mfr.	1853–1914	H
Ames Manufacturing Co.		Chicopee MA	USA	Mfr. (& Whol.?)	1829–1900	H
Anglo-Pacific Cutlery Co.			England	Import brand	19th Cent.	H
Anheuser Busch	by Kastor, Wester, and Konejung	St. Louis MO	Germany	Brewer Advt.	c1880–1914	V
Anheuser Busch	made by Camillus	St. Louis MO	USA	Brewer Advt.	c1932–1948	H
Anvil	see Colonial Knife Co. (current) or Meriden Cutlery Co. (pre-1921)					
Arbolito = Little Tree (Spanish)	see H. Boker, Germany					
Ardobo Cutlery Co.			Germany	Import brand	c1930	L
Argyle Cutlery Co.			Germany	Import brand	c1910	L
Arkansas Traveler	see Fones Bros.					
Arnold	(On a folding cutlass)	Namur	Belgium	Mfr. or Retail	c1900	H
Arrow Brand	see Adolph Blaich					
Arrow Co.			Germany	Import brand	c1920s?	L
Arrows (five) around circle	see Mueller & Schmidt		Germany			
Arrows (two) crossed, in circle	see China Light Ind	Shanghai	China			
Atco			Japan	Import brand	recent	L
Atkins, William	Turtle (picture)	Sheffield	England	Mfr.	c1848–1913	M
Atkinson Bros.	Bear (picture)/In Mind	Sheffield	England	Mfr.	c1845–pres.	M
Atlantic Cutlery Co.			Germany	Import brand	pre–1915	L
Auto(matic) Knife Co.	Wilzin's patent	Middletown CT	USA	Mfr.?	c1889–?	H
Autopoint		Chicago IL	USA	Ad. Specialties	c1950	L
B. & B.	see Brown & Bigelow					
B. B. Knife Co.	see Beaver Brook					
B. P. Co. Ltd.	see Butterick Pattern Co.					
B. T. Co.	see Bridgeport Tool Co.					
Bagshaw, William		Sheffield	England	Mfr.	c1830s–50s	H
Baker & Hamilton	(on tang c1915–1918)	San Francisco CA	US	Hdw. Whol.	1853–1981	H
Baker & Hamilton	(Golden Gate Cutlery Co. c1890s)	San Francisco CA	US/Ger/Eng	Hdw. Whol.	1853–1981	H
Baker & Hamilton	(Damascus by New Haven or Eclipse, pre-1918)	San Francisco CA	US/Ger/Eng	Hdw. Whol.	1853–1981	H
Baker Hamilton & Pacific	Stiletto (Cutlery Co.)	San Francisco CA	USA	Hdw. Whol.	1918–c1945	H
Baker, W. Jno.		Sydney, Australia	England	Retail Importer	1888–pres.	M
Baldwin Cutlery Co.		Tidioute PA; Jamestown NY	USA	Mfr.	c1912–1932	M
Baldwin, A., & Co.		New Orleans LA	USA	Hdw. Whol.	1874–pres.	H
Balke & Schaaf	Lamb (picture)	Solingen	Germany	Mfr.?	c1910?	M
Banner Cutlery Company		New York NY	Germany	Import Brand	pre–1915?	L
Barber, James	ERA. see Thomas Ellin					
Barber, John		Sheffield	England	Mfr.	1810–1834	H
Barber, John, & Son		Sheffield	England	Mfr.	1834–c1852	H
Barge, Henry		Sheffield	England	Mfr.	c1850	H
Barker, C. B., & Co.	see Howard Cutlery Co.					
Barker, C. C.	(on handle)	Cumby TX	USA	Mfr., Blacksmith	1920–1974	M
Barlow, Samuel	BARLOW Z ° Scimitar (picture)	Neepsend, Sheffield	England	Mfr.	c1780–1840	V
Barnes, Edward, & Sons	U.★S.	Sheffield	England	Mfr.	c1856–1865	H

POCKETKNIFE BRAND	TRADEMARK (or Reference)	LOCATION	MADE IN:	TYPE OF FIRM	DATES	$
Barnes, Isaac		Sheffield	England	Mfr.	c1837–1870	H
Barnett, O(scar), Tool Co./J. C. Lewis Patent; H. H. H.		Newark NJ	USA	Mfr.	1900–c1915	H
Barnsley, T. C. Mfg. Co.		Oklahoma City OK	USA	Mfr.	c1898	H
Barnsley Brothers		Monett MO	USA	Mfr. & Whol.	1898–1906	M
Barnsley, George & Sons	Wide Awake	Sheffield	England	Mfr.	c1839–1938	M
Barrel (picture)	see Daniel Peres					
Barrett Hicks Co.		Fresno CA	USA?	Whol. or retail	c1920s?	H
Battle Axe Cutlery Co.	see A. R. Justice Co.	Philadelphia PA		Hdw. Whol.	c1897–1937	M
Battle Axe Knives		Winston-Salem NC	Germany	Retail Ltd. Ed.	current	M
Bauer			Germany		c1930	L
Bay State Mfg. Co		Worcester MA	USA			M
Bayonne Knife Co.		Bayonne NJ	USA	Whol. (Mfr.?)	1888–1898	M
Beach, W.		Salisbury	England	Mfr.	c1850	H
Beal, Josh., (& Sons)	Endure, Sound, Boar	Sheffield	England	Mfr.	c1870s–90s	H
Bean, L. L.		Freeport ME	USA	Retail	1912–pres.	M
Beaver Brook Knife Co.	B. B. Knife Co.	Beaver Brook MA	USA	Mfr.	c1880	H
Beaver Falls Cutlery Co.	(equipment sold to Cattaraugus 1890)	Rochester PA	USA	Mfr.	1866–1886	H
Beck & Gregg Hdwe. Co.	Dixie Knife	Atlanta GA		Hdw. Whol.	c1890–30s	M
Bee Hive (picture)	see Slater Bros.					
Belknap Hardware Co.	Primble, Blue Grass	Louisville KY	US/Ger.	Hdw. Whol.	c1840–pres.	M
Bench Mark Knives		Gastonia NC	USA	Mfr.	1970s–1984	M
Bench Mark Knives	made by Gerber	Portland OR	USA	Mfr.	1984–pres.	M
Berg, Erik Anton		Eskilstuna	Sweden	Mfr.	c1880–1920	M
Berkshire Cutlery Co.	O-U-NO		Germany	Import Brand	c1890	L
Berns, Gebruder (Bros.)	Otter	Solingen	Germany	Mfr.	1840–pres.	M
Bernstein, Samuel E. (Nat'l. Silver)	Royal Brand Sharp Cutter	New York NY	US/Ger/Jap	Whol. & Importer	c1890–50s	M
Bertram, Carl	Hen & Rooster	Solingen	Germany	Mfr.	1864–1983	H
Besteel Warranted			USA?	Discount brand	c1930s	L
Best English Cutlery			Eng./Ger.	Import mark	c1800–1860	H
Biddle Hardware	was Robbins Clark & Biddle?	Philadelphia PA		Hdw. Whol.	20th cent.	M
Biffar, Fred (made by Camillus)	Dixie Switch	Chicago IL	USA	Retail?	1917–1922	M
Bigelow & Dowse		Boston, Springfield MA		Whol. & Retail	1872–1954	M
Billings & Spencer Co., The	(knives c1890–1914)	Hartford CT	USA	Tool Mfr.	1872–1963	V
Billings, J. W.	X. X. L. Cutlery	Sheffield			c1880s	M
Bingham, W., Co.	XLCR, BBB. Ulster's agent	Cleveland OH	USA	Whol.	c1841–1930	M
Birmingham Knife Factory		Birmingham (Derby) CT	USA	Mfr.	c1849	V
Blaich, Adolph/J.S. Holler	Arrow Brand	San Francisco CA	Germany	Whol. Importer	c1893–1915	H
Blaich, Adolph, Inc.	moved to Reno NV 1954	San Francisco CA		Whol. Spt. Gds.	1915–pres.	M
Blake & Lamb	made by Utica	Utica NY	USA	Trap mfr.	c1930	M
Bleckmann, J. E.	exported to England	Solingen	Germany	Mfr.	1808–c1980	M
Blish Mize Silliman Hardware Co.	Mohawk	Atchison KS	USA	Hdw. Whol.	1871–pres.	M
Blue Grass	see Belknap Hdw. Co.					
Blue Ribbon Cutlery Co.	see Belknap Hdw. Co.				1910–ff.	M
Blyde, John	Genius	Sheffield	England	Mfr.	c1875	M
Boden, James		Sheffield	England	Mfr.?	c1860?	M
Boentgen & Sabin, Bonsa-Werk	many trademarks	Solingen	Germany	Mfr.	1867–1983	L
Bofil		Vich, Catalonia	Spain	Mfr.	current	L
Boker's, H(ermann), Improved Cutlery	merged into Boker U.S.A.	Newark NJ	USA	Whol. & Import	1837–1917	M
Boker, Heinrich	Tree Brand. Arbolito	Solingen	Germany	Mfr.	1868–pres.	M
Boker, U.S.A.	sold to J. Wiss 1969	Newark & Maplewood NJ	USA	Mfr.	1899–pres.	M
Boker, Henry HB/2 bird heads (pic)	(made for Australia?)	Solingen	Germany	Mfr.	c1950s	M
Bonsa	see Boentgen & Sabin					
Bonsmann, E.		Solingen	Germany	Mfr.?	1861–c1920	M
Boom Fixer	see Union Cutlery Co.					
Booth Bros.	Exhibited at 1867 Paris Exposition	Newark NJ	USA	Mfr.	1864–1879	H
Booth Bros.		Boonton NJ	USA	Mfr.	1879–1889	H
Booth Bros.		Stockholm NJ	USA	Mfr.	1889–1903	H
Booth Bros.		Sussex NJ	USA	Mfr.	1903–1909	H
Borgfeldt, George, & Co.	Twig, Nifty. Eagle agent	New York NY		Whol. & Imp.	c1895–1927	M

POCKETKNIFE BRAND	TRADEMARK (or Reference)	LOCATION	MADE IN:	TYPE OF FIRM	DATES	$
Bostwick Braun Co.		Toledo OH	USA	Hdw. Whol.	1873–pres.	M
Bowen Knife Co.	Bullet	Waycross GA	USA	Mfr.	1973–pres.	M
Boy of America, The (on handle)	see J. Russell					
Bracht, Fritz	(now owns Hartkopf) Dovo, Raucherkopf (now)	Solingen	Germany	Mfr.	1887–pres.	M
Bradford & Anthony	became Dame Stoddard & Kendall	Boston MA		Retail & Whol.	1856–1883	H
Bradford, Martin L., (& Son)	became Bradford & Anthony	Boston MA		Retail	1845–1856	H
Bradford, R. & W.	9 Patricks Road	Cork	Ireland	Mfr.	c1850	H
Bradford, Samuel		Clonmel	Ireland	Mfr.	c1850	H
Bradlee, Samuel	sold to M. L. Bradford	Boston MA		Retail	1799–1845	H
Bradley, L(yman), & Co.		Naugatuck CT	USA	Mfr. & Whol.	c1841–1896	H
Brantford Cutlery Co.	Warranted Never Dull	?			c1900?	M
Bridge Cutlery Co.	(sold by Shapleigh Hdw.)	St. Louis MO	USA	Mfr.?	c1915	H
Bridgeport Tool Co.	B. T. Co., Pequot Brand	New Haven CT	USA	Whol. (Mfr.?)	c1910s–20s	M
Brighton Cutlery Works			Germany	Import brand	c1900?	M
Bristoline			Germany	Ad. Spec.?	c1950s	M
Brit-Nife		St. Louis MO				L
Britnal Terry & Belden	imported Wester & Butz	Chicago IL		Whol. & Imp.	?–1876	H
Brokhahne, William	W. B., Speed (to Wiebusch 1906)	New York NY		Whol. Importer	c1875–1906	M
Brookes & Crookes	Bell (picture)	Sheffield	England	Mfr.	c1859–1947	H
Brooksbank, Abram	Defiance	Sheffield	England	Mfr.	c1849–1864	M
Brown & Bigelow	B & B, mfd. by Colonial	St. Paul MN	USA	Advt. Specialty	1931–1950s	L
Brown Bros.	became Union Razor Co.	Tidioute PA	Ger./US	Whol. & Imp.	c1890–1902	H
Brown Camp Hardware Co.	I. O. A.	Des Moines IA		Hdw. Whol.	c1907–1959	M
Brown, Buster, Shoe Co.	by Camillus via Shapleigh	St. Louis MO	USA	Shoe Mfr. Ad.	c1930s	H
Brown, John,	Columbia Works c1830s Atlas Works after 1875	Sheffield	England	Mfr.	19th Cent.	H
Brown, The Ralph, Co.		San Francisco CA		Wholesale	c1910	M
Browning		Morgan UT	US/Ger/Jap	Mfr. & Imp.	1969–pres.	M
Brueckmann, Ernst	Bridge (picture)	Solingen-Ohligs	Germany	Mfr.	1891–c1956	M
Brunswick Cutlery Co.	D. C. & H. economy brand	San Francisco CA	Germany	Hdw. Whol. Imp.	c1897–1907	L
Buck (lockback folders)	(Buck established before WWII)	San Diego/El Cajon CA	USA	Mfr.	1963–pres.	M
Buck (multiblades)	made by Schrade, Camillus	San Diego/El Cajon CA	USA	Whol. (mfr. '84–pres.)	1966–pres.	M
Buck Creek		London KY	Ger./Japan	Whol. Importer	1970–pres.	M
Bud Brand Cutlery Co.		Winsted CT	USA	Mfr.	c1922	H
Buffalo Cutlery Co.				Whol.?	c1915?	M
Bull Head Cutlery Co.			USA?		c1930?	M
Bulldog Brand		Kingsport TN	Germany	Whol. Importer	1980s–pres.	M
Bunting, R., & Sons		Sheffield	England	Mfr.	c1837–1868	H
Burgon & Ball	Sound	Sheffield	England	Mfr.	c1873–1917	M
Burkinshaw, Aaron	Exile, Pain	(in CT 1846) Pepperell MA	USA	Mfr.	1853–1920	V
Burnand, James, & Sons	Indian (picture), Self Defence	Sheffield	England	Mfr.	c1865–70s	H
Busch, Adolphus	see Anheuser Busch					
Busch, Wilhelm, Soehne	part of Exportring Solingen	Solingen-Ohligs	Germany	Mfr.	c1950s	L
Buster, Frank, Cutlery Co.	Fight'n Rooster	Lebanon TN	Germany	Ltd. Edit. Imp.	1977–pres.	H
Butcher, W(illiam) & S(amuel)	Wade & Butcher, X.C.D.	Sheffield	England	Mfr.	c1819–1947	H
Butler Brothers (by Brantford?)	Warranted Never Dull	Chicago IL	USA	Whol. (?)	c1888–1907	M
Butler, George (& James), & Co.	Key, Cavendish	Sheffield	England	Mfr.	c1681–1972	M
Butterick Pattern Co.	B. P. Co. Ltd.		Germany	Sewing Advt.	c1910	M
C. C. Knife Co.	see Central City Knife Co					
C. J. (in flag)	see Christopher Johnson					
C. K. Co.	see Colonial Knife Co.					
Cadman, Thomas R., & Sons		Sheffield	England	Mfr.	c1870–1947	M
Caldwell, A. B., Cutlery Co.	sold by Van Camp Hdw. Co.	Indianapolis IN	Germany	Hdw. Whol.	c1910	M
California Notion & Toy Co.		San Francisco CA		Whol. Import	1894–c1930	M
Cam III Enterprises		Vacaville CA	Japan	Whol. Importer	current	M
Cambridge Cutlery Co.	(US Navy contractor)	Sheffield (?)	England	Export Brand	c1865	H
Camco	(Camillus economy brand)	Camillus NY	USA	Mfr.	1948–pres.	L

POCKETKNIFE BRAND	TRADEMARK (or Reference)	LOCATION	MADE IN:	TYPE OF FIRM	DATES	$
Cameron Knife Co.			USA?		c1920s?	M
Camillus/Cutlery Co./Camillus NY/ USA	(mark used through WWII)	Camillus NY	USA	Mfr.	1902–pres.	M
Camillus/New York/USA	(mark used after WWII)	Camillus NY	USA	Mfr.	1902–pres.	M
Canastota Knife Co.		Canastota NY	USA	Mfr.	1875–1895	V
Canton Cutlery Co.	W. S. Carnes	Canton OH	USA	Mfr.	1879–c1930	M
Canton Hardware Co.	Keen Edge	Canton OH	US/Ger.	Hdw. Whol.	c1910	M
Canton Knife Co.	see Novelty Cutlery Co.					
Capitol Cutlery Co.	owned by Van Camp Hdw.	Indianapolis IN	USA	Mfr.	1904–1948	M
Capitol Knife Co.		Winsted CT	USA	Mfr.	c1920s	M
Car-Van S(teel) P(roducts)	see Canton Cutlery Co.				1911–c1930	
Carrier Cutlery Co.	see Cronk & Carrier	Elmira NY	USA	Mfr.	1900–1921	M
Carters/Hen & Rooster	made by Bertram	Scottsville KY	Germany	Retail	1969–1983	H
Case Brothers & Co.	made by C. Platts & Sons	Gowanda NY	USA	Whol.	1896–1900	V
Case Brothers Cutlery Co.	Tested XX (by itself)	Little Valley NY	USA	Mfr.	1900–1912	V
Case Cutlery Co. (branch of Case Bros. Cut. Co., L.V. NY)		Kane PA	USA	Mfr.	1907–1911	V
Case Brothers Cutlery Co.	Tested XX (by itself)	Springville NY	USA	Mfr.	1912–1915	V
Case Mfg. Co.		Little Valley NY	USA	Whol.	c1898–1899	V
Case, J. D.	see Case Mfg. Co.	Little Valley NY	USA	Whol.	c1898–1899	V
Case, Jean	see Kinfolks Inc.				1928–1948	
Case, W. R., & Son Cutlery Co.	(made by Napanoch)	Little Valley NY	USA	Whol.	1902–1905	V
Case, W. R., & Sons Cutlery Co.	(made by Platts)	Little Valley NY	USA	Whol.	1904–1905	V
Case, W. R., & Sons Cutlery Co.		Bradford PA	USA	Mfr.	1905–1920	V
Case, W. R., & Sons Cutlery Co.	W. R. Case & Sons	Bradford PA	Germany	Import	pre-1914	H
Case, W. R., & Sons Cutlery Co.	Case/Tested XX	Bradford PA	USA	Mfr.	1920–1940	V
Case, W. R., & Sons Cutlery Co.	CASE/XX	Bradford PA	USA	Mfr.	1940–1965	H
Case, W. R., & Sons Cutlery Co.	CASE XX/Made in U.S.A.	Bradford PA	USA	Mfr.	1965–pres.	M
Case XX Metal Stampings Ltd.	by Case for Canadian gov't.	Bradford PA	USA	Mfr.	1940s	H
Cattaraugus Cutlery Co.		Little Valley NY	USA	Whol.	1886–1891	H
Cattaraugus Cutlery Co.		Little Valley NY	USA	Mfr.	1891–1963	H
Cattaraugus (limited edition)	by Knife Collector's Club	Springdale AR		Retail	1984–pres.	M
Central City Knife Co.	C. C. Knife Co.	Phoenix NY	USA	Mfr.	1880–1892	H
Central Cutlery Co.		Elizabeth NJ	USA	Mfr.?	c1926	M
Challenge Cutlery Co.	owner: Wiebusch & Hilger	Sheffield or NYC	Eng./Ger.	Importer	1867–1914	M
Challenge Cutlery Co.	owner: Wiebusch & Hilger	Bridgeport CT	USA	Mfr.	1899–1926	H
Chalmers, (Thomas), & Murray		New York NY		Whol.	c1890s	M
Chapman (E. Byron) Cut. (or Mfg.) Co.	Chapman Hand Forged	Muncie IN	USA	Whol.	1915–1931	M
Chatellerault	(place name)		France			
Chatillon, John, & Sons		New York NY	USA	Mfr.(or Whol.?)	c1894–1937	H
China Light Ind. Prod. Imp. & Exp.	Fong Yuon/Whirling Square	Canton, Guangdong	P.R. China	Mfr.	current	L
China Light Ind. Prod. Imp. & Exp.	Crossed arrows	Shanghai	P.R. China	Mfr.	current	L
China Light Ind. Prod. Imp. & Exp.	Rose in circle	Tsingtao, Shantung	P.R. China	Mfr.	current	L
Chipaway Cutlery Co.	for E. C. Simmons Hdw.			Whol.	c1891–1907	M
Christians, Gebruder (Bros.)	Fork (picture)	Solingen	Germany	Mfr.	1824–pres.	M
Christy (Russ J.) Knife Co.		Fremont OH	USA	Mfr.	1890–pres.	L
Claflin, H. B., & Co.	(US Navy contractor)				19th Cent.	H
Clarenbach & Herder	see Herder's					
Clark Brothers	bought Northfield in 1919	Kansas City MO	US/Eng/Ger	Mfr. & Imp.	1895–1929	M
Clarke, John, & Son	Wm. Rodgers, John Holmes	Sheffield	England	Mfr.	1848–pres.	M
Clauberg, Wilhelm	Knight (sub. of A. Wingen)	Solingen	Germany	Mfr.	1857–pres.	M
Clauss Cutlery Co.	S. & M. made some c1925	Fremont OH	USA	Whol. & Mfr.	1887–pres.	M
Clay Cutlery Co.	made by Robeson (?)	Andover NY	USA		?	M
Clean Cut (Clover)	(imp. by Kastor for Dunham Carrigan)	San Francisco CA	Austria?	Hdw. Whol.	c1884–1912	M
Clearcut	see George Worthington					
Clements	Hand Forged	Sheffield	England	Mfr.	20th cent.	M
Clim(Axe)	see Schmachtenberg					
Clipper Cutlery Co.	see Watkins Cottrell					
Clover Brand	see Kastor and Camillus	Camillus, N.Y.C.	US/Ger.	Mfr. Importer	pre-WWII	L
Clover Brand	made by Camillus	"Syracuse" NY	USA	Mfr.	c1941–42	L
Clyde Cutlery Co.	sold po'k's c1930s	Clyde OH	USA	Mfr.(& whol.?)	1850–pres?	M
Coast Cutlery Co.		Portland OR	USA	Whol.	1919–pres.	M
Coca Cola (genuine)	made by Camillus	Atlanta GA	USA	Bottler Advt.	1930s–40s	H
Coca Cola (counterfeit)			Germany		1970s–80s	L

POCKETKNIFE BRAND	TRADEMARK (or Reference)	LOCATION	MADE IN:	TYPE OF FIRM	DATES	$
Coca Cola 5¢ on handle, USA on tang	(fantasy by Colonial)	Providence RI	USA		1980s	L
Cole National Corp.	markets Kabar (USA), Khyber (Japan)	Cleveland OH	US/Japan	Whol. & Imp.	c1960s–pres.	
Coles	Hand Forged	New York NY	Germany	Whol. Importer	c1960s	M
Colonel Coon Knives	Racoon	Columbia TN	USA	Mfr.	1978–pres.	H
Colonial Cutlery Co.	see Schwabacher Hdw. Co.					
Colonial Knife Co.	many trademarks	Providence RI	USA	Mfr.	1926–pres.	L
Colt	by Barry Wood, Venice CA	Hartford CT	USA	Whol., Gun.Mfr.	1969–1973	H
Columbia Knife Co					c1900	M
Commander	(probably made for Metropolitan Cutlery Co.)					
Concord Cutlery Co.			Germany?	Import brand	c1880	M
Congreve, C(harles)	W(crown)R	Sheffield	England	Mfr.	1829–1843	V
Conn(ecticut) Cutlery Co.		Naugatuck CT	USA	Mfr.	1867–1883	H
Conn(ecticut) Cutlery Co.		Thomaston CT	USA	Mfr.?		H
Continental Cutlery Co.	see Clark Bros.	KC/NYC/Sheffield		Whol.?	1915–1920	M
CoO Knife Co.	see Cooperative Knife Co.					
Cook Bros.		Sheffield	England	Mfr.?	c1890	M
Cooperative Knife Co.	became Ulster	Walden/Ellenville NY	USA	Mfr.	1871–1876	V
Copley, J., & Sons	XX	Sheffield	England	Mfr.	c1876–1924	M
Coppel, Alexander	Balance, Alcoso, A. C. S.	Solingen	Germany	Mfr.	1821–pres.	L
Corning Knife Co.		New York (?) NY		?	c1930s	M
Cornwall Knife Co.		Cornwall (?) CT	USA	Mfr.?	19th Cent.	H
Cornwall Knife Co.	(possibly William M. Cornwall?)	New York NY		Whol.	c1880s?	M
Corsan Denton Burdekin		Sheffield	England	Mfr.	c1860	H
Craftsman (Sears Roebuck)	by Camillus, Schrade, Ulster	Chicago IL	USA	Retail	1940s–pres.	M
Cranberry	see Luttrell, McClung Hdw.					
Crandall Cutlery Co.	merged with W. R. Case	Bradford PA	USA	Mfr.	1905–1912	H
Cresta		Sheffield	England		20th Cent.	L
Creutzberg, George F.	Eagle/Phil'a	Philadelphia PA	USA	Whol. & Seconds	c1875–1943	M
Cripple Creek	by Bob Cargill	Lockport IL	USA	Mfr. Ltd. Edit.	1981–pres.	H
Criterion	see Alfred Field		Ger./Eng.?	Import Brand		
Croisdale		Leeds	England	Retail?		M
Cromwell Criterion	probably Alfred Field					
Cronk & Carrier Mfg. Co.	Carrier Cutlery Co.	Elmira NY	USA	Mfr.	1900–1921	M
Crookes, G. or H., & Co.		Sheffield	England	Mfr.	c1836–1867	M
Crookes, Jonathan	Heart and Pistol	Sheffield	England	Mfr.	c1780–1827	H
Crookes, Jonathan, & Son	Heart and Pistol (to H. Slater 1947)	Sheffield	England	Mfr.	1827–pres.	M
Crosman Blades		Wichita KS	USA	Whol.	1982–pres.	M
Crouch, Jess (stamped on blade)	see Queen Cutlery Co.					
Crown Cutlery Co.		New York NY	Germany	Whol. importer	1910s–20s	L
Crown with wings	see Olbertz					
Crucible Knife Co.	sold by W. T. Grant, NYC	Lynn MA	USA	Mfr.?, Retail	1921–1932	M
Cunningham Hdw. Co.				Hdw. Whol.		M
Curley, J., & Brother (Terrence)		New York NY		Whol/Imp/Invent	c1880–1925	M
Curtin & Clark Cutlery Co.		St. Joseph and Kansas City MO	USA	Whol.	c1910	M
Cussin & Fearn			USA	Retail (prize)	1930s	M
Cut Sure	see Kruse & Bahlman					
Cutino Cutlery Co.	some made by Challenge	Kansas City MO	USA	Retail?	c1914–1935	M
Cutter (boat)	see Thomas Ellin					
D. C. & H.	see Dunham Carrigan & Hayden					
D. E.	see Diamond Edge					
D.R.G.M. = Registered pattern (German)						
D.R.P. or D.R.Pat. = Patented (German)						
D. S. & K.	see Dame Stoddard & Kendall					
Dahmann, Herman	has merged with A. Wingen	Solingen	Germany	Mfr.	1950s	L
Damascus (for Baker & Hamilton)	see Eclipse or New Haven					
Damascus Steel Products Corp.	DASCO	Rockford IL	USA	Whol.?	1922–1962	M
Dame Stoddard & Kendall	(DS&K, Hub) was Bradford & Anthony	Boston MA		Retail & Whol.	1883–c1932	H
DASCO	see Damascus Steel Products					

POCKETKNIFE BRAND	TRADEMARK (or Reference)	LOCATION	MADE IN:	TYPE OF FIRM	DATES	$
Davy, Abraham (& Sons, after 1856)		Sheffield	England	Mfr.	c1836–1870	H
Dawes & Ball		Sheffield	England			M
Dawson Hardened Copper Co.	see Hardened Copper Cut. Co.?	New York NY				
Deakin	Lamp	Sheffield	England	Mfr.	c1847–1870	M
DeBoer & Bach		New York NY	US/Eng/Ger	Whol. Importer	c1915–1920	L
Deerslayer Brand	see Precise					
Defender	(on .22 knife-pistol)		USA?		c1912?	H
Delmar Cutlery Co.			Germany?	Import Brand?	c1910	M
Delta	see Hugo Linder					
DeLuxe	see Salm	Torrance CA	USA	Mfr.?	1918–1925	L
Depend-on Me Cutlery Co.		New York NY	USA?		c1945	M
Dewing Tyler & Co.		Worcester MA			c1820	V
Diamond Edge (D-E)	Shapleigh until 1960, then Imperial.					
Dickinson, E. M.		Sheffield	England	Mfr.	c1870–1912	M
Dictator			USA	Retailer brand?	c1930s	L
Dinger, H.	(made in Solingen)	Kaiserslautern	Germany	Retail?	c1930s?	M
Dispatch	see Peter L. Schmidt					
Disston Steel	(commemorative, probably by Camillus)	Philadelphia PA	USA	Saw Mfr.	1940	H
Divine, Dwight, & Sons	Ulster Knife Co., Kingston	Ellenville NY	USA	Mfr.	1876–1941	H
Dixie Knife	see Beck & Gregg					
Dixon Cutlery Co.	made in Werwolf Work	?	Germany	Whol. Importer	c1920s?	M
Dobson, George		Sheffield	England	Mfr.?	c1880s	M
Dodson Mfg. Co.		Chicago IL	USA	Ad. specialty?	c1937	M
Dollar Knife Co.	see Schatt & Morgan	Titusville PA	USA	Mfr.	c1927	M
Dolphin Cutlery Co.		New York NY	Germany	Whol. Importer	1918–1920s	M
Domar Cutlery Co.	Theodore M. Green Co.	Oklahoma City OK	USA	Whol.	c1916–1920	M
Dooley	D with arrow	Cincinnati (?) OH	USA	Mfr.	c1950s?	M
Dreiturm (Three Spires)	see J. A. Schmidt					
Dreizack (Trident)	see Ed. Wusthof					
Droescher, Severin R.	S.R.D./Arrow	New York NY	Sweden &?	Whol. Importer	c1891–1924	L
Duane Cutlery Co.	(Kastor brand?)		Germany	Import brand	c1910	L
Duke Peterson Hdw. Co.				Hdw. Whol.	c1920s?	M
Dunham Carrigan & Hayden	Clean Cut, Springbrooke, Volka	San Francisco CA	US/Ger.	Hdw. Whol.	1848–1964	M
Dunlap, J.	dist. by Schmachtenberg	New York NY	Germany	Whol. Importer	1916–c1939	L
Dunn Bros.		Providence RI	USA	Jewelry Mfr.	1927–pres.	L
E. F. & S.	see Furness					
E. K. A.	see Eskilstuna Knivfabriks Aktiebolag					
E. P. Co.	see Eagle Pencil Co.					
E/crowned anchor	see Eskilstuna Jernmanufaktur Aktiebolag					
Eagle	has Frary patent bolster	Bridgeport CT	USA?		c1890	M
Eagle Brand	see Parker Cutlery		Japan			
Eagle Knife Co. (sold to Winchester 1919)	Hemming Pat. 10/1/1918	New Haven CT	USA	Mfr. & Inventor	1916–1919	H
Eagle Pencil Co.		New York NY	USA	Mfr.	c1883–1945	L
Eagle/Phil'a	see Creutzberg					
Ebro	see Adolph Kastor					
Eclipse Cutlery Co. "Damascus"	see Baker & Hamilton	San Francisco CA	US or Ger.?	Hdw. Whol.	c189?–1918	M
Edge Mark	for Gutmann Cutlery, Inc.	Mount Vernon NY	Ger./Japan	Whol. Importer	c1950–pres.	M
El Gallo = Rooster (Spanish)	see Carl Schlieper					
Elberfield Cutlery Co.	made by Wester & Butz		Germany	Export brand	c1866–1891	M
Electric Cutlery Co./Newark N.J.	Friedmann & Lauterjung	New York NY	USA	Whol.	1873–c1901	M
Electric Cutlery Co./Walden N.Y.	Friedmann & Lauterjung	New York NY	USA	Whol.	c1901–?	H
Electron	see J. A. Schmidt					
Elinox	see Elsener, Victoria					
Elk	see Premier Cutlery Co.					
Ellenville Knife Co.	see Dwight Divine & Sons	Ellenville NY	USA	Mfr.	1876–?	H
Ellin, Thomas	J. Barber ERA, Vulcan	Sheffield	England	Mfr.	c1840–1970	M
Elliot, William	(owned by Adolph Strauss 1907–1918)	New York NY		Whol.	c1880–1918	M
Elliott, Joseph		Sheffield	England	Mfr.	1795–pres.	M
Elsener, Karl	Elinox, Victoria, Victorinox	Ibach	Switz.	Mfr.	1884–pres.	
Elyria Cutlery Co.	became Clauss Cutlery Co.	Elyria OH	USA	Mfr. & Whol.	1878–1887	H

POCKETKNIFE BRAND	TRADEMARK (or Reference)	LOCATION	MADE IN:	TYPE OF FIRM	DATES	$
Emmons-Hawkins Hardware Co.	EMHAWCO (by Utica)	Huntington WV	US/Ger.	Hdw. Whol. Ret.	1899–1969	M
Empire Knife Co.	in West Winsted post-1880	Winsted CT	USA	Mfr.	1856–1930	H
Enderes		Albert Lea MN			c1918	M
Enders, Wm.	Oak Leaf, division of E. C. Simmons	St. Louis MO	US/Ger.	Whol.	c1908–1913	M
Endure	see J. Beal					
English Steel (NOT marked Sheffield)	see A. Feist & Co.					
Engstrom, John	(JE/18/74) Wiebusch import	Eskilstuna	Sweden	Mfr.	1874–c1893	M
Enterprise Cutlery Co.	(probably by Camillus and Kastor)	St. Louis MO	US/Ger.	Whol.?	c1920s	M
Erma			Germany	Import brand	c1950s?	L
Ern, C. Friedrich	Crown & Sword	Solingen-Wald	Germany	Mfr.	1873–pres.	L
Eskilstuna Jernmanufaktur Aktiebolag	E on crowned anchor	Eskilstuna	Sweden	Mfr.	1885–1949	M
Eskilstuna Knivfabriks Aktiebolag	E. K. A.	Eskilstuna	Sweden	Mfr.	1917–pres.	M
Eureka Cutlery Co.	became Lackawanna	Nicholson PA	USA	Mfr.	1911–1915	H
Ever-Sharp		Baltimore MD	USA	Retail	1920s	M
Everlastingly Sharp	see Schrade Cutlery Co.					
Excelsior Knife Co.	sold to Northfield c1884	Torrington CT	USA	Mfr.	1880–1884	H
Exclusive Cutlery Shop, The	T. E. C. S.	San Francisco CA	Ger./France	Retail	1911–pres.	M
Executive	see Colonial Knife Co.					
Explorer	see Gutmann Cutlery Co.					
Eye Brand	see Carl Schlieper					
Eyre Ward & Co.	Sheaf Works	Sheffield	England	Mfr.	c1840–1869	H
Eyre, B. J., & Co.	Late W. Greaves & Son	Sheffield	England	Mfr.	1850–c1876	H
Eyre, B. J., Co.	(Wiebusch trademark)	New York NY	Eng./Ger.	Whol. Importer	c1876–1915	M
F. B. Trade Mark	see Forquignon					
Fabyan Knife Co.	Q. E. D.	? NY	Germany?	Importer?	c1890?	M
Fairmount Cutlery Co.	Camillus brand	Camillus NY	USA	Mfr.	1930s	M
Fall River Knife Co.		Fall River (?) MA	Germany	Import brand	c1900	M
Famex or Famexi	see E. & F. Horster					
Fan Brand	(not exported to U.S.) see Carl Schlieper					
Farr, John		Sheffield	England	Mfr.	c1821–1852	M
Farwell Ozmun Kirk & Co.	owned Henry Sears/1897–1959	St. Paul MN	USA	Hdw. Whol.	1881–1959	M
Fayetteville Knife Co.	F. K. Co.	Fayetteville NY	USA	Mfr.	?–1911	H
Featherweight (aluminum frame)	see Utica Cutlery Co.				1932–pres.	
Federal Knife (Cutlery?) Co.	by Camillus (?)	Syracuse NY	USA		c1920s	M
Fein Stahl = Fine steel (German)	usually not made for export					
Feist, A., & Co.	Omega, Lunawerk, English Steel	Solingen	Germany	Mfr.	c1870–1948	M
Felix, Gustav	Gloria-Werke	Solingen	Germany	Mfr.	1850–pres.	L
Fenney, Frederick	Fox, Tally-Ho	Sheffield	England	Mfr.	1824–1852	H
Fenton, Joseph, & Sons		Sheffield	England	Mfr.	c1860	M
Field, Alfred, & Co.	Criterion. agent of J. Rodgers, G. Korn	New York NY	Eng/Ger/US	Whol. Importer	1886–1942	M
Fife Cutlery Co./Hen & Rooster	made by C. Bertram	Mount Sterling KY	Germany		1968–1974	H
Fight'n Rooster	see Frank Buster Cut. Co.					
Fine Steel			Germany?	Import mark	c1890?	M
Finedge Cutlery Co.	Ostiso	New York NY	Germany	Whol.	1920s	M
Firth, Luke		Sheffield	England	Mfr.	c1850?	H
Fisher, J. A., & Co.		New York NY		Whol.?	c1910?	M
Fiskars			Finland	Mfr.	1649–pres.	M
Fleron		Trenton NJ	USA?		c1910?	M
Fletcher Knife Co.		Detroit MI		Hdw. Whol.	c1863–1913	M
Flint, A. W.		Sheffield	England	Mfr. or Exp.	20th Cent.	M
Flylock Knife Co./Challenge Cut. Co.	Geo Schrade pat. 3/5/1918	Bridgeport CT	USA	Mfr.	1918–1928	H
Fones Brothers	Arkansas Traveler	Little Rock AR		Hdw. Whol.	c1881–1914	M
Fong Yuon	see China Light Ind. . . .	Canton, Guangdong	China			
Ford & Medley		Sheffield	England	Mfr.	1872–c1930	M
Forestmaster, Fishmaster	see Colonial	Providence RI	USA	Mfr.	1930s–pres.	L
Fork (picture)	see Gebruder Christians					
Forquignon (Bros.)	F.B., LeRoi Corn Knife	Solingen?	Germany	Mfr.	c1900	M

POCKETKNIFE BRAND	TRADEMARK (or Reference)	LOCATION	MADE IN:	TYPE OF FIRM	DATES	$
Forschner (R. H.) Group	agent for Victorinox	Shelton CT		Whol.		
Fox Cutlery Co.	called Koeller & Schmitz until 1915	Milwaukee WI		Whol.	c1884–1955	M
Frary Cutlery Co. (James D. Frary)	A1 Warranted	Bridgeport CT	USA	Mfr.	1876–1884	H
Frenzel, Franz	imported by Wiebusch	Nixdorf, Bohemia	Aust.-Hung.	Contract Mfr.	c1898	M
Friedmann & Lauterjung Celeb.Cut.	F & L (see also Electric)	New York NY	Ger./USA	Whol.	c1866–19?? current	M
Frontier	see Imperial					
Frost Cutlery Co.	Surgical Steel	Chattanooga TN	Japan USA?	Whol/Ret/Imp.	1978–pres.	M
Frye Phipps & Co.						M
Fulton Cutlery Co.		New York NY		Whol.?	c1910	M
Fulton or Fulltone	see John Kenyon & Co.					
Funke, Leopold	(Bridge Cutlery ??)	St. Louis MO	USA	Mfr.?	c1876	H
Furness, Enoch, & Sons	(E. F. & S.) imported by Wiebusch	Sheffield	England	Mfrs.	c1870–1915	M
G-96	see Jet-Aer					
G. & J. B.	see George & James Butler					
G. C. CO.	see Gutmann Cutlery Co.					
G. R. C. Co.	see Golden Rule Cutlery Co.					
G. W. & H. Hdw. Co.	see Geller Ward Hosner					
Gamble Stores	by Camillus (?)	Minneapolis MN	USA	Retail Hdw.	c1930s–50s	M
Gardner, Joseph (supt. of L. & G.)	GARDNER 1876	Shelburne Falls MA	USA	Mfr.	1876–1883	V
Gebr(uder) = Brothers (German)						
Geller Ward Hosner Hdw. Co.	G. W. & H. Hdw. Co.	St. Louis MO	USA	Hdw. Whol.	c1903–1937	M
Geneva Cutlery Co.	became Geneva Forge 1934	Geneva NY	USA	Mfr.?	1902–1934	M
Geneva Forge, Inc.	div. of E. Katzinger (EKCO)	Geneva NY	USA	Mfr.?	1934–c1948	M
Gerber	Legendary Blades	Portland OR	USA (Jap.)	Mfr. (some imp.)	1939–pres.	M
Germania Cutlery Works	see Edw. Parker & Sons					
Ges. Gesch. = Design patent (German)						
Giesen & Forsthoff	G(man)F. Timor	Solingen	Germany	Mfr.	1920–pres.	L
Gilbert	Saville Works		Eng./Ger.		c1900?	M
Gits Razor Knife (Gitsnife)	by Gits Molding Co.	Chicago IL	USA	Plastics Mfr.	1923–1950	L
Glamorgan Works	see Joseph Haywood					
Globe Cutlery Co.	Pat. 4-25-05	New York NY	USA?	Whol.?	c1922	M
Golden Gate Cutlery Co.	see Baker & Hamilton	San Francisco CA	Ger./US?	Hdw. Whol.	c1890s	H
Golden Rule Cutlery Co.	G. R. C. Co.	Chicago IL	USA	Mfr.	1911–c1924	H
Graef & Schmidt	agency for J. A. Henckels	New York NY	US/Ger.	Whol. Importer	1883–c1948	M
Graef & Schmidt	G. & S. Welkut	Irvington NJ	USA	Mfr.	c1940	M
Grafrath, Gebruder (Bros.)	Grawiso	Solingen	Germany	Mfr.	1869–pres.	M
Graves, J. G.	Enterprise	Sheffield	England	Mfr.	c1869 ff.	M
Grawiso	see Grafrath					
Gray & Dudley Hdw. Co.	Washington Cut. Co.	Nashville TN		Hdw. Whol.	c1885–1927	M
Greaves, W(illiam)	Fame	Sheffield	England	Mfr.	1780–1816	V
Greaves, W(illiam), & Son	sold to B. J. Eyre	Sheffield	England	Mfr.	1816–1850	V
Green, Theo. M.	see Domar Cutlery Co.					
Griffon Cutlery Works	Griffon XX. Carbomagnetic	New York NY	USA	Whol. & Mfr.	c1918–1966	H
Griffon XX	see Griffon Cutlery Works	Worcester MA	USA		c1918–1921	H
Griffon XX	see Griffon Cutlery Works	Bridgeport CT	USA		1921–c1966	H
Guss Stahl = Cast Steel (German)						
Gutmann Cutlery Co.	Explorer; Edge; G.C.CO.	Mount Vernon NY	US/Ger/Jap	Whol. Importer	1947–pres.	M
H. & B. Mfg. Co.	see Humason & Beckley					
H. H. H.	see O. Barnett Tool Co.					
H. H. S.	see E. & F. Horster					
H. S. B. & Co.	see Hibbard Spencer Bartlett					
H'Ville Knife Co.	see Hotchkisville Knife Co.					
Hagg & Co.		Eskilstuna	Sweden	Mfr.	c1920	M
Hague, Samuel		Sheffield	England	Mfr.	c1830s–50s	H
Hale Brothers		Sheffield	England	Mfr.	c1871–1907	M
Hall, Charles	C. Hall	Sheffield	England	Mfr.	c1836–1872	H
Hall, Jonathan	I. Hall	Sheffield	England	Mfr.	1795–1830	H
Hammer Brand (solid bolsters)	see New York Knife Co.	Walden NY	USA	Mfr.	c1880–1931	H
Hammer Brand (shell handles)	see Imperial Knife Co.	Providence RI	USA	Mfr.	1938–pres.	L
Hammesfahr, Gottlieb	Nirosta, Pyramide	Solingen-Foche	Germany	Mfr.	1684–pres.	L

POCKETKNIFE BRAND	TRADEMARK (or Reference)	LOCATION	MADE IN:	TYPE OF FIRM	DATES	$
Hancock, Samuel, & Sons	Mazeppa, Zephyr	Sheffield	England	Mfr.	c1836–1924	M
Hardened Copper Cutlery Co.	(copper blade)	New York (office)	USA?	Mfr.	c1920	V
Hargreaves Smith & Co.		Sheffield	England	Mfr.	c1866–1920	M
Harrington, Henry	Cutler to the People	Southbridge MA	USA	Mfr.	1818–1876	V
Harrison Brothers & Howson	Alpha	Sheffield	England	Mfr. & Retailer	c1853–1919	H
Hart Cutlery Co.	probably by Camillus	New York NY	USA		c1920s	M
Hartford Cutlery Co.		Tariffville CT	USA	Mfr.	c1880	H
Hartford Cutlery Co.		Duluth MN	USA	Mfr.?	c1928	M
Hartkopf, Robert, & Co.	Winged lions. Some made for Utica Knife & Razor	Solingen	Germany	Mfr.	c1855–1957	M
Harvard	see George Worthington					
Harwell, W.F.	Blitzknife	Charlotte NC	USA		c1947	L
Hassam Brothers (Kingman & Hassam)	succ. to N. Hunt & Co.	Boston MA	US/Eng.	Retail	c1853–1872	V
Hatch Cutlery Co.	moved to Wisconsin	Bridgeport CT	USA	Mfr.	1892–1898	H
Hatch Cutlery Co.		So. Milwaukee WI	USA	Mfr.	1898–?	H
Haugh & Frisbie		New Haven CT	USA	Mfr.?	c1857	V
Haven, R. M.		Norwich CT	USA	Mfr.?	c1857	V
Haynes Stellite		Kokomo IN	USA	Mfr. Retailer	1911, 1919	V
Hayward Key Knife	see Empire					
Haywood, Joseph	Tea-kettle (picture), to Turner c1869	Sheffield	England	Mfr.	c1850–1869	H
Hecho en Mexico = Made in Mexico						
Hedengram &Son		Eskilstuna	Sweden	Mfr.	c1900?	M
Heljestrand, C. V.		Eskilstuna	Sweden	Mfr.	c1900	M
Hellberg, J. A.		Eskilstuna	Sweden	Mfr.?	c1900–pres.	M
Hen & Rooster	see Carl Bertram					
Henckels, J. A., (Twinworks)	In USA 1883–pres. Pocketknives 1960.	Solingen	Germany	Mfr.	1731–pres.	H
Henckels International	Half Twin with halberd		Brazil	Mfr.	c1970s	L
Henkels, Paul A.		Solingen	Germany	Mfr.	1887–pres.	L
Henkle & Joyce Hdw. Co		Lincoln NE	USA	Hdw. Whol.	c1900–1934	M
Herder's (L. Herder & Son)	orig. Clarenbach & Herder	Philadelphia PA	USA	Retailer & Mfr.	1847–pres.	M
Herder, Friedr., Abr. Sohn	Spade (since 1727)	Solingen	Germany	Mfr.	1623–pres.	M
Herder, H(enriette)	Spade in frame	Solingen	Germany	Mfr.	1806–pres.	M
Herder, Richard Abr.	4-pointed star	Solingen	Germany	Mfr.	1885–pres.	M
Herder, Robert	4-leaf clover, Windmill	Solingen	Germany	Mfr.	1872–pres.	M
Hessenbruch, T. (later Herman)	Bear with cane (picture)	Philadelphia PA	US/Ger.	Whol. & Imp.	1873–1926	M
Hibbard Spencer Bartlett & Co.	(OVB) by Napanoch, Camillus, Ulster	Chicago IL	USA	Hdw. Whol.	1855–c1960	H
Hickok Mfg. Co.	KoiNife	Rochester NY	USA	Jewelry Mfr.	1937–1950s	L
Hickory	see Kelly How Thomson					
Hickory Hand Forged	see J. H. Sutcliffe & Co.					
High Carbon Steel	Camillus brand	Camillus NY	USA	Mfr.	1930s	M
Hilger & Sons	see Wiebusch					
Hilliard & Chapman		Glasgow	Scotland	Mfr.	c1850	H
Hinchcliffe, John		Sheffield	England	Mfr.	c1850	V
Hobson, Alfred, & Sons	Current	Sheffield	England	Mfr.	19th Cent.	H
Hobson, Henry, & Son	Express	Sheffield	England	Mfr.	c1860s	H
Hobson, John M.		Sheffield	England	Mfr.	19th Cent.	M
Hoffritz		New York NY	Ger./France	Whol/Ret/Imp	c1930–pres.	M
Holler, J. S.	also see A. Blaich	New York NY	Germany	Whol. Importer	c1867–1906	M
Holley & Co.		Salisbury CT renamed Lakeville in 1846	USA	Mfr.	1844–1846	V
Holley (& Merwin) (Mfg. Co.)	ceased distribution c1904	Lakeville CT	USA	Mfr.	1844–c1930	V
Hollingsworth Knife Co.	formerly Kane Cutlery	Kane PA	USA	Mfr.	c1916–1930	M
Holmberg, P.		Eskilstuna	Sweden	Mfr.	c1900	M
Holmes, John, & Co.	sold to J. Clarke before 1900	Sheffield	England	Mfr.	1860–pres.	M
Honk Falls Knife Co.	in old Napanoch building	Napanoch NY	USA	Mfr.	1921–1929	H
Hoppe, Gebruder (Bros.)	owner Karl Joest	Solingen	Germany	Mfr.	1919–pres.	M
Horster, E. & F., Co.	HHS, Famex, Monika	Solingen-Wald	Germany	Mfr.	1850–pres.	M
Hotchkissville Knife Co.	made by Am. Shear & Knife	Hotchkissville CT	USA	Mfr.?	c1870?	M
Howard Cutlery Co.	C. B. Barker Co.	New York NY	Germany	Whol. Importer	c1880s–90s	M
Howard Cutlery Co.	(C. B. Barker Co.) made by Canastota	New York NY	USA	Whol.	c1881–1890	H

POCKETKNIFE BRAND	TRADEMARK (or Reference)	LOCATION	MADE IN:	TYPE OF FIRM	DATES	$
Howes Cutlery Co.			Germany	Import brand	c1900	L
Hubertus Schneidwarenfabrik	Kuno Ritter, owner	Solingen	Germany	Mfr.	1932–pres.	L
Hudson Knife Co			Germany	Import brand	c1920s	L
Hudson Valley Cutlery Co.		? NY	USA?		c1890?	H
Hudson's Bay Company (on tang)	marked pocketknives c1880	Winnipeg MB	US/Eng.	Retail, Trading	1670–pres.	V
Humason & Beckley Mfg. Co.	(H. & B.) sold to L.F. & C. 1912	New Britain CT	USA	Mfr.	1852–1916	H
Humphreys, W. R., & Co.	Radiant	Sheffield	England	Mfr.	c1875–pres.	L
Hunt, N., & Co.	sold to Kingman & Hassam	Boston MA	US/Eng.	Retail	c1840–1853	V
I. & J. Mfg. Co.	Shur-Lock	Plainfield NJ	USA	Mfr.?	c1950	M
I. K. CO. or IKCO	see Imperial Knife Co.	Providence RI	USA	Mfr.	1920s–40s	L
I*XL	see George Wostenholm					
Ibberson, George, & Co.	Violin (after 1880)	Sheffield	England	Mfr.	1700–pres.	H
Ibbotson Brothers & Co.	Globe	Sheffield	England	Mfr.	1841–c1925	H
Ibbotson Peace & Co.	became W. K. Peace & Co.	Sheffield	England	Mfr.	c1847–1864	H
Ibbotson, Charles, & Co.		Sheffield	England	Mfr.	c1868–1896	H
Ideal	(I-D-L) for Belknap Hdw. Co.	Louisville KY		Hdw. Whol.	1890s	M
Ideal Knife Co.	IDEAL/U.S.A.	Providence RI	USA	Mfr.	1924–pres.	L
Illinois Cutlery Co.	(? Golden Rule?)	Chicago IL	USA		c1911	H
Imperial Knife Associated Cos.	owns Ulster, Schrade, Imperial	New York NY	USA	Mfrs.	1947–1984	
Imperial Schrade	was Imperial Knife Associated Cos.				1984–pres.	
Imperial Knife Co.	IKCO, Crown, Hammer, Jackmaster	Providence RI	USA	Mfr.	1917–pres.	L
Imperial Knife Co.	(multi-colored handles)	Providence RI	USA	Mfr.	c1925–1942	M
Imperial Knife Co.			Ireland	Mfr. & Exp.	current	L
Imperial			Mexico		recent	L
Imperial R(azor) Co.	(Cutwell) Kastor's first brand	New York NY	Germany	Whol. Importer	c1880s–90s	M
India Steel Works (John Primble)	see Belknap Hdw. Co.					
Indiana Cutlery Co.	see Wabash Cutlery Co.	Terre Haute IN	USA	Mfr.	c1932	H
Industry Novelty Co.		Chicago IL	USA?	Ad Specialty?	1908–1917	M
Inox(ydable) = Stainless (French)						
International Cutlery Co.		Fremont OH		prob. Whol.	1922– ?	M
Iowan Novelty (Cutlery) Co.	I. N.Co. or I.N.C.Co.	Cedar Rapids, Keota IA	USA	prob. Whol.	c1910s	M
Iroquois	probably by Utica	Utica NY	USA	Mfr.	c1930s–40s	L
Iver Johnson S(porting) G(oods) Co.	by Russell, N.Y.K.Co., etc.	Boston MA	USA	Retail	c1912	H
Iversen & Albrecht	agent for J. A. Henckels	New York NY	Germany	Whol. Importer	c1948–1960	M
Ives, W. A., Mfg. Co.		Meriden CT	USA	Mfr.	19th Cent.	H
J. C. N. Co. (Pat. 11-9-37)	made by G. Schrade	Jersey City NJ (?)	USA	Ad Spec.?	c1940	M
Jack Knife Ben		Chicago IL	USA	Retail	1887–1940s	H
Jack Knife Shop	Union Stockyards	Chicago IL	USA	Retail	?	M
Jack-O-Matic	made by Imperial Knife	Providence RI	USA	Mfr.	1943–1958	M
Jackmaster	see Imperial Knife Co.	Providence RI	USA	Mfr.	1938–pres.	L
Jackson Knife & Shear Co.		Fremont OH	USA	Mfr.	c1900–1914	M
Jackson, William		Sheffield	England	Mfr.	c1859	H
Jacoby & Wester	became Wester Bros.	New York NY	Germany	Whol. Importer	1891–1902	H
Jaeger Bros.	see Aerial Cutlery Co.					
Jaeger, Joseph	Palm	Los Angeles CA		Whol. or Retail	c1891–1909	M
Jet-Aer Corp.	G-96	Paterson NJ		Whol. Importer	current	L
Jim Bowie	see Carl Schlieper					
John Jay	see Union Cutlery Co.					
Johnson, Christopher, & Co.	CJ in flag; to I*XL 1955	Sheffield	England	Mfr.	1865–c1977	M
Johnson, George, & Co.	Seven stars (picture)	Sheffield	England	Mfr.	1810–1855	H
Johnson, James		Sheffield	England	Mfr.	c1818–1853	M
Jordan, A(ndrew) J.	AAA1, Adolphus, Old Faithful	St. Louis MO	Eng./Ger.	Whol. Importer	c1870–1926	H
Jordan, F. W.	probably by Krusius Bros.	New York?	Germany	Import brand	c1920s	M
Joseph, Nathan	Queen's Own Co.	San Francisco CA	England	Whol. Importer	c1873–1894	V
Jowett, John		Sheffield	England	Mfr.	c1870s	M
Judson Cutlery Co.		New York NY	Ger./US	Whol.	c1900–1940	M
Justice, A(lfred) R., Co.	Battle Axe Cutlery Co.	Philadelphia PA		Hdw. Whol.	c1897–1937	M
K. & B. Cutlery Co.	see Kruse & Bahlman Hdw.					
K. B. Extra	see Krusius Brothers					

POCKETKNIFE BRAND	TRADEMARK (or Reference)	LOCATION	MADE IN:	TYPE OF FIRM	DATES	$
K55K Black Cat	see Heinrich Kauffmann					
KA-BAR (only mark)	see Kabar Cutlery Co.					
KA-BAR/UNION CUT. CO.	see Union Cutlery Co.	Olean NY	USA	Mfr.	1923–1951	V
KA-BAR/OLEAN N.Y.	see KA-BAR/UNION CUT.CO.					
KA-BAR/U.S.A.	see Kabar Cutlery Co.					
KA-BAR/[number] USA	see Kabar (Cole National)					
Kabar Cutlery Co. (succ. to Union)	KA-BAR, KA-BAR/U.S.A.	Olean NY	USA	Mfr.	1951–c1966	H
Kabar	see Cole National	Cleveland OH	USA	Whol.	c1966–pres.	M
Kaliakin, John		Vyatka (Kirov)	Russia	Mfr.	c1876	H
Kammerling, Carl, & Co.	owns P. L. Schmidt, Wintgen	Elberfeld	Germany	Mfr.	1904–pres.	M
Kamp Cutlery Co.			Germany		c1910	L
Kamp King	see Imperial Knife Co.				1935–pres.	L
Kamphaus, P. (owner K. B. Dorndorf)	Granate	Solingen	Germany	Mfr.	c1797– pres.	L
Kamphausen & Pluemacher		Solingen-Ohligs	Germany	Mfr.	1860–19??	L
Kane Cutlery Co.	became Hollingsworth	Kane PA	USA	Mfr.	c1910–1916	H
Kase (with soccer ball and foot)	by Boentgen & Sabin	Solingen	Germany	Mfr.	c1960s?	M
Kastor, Adolph, & Bros.	XLNT, EBRO, Clover, Camillus, Morley, Duane	New York NY	Ger./US	Whol./Imp./ Mfr.	1876–c1947	M
Kastor, N(athan)	buyer for Adolph Kastor	Solingen-Ohligs	Germany	Exporter	c1885–30s?	M
Kaufmann, Heinrich, & Soehne	Mercator, K55K, Indiawerk	Solingen	Germany	Mfr.	1856–pres.	L
Kay, John		New Haven CT	USA	Mfr.?	c1857	V
Keen Edge	see Canton Hdw. Co. or Keith Simmons & Co.					
Keen Kutter	see E. C. Simmons 1868–1940, Shapleigh 1940–60, Val-Test by Schrade 1960–65					
Keen(e?) Cutlery Co.	made by Napanoch (1)					
Keener Edge	see C. M. McClung Hdw.					
Keenwell Mfg. Co.	by Union Cutlery Co.	Olean NY	USA	Mfr.	c1910	H
Keith Simmons & Co.	Keen Edge	Nashville TN		Hdw. Whol.	c1901–pres.	M
Kelly How Thomson Co.	Hickory (some by Napanoch)	Duluth MN	USA	Hdw. Whol.	1902–1947	H
Kendal		Winsted CT	USA			M
Kent (Made for F. W. Woolworth)	made by Camillus	Camillus NY	USA	Retail brand	c1934	L
Kenyon, John, & Co.	Fulton, Fulltone, IK	Sheffield	England	Mfr.	c1870–1920	M
Kershaw Cutlery Co.		Lake Oswego OR	Japan	Whol. Importer	current	M
Keschner, H.	Diamond		Germany	Ad. Spec.?	c1920s?	M
Keyes Cutlery Co.		Unionville CT	USA	Mfr.	pre-1893	H
Keystone Cutlery Co.		Milwaukee WI		Hdw. Whol.	c1925–1938	H
Khyber	see Kabar (Cole National)	Cleveland OH	Japan	Whol. Importer	recent	L
Kinfolks Inc.	Kinfolks, K.I., Jean Case	Little Valley NY	USA	Mfr.	1925–c1951	H
King's head in profile	see Weyersberg					
Kingman & Hassam	became Hassam Brothers qv					
Kingston	Joint venture by Ulster & Imperial	Ellenville & Prov.	USA	Mfr.	1943–47	M
Kippax	see Nowill & Kippax					
Kipsi Kut	Pokipsi, N. Y.	Poughkeepsie NY	USA?	Whol.	c1900	H
Kitchen, S(amuel) & J.	Snake (picture), Fame	Sheffield	England	Mfr.	c1865 ff.	H
Klaas, Robert	Two Cranes "Kissing"	Solingen	Germany	Mfr.	1834–pres.	H
Klauberg, Carl, & Bros.		New York NY	Germany	Whol. Importer	c1883–1940	L
Klein, M(athias), & Sons	(pocketknives 1911–present)	Chicago IL	USA	Electric. Whol.	1857–pres.	L
KlicKer	see Shapleigh	St. Louis MO	USA	Hdw. Whol.	c1958	M
Knapp & Spencer	Regent	Sioux City IA		Retail?	c1895–1905	M
Knauth, G(ustav) C.		Spring Valley NY	USA	Mfr.?	c1900–1941	M
Knife Collector's Club	A. G. Russell III	Springdale AR	US/Ger.	Retail	c1974–pres.	H
Koch, F. A., & Co.		New York NY	Ger./US	Whol.	c1880–1933	M
Koeller (Koller), F., & Co.	Elephant, Magna, WEXL	Solingen-Ohligs	Germany	Mfr.	1855–pres.?	L
Koesters, J., Sons	imported by Kastor	Ohligs	Germany	Mfr.?	c1930s	M
KoiNife	see Hickok Mfg. Co.					
Koller, F.	variant of Koeller					
Koller, Hugo	Eagle	Solingen	Germany	Mfr.	1861–pres.?	M
Kondratov, Demetrius	Imperial Eagle (picture)	Vyatka (Kirov)	Russia	Mfr.	1870–1917?	V
Konejung, Hermann	Spectacles, Hammers	Solingen	Germany	Mfr.	1873–pres.	M
Korn, George W.	(prob. not a Mfr.)	N.Y.C. & Little Valley NY		Inventor & Imp.	c1880–1925	H
Krebs, Peter Daniel	Lobster (picture)	Solingen	Germany	Mfr.	c1870–1924	M
Kruse & Bahlman Hdw. Co.	K. & B., Cut Sure	Cincinnati OH	USA	Hdw. Whol.	c1896–1962	M
Krusius Brothers	K. B. Extra	New York NY	Germany	Whol. Importer	c1888–1927	M
Krusius, Gebruder (Brothers)		Solingen	Germany	Mfr.	1856–1983	M

POCKETKNIFE BRAND	TRADEMARK (or Reference)	LOCATION	MADE IN:	TYPE OF FIRM	DATES	$
Kunde & Co.		Remscheid	Germany		current	M
Kutmaster	see Utica Cutlery Co.	Utica NY	USA	Mfr.	1937–pres.	M
Kutwell	made by Union	Olean NY	USA	Mfr.	c1930s	H
L. C. Co.	see Lackawanna Cutlery					
L. F. & C.	see Landers Frary & Clark					
L. K. Co.	see Liberty Knife Co.					
L. L. H. Co.	see Lockwood Luetkemeyer Henry					
L. V. Knife Association	see Little Valley Knife Assoc.					
La Barge = the godwit (bird)		Thiers?	France	Mfr.	c1900?	M
LaBelle Cutlery Works	Smith Sutton & Co.; Harry L. Frary	Bridgeport CT	USA	Mfr.	c1884–1888	H
Lackawanna Cutlery Co.	L. C. Co.	Nicholson PA	USA	Mfr.	1917–c1930	H
Lafayette Cutlery Co.		New York	Germany	Whol. Importer	c1910s–20s	L
Laguiole	(place and pattern name)		France			
Lakeside Cutlery Co.	(by Challenge) sold by Montgomery Ward's	Chicago IL	USA	Retail brand?	c1922–1928	H
Lakota Corp.		Riverton WY	USA	Mfr.	current	M
Lamson & Goodnow	(folding knife & fork sets c1862–1880s)	Shelburne Falls MA	USA	Mfr.	1844–pres.	V
Lamson & Goodnow	(pocketknives 1870s–80s by Waterville, Gardner)	Shelburne Falls MA	USA	Whol.	1844–pres.	H
Landers Frary & Clark (Universal)	(pocketknives 1912–1930s)	New Britain CT	USA	Mfr.	1863–1954	H
Landis Brothers (Henry and Reuben)	Pat. Nov. 11, 1879	Canton OH	USA	Inventors (Mfr.)	c1879	H
Langbein, Charles		New York NY		Retail & Whol.	c1880s–90s	H
Langbein, William, & Bros.		New York NY		Whol. & Retail	c1900–40s	M
Laufbrunnen = flowing well (German)	see W. Weltersbach					
Lauterjung & Co. (owned by Eicker)	Tiger Brand, Cervo	Solingen	Germany	Mfr.	1813–pres.	M
Lauterjung & Sohn	now called Puma-Werk qv					
Law, Joseph	LIBERTY on bolster	Sheffield	England	Mfr.	c1820	V
Lawrence, G(eorge). H.	Laurel	Sheffield	England	Mfr.	c1919–1952	M
Lawton Cutlery Co.		Chicago IL			c1895	M
Layman Carey Co.		Indianapolis IN		Hdw. whol.	c1920	M
Lee Hdw. Co.		Salina KS		Hdw. Whol.	? –pres.	M
Lee, J.		Medway MA	USA	Mfr.?	c1830	V
Lehrkine & Daevel Co.		Milwaukee WI				M
Lenox Cutlery Co.			Germany	Import brand	c1910	L
Leon, Abraham		Sheffield	England	Mfr.	c1850	H
Leonard, A. M., Inc.	marked knives by Schrade before 1960	Piqua OH	US/Ger/Eng	Hortic. Supply	1885–pres.	M
LeRoi Corn Knife	see Fourquignon					
Lever Cutlery Co.		New York NY	USA?	Mfr.?	1898– ?	H
Lewis, J. C., Pat. 1900	see O. Barnett Tool Co.					
Liberty Knife Co.		New Haven CT	USA		? –1925	M
Lincoln		Sheffield	England	Mfr.?	19th Cent.	M
Linder & Co.	Junkerwerk	Solingen	Germany	Mfr.	1887–pres.	L
Linder, C(arl) & R(obert)	crown/pruning knife	Solingen-Weyer	Germany	Mfr.	1842–19??	M
Linder, Carl	Rehwappen	Solingen	Germany	Mfr.	1908–pres.	M
Linder, Hugo	Deltawerk	Solingen	Germany	Mfr.	1878–1957	L
Lindstrom, C. J.		Eskilstuna	Sweden	Mfr.	c1900	M
Lingard, Joseph	I-Fly, Shuttle (picture)	Sheffield	England	Mfr.	c1842–1925	M
Lingard, Robert		Sheffield	England	Mfr.	19th Cent.	H
Lion lying down (picture)	see C. Lutters					
Lion standing up (picture)	see Carl Spitzer					
Lipic, Joseph, Pen Co.		St. Louis MO	USA	Ad. Specialties	? –pres.	L
Lipscomb, H. G., & Co.	Watauga	Nashville TN	USA	Hdw. Whol.	1891–1913 +	M
Little Valley Knife Association	forerunner of Crandall	Little Valley NY	USA	Whol.	1900–1905	H
Lockwood Bros.	C + X, Pampa, Rhea (bird)	Sheffield	England	Mfr.	c1849–pres.	M
Lockwood Luetkemeyer Henry Hdw. Co.	Thelco, LLH; was McIntosh	Cleveland OH	US/Eng.	Hdw. Whol.	1911– ?	M
Long		Oxford	England	Retail?	c1880	M

POCKETKNIFE BRAND	TRADEMARK (or Reference)	LOCATION	MADE IN:	TYPE OF FIRM	DATES	$
Long, H. G., & Co.	(now a division of H. M. Slater)	Sheffield	England	Mfr.	c1846–pres.	M
Lord Bros.			Germany?	Import brand	c1880s	M
Lubin	perhaps Weinstock Lubin	San Francisco? CA	Austria?	Retail?	c1890s	H
Luna, Lunawerk	see A. Feist & Co.					
Luthe Hdw. Co.	marked knives c1917 ff.	Des Moines IA	USA	Hdw. Whol.	c1900–1955	M
Lutters, C., & Co.	Lion lying down (picture)	Solingen	Germany	Mfr.	1840–pres.	M
Luttrell, S(amuel) B(ell), & Co.	Cranberry. to McClung Hdw	Knoxville TN		Hdw. Whol.	c1880	H
Lux, Louis		New York NY	Germany	Whol. Importer	c1920	L
Luxrite		Hollywood CA				M
Lyon Cutlery Co.	resemble Frary knives	Bridgeport? CT	USA?	Mfr.?	1880s	H
M. C. Co.	Anvil. see Meriden Cut.					
M. Fruit Knife Pat. Apr. 26, '81	see Miller Brothers					
M. S. A. Co.	see Marble's Safety Axe					
M.S. Ltd. XX	see Case XX Metal Stampings Ltd.					
M. W. H. Co.	see Marshall Wells Hdw.					
Magnetic Cutlery Co.	(O. & F. Maussner) Blue Bird (by Peres)	Philadelphia PA	Germany	Whol. (Retail?)	c1900–1932	M
Maher & Grosh	to Clyde OH 1963	Toledo OH	USA	Retail, Whol.	1877–pres.	H
Mairowitz & Buscher	M. & B. S., key and rope	Solingen	Germany	Mfr.?	c1860s	H
Majestic Cutlery Co.			Germany	Import brand	c1910	L
Manchester			USA	Po'k. skeletons	c1920s?	M
Manhattan Cutlery Co.	see H. Boker's, Newark NJ	Sheffield	England	Import Brand	c1868–1916	M
Maniago	(place name)		Italy		c1400–pres.	
Manson		Sheffield	England	Mfr.	19th Cent.	M
Mappin & Webb	Trustworthy. Sun (?)	Sheffield	England	Mfr.	c1835–1964	M
Mappin Brothers	Queen's Cutlery Works. Sun	Sheffield, London	England	Mfr. & Retail	c1840–1872	H
Mar, Al		Lake Oswego OR	Japan	Whol. Importer	1979–pres.	M
Marble's Safety Axe Co.	(Marble's folding hunter: c1900–42)	Gladstone MI	USA	Mfr.	1898–pres.	V
Marble's Safety Axe Co.	(M.S.A.Co. pocketknives: c1902–08)	Gladstone MI	USA	Whol.	1898–pres.	V
Marriott (Marriott & Atkinson)		Sheffield	England	Mfr.	c1840–1875	M
Marsden, William W.		Sheffield	England	Mfr.	c1850–1870	H
Marsh Bros.	succ. to W. & T. Marsh?	Sheffield	England	Mfr.	c1850–1947	H
Marsh, W(illiam) & T(homas)		Sheffield	England	Mfrs.	c1780–1840	H
Marshall Field & Co.		Chicago IL	Ger./?	Retail	18??–pres.	M
Marshall Wells Hdw. Co.	M.W.H.Co., Zenith (before 1917)	Duluth MN & branches	USA	Hdw. Whol.	1893–1963	H
Marshes & Shepherd	Pond Works	Sheffield	England	Mfr.	1818–1850	H
Martin Bros. (& Naylor)		Sheffield	England	Mfr.	c1860	M
Marx & Co.			Germany	Whol. Imp.	c1880s	M
Massillon Cutlery Co.	successor to Ohio Cutlery Co.	Massillon OH	USA	Mfr.	c1924–5	M
Master Barlow, Master	made by Colonial	Providence RI	USA	Mfr.	1939–pres.	L
Maussner, Otto	in Solingen 1855–87, Riga 1887–90, Phila. 1900–10	Ger/Latvia	Whol. (Retail?)	c1855–1910	M
Maussner, Otto (& Frank, after 1910)	see Magnetic Cutlery Co.	Philadelphia PA	Germany			
Mazeppa (with running horse)	see Samuel Hancock & Sons					
McClung, C(alvin) M(organ), & Co.	Cranberry, Keener Edge	Knoxville TN	US/Ger.	Hdw. Whol.	1882–c1960	M
McIlwaine Linn & Hughes	Sterling Cutlery Co.	New York NY	Ger./Engl.	Whol. Importer	c1896–1914	M
McIntosh Hdw. Co.	Heather; became L.L.H.	Cleveland OH		Hdw. Whol.	1875–1911	M
McL(endon) Hdw. Co.	some by Schatt & Morgan	Waco TX	USA	Whol. (Retail?)	c1890–1945	M
McLory, John, & Sons	Scotia, Thistle (picture)	Sheffield	England	Mfr.	c1870–pres.	M
Mehasco		Calgary AB	USA?	Hdw. Whol.?	c1930s	H
Mercator	see Heinrich Kauffmann					
Meriden Cutlery Co.	(to LF&C 1916)pocketknives by Southington, Valley Forge	Meriden CT	USA	Mfr. & Whol.	1855–c1925	M
Meriden Knife Co.	made for Miller Bros.	Meriden CT	USA	Contract Mfr.	1917–c1932	M
Merit Import Co.	(Peter J. Michels Inc.)	New York NY	Germany	Whol. Import	c1922–1940	M
Metropolitan Cutlery Co.	Commander (?)	New York NY	Ger./US	Whol. & Imp.	c1918–1951	M
Miller Brothers	moved to Meriden CT c1872	Yalesville, W'ford CT	USA	Mfr.	1863–1872	H
Miller Brothers Cutlery Co.	many w/screws in handles	Meriden (post-1872) CT	USA	Mfr.	1863–1926	H
Miller Sloss & Scott (Stiletto)	sold to Pac. Hdw. & Steel	San Francisco CA	USA	Hdw. Whol.	1891–1901	H

POCKETKNIFE BRAND	TRADEMARK (or Reference)	LOCATION	MADE IN:	TYPE OF FIRM	DATES	$
Missoula Mercantile Co.	Buffalo Brand (–c1917)	Missoula MT	USA	Whol. & Retail	1885–c1972	H
Mitchell & Co. Ltd.		Manchester	England	Mfr.?	c1910?	M
Mogal, Mitchell, Inc.	MOGAL/MADE IN U.S.A.	New York NY	USA	Whol.	c1924–1951	M
Mogal, Mitchell, Inc.	ROMO	New York NY	Ger/It/Jap	Whol.	1924–pres.	L
Monarch	see Cole National					
Mongin, Jacques		Biesles, near Nogent	France	Mfr.	current	H
Monika	see E. & F. Horster					
Montgomery Ward	Lakeside, Wards, Power Kraft	Chicago IL		Retail	1872–pres.	
Monumental Cutlery Co.	see Wiebusch	New York NY	Ger./Eng.	Whol. Importer	c1874–1893	M
Moore Handley Hdw. Co.	many by Camillus	Birmingham AL	USA	Hdw. Whol.	c1882–pres.	M
Morley Bros. Hdw. Co.	Wedgeway Cutlery Co. 1887–1933	Saginaw MI	USA?	Hdw. Whol.	1865–pres.	M
Morley, W. H., & Sons	part of A. Kastor & Bros.	New York NY	Aust./Ger.	Whol. Importer	c1913–1927	M
Morris Cutlery Co.		Morris IL	USA	Mfr.	1882–c1930	H
Morse, B. H.	see Waterville Co.					
Mount Vernon Cutlery Co.			Germany?	Import brand	c1890	M
Mueller & Schmidt Pfeilringwerk	Five arrows around circle	Solingen	Germany	Mfr.	1896–pres.	L
Mumbly Peg	Camillus brand				c1937–1948	M
N. B. Knife Co., The	see New Britain Knife Co.					
N. C. Co.	see Novelty Cutlery Co.					
N. Shore Co.	see North Shore Co.					
Nachf(olger) = Successor (German)						
Nagle Reblade Knife Co.		Poughkeepsie NY	USA	Mfr.	1912–1916	V
Napanoch Knife Co. (1)	to Winchester & Honk Falls	Napanoch NY	USA	Mfr.	1900–1919	V
Napanoch Knife Co. (2)	J. Cushner, ex-Napanoch (1)	Napanoch NY	USA	Mfr.	1931–1939	V
Nash Hardware Co.		Fort Worth TX	USA	Hdw. Whol.	1873–1975	M
Naugatuck Cutlery Co.		Naugatuck CT	USA	Mfr.	1872–1888	H
Naylor & Sanderson		Sheffield	England	Mfr.	c1810–1830	V
Needham Bros.	Repeat (Wiebusch import)	Sheffield	England	Mfr.	c1860–1900	H
Needham Veall & Tyzack (Taylor Eyewitness, Llama, Isonit & c.)		Sheffield	England	Mfr.	1836?–pres.	M
Neft Safety Knife		Newark NJ	USA		1920–?	M
New Britain Knife Co., The	The N. B. Knife Co.	New Britain CT	USA	Mfr.?		M
New Century Cutlery Co.				Import brand	c1900	M
New England Cutlery Co.		Wallingford CT	USA	Mfr.?	c1860	H
New England Knife Co.				Whol.?	c1910?	H
New Haven Cutlery Co. "Damascus"	see Baker & Hamilton	San Francisco CA	US or Ger.?	Hdw. Whol.	c1890s	H
New Holland (on Kutmaster bolster)	for New Holland Co.	New Holland PA	USA	Farm Eqpt. Ad.	c1960	M
New Jersey Cutlery Co.	American Ace	Newark NJ			c1921	M
New York Cutlery Co.	became Schatt & Morgan	Gowanda NY		Wholesaler	1890s	H
New York Knife Co.	moved to Walden 1856	Matteawan (Beacon) NY	USA	Mfr.	1852–1856	V
New York Knife Co.	Hammer Brand (post–c1880)	Walden NY	USA	Mfr.	1856–1931	H
Newton, Francis, & Sons	J. & R. Dodge	Sheffield	England	Mfr.	c1838–pres.	M
Newton, John	see H. Boker, Newark NJ	Sheffield	England	Import Brand	c1906	M
Nicholson, William		Sheffield	England	Mfr.	c1846–1864	H
Nifty	see Borgfeldt				c1913	L
Nilsson, Axel	some imported by Thompson Hdw.	Solingen?	Germany	Mfr.	pre-1914	M
Nirosta = No Rust (German)	see Gottlieb Hammesfahr					
Nogent	(place name)		France			
NON-XLL	see Joseph Allen					
Normark	Mfd. by E. K. A.	Minneapolis MN	Sweden	Whol. Importer	1959–pres.	M
Norris, Samuel	☆P Cast Steel	Sheffield	England	Mfr.	c1795–1815	H
North American Knife Co.		Wichita KS			c1920s	M
North Shore Co.		Chicago, IL	USA	Ad. Specialty?	c1930s	M
North West Cutlery Co.			Germany	Import Brand	c1890	L
Northfield Knife Co.	UN-X-LD	Northfield CT	USA	Mfr.	1858–1919	H
Norvell Shapleigh Hdw. Co.	see Shapleigh Hdw. Co.				1902–1920	
Norvell, S(anders)	see Shapleigh Hdw. Co.				1902–1920	
NOVCO or NOV. CUT. CO.	see Novelty Cutlery Co.					
Novelty Cutlery Co.	(Canton Knife Co.) NOVCO, A. Vignos	Canton OH	USA	Mfr.	1879–c1949	H
Nowill, John, & Sons	Krosskeys, *D	Sheffield	England	Mfr.	c1848–pres.	M

POCKETKNIFE BRAND	TRADEMARK (or Reference)	LOCATION	MADE IN:	TYPE OF FIRM	DATES	$
Nowill, Joseph, & John Kippax	NOWIL/KIPPAX	Sheffield	England	Mfr.	c1780	V
O. C. Mfg. Co.	see Ohio Cutlery Co.					
O. M. F.	(on W.W.I Canadian sailor knives)				c1915	V
O. N. B., O. N. B. Barlow			Germany	Import Brand	c1910	M
O. S. T. Cutlery Co.		Newark NJ				M
O. V. B. (Our Very Best)	see Hibbard Spencer Bartlett				c1884–1960	
Oak Leaf	see William Enders (Simmons)					
Oakman Bros.		New York NY		Retail or Whol.	c1900	M
Oates, S. E., & Sons	S.E.O. & S. (by Furness?)	Sheffield	England	Mfr.?	pre-1915	M
Occident Cutlery Co.	sold by Seattle Hdw. Co.	Seattle WA		Hdw. Whol.	1908–?	M
Odell Hdw. Co.	Southern + (cross) Cutlery	Greensboro NC		Hdw. Whol.		M
Oehm (& Co.)	Some made by Miller Bros.	Baltimore MD	USA/ ?	Retail	c1860–1936	M
Ohio Cutlery Co.	O. C. Mfg. Co., Tru-Temper	Massillon OH	USA	Mfr.	1919–1923	H
Olbertz, Friedrich	Olbos, Winged crown	Solingen	Germany	Mfr.	1915–pres.	L
Olcut	see Olean Cutlery Co.	Olean NY	USA	Mfr.	c1911–1914	H
Old Cutler	by Colonial Knife Co.	Providence RI	USA	Mfr.	c1978–pres.	M
Old Faithful	see A. J. Jordan					
Old Hickory	see Ontario Knife Co.					
Olean Cutlery Co.	Olcut. Div. of Union Cut.	Olean NY	USA	Mfr.	c1911–1914	H
Olsen Knife Co.	(Mfr. of sheath knives)	Howard City MI	Germany	Mfr. & Imp.	Current	M
Olsson, Emil		Eskilstuna	Sweden	Mfr.		M
Omega	see Joseph Feist					
Ontario Knife Co. (po'k's 1971–)	Old Hickory (by Queen)	Franklinville NY	USA	Kit. Knf. Mfr. Whol.	1889–pres.	M
Opinel (now imported by Gutmann)	Crowned Hand	Cognin, Savoie	France	Mfr.	c1890–pres.	L
Orange Cutlery Co.	(ex Walden Knife employees)	Walden NY	USA	Mfr.	1923	H
Osborn, Samuel, & Co.	Hand & Heart (pictures)	Sheffield	England	Mfr.	c1841–1928	M
Osgood Bray & Co.	(Three Stars) made by Burkinshaw		USA	Whol.?	19th Cent.	H
Ostwald, P. W.	-O- [crude hand-made]	Baker OR	USA	Mfr. (Machinist)	c1930s–60s	M
Othello	see Anton Wingen, Jr.					
P. N. Mfg. Co.	Novelty Pat. 11-11-84		USA		1880s	H
Pacific Hardware & Steel	(Stiletto) sold to Baker & Hamilton	San Francisco CA	USA	Hdw. Whol.	1901–1918	H
Pal Brand/Czechoslovakia	imported by Utica	Utica NY	Czecho.	Whol. Importer	c1924–1929	M
Pal Blade Co./Pal Cutlery Co.	by ex-owners of Utica	Montreal/Plattsburgh	Canada/US	Mfr.	c1929–1953	M
Pal/Remington (blades on same knife)	Pal bought Rem. Cut. 1940	Plattsburgh NY	USA	Mfr.	c1940–1942	H
Pape Theibes Cutlery Co.	Unitas	St. Louis MO	Germany	Whol. Importer	c1903–1929	M
Paris Bead		Chicago IL			c1920s	M
Parisian Novelty Co.		Chicago IL	USA?	Advt. Specialty	c1915	M
Parker Cutlery Co.	Eagle, Parker Bros., Amer. Blade	Chattanooga TN	Japan	Whol/Ret/ Import	c1970– pres.	M
Parker Frost Cutlery Co.		Chattanooga TN	Japan	Whol/Ret/Imp.	1976–1978	M
Parker, Edw., & Sons	Germania Cutlery Works	New York?	Germany	Whol. importer	c1900	M
Pauls Bros.	Echo	N.Y.C. & Solingen	Germany	Mfr. & Imp.	c1880–1900	L
Pavian (-Adams) Cutlery Co.	Summit	St. Paul MN		Whol.	1906–c1920	M
Paxton & Gallagher	CutAway	Omaha NE	USA	Hdw. Whol.	c1864–1959	M
Peace, W. K., Co.	Eagle. Was Ibbotson Peace	Sheffield	England	Mfr.	c1867–pres	M
Pennsylvania Knife Co.		Tidioute (?) PA	USA	Mfr.?	c1914–1921	M
Peres, Daniel, & Co.	Ale Barrel	Solingen	Germany	Mfr.	1792–pres.	M
Perkins, J. (or N.)		Newburyport MA		?	c1820s	V
Perlmann, Louis	Two fencers (picture)	Solingen, Leipzig	Germany	Retail?	1883–pres.	M
Peters, Gebruder (Bros.), Cutlery		Solingen-Merscheid	Germany	Mfr.	c1880	M
Peters, Walter	Laurus tool kit knives	Solingen	Germany	Mfr.	1936–pres.	M
Pfeilringwerk	see Mueller & Schmidt					
Phelps, H. M.	see Waterville (?) c1857					
Phoenix Knife Co.	was Central City Knife Co.	Phoenix NY	USA	Mfr.	1892–1916	H
Pilatus			Germany		c1890?	L
Pine Knot (bird) James W. Price	by Belknap Hdwe. Co.	Louisville KY		Hdw. Whol.	1930s	H
Pitkin Cutlery Co.			Germany	Import brand		M
Platts, C., & Sons	in old S. & M. plant	Gowanda NY	USA	Mfr.	1896–1897	H
Platts, C., & Sons	became C. Platts' Sons	Eldred PA	USA	Mfr.	1897–1900	H
Platts', C., Sons	merged with W.R. Case 1905	Eldred PA	USA	Mfr.	1900–1905	H

POCKETKNIFE BRAND	TRADEMARK (or Reference)	LOCATION	MADE IN:	TYPE OF FIRM	DATES	$
Platts Brothers		Union NY	USA?	Whol.	1905–1907?	H
Platts Brothers Cutlery Co.		Andover NY	USA	Mfr.	1907–c1909	H
Platts N'field (usu. overstamped)	from parts, by Ray Platts	Northfield CT	USA	Mfr.	post–1919	M
Pli-R-Nif Co.		S. F., Berkeley CA	USA	Mfr.	1905–?	V
Plum, (Robert)		Bristol	England	Mfr.	c1822–1939	H
Pocket Pard	see Utica Cutlery Co.					
PocketEze	see Robeson					
Pocketknives crossed (picture)	see Carl Spitzer					
Power Kraft	made for Montgomery Ward	Chicago IL	USA	Retail	c1939–pres.	M
Pradel, C.	1er Choix (first choice)		France			M
Precise (International)	Deerslayer	Suffern NY	Switz./Jap.	Whol. Importer	current	M
Premier Cutlery Co.	Elk, Lifetime	New York NY	Ger. & ?	Whol. Importer	c1921–1955	L
Prentiss Knife Co.		New York NY	USA?	Whol.?	c1910?	H
Press Button Knife Co.	(Geo. Schrade) div. of Walden Knife Co.	Walden NY	USA	Mfr.	c1892–1923	H
Presto	see George Schrade Knife Co.	Bridgeport CT	USA	Mfr.	1925–1945	H
Pribyl Brothers			Germany?	Import brand	c1880s	M
Price, M(ichael)		San Francisco CA	USA	Mfr.	1856–1889	V
Primble, John (India Steel Works)	see Belknap Hdwe. Co.					
Princeton Knife Co.	(Wiebusch brand)	New York NY			c1905	M
Pritzlaff, J., Hdw. Co.	Everkeen	Milwaukee WI		Hdw. Whol.	c1850–1957	M
Progress	see Alfred Field		Germany	Import Brand		
Pronto	see Colonial Knife Co.	Providence RI	USA	Mfr.	c1926–1952	M
Providence Cutlery Co.		Providence RI	USA	Mfr.	c1917–pres	L
Providence Cutlery Co.			Germany	Import Brand	c1890–1915	M
Puma, Puma-Werk	was Lauterjung & Sohn	Solingen	Germany	Mfr.	1769–pres.	H
Q/Crown	see Queen Cutlery Co.					
Queen City Cutlery Co.	now Queen Cutlery Co.	Titusville PA	USA	Mfr.	c1920–45	M
Queen Cutlery Co.	Q/Crown, Queen Steel	Titusville PA	USA	Mfr.	1945–pres.	M
Queen's Cutlery Works	see Mappin Brothers					
Queen's Own Co.	see Nathan Joseph	San Francisco CA				
Quick Point	some made by Remington	St. Louis MO	USA	Advt. Specialty	c1930s	M
Rabone Bros. & Co.	(US Navy contractor)		England	Export brand	c1865	H
Rainbow	(made for Boker USA)	Providence RI	USA		c1933–1954	L
Rampur U(ttar) P(radesh)	(place name)		India			
Ranger	see Colonial				1938–pres.	
Raucherkopf (smoking head)	see Voelker et al. or Bracht					
Rawson & Nourse		Grafton MA			c1860	V
Rawson Bros.		Sheffield	England	Mfr.	c1860	H
Ray, Tom, Cutlery Co.		Kansas City MO		Whol.	c1910	M
Razor (picture)	see R. J. Roberts					
Red Devil S. & H. Co.	see Smith & Hemenway					
Red Stag		Chattanooga TN	Germany	Ltd. Edit. Imp.	current	M
Remington (circle) (UMC)	Usu. have pattern # on reverse tang	Bridgeport CT	USA	Mfr.	1919–1940	V
Remington (circle) S	Stainless blades	Bridgeport CT	USA	Mfr.	c1939–1940	V
Remington/straight line script mark	cheap assortment knives	Bridgeport CT	USA	Mfr. & Whol.	c1933–1940	H
Renshaw, T.	Stand	Sheffield	England	Mfr.	c1870	M
REV-O-NOC	see Hibbard Spencer Bartlett					
Reynolds, Frederick		Sheffield	England	Mfr.	18??–1920s	M
Richard, S(tephen), Co.	Richard's	Southbridge MA	US/Ger/Eng	Whol	c1862–1908	M
Richards & Conover Hdw. Co.	Rich-Con., R. & C.	Kansas City MO		Hdw. Whol.	c1894–1956	M
Richards Bros. & Sons Ltd.	owned by Imperial K.A. Cos.	Sheffield	England	Mfr.	?–pres.	L
Richartz, Gebruder, & Soehne	Whale	Solingen-Ohligs	Germany	Mfr.	1900–pres.	L
Richmond Cutlery Co.			Germany?		19th Cent.	M
Rigid Knives		Santee CA	USA	Mfr.	c1970– pres.	M
Ritter, Kuno	see Hubertus					
Riverside Cut. Co. N.Y.	(by BokerUSA?) see Dunham Harrigan & Hayden	San Francisco CA	USA	Hdw. Whol.	c1918	M
Rivington Works	see Alfred Williams					
Robbins Clark & Biddle	became Biddle Hdw. (?)	Philadelphia PA		Hdw. Whol.	19th Cent.	M
Roberts, R(obert) J., Razor Co.	Razor. Sold to Boker 1905	New York NY	Germany	Whol. Importer	c1870–1940	M

POCKETKNIFE BRAND	TRADEMARK (or Reference)	LOCATION	MADE IN:	TYPE OF FIRM	DATES	$
Robeson Cutlery Co.	ShurEdge, PocketEze	Rochester & Perry NY	USA	Mfr. & Whol.	c1894–1977	M
Robinson Bros. & Co.		Louisville KY		Hdw. Whol.	c1880–1925	M
Robinson, Herbert	Grinder (picture)	Sheffield	England	Mfr.	c1873	M
Robinson, Samuel		Sheffield	England	Mfr.	19th Cent.	H
Rochester P'a	see Beaver Falls					
Rodgers Wostenholm Ltd.	Division of Imperial 1977–82	Sheffield	England	Mfr.	1971–1984	L
Rodgers, James		Sheffield	England	Mfr.	c1830s–50s	H
Rodgers, Joseph, & Sons	*‡, No. 6 Norfolk St.	Sheffield	England	Mfr.	1682–1971	H
Rodgers, William	I Cut (Ax) My Way; sold to J. Clarke c1855	Sheffield	England	Mfr.	1830–pres.	M
ROMO	(Rosenbaum & Mogal: 1917–1924) Mitchell Mogal, Inc. 1924–	New York NY	Ger/It/Jap	Whol.	1917–pres.	L
Rose (picture) in circle	see China Light Indust. . .	Tsingtao, Shantung	China			
Rostfrei = Stainless (German)						
Rowbotham, T. E., & Son		Sheffield	England	Mfr.	c1820	H
Royal Brand Sharp Cutter	see Samuel E. Bernstein					
Runkel Bros.	made by Wester & Butz		Germany	Chocolate Advt.	c1920s	M
Russell	Locknife	Pictou NS	Canada	Mfr.	c1970s?	M
Russell 100th Anniv. reissue Barlow	made by Schrade				c1975	M
Russell, A. G.	see Knife Collectors Club					
Russell, J., & Co. Green River Wks.	R(arrow)po'k's 1875–1941	Turners Falls, MA	USA	Mfr.	1834–pres.	V
Ryals & Heathcote		Sheffield	England	Mfr.	c1836–1870	M
S. & A.	see Sperry & Alexander					
S. & M.	see Schatt & Morgan					
S. C. Co.	see Schrade Cuterly Co.	Walden NY				
S. E. O. & S. (on bolster)	see S. E. Oates					
S. M. F. under picture of king	see Stocker & Co.					
S. R. D. / Arrow	see Severin R. Droescher					
Sabre (by Mitsubishi)	see Cole National	Cleveland OH	Japan	Whol. Importer	1960–1980	L
Saint Lawrence Cutlery Co.	see Schmachtenberg					
Salm, John	marked DeLuxe (1918–1925)	Torrance CA	USA	Mfr.?	1918–1935	M
SAMCO	see Sanders Mfg. Co.					
Sanders Manufacturing Co.	SAMCO	Nashville TN	USA	Ad. Specialties	current	M
Sanderson Bros. & Newbould	1776, many other marks	Sheffield	England	Mfr.	c1860–1933	H
Savage, George, & Sons		Sheffield	England	Mfr.	c1855	M
Saynor Cooke & Ridal	Saynor's, Obtain	Sheffield	England	Mfr.	c1868–pres.	M
Saynor, Samuel, & Sons	Saynor's	Sheffield	England	Mfr.	c1840–1868	M
Schatt & Morgan	was N.Y. Cutlery Co.	Gowanda NY	USA	Mfr.	189?–1896	H
Schatt & Morgan	S. & M.; sold to Queen City	Titusville PA	USA	Mfr.	1896–1931	H
Schlieper, Carl	Eye Brand, Fan, El Gallo, Jim Bowie	Solingen	Germany	Mfr.	1769–pres.	M
Schmachtenberg Bros.	Dunlap, Clim(Axe), Anchor/ Swords	N.Y.C. & Solingen	Germany	Mfr. & Whol. Imp.	1887–c1939	M
Schmid, J(ohn) M., & Son		Providence RI		Retail	1857–1964	H
Schmidt, Carl, Sohn	Church (or house?), Ram	Solingen	Germany	Mfr.	1829–pres.	M
Schmidt, J. A., & Sohne	Dreiturm (Three Spires)	Solingen	Germany	Mfr.	1829–pres.	M
Schmidt, Peter Ludwig	now part of Kammerling	Elberfeld	Germany	Mfr.	c1895–pres.	M
Schmidt & Ziegler	Bull head shield	Solingen	Germany	Mfr.	c1930?	M
Schmidtberg, P.		Solingen	Germany	Mfr.	c1930	M
Schneider, Wenzel		Prague, Bohemia,	Aust.-Hung.	Contract Mfr.	19th Cent.	M
Schrade Cutlery Co.	sold to Imperial 1946	Walden NY	USA	Mfr.	1904–1946	H
Schrade Walden	(div. Imperial Knife A. Cos.) became "Schrade" 1973	Walden NY	USA	Mfr.	1946–1973	H
Shrade	(div. Imperial Schrade) Uncle Henry, Old Timer	Ellenville NY	USA	Mfr.	1973–pres.	M
Schrade, George, Knife Co.	Presto [H], Commando	Bridgeport CT	USA	Mfr.	c1925–1945	M
Schwabacher Hardware Co.	Colonial Cutlery Co.	Seattle WA	US/Ger.	Hdw. whol.	1869–pres.	M
Sears Roebuck & Co.	(on tang: prob. sold before 1902)	Chicago IL	USA	Retail	1886–pres.	M
Sears Roebuck & Co.	see Craftsman, Sta-Sharp, T.T.C., Wilbert					
Sears, Henry, & Co.	son Edward B. joined 1878	Chicago IL	USA	Mfr.	1865–1878	H
Sears, Henry, & Son.	(1865) see Farwell Ozmun Kirk	Chicago IL	USA	Mfr.	1878–c1959	M
Seattle Hardware Co.	Occident Cutlery Co.	Seattle WA		Hdw. Whol.	c1908	M

POCKETKNIFE BRAND	TRADEMARK (or Reference)	LOCATION	MADE IN:	TYPE OF FIRM	DATES	$
Sellers, John, & Sons	Signal	N.Y.C., Sheffield	England	Mfr. & Imp.	1820–c1900	H
Seneca Cutlery Co.	see Utica Cutlery Co.	Utica NY	USA	Mfr.	c1932–1942	M
Shapleigh, A. F., Hdw. Co.	Diamond Edge (after 1888)	St. Louis MO	US/Ger.	Hdw. Whol.	1843–1960	M
Shapleigh, A. F., Hdw. Co.	Keen Kutter (after 1940)	St. Louis MO	USA	Hdw. Whol.	1843–1960	M
Sharp Cutter, Royal Brand	see Samuel E. Bernstein					
Shaw, William	W. S.	Sheffield	England	Mfr.	c1847–1871	H
Sheffield	(place name)		England			
Shelburne Falls Cutlery Co.	by Waterville for L. & G.	Shelburne Falls MA	USA	Mfr.	c1870s–80s	V
Shelton, Clark R.		Birmingham and Westville (Derby) CT	USA	Mfr.	c1849–51	V
Sherwood (Charles E.)	became Camillus 1902, A. Kastor	Camillus NY	USA	Mfr.	1894–96–01	V
Shipley, Howard W.	Coquanoc Works	Philadelphia PA	USA	Mfr.?	c1876	H
ShurEdge	see Robeson					
Shur-Lock	see I. & J. MFG. Co.					
Shur-Snap	see Colonial Knife Co.	Providence RI	USA	Mfr.	c1948	M
Silver Sword	see Camillus				c1982–pres.	
Simmons, E.C., Hdw. Co.	KEEN CUTTER to Winch. 1922–9, Shapleigh 1940	St. Louis MO	USA	Hdw. Whol.	1868–1960	H
Simmons Hardware Co.	economy brand tang stamp	St. Louis MO	Germany	Hdw. Whol. Imp.	c1890–1940	M
Simmons Worden White Co.	SWWCo, advt. knife by Camillus	Dayton OH	USA	Tool Mfr. Advt.	c1937 ff.	M
Singleton & Priestman		Sheffield	England	Mfr.	c1861–19??	M
Slater Brothers (Bee Hive picture)	see Slater, Herbert M.					
Slater, Herbert M(arriatt)	Venture, Bee Hive	Sheffield	England	Mfr.	1853–pres.	M
Slater, Herbert Marriatt	now owns J.Crookes, H.G.Long					
Smethport Cutlery Co.	sold to W. R. Case	Smethport PA	USA	Mfr.	1907–1909	H
Smith & Clark		Bronxville NY	USA	Mfr.?	c1850	H
Smith & Hemenway	Red Devil S. & H. Co.	Utica NY	USA	Hdw. Whol.	c1890–1920	M
Smith & Hopkins		Naugatuck CT	USA	Mfr.	1848 ff.	H
Smith & Wesson	S & W	Springfield MA	USA	Gun Mfr.	c1974–pres.	M
Smith Brothers Hdw. Co.	CutEasy	Columbus OH	USA	Hdw. Whol.	1903–1959	M
Smokey Mountain Knife Works		Sevierville TN		Retail	current	M
Snappy, Shur-Snap	see Colonial	Providence RI	USA	Mfr.	1948–c1958	M
Solingen	(place name)		Germany			
Son Bros. & Co. (Son & Briggs 1869–72)	owned Yale Cut. Co. (CT)	San Francisco CA	US & ?	Whol. & Import	1869–c1919	H
Southern & Richardson	Nest, Cigar, Squatter	Sheffield	England	Mfr.	1846–pres.?	M
Southington Cutlery Co.	dist. by Meriden Cut. Co.	Southington CT	USA	Mfr.	1867–c1914	H
Spear & Jackson	Aetna	Sheffield	England	Mfr.	c1850–pres.	H
Spear Cutlery Co.	?		Ger./Austria		pre-1915	L
Sperry & Alexander	S. & A.	New York NY	USA?	Whol.	1893–1920s	H
Spitzer, Carl Gustav	Standing Lion, Po'K., etc.	Solingen	Germany	Mfr.	1863–197?	M
Spratt's	(dog stripper)	Newark/Berlin/ London	England	Dog Food Mfr.	c1912	M
Spring Cutlery Co.		Sheffield	England		c1890	M
Springbrooke Knife Co.	for D.C.&H. by N.Y. Knife Co.	San Francisco CA	USA	Hdw. Whol.	c1914–1920	H
Springer (on handle of switchblade)	see W. Weltersbach					
Spyderco	Clipit	Golden CO	Japan	Whol. Importer	current	M
Sta-Sharp (sold by Sears Roebuck)	made by Camillus	Chicago IL	USA	Retail brand	c1924–1941	M
Stacey Bros. & Co.	Ark. (to Thos. Ward?)	Sheffield	England	Mfr.	1847–19??	M
Stainless Cutlery Co./N.Y. City	Camillus brand/Kastor	Camillus NY	USA	Mfr.	1924–30s	M
Stamm, Gebruder (Bros.)	Original Tidax	Solingen?	Germany	Mfr.	c1930?	M
Standard Cutlery Co.			Eng/Ger/US	Whol.?	c1900?	M
Standard Knife Co.	owned by 2 Case Brothers	Little Valley NY	USA	Whol.	1901–1903	H
Standard Knife Co.	made by W. R. Case & Sons	Bradford PA	USA	Mfr.	1920–1923	H
Staniforth, William Thomas	Ascend, wings	Sheffield	England	Mfr.	1852–c1906	H
Star Sales Co.	agent for R. Klaas	Knoxville TN		Whol. & Imp.	current	
Stellite	see Haynes Stellite					
Sterling Cutlery Co.	see McIlwaine Linn & Hughes					
Sterling Service	see Thompson Hdw. Co.					
Stiletto	(made for Miller Sloss & Scott/ Pacific Hdw. & Steel/ Baker Hamiton & Pacific)					
Stiletto Cutlery Co., New York	made for the above firms	San Francisco CA	USA	Hdw. Whol.	c1900–1942	H
Stocker & Co.	Solingen Metallwarenfabrik S.M.F. (after c1933)	Solingen	Germany	Mfr.	1897–197?	M

POCKETKNIFE BRAND	TRADEMARK (or Reference)	LOCATION	MADE IN:	TYPE OF FIRM	DATES	$
Stoddard's	was Dame Stoddard & Kendall	Boston MA		Retail	c1932–pres.	M
Strauss, A(dolph), Company	bought William Elliot	New York NY		Whol. Importer	c1907–1918	M
Streamline	see Camillus				1936 ff.	
Summit Cutlery Co.	see Pavian Cutlery Co.					
Superota, Le			France	Mfr.?	current	L
Sutcliffe, J(ohn) H., & Co.	Hickory Hand Forged	Louisville KY	USA	Ret. mail order	c1900	M
Svoboda, B.	imported by Liberty Organization (?)	Montrose CA	Ger./Japan	Whol. Importer	c1950–pres.	L
Swan Works	see Altenbach					
Swanner Cutlery Co.	Swans	Fairfield OH	US/Ger.	Retail, Whol.	1979–pres.	M
Sword & Shield			Germany	Import Brand	recent	L
Sword (Sword Brand after 1942)	see Kastor and Camillus				c1906–pres.	M
Syracuse Knife Co.	Camillus brand	Camillus NY	USA	Mfr.	1930s	M
Syracuse Knife Co.	Imported by Camillus		Poland	Import brand	1975–6	L
T. B. & M.	see Turton Bros. & Matthews					
T. E. C. S.	see Exclusive Cutlery					
T. T. C. Diamond Brand, N. Y.	sold by Sears Roebuck	Chicago IL	USA	Retail	c1909	M
Tampa Hdw. Co.	W. C. T.	Tampa FL		Hdw. Whol.	c1910	M
Tarry/Levigne	Salamander (picture)	Thiers?	France	Mfr.	c1900	M
Taylor (eye) Witness	see Needham Veall Tyzack					
Taylor Cutlery Co.		Kingsport TN	Japan	Whol. Importer	current	L
Taylor, H. H., & Bro.	(US Navy contractor)	Sheffield	England	Mfr.	c1855 ff.	V
Taylor, Henry	Acorn	Sheffield	England	Mfr.	c1858–1927	M
Terrier Cutlery Co.	made by Robeson	Rochester NY	USA	Mfr.	c1910–1916	M
The W. & H. Co.	see Whitehead & Hoag					
Theile & Quack	(by Wester, Weyers.) Wade B(ros.), Tyler, A☆1	Elberfeld	Germany	Whol. Export	c1866–1890	M
Thelco	The L. Co., see Lockwood Luetkemeyer Henry					
Thickett, James		Sheffield	England	Mfr.?	19th Cent.	M
Thiers	(place name)		France			
Thomas Mfg. Co.	sold HHH, American Shear & Knife	Dayton OH	USA	Retail	1907–1911	M
Thomaston Knife Co.		Thomaston CT	USA	Mfr.	1887–c1930	M
Thompson & Gascoigne	became Empire Knife Co.	Winsted CT	USA	Mfr.	1852–1856	V
Thompson, J. M., Hdw. Co.	Sterling Service	Minneapolis MN	US/Ger/Eng	Hdw. Whol.	c1910–1922	M
Thornhill, W.		London	England	Mfr. & Retailer	19th Cent.	H
Thornton			USA	Mfr.?	c1950s?	L
Thorpe, Joseph		Sheffield	England	Mfr.	c1853–1873	M
Tidioute Cutlery Co.	sold to Union Razor Co.	Tidioute PA	USA	Mfr.	1897–1902	H
Tiger Brand	see Lauterjung & Co.					
Tillotson & Co.		Sheffield	England	Mfr.	c1840	H
Timpson, C(ornelius) B.,& Tucker, (Joseph A.) 167 South St.		New York NY	USA?	Hdw.Whol.& Mfr.	1863–1872	V
Tina			Germany		c1890–pres.	M
Toledo	(place name)		Spain			
Topper, Junior Topper, Sport Topper	see Colonial					
Torrey, J. R., Razor Co.		Worcester MA	USA	Mfr.	1858–1963	H
Towika (or Jowika)			Irel./Ger.	Import brand	current	L
Townley Hdw. Co.		Kansas City MO		Hdw. Whol.	1884–pres.	M
Trail Blazer	see George Worthington					
Trident (Dreizack)	see Ed. Wusthof					
Tritch, George, Hdw. Co.	made by Ulster		USA	Hdw. Whol.	c1910	M
Troll			Germany	export brand?	c1920s	L
Trout Hardware Co.	Square Deal	Chicago IL		Hdw. Whol.	c1896–1907	M
Tru-Temper	see Ohio Cutlery Co.					
True Value	see Hibbard Spencer Bartlett					
Trumpet or cornet (picture)	see Gebruder Weyersberg					
Tryon, Edward K.	3/T. Some by Utica.	Philadelphia PA	US/Eng.	Retail & Whol.	c1811–1952	H
Turner, Thomas, & Co.	Encore, Suffolk, Haywood	Sheffield	England	Mfr.	1830–1932	M
Turton Brothers & Matthews	T. B. & M., Torpedo	Sheffield	England	Mfr.	c1860–1914	M
Tuska Moto			Japan?			M
Twig Brand	see Borgfeldt				c1911	L
Twitchell Bros.		Naugatuck CT	USA	Mfr.		H
Tyler Celebrated Cutlery	see Theile & Quack					
Tyzack, W. A., & Co.		Sheffield	England	Mfr.	c1850–1953	M

POCKETKNIFE BRAND	TRADEMARK (or Reference)	LOCATION	MADE IN:	TYPE OF FIRM	DATES	$
U. K. & R.	see Utica Knife & Razor					
U.M.C. (Union Metallic Cartridge)	see Remington (circle)					
U. S. A. (bone handles)	made by Kingston for U.S. Army					M
U. S. A. (plastic handles)	usually Colonial					L
U. S. Small Arms Co.	small knife-pistol	Chicago IL	USA	Mfr.	c1914–1923	H
Ulery, U(lysses) J., Co.	metal handles, by Napanoch	New York NY	USA	Whol.	c1902–1919	M
Ulmer, A(dolph)	C. F. Ulmer after 1890	Portland ME	Germany	Retail	1869–1928	M
Ulster Knife Co.	owned by Dwight Divine & Sons	Ellenville NY	USA	Mfr.	1876–1941	H
Ulster USA	owned by Albert and Henry Baer	Ellenville NY	USA	Mfr.	1941–pres.	L
UN-X-LD	see Northfield Knife Co.					
Underwood, H.	56 Haymarket	London	England	Mfr. & Retailer	c1820–19??	H
Union Knife Co.	(beware of counterfeits)	Naugatuck CT	USA	Mfr.	1851–1885	V
Union Knife Works		Union NY	USA	Mfr.	c1911–1913	H
Union Razor Co.	became Union Cutlery	Tidioute PA	USA	Mfr.	1898–1909	V
Union Cutlery Co.		Tidioute PA	USA	Mfr.	1909–1911	V
Union Cutlery Co.	KA-BAR (first used 1923)	Olean NY	USA	Mfr.	1911–1951	V
Union (in map of N. America)	see Union Cutlery Co.					
United Cutlery Co.			Aust./Ger.	Import brand	pre-1915	L
United Machine Tool Co.	United	Grand Rapids MI	USA	Mfr.	WWII	M
Unwin & Rogers	made knife pistols	Sheffield	England	Mfr.	c1848–1867	H
Utica K(nife) & R(azor) Co.	became Utica Cutlery Co.	Utica NY	US/Ger.	Mfr. & Whol.	1910–1929	H
Utica Cutlery Co.	Kutmaster, Seneca	Utica NY	USA	Mfr.	1929–pres.	M
V. C. & Co.	see Vom Cleff & Co.					
Valley Forge Cutlery Co.		Newark NJ	USA	Mfr.	1892–1916	H
Valley Forge (VF in circle)	owned by Boker	Newark NJ	USA	Mfr.	1916–c1950	M
Valor Corporation	also Valco	Miami FL	Ger/Jap/Pak	Importer	1970–pres.	L
Van Camp Hdw. & Iron Co.	owned Capitol Cut. Co.	Indianapolis IN	US/Ger.	Hdw. Whol.	c1876–1960	M
Venture	see Slater					
Veritable = Genuine (French)						
Vermont Cutlery Co.	made by Wester & Butz?			Whol.?	c1920s	M
Victoria (1909–), Victorinox (1921–)	(Swiss Army) Karl Elsener	Ibach, near Zurich	Switz.	Mfr.	1884–pres.	M
Victory Cutlery Co.		New Haven CT	USA	Mfr.?	c1925	M
Vignos, August	see Novelty Cutlery Co.					
Viking	see Eric Wedemeyer					
Voelker Forst & Merten	Raucherkopf (smoking head)	Solingen-Hoehscheid	Germany	Mfr.	1920–19??	M
Volka	see Dunham Carrigan & Hayden	San Francisco CA	Germany	Hdw. Whol. Imp.	c1903	L
Vom Cleff & Co.	V. C. & Co.,	New York NY	Ger./Eng.	Whol. Importer	1887–c1930	M
Voos Cutlery Co.	Voos/Arrow (also Empire?)	Cheshire/New Haven CT	USA	Import (& Mfr?)	c1920s–81	M
Voss, August, & Co.	Voss Cutlery Co.	New York NY	Germany	Whol. Importer	c1900–1939	M
Vulcan (Knife Co.)	see Thomas Ellin (?)					
W. & H. (in a flag)	see Walker & Hall					
W. & H. Co., The	see Whitehead & Hoag					
W. B. / Speed	see Brokhahne or Wiesbusch					
W. C. T.	see Tampa Hdw. Co.					
W. R. B. Co.	see Will Roll Bearing Co.					
W'vill Co.	see Waterville Co.					
Wabash Cutlery Co.	(Indiana Cut. Co. c1932)	Terre Haute IN	USA	Mfr.	1921–1935	H
Wade, Robert (joined W & S Butcher)	Wade	Sheffield	England	Mfr.	c1810–1819	H
Wade & Butcher	see W. & S. Butcher	Sheffield	England	Mfr.	c1819–1947	H
Wade Wingfield & Rowbotham		Sheffield	England	Mfr.	c1830–50s	H
Wade B(ros.) Celebrated Cutlery	see Theile & Quack					
Wadsworth, A. W., & Sons	part of A. Kastor & Bros.	New York NY	Aust./Ger.	Whol. Importer	c1905–1922	M
Wagner, Wilhelm	W/W	Solingen	Germany	Mfr.	1876–197?	M
Walden Knife Co.	sold to E.C. Simmons 1902	Walden NY	USA	Mfr.	c1870–1923	H
Walker & Hall	W. & H. (in a flag)	Sheffield	England	Mfr.	1867–c1900	M
Wallkill River Works	N. Y. Knife Co. brand	Walden NY	USA	Mfr.	1928–1931	H
Walter Bros.			Germany	Import brand	pre-WWI	L
Walters, John, & Co	Globe Works	Sheffield	England	Mfr.	c1846–1862	M

POCKETKNIFE BRAND	TRADEMARK (or Reference)	LOCATION	MADE IN:	TYPE OF FIRM	DATES	$
Ward & Co.		Bronxville NY	USA	Mfr.?	c1860s	H
Ward, Asline	agent for Wostenholm	New York NY	England	Whol.	c1880	
Ward, F., & Co.	B 4 ☆ ANY (regis. 1867)	Sheffield	England	Mfr.	c1850s–79	M
Ward, Thomas, & Sons	see Stacey Bros.	Sheffield	England	Mfr.	c1850s–pres.	M
Wardlow, S. & C.	Terrifik	Sheffield	England	Mfr.	1855–c1920	M
Wards	made for Montgomery Ward by Utica (& Winchester?)	Chicago IL	USA	Retail	c1935–50s	M
Wards (blade etched Western Pride)	by Western for Montgomery Ward	Chicago IL	USA	Retail	1930s–?	M
Warther, Ernst	died 1972	Dover OH	USA	Mfr., carver	1920s–40s	V
Warther, Thomas	son of Ernst Warther	Dover OH	USA	Mfr.	d. 1984	V
Warwick Knife Co.		Warwick NY	USA	Mfr.	c1907–1928	M
Washington Cutlery Co.	see Gray & Dudley Hdw.					
Watauga	see H. G. Lipscomb & Co.					
Waterville (Cutlery or Mfg.) Co.		Waterbury CT	USA	Mfr.	1843–c1913	H
Watkins Cottrell Co.	Clipper (after 1901)	Richmond VA		Hdw. Whol.	1967–pres.?	M
Watts, John	''Estb. 1765''	Sheffield	England	Mfr.	c1855–pres.	M
Weck, Edward, & Sons		New York NY		Whol. Imp.	c1893–1943	M
Wedemeyer, Eric	Viking E. W.	New York NY	USA	Retail?	c1930s	M
Wedgeway Cutlery Co.	for Morley Bros. Hdw. Co.	Saginaw MI	USA?	Hdw. Whol.	1887–1933	M
Weidmannsheil = Good hunting (German)	Stag (picture), see W. Weltersbach					
Weiss, John (& Son 1830–83) (& Sons 1883–pres.)		London	England	Mfr. & Retailer	1878–pres.	H
Weltersbach, Wilhelm	Springer, other marks	Solingen	Germany	Mfr.	1882–pres.	M
Wenger (Swiss Army)	Wengerinox	Delemont	Switz.	Mfr.	c1908–pres.	M
Werwolfwerk	imp. by Dixon Cut. Co.		Germany	Mfr.?	c1920s	M
Weske Cutlery Co.		Sandusky OH		Retail?	c1946–1952	M
West Virginia Cutlery Co.				Whol.?		M
Westaco	see Western States Cutlery					
Wester & Butz	many trademarks; Wester Bros.	Solingen	Germany	Mfr.	1832–1966	M
Wester Bros.	agent of Wester & Butz, Anchor-Star-Arrow	New York NY	Germany	Whol. Importer	1902–c1967	M
Western Cutlery Co.	imported by Wiebusch & Hilger	New York NY	Ger./Aust.	Whol. Importer	c1874–1914	L
Western States Cutlery Co.	(became Western Cutlery Co. 1951)	Boulder CO	USA	Mfr.	1911–1951	H
Western Cutlery Co.		Boulder CO	USA	Mfr.	1951–1978	M
Western Cutlery Co.	sold to Coleman 1984	Longmont CO	USA	Mfr.	1978–pres.	M
Westersson, A. J.		Eskilstuna	Sweden	Mfr.	c1900	M
Westmark	see Western Cutlery Co.					
Westpfal (August) Cutlery Co.	Standpoint	New York NY		Retail	c1920–1951	M
Westpfal, Frederick (& Bro.)	Acme	New York NY	Ger./US	Whol. & Retail	c1884–1940	M
Weyersberg, Gebruder (Bros.)	Cornet, King, A☆1, etc.	Solingen	Germany	Mfr.	1787–pres.	M
Whale (picture)	see Richartz					
Whirling square (picture) in circle	see China Light Ind. ...	Canton, Guangdong	China			
White, Matthew	OVO	Sheffield	England	Mfr.	c1847–1869	H
Whitehead & Hoag, The, Co.	made by Boker USA	Newark NJ	USA	Advt. Specialty	1892–1940s	M
Whittles & Froggart		Sheffield	England	Mfr.	c1850	H
Wibbeltrath, Hermann	Steeple (picture)	Solingen-Ohligs	Germany	Mfr.	c1860	H
Wichita Cutlery Co.		Wichita KS				M
Wick, Albert or William		New York NY	Germany	Whol.	19th Cent.	M
Wiebusch, F. / Wiebusch & Hilger	Challenge, Western, Monum'l	New York NY	US/Ger/Eng	Whol/Imp/Mfr	C1874–1928	M
Wilbert Cutlery Co. (Sears Roebuck)	made by Napanoch, Empire	Chicago IL	USA	Retail	c1909	H
Wilcox / 45 Edgeware Road	(made in Sheffield)	London	England	Retail	c1900	M
Wilford & Co. Cutlery Co.		Sheffield	England	Mfr.?	c1880s	H
Wilkinson Sword Ltd.		London & Sheffield	England	Whol. & Mfr.	c1905–pres.	L
Wilkinson H. Y., Cutlery Co.		Sheffield	England	Mfr.?	c1900	M
Wilkinson, W(illiam), (& Son)		Sheffield	England	Mfr.	c1760–1892	M
Will & Finck	(factory 1863–1905), marked po'k's imported	San Francisco CA	Ger./Eng.	Mfr. & Retail	1863–1932	V
Will Roll Bearing Co.	W.R.B. Co. (by Baldwin?)	Terre Haute IN	USA	Whol.?	c1920s	M
Williams (Brothers) Cutlery Co.		San Francisco CA		Retail	c1900–pres.	M

POCKETKNIFE BRAND	TRADEMARK (or Reference)	LOCATION	MADE IN:	TYPE OF FIRM	DATES	$
Williams, Alfred	(Rivington Works) EBRO, imported by Kastor	Sheffield	England	Import brand?	c1890–1920	M
Wilson Hawksworth & Moss (or W. H. & Ellison)		Sheffield	England	Mfr.	19th Cent.	M
Wilzin's patent	see Auto(matic) Knife Co.					
Winchester	bought Napanoch, Eagle, Simmons	New Haven CT	USA	Mfr. Whol. Retail	c1919–1942	V
Wingen, Anton, Jr.	Othello	Solingen	Germany	Mfr.	1888–pres.	M
Wingfield Rowbotham & Co.	see Wade Wingfield & Rowbotham					
Wintgen, Ewald, & Co.	now part of Kammerling	Elberfeld	Germany	Mfr.		
Witte Hdw. Co.		St. Louis MO		Hdw. Whol.	c1865–pres.	M
Wolf, Chris (stamped on blade)	see Queen Cutlery Co.					
Wolfertz, C. F., & Co.	(Mfr. 1862–c1920)	Allentown PA		Mfr. then Whol.	1862–c1944	H
Woodbury Cutlery Co.		Woodbury CT	USA	Mfr.?	19th Cent.	H
Woodhead, George (& Son)	G. W.*I.	Sheffield	England	Mfr.	c1845–70s	H
Worth, B., & Sons		Sheffield	England	Mfr.	c1874–1919	M
Worthington, George, Co.	Trail Blazer, Harvard, Clearcut	Cleveland OH		Whol.?	c1902–1949	M
Wostenholm, George	I*XL (see other listings)	Sheffield	England	Mfr.	1745–c1971	
Wolstenholm, George	(1st US sale 1830) Rockingham Works	Sheffield	England	Mfr.	1815–1848	V
Wostenholm, George	I*XL Washington Works	Sheffield	England	Mfr.	1848–c70s	V
Wostenholm, George	I*XL Celebrated	Sheffield	England	Mfr.	c1860s–90s	H
Wolstenholm, George	I*XL, ENGLAND on blade	Sheffield	England	Mfr.	c1891–1971	M
Wostenholm, George	I*XL, Oil The Joints	Sheffield	England	Mfr.	c1930s–77	M
Wragg, Samuel C. (& Sons)		Sheffield	England	Mfr.	c1830s–60s	H
Wusthof, Carl, KG	Gladiator, Hejo, James	Solingen	Germany	Mfr.	1895–pres.	M
Wusthof, Eduard	Dreizack (Trident)	Solingen	Germany	Mfr.	1814–pres.	M
Wyeth Hdw. & Metal Co.	Wyeth's Warranted Cutlery	St. Joseph MO	US/Ger.	Hdw. Whol.	c1884–pres.	M
X. C. D.	see W. & S. Butcher					
X. L. C. R	see W. Bingham					
X. L. N. T.	see Adolph Kastor					
X. X.	see Case or Copley					
Yale Cutlery Co.	owned by Son Bros. S.F.CA.	Meriden CT	USA	Mfr.?	c1883–?	H
Yankee	see Colonial Knife Co.					
Yankee Cutlery Co.		New York NY	Germany	Import Brand	c1910s	L
Yudelman, Israel	Sjambok	Sheffield	England	Mfr.	c1880	H
Zak			Germany	Import brand	c1910?	L
Zavialoff, Alexis		Vyatka (Kirov)	Russia	Mfr.	c1876	H
Zenith	(some made by N.Y. Knife Co.) see Marshall Wells Hdw.	Duluth MN	USA	Hdw. Whol.	c1893–1917	H
Zinn, Edward	Open Easy		Germany?	Mfr.	c1920	M
Zippo		Bradford PA		Lighter Mfr.	c1950s	M

Late 18th Century Sheffield Cutlers' Marks

THE FIRST Sheffield city directory was published in 1740, but the most comprehensive Sheffield directory of the 18th century was the one of 1787. The 1787 directory includes an extensive classified section. For all the makers and factors of finished cutlery, the classified listings show name, address, and touch-mark.

A factor was a person (or firm) who sold cutlery made for him which was marked with his brand by independent workmen called "little masters." In Sheffield, the factoring system was called "liver and draw." The workmen (forgers, grinders, handle and fitting makers, and "cutlers" or final assemblers) delivered the week's finished goods to the factor, and then drew their pay, as well as their parts and material for the following week.

Most of the knives made in Sheffield at that time were marked only with a maker's or factor's touch-mark. Therefore, to identify the mark on an 18th century Sheffield knife, you need to have a listing like the one included in the 1787 directory.

Within a generation of 1787, legal and guild rules had changed, permitting the use of the maker's or factor's full name on finished cutlery. If he chose, he could add his address, and he could include his word or pictorial mark, as well. Advances in die-sinking technology made such elaborate stamping dies affordable.

Although the 1787 Sheffield directory was reproduced in 1969 (by Da Capo Press), those reproductions are now almost as difficult to find as original copies. Therefore, I have here reproduced all parts of that directory which identify cutlers' touchmarks. I would like to thank Tom Heitzman for permission to reproduce from his copy of the directory.

Knives in Excellent condition with any of these touchmarks are very rare. Their values range from High to Very High.

The high values are due in part simply to age and rarity. More important, however, is that the large majority of cutlery sold in the infant United States in the decades around 1800 was made in Sheffield by or for people listed in the 1787 Sheffield city directory. To the contemporary American collector or historian, these knives are therefore of particular interest.

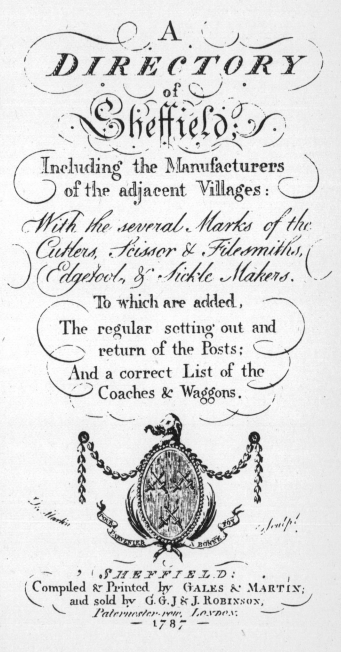

A DIRECTORY of Sheffield; Including the Manufacturers of the adjacent Villages: With the several Marks of the Cutlers, Scissor & Filesmiths, Edgetool, & Sickle Makers. To which are added, The regular setting out and return of the Posts; And a correct List of the Coaches & Waggons. SHEFFIELD: Compiled & Printed by GALES & MARTIN; and sold by G. G. J & J. ROBINSON, Paternoster-row, LONDON. — 1787 —

PEN and POCKET KNIVES
in general.

Manufacturers in SHEFFIELD.

BARNES Isaac, Campo-lane	BARNS
Barnes Thomas, Smithfield	LOVE
Barlow John, Campo-lane	BARLOW
Bateman George, Smithfield	BATEMAN
Beardshaw William, Silver-street	PASTO
Beardshaw John, Holles Croft	BEARDSHAW
Beet and Senyers, Pea Croft	BRET
	OBTAIN
	RAINBOW
Bradshaw Wm. Holles Croft; *Pockets only*	BRADSHAW
Briddock Martin, Lambert Croft	BRID-DOCK
Brightmore William, Broad-lane	LONDON
	CITY
Broadhead William, Holles Croft	BO→W
Broomhead, Hinchsliffe, and Co. Brinsworth's Orchard	BROOMHEAD
Broomhead Joseph, Lambert Croft; *Jacks*	⚚ PYL
Brown George, Coalpit-lane	BROWN
Burch George, Spring-street	SMEG ✠
Butler William, Trinity-street	BUTLER
Cadman George, Back-lane	CUPID
Cawton Joshua, and Sons, Snighill	⊙ CAWTON
Clark Jonathan, Norfolk-street	LARK
Crabtree Thomas, Pea Croft	CRABTREE
Creswick Joseph, Queen-street	LAVORO
Crookes James, and Son, New-street	W'D DAY
Davison Lemuel and Co.	IMPERIAL
	CROS
Fowler Isaiah, Coalpit-lane	P ROOM
Fox and Norris, Westbar	METAS
Fox William, do.	FOX ✠
Green James, Norfolk-street	J. GREEN
Green Jonathan, Bailey Field	✠ZA✠
Hague and Nowil, Garden-street	D EHONG
Hall Thomas, Meadow-street	FUEL
Hall Henry, Union-street; *spotted and Wood Pockets*	↲ ⊟ →
	⊹
Harrison John, and Son, Holles Croft	I H
Hawksworth Christopher, Silver-street	O CH
Higginson Samuel, Burgess-street	STAR
Ibberson John and George, Gibralter	◇ K
Jervis William, White Croft	✠⊙✠
Jervis John, Meadow-street	♔ C

Justice-Paris, Spring-street	PARIS
Kay Samuel, Pinston-lane	WAR
Kelk Charles, Westbar-green	♟
Kemp Isaiah N. Norfolk-street	KEMP
Kennington James, Blind-lane	PIT
Kippax John, China-square	PEARL
	ESAU
Kirkby and Borwick, Longstone-lane	SULTAN
Kirkby Mary, Brinsworth's Orchard	EDEN
Knowles Francis, White Croft	✠ S L
Levick John, and Son, Pond-lane	LEVIK
	MERIT
Loy William, Far-gate	♋⊙✠
Ludlam Widow, and Sons, Burgess-street	ETNA
Marriot Luke, Coalpit-lane	⋉<✠✠
Martin Charles, Pond-lane	ORMUS
Matthews John, Smithfield	TOURS
Mickelthwaite, and Co.	ZACA
Mycock John and Joseph, Burgess-street	+ PENS
Mycock Joseph, Church-lane; *Pockets*	⋉◁✠
	IM
Naylor and Son, Coalpit-lane	PRET
Nowil and Kippax, High-street	NOWIL
	KIPPAX
Nowil Joseph, Copper-street; *also Jacks*	GENEVA
Newton Edmund, Back-lane	ACUTE
Owen Robert, Westbar-green	GOLD
Patten Hannah, and Son, Silver-street	NANTZ
Patten George, Coalpit-lane; *also Jacks*	PATEN
Priest Francis, Pea Croft	PRIEST
Proctor Charles, and Luke, Milk-street;	⏚ ↝ ⌇
Hunters Knives and Butchers Steels only	PROSPER
Ratcliff Widow, Paradise Square	CROIX
Roberts John, Pinston-lane	HOTEL
Rodgers Joseph, and Maurice, Norfolk-str	✷ ✠ ✠
Roebuck, and Co. Lambert Croft	ROEBUCK
Rose William, Coalpit-lane	✠ ⊛
Shepherd Robert, Norfolk-street	◁∼✠
Shipman Æneas, Silver-street	ANON
Smith William, and Co. Coalpit-lane	✧✠✠ IFS
Smith John, Grindle-gate	SPARLIN
Spurr Peter, Church-lane	SPUR
Staniforth, Parkin, and Co. Sycamore-str.	HAGUE
	SHEMEL
Stead Richard, Silver-street	STEAD
Sutton Jonathan, Meadow-street	BAM✠
Sykes Samuel, Holles Croft	BUDA
Tarbotton Thomas, Scotland-street	QUEEN
Taylor Samuel, Pea Croft	BEET

Name	Mark
Travis Nathaniel, White Croft	IN
Urton William, and George, Colston Croft	BILBO URTON
Water Godfrey, and Son, Pond-lane	TAGLIO WATER
Wigfall William, Pea Croft	REMUS
Watkinson Jonathan, Silver-street	J. WATKINSON
Wild Jonathan, Sims Croft	SIAM
Wild William, Trinity-street	GLOBE
Wilkinson John, Lambert Croft	AN & C
Withers Benjamin, and Co. Far-gate	ESPANGE
Wright William, John, and Robert, Smithfield	◇ ♡ ♌ ✠ 8 CV ✗

Manufacturers the NEIGHBOURHOOD.

Name	Mark
BARLOW Samuel, Neepsend	N°
Baxter John, Bridgehouses; *Hunters only*	24 N
Carr John, Neepsend	CARR
Hawksworth Thomas and Jonathan, Attercliff	+ + SX CASAN +
Warburton Samuel, Bridgehouses	LIFE
Yates George, Bridgehouses	♦ R 3

Common POCKET and PENKNIVES.

Manufacturers in SHEFFIELD.

Name	Mark
ALSOP Luke, Coalpit-lane	HA
Bishop Thomas, China Square	+ STATE
Butler Stephen, Townhead Well	◇ BAKU
Crookes Jonathan, Scotland-street	⊸◁
Dixon James, Campo-lane	+ DIXON
Duke Henry, Trinity-street	READ
Dungworth Jonathan, Meadow-street	1772
Drabble Enoch, Green-lane	USE
Fox John, Park	+ FOX
Hancock Charles, Scotland-street	QUEBEC
Hibbert Samuel, Bailey Field	SOL
Hutton Henry, Coalpit-lane	HUTTON
Lindley William and Son, Ponds	SAILOR BOLD
Littlewood and Hatfield, Park	⚥ IL UPHONY
Marsh Hannah, Park	Y✱
Oates John, Little Sheffield	OATES
Osborne George, Porto Bello	DRAFT

Name	Mark
Parkin Thomas, Scotland-street	LOUIS
Priest Joseph, Young-street	DUNBAR
Revel Joseph, do.	+ PINK
Revel Benjamin, Pea Croft	JOLLY SAILOR
Spencer Widow, Westbar-green	∽♡♌
Smith Widow, Broad-lane End	+♌+✱
Swinden Matthew, Holles Croft	♆
Taylor Paul, Pond-lane	♛ PT
Turner Samuel, China-square	◊ IVORY
Twigg Jonathan, Broadlane End	² TWIGG
Ward James, Spring-street	WDS
Waterhouse Jeremiah, Scotland-street	▷◇+
Wild John, Holles Croft	✠ WILD

Manufacturers in the NEIGHBOURHOOD.

NOTE. Those who make Penknives, have the Word *Pen* put against their Names; the others make only *Couteaux*.

Name	Mark
ALMON John, Cherry-tree Hill	ALMON
Ashell George, Attercliff, *Pen*	✠ CRUZ
Abel John, Bents Green	ABEL
Abel William, Little Common	+∽♌✠
Barker William, Wadsley	✠N✠
Bateman Ralph, Wadsley	ROD
Beatson George, Gleadles	+MYR
Beatson Luke, do.	✠▷◁
Beighton, William, Edge	⊙N✠
Boulsover Timothy, Park	JOVIL
Bowden Joseph, Worral	✿
Bradshaw William, Crooks	ENE
Bradshaw James, do.	✿✠⊢
Briggs William, Toadhole	BRIGS
Bruck John, Hill-top	BRUCK
Brookshaw Sampson, Little Common	SAMP
Brown George, Heely	FIR
Brown John, do.	Γ<
Burdekin John, Stannington	²³ B
Burley Nicholas, Onesacre	Z♌✱
Burley George, do.	ASTRON
Close Godfrey, Heely	♌✠✚
Close Francis, Newfield Green	CLOSE
Coldwell Joseph, Dungworth	GES
Denton William, Bents Green	SOU
Dewsnap Thomas, Tom-lane	DUSNAP
Drabble Enoch, Dungworth	▷♌◀

Name	Mark
Drabble William, do.	GOSLAR
Drabble Joshua, do.	SADU
Dungworth Joseph, Hirst	◁ϵ◣
Dyson William, jun. Shotnell	AJAX
Garret Joseph, Birley Edge	1765
Gill Samuel, Heely	ASHDOD
Gill Thomas, do.	⊀⊢◁
Gill Jonathan, do.	VENLO
Gill Joshua, do.	SEALED
Gillat Samuel, do.	⊞⊙⧻
Gillat William, do.	SYNO
Gillat Henry, do.	⊢⊙⧻
Gillat Thomas, do.	z⊣ϕ⊱
Goddard John, Attercliff; *Pen*	⊗⧻+
Green Moses, Wadsley	888 / 888
Green Widow, Worral	⊢⊙⌒
Hague William, Dungworth	DRIVE
Hallam Francis, Darnall; *Pen*	F H + HALM
Hallam Thomas, sen. Heely; *Pen*	♔ HALM
Hallam Thomas, jun. do.	CEYX
Hallam Jonathan, Heely	SPELL
Hallam Joseph, Little Common	SPELL
Hartley Joshua, Mill Lee	HARTLY
Hawksworth George, Dungworth	³G H
Hill James, Piper House	⊢H⊳ N I ⌒
Hobson John, Bell Hague	P ⊳⧻⊣
Hobson Amos, Malin Bridge	◁⧻⊙
Hobson Joseph, Owlerton	⊙ω⧻
Hobson Jacob, do.	⊏∃⊣
Hoole William, Crooksmoor	⧻⊢ϵ
Howard Joseph, Storrs	ANCONA
Hoyle Ralph, Dungworth	PASO
Ibbotson Widow, Coldwell	⚓ LUTON
Innocent John, Darnall; *Pen*	JONES
Jones Widow, and Sons, Greenhill	+ BOSTON
Kinder John, Attercliff; *Pen*	X⊗ UBIA
Kinder John, Hirst	TOR+
Kirkby and Himsworth, Cross Pool	⊳⊣+⊙
Leadbeater George, Stannington	z⊆+
Lingard Joseph, Milnhouses	z⊆+◁
Lingard John, do.	⊢⊣ON
Lingard Thomas, do.	ω⊣+C
Lowe Richard, Stannington	+ω⊙+
Marshall William, Bents Green	z⊙+
Memmot George, Heely	

Name	Mark
Memmot Amos, Heely	⊀⊙⊙
Memmot Samuel, do.	RUSO
Middleton John, Wadsley	ARM
Newton John, Sharrowmoor; *Pen*	⟶◢⊙
Nicholson John, Darnall; *Pen*	SAX
Nichols Abraham, Stannington	JAN. 20
Nichols John, Storrs	⊃+⊗
Nixon Thomas, Dungworth	◁ 20
Oates Matthew, Bents Green	+ ELT
Owen George, Bridgehouses	STEADY
Platt William, Cowms	W. PLAT
Priest John, Bents Green	NINE
Priest William, do.	PRIEST
Ransley Henry, Stannington	◁⊞⧻ϵ
Revel Abraham, Little Common	EPHOD
Rose John, Wadsley	⧻⊞C
Rose John, jun. do.	MOPED
Senior Joseph, Slaylee	I C
Shaw Samuel, Heely	⌒ +ϵ
Slack Isaac, and Co. Crooksmoor	⊙ 4
Slack Jonathan, Steel Bank	⊃⊞◀
Staniforth George, Bridgehouses	+ SENT
Stones Joseph, sen. Park	STONES
Stones Joseph, jun. Heely	93⧻
Stones Thomas, do.	z ϵ+
Stringer Joseph, Slaylee	ϖ⊙⧻ W
Taylor Philip, Birley Car; *Pen*	z⊙⌒
Thompson John, and Son, Heely	BON COUTEAU
Turner Stephen, Hirst	♔ S T
Turner Joseph, Hilltop	P Y
Turner John, do.	⊙+P
Tricket William, Morwood	AEUN
Tricket William, Storrs; *Pen*	z⊣ϵ N⌒
Tricket John, Wadefield House	EMER
Tricket John, Dungworth	z⊙
Tricket James, Bierly Car	EDG
Twigg John, Attercliff	LUCK
Watson John, Sandygate	6 V
Watson Thomas, do.	⊙ V
West John, Storrs	WEST
Wigley Joshua, Bradfield	EWTO
Wright John, Dungworth	WRIGHT

Names omitted in their proper Places.

Name	Mark
ABDY John, Howard-ſtreet; *Couteau and Graver Maker*	✳ A
Cooper Sheldon, Gibralter, *Pen and Pocket Knives in general*	COOPER
Drabble Samuel, Broad-lane, do.	ORRERY
Greaves Thomas, Church-lane, do.	◀♀▶

RAZORS.

Manufacturers in SHEFFIELD.

Name	Mark
ASH Richard, Young-ſtreet	RAY ♔
Birks William and John, Norfolk-ſtreet	♗ & ♗ &
Brammall Nicholas, White Croft	CALVIN
Brightmore John, Croſs Field	CITY
Brittain, Wilkinſon, and Brownell, Arundel-ſtreet	EXCELLENT FRANCE VRAI
Broomhead, Hinchſliffe, and Co. Brinſworth's Orchard	BROOMHEAD
Broomhead Joſeph, Lambert Croft	♗ PYL
Cadman Luke, Surrey-ſtreet	BENGALL
Cadman David, Longſton-lane	SENEGAL
Dewſnap George, and William, Lambert Croft	SORBON MECA
Dewſnap Francis, Wicker	FARA ♗ P ROOM MARKS
Fox and Norris Weſtbar	FOX ✚
Fox William, do.	
Greaves William, Burgeſs-ſtreet	GREAVES
Hall Jonathan, China-ſquare	GRATIAN
Hallam James, Norfolk-ſtreet	✈ PARIS
Harriſon John, Campo-lane	HARRISON
Hudſon John, Weſtbar-green	CUSCO ✚ PARIS
Juſtice Paris, Spring-ſtreet	♗ R M
Kirkby Samuel, Lambert Croft	J. GREEN
Green James, Norfolk-ſtreet	ITALY
Leadbeater John, Copper-ſtreet	
Lindley John, Spring-ſtreet	⟶ ✚
Marriot Luke, Coalpit-lane	ⵦ ◀✳✚
Parkin Joſephus, Campo-lane; *alſo Jacks*	HOLLAND
Parker Widow, Pea Croft	✚ PARKER
Patten Hannah, and Son, Silver-ſtreet	✚ NANTZ

Name	Mark
Pryor Michael, Burgeſs-ſtreet	N ⟝ ♾
Revel George, Ratten Row; *alſo Jacks*	♗ ✚ GR BELVOIR AMSTERDAM
Roberts Joſeph, and Co. Garden-ſtreet	
Rodgers Joſeph, and Maurice, Norfolk-ſtreet	✳ ✚ RODGERS
Roebuck, and Co. Lambert Croft	ROEBUCK
Rowland Widow, Back-lane	♔ R
Shepherd John, Holles Croft	WOLF
Smith Thomas, Scotland-ſtreet	LEIPZIG ✚ SMITH
Staniforth, Parkin, and Co. Sycamore-ſtreet	SHEMEL PARKIN ⚓
Staniland Richard, Burgeſs-ſtreet	RICH ◆
Warburton Thomas, Burgeſs-ſtreet	✚ LISBON
Withers Benjamin, and Co. Far-gate	ESPANGE
Wright William, John, and Robert, Smithfield; *alſo Jacks*	◀✚ ⊢ C ∞ ◁♡ ✕ ✚

Manufacturers in the NEIGHBOURHOOD.

Name	Mark
BRAMMALL John, Storrs	JOPPA
Hall John, Sharrowmoor	LIMRICK
Lindley Samuel, Attercliff	LONDON
Palfreyman George, Stannington	N 3 CC
Pitchford Jonathan, Stumperly	P ⟶ FORD
Revet John, Stannington	VIRGIL
Revet Richard, do.	●∞ HOMER
Shaw John, do.	CLAYTON
Worrall John, do.	♔ HORACE
Warburton Samuel, Bridgehouſes	LIFE

LANCETS and PHLEMES.

Name	Mark
ASH Richard, Young-ſtreet; *Lancets*	RAY ♔
Brightmore John, Croſs Field	CITY
Butler William, Trinity-ſtreet; *Phlemes*	BUTLER
Creſwick Joſeph, Queen-ſtreet; *Phlemes*	LAVORO
Fox William, Weſtbar	FOX ✚
Hallam Mary, Norfolk-ſtreet; *Lancets*	✈ PARIS
Hallam James, do. do.	✈ PARIS
Proctor Jonathan, Coalpit-lane; *Phlemes*	PROCTOR
Pryor Michael, Burgeſs-ſtreet; do.	N ⟝ ♾
Roebuck, and Co. Lambert Croft	ROEBUCK
Watkinſon Jonathan, Silver-ſtreet	J. WATKIN-SON

SPOTTED KNIVES.

Manufacturers in SHEFFIELD.

Name	Mark
BEELY Thomas, Ponds	MARS
Beet Edward, Lambert Croft	BEET
Hall Henry, Union-street	⇁ Ⅱ ↗
Marples Samuel, Holles Croft	N ⊃ +
Race Richard, Cleekham Bowling-green	℞ ℞ ℳ
Shipman Æneas, Silver-street	VERNON
Swallow Joseph, Smithfield	⊃ ⊦ K
Swann Joseph, Gibralter	ᗉ ⊢ ✲
Townsend James, Holles Croft	66 T

Manufacturers in the NEIGHBOURHOOD.

Name	Mark
ASHALL John, Darnall	1756
Atkinson Richard, Graystones	🐦 R A
Bancroft Robert, Stannington	⊢ ◌ ✳
Barnes Joseph, Owlerton	⸮
Bateman Ralph, Wadsley	I B
Beldon Joseph, Darnall	ROD
Brammall Thomas, Wisewood	ᗉ ✿ +
Briddock Martin, do.	M
Burch Joseph, Stannington	GHUR
Burley John, Stannington	I⅄N +
Carr Thomas, do.	✳ ♡
Carr James, do.	✳
Creswick John, Sandy-gate	ᗞ 2 ✳
Crownshaw Ralph, Wadsley	CAVE
Dyson William, sen. Shotnell	ICUNE
Dyson Charles, Stannington	DYSON
Ellis John, Wadsley	ROPA
Eyre William, Darnall	⊢ ◌ ✳
Fearn Thomas, Roebuck House	Q KING
Fenton Hugh, Malin Bridge	TABLE
Furnace Luke, Stannington	DISH
Grason Joseph, Darnall	1760
Green Jeremiah, Worrall	FIRMUM
Hague William, Dungworth	M ᗕ Ꝏ +
Hague John, Wadsley	DRIVE
Hallam John, Walkley	⊲ ⅋ +
Hallam Robert, Dungworth	ASAY
Hallam George, Owlerton	ISAY
Hawley John, Stannington	C + C
Hobson Benjamin, Hilltop	IH 70
	MINE

Name	Mark
Hobson Jonathan, Wadsley	NORCOPPIN
Hobson Thomas, Bradfield	HOBSON
Hobson George, sen. Worrall	LASS
Hobson George, jun. Bradfield	◇ LASS
Hoyle Jeremiah, Wadsley	ᗉ ♣
Howard John, do.	℞ ✶ ✳
Howard Jonathan, Toadhole	ᗕ ᗉ
Ibbotson John, Stannington	IBBOTSON
Ibbotson Henry, Sowden	◌ ◌ ◦
Jebson Joseph, do	GLAD
Jenkin James, Attercliff	ᗦ ⊢ ✕ ᗇ
Johnson Samuel, Wadsley	GLUTIA
Kay Thomas, do.	✳ ONE
Lingard Joseph, Worrall	N ᗉ ✳
Marsh Thomas, Darnall	ᗉ ᗗ +
Marsh William, do.	IRISH
Matthewman William, Wadsley	✤ ✤ ✤
Milnes Benjamin, Worrall	MILNS
Nichols Sarah, Stannington	ᗉ ᗕ +
Nichols Abraham, do.	JAN. 20
Nut Joseph, Wadsley	z ᗕ
Oates Matthew, Stannington	ᗡ ⊲ ᗷ
Oates William, do.	✳ W
Oxley Thomas, Stannington	⊦ ᗉ C
Parkin William, Tom-lane	✚ P ✚
Rose Benjamin, Wadsley	ᗉ ⊢
Rose John, jun. Wadsley	ROSE
Rose Joseph, do.	DONIA
Saunderson Jeremiah, Holdworth	MERE
Staniforth Aaron, Worrall	A ᗕ +
Stringer Joseph, Wadsley	✲ ᗩ ᗕ
Stringer Charles, do.	C SER
Skelton Jonathan, Stumperley	VINE
Tricket John, Stannington	EMIR
Tricket John, Dungworth	z ᗕ
Turner Samuel, Fullwood	TURNER
Walker Samuel, Sowden	SALAD
Webster William, Whiteley Wood	✕
Whiteley Joseph, Edgefield	OGNIL
Wilkinson and Twigg, Attercliff	LA ✠ ✳ ◌ ⊸ ✳ ◌
Wilson, Robert, Wadsley	WILSON
Wilson Joseph, Damflask	RAPAN
Wood George, Darnall	ᗕ ᗇ
Wood John, do.	EPIC
Woolhouse Michael, Worrall	TREE
Youle Robert, Darnall	ALO ✳

LATE 18TH CENTURY SHEFFIELD CUTLERS' MARKS

Stamped Brass, White Metal, and Metal Framed KNIVES.

Maker	Mark
BEELY Thomas, Ponds; *Brass stamped*	MARS
Baxter John, Bridgehouses; *White Metal, and Metal framed, only*	24 N
Binney Joseph, Broad-lane End; *White Metal, Metal framed & Japanned*	THAT
Greaves Thomas, Church-lane; *Brass framed, only*	◄⌂►
Harrison John, and Son, Holles Croft; *White Metal, and Metal framed, only*	⊞
Harwar Charles, High-street; *Japanned only*	DECEM
Jervis William, White Croft	✠⊙✠
Jervis John, Meadow-street; *White Metal, and Metal framed*	☿ C
Ludlam Widow, and Sons, Burgess-str. do.	ETNA
Naylor and Son, Coalpit-lane; do.	PRET
Patten Hannah, and Son, Silver-street	✠ NANTZ
Patten George, Coalpit-lane	✠ PATEN
Ratcliff Robert, Lambert Croft; *Brass stamped only*	+ RR
Rodgers Joseph, and Maurice, Norfolk-street; *White Metal, and Metal framed*	✱ ✠ RODGERS
Smith William, and Co. Coalpit-lane	⊹✠ IES
Turner Samuel, China-square; *White Metal Metal framed, and Japanned*	◊ IVORY
Water Godfrey, and Son, Pond-lane; do	WATER
Webster Joseph, Hartshead; *Brass stamped*	⋈⊙
Wilson Samuel, Eyre-street; do.	O TW
Wilson John, Brinsworth's Orchard; *Wh. Metal and Metal framed only*	BILBOA
Wilson Joseph, Carver-street; *White Metal, and Metal framed only*	IDEA
Withers Benjamin, and Co. Far-gate	ESPANGE

TABLE KNIVES, Silver and Plated.

Maker	Mark
BELDON, Hoyland, and Co. Burgess-street	PLUTUS ⚷←⚸ →
Birks William, and John, Norfolk-street	FABRE
Dewsnap John, Queen-street	♆ SOUND
Dewsnap Joshua, Trinity-street	W. GREEN & Co ←
Green William, and Co. Eyre-street	SUPER Z C CLARBOUR
Hoyland, Clarbour, and Barnard, Hill-Foot	+ SURIOUS WATCH HUMBLE
Hunter and Twigg, Back-lane	✠ LAW L&Co. ARGENT
Law Thomas, and Co. Norfolk-street	☿
Littlewood John, Silver-street	+ + PAPA ABBA
Roberts Jacob, and Samuel, Union-street	✠ SET
Settle Thomas, and Co. Brinsworth's Orchard	☿+⚔ N S
Smith Nathaniel, and Co. Wain-gate	⚔✠⚔ PARKIN SHEMEL
Staniforth, Parkin, and Co. Sycamore-street	S. S. & Co.
Sutcliff, Sporle, and Co. King-street	SYKES ♘
Sykes, and Co. Pinston-lane	✠ OVA OPUS
Tricket, Haslehurst, Whiteley, and Pryor, Hill Foot	

TABLE KNIVES, in general.

Maker	Mark
BARNES Thomas, Smithfield	LOVE
Beet John, Norfolk-street	CIRCLE
Beet Widow, and Sons, Broad-lane	BEET
Birkinshaw Francis, Silver-street	MIZZEN
Bramhall James, Porto Bello	BEST STEEL
Brightmore John, Cross Field	CITY
Bright Lydia, Holles Croft	CHEAPSIDE
Brittain, Wilkinson, and Brownell, Arundel-street	✠ GB VRAI FRANCE
Brittain Benjamin, Hawley Croft	EXCELLENT PRIVATEER
Broomhead, Hinchsliffe, and Co. Brinsworth's Orchard	BROOMHEAD
Broomhead and Ward, Eyre-street	↫←
Butler Stephen, Townhead Well	⊕ BAKU
Carlton John, Far-gate	P
Carnell Joseph, Westbar-green	PLANT ARMIS

Name	Mark
Cawton Joshua, and Sons, Snig-hill	⊙ CAW-TON
Colley and Brady, Burgess-street	WALDO OCOLOS
Crooks John, Smithfield	OPHIR
Dickinson Thomas, Furnace-hill	✣ RIR
Dunn William, and Co. Grindle-gate	W DUNN
Emerson Robert, Burgess-street	JACHIN
Eyre John, and Co. China-square	EXTRA
Green John, Sims Croft	W. LOY
Green Thomas, Spring-street	✠ SOLYMA
Hawksworth and Sharrow, Grindle-gate	HAWKS-WORTH
Holmes and Nicholson, Pond-lane	♛ PHARPAR
Hoyland, Clarbour, and Barnard, Hill-Foot	♛ SUPER z c CLARBOUR + SURIOUS
Hudson Joseph, and Co. Coalpit-lane	EMB+
Hunter and Twigg, Back-lane	WATCH HUMBLE
Jebson Matthew, Westbar-green	GOZO
Loy William, and Co. Pond-lane	⋖☐✣
Loy Jonathan, Coalpit-lane	LOY
Naylor George, and Son, do.	PRET
Oates Christopher, Holles Croft	C. OATES
Owen Robert, Westbar-green	✠ GOLD
Parker Ebenezer, Eyre-street	WITSIUS
Parker Ann, Pea Croft	✠ PARKER
Roberts Jacob, and Samuel, Union-street	+ + PAPA ABBA
Salt John, Holles Croft	☐⊥⊙✠
Shepherd Edward, Far-gate	⋖ Υ ✠
Shepherd Robert, Norfolk-street	⊙━☐
Smith Samuel, Scotland-street	S S
Smith Widow, Broad-lane End	✳+☉+
Staniland John, do.	⌐GRACE & STANLEY
Stanley Samuel, Scotland-street	
Staniforth, Parkin, and Co. Sycamore-street	⋇⋌⋔ PARKIN SHEMEL
Teal William, Shudehill	TEAL
Tillotson Thomas, Coalpit-lane	ALBION
Trickitt William, and Thomas, Arundel-street; also Desk Penknives	KOLA TURIN
Walton Richard, White Croft	━ WALTON
Warburton Samuel, Holles Croft	WARBURTON
Wilkinson Thomas, Blind lane	+ PLANT

Name	Mark
Windle Edmund, Lambert Croft	🐦 E W
Woolhouse Joseph, do.	SWAIN
Wright William, John, and Robert, Smithfield	Cᕵ━c ∞૩◇ X✣

TABLE KNIVES, common.

Manufacturers in SHEFFIELD.

Name	Mark
ASHFORTH Samuel, Park	⪡+
Broomhead Benjamin, and Joseph,	E Y H ⪢+ ⪡⪡ YH IS ⪡
Cadman Peter, and Co. Norfolk-street	
Kent Richard, and Son, do.	W. KENT
Midgley Thomas, Dixon-lane	NIZZA
North William, Little Sheffield	2 NORTH
Parker Samuel, Scotland	YTHEL
Pass John, Sheffield Moor	PASS TEEN
Ryals Joshua, and Son, Brinsworth's Orchard	◊ I S
Timm John, Back-lane	+ UGGU
Waterhouse Jeremiah, Scotland-street	▷O+

Manufacturers in the NEIGHBOURHOOD.

Name	Mark
ASHFORTH John, Shire Green	⸮ W A
Green George, Storrs	XERXES
Holland Robert, Grimestorpe	⊃c⪡
Hydes Thomas, Pitsmoor	P⪡━x
Kent Richard, Brightside	☐☐⊲⪡
Milner George, do.	⊔⊲◇+

SCISSORS, fine.

Manufacturers in SHEFFIELD.

Name	Mark
Bailey and Eadon, Westbar	DEI &C
Barlow, and Co. Meadow-street	BARLOW
Bells and Shepherd, Gibralter	SCU XX X&Y
Blonk and Son, Norfolk-street	S
Brookfield William, Trinity-street	DEY
Broomhead, Hinchsliffe, and Co. Brinsworth's Orchard	♥ * IH
Corker John, Meadow-street	* ⋈
Colley Emmanuel, China-square	BATH
Dearden John, Smithfield	KING HEROD
Eyre Samuel, Westbar-green	EASY
Fowler William, Westbar-green	(mark)
Fowler Samuel, Westbar	(mark)
Furniss John, Milk-street	8 IF
Greaves Thomas, Gibralter	ORB
Henfrey John, Norfolk-street	E D
Hinchsliffe Robert, China-square	G SARUM
Hinchsliffe Joseph, Pond-lane	(mark)
Hinchsliffe John, Gibralter	LAMPREY
Kent George, Barker-pool	SHIRE
Lindley George, Queen-street	45
Matthews Widow, Brickyard	2
Nelson John, Brinsworth's Orchard	(mark)
Norcross William, and John, Barker-pool	CROSS
Oaks Widow, Pond-lane	C 3
Pinder Samuel, China-square	PONTY
Pryor Thomas, Gibralter; also Surgeon's Instruments	TRI
Sadler Tobias, Barker-pool	RED
Swift Thomas, Smithfield	+ E G
Smith William, Hawley Croft	CARE
South Widow, Burgess-street	XOX
Timm Nicholas, Far-gate	LUPO
Tricket, Haslehurst, Whiteley, and Pryor, Hill Foot	+ OVA OPUS
Vickers Benjamin, Spring-street	B.V.
Vickers William, Sims Croft	VICKERS
Whitely James, Gibralter	ULM
Wood George, Pea Croft	(mark) +
Wortley John, Gibralter	AIM

Manufacturers in the NEIGHBOURHOOD.

Name	Mark
Oaks Jonathan, Attercliff	(mark) +
Shepherd John, Brightside	(mark) +

SCISSORS, common.

Manufacturers in SHEFFIELD.

Name	Mark
Brammall George, Pinston-lane	◊ GB
Broadbent Dennis, Brinsworth's Orchard	SY
Colley Widow, Campo-lane	S (mark)
Colley George, Barker-pool	TAY
Cooper William, and Robert, Ratten-row	(mark)
Gold Jonathan, Park	1777
Hoyland Samuel, Blind-lane	W
Hufton Thomas, Ratten-row	PEGU
Kent Titus, Wicker	Pa
Lockwood Abraham, Little Sheffield	+ GP
Oates John, Blind-lane	(mark)
Pass Ann, and Son, Coalpit-lane	PASS HERO
Ratcliffe John, Sheffield Moor	(mark)
Ratcliffe Isaac, Little Sheffield	(mark)
Redfearn Mary, Sims Croft	PARIS
Skidmore Robert, New-street	EYAM
Smith William, Hawley Croft	CARE
Smith John, Sims Croft	+ O
Stringer Joseph, Burgess-street	VIS
Twigg William, Wicker	(mark)
Unwin John, Brinsworth's Orchard	HOPE
Ward Widow, Burgess-street	WARD
Wood George, Pea Croft	(mark) +
Young Joseph, Park	YOUNG

Manufacturers in the NEIGHBOURHOOD.

Name	Mark
Beal Thomas, Lee House	+ GAS
Beal Isaac, Bradfield	◊ ROYAL
Beal Enoch, Bradfield	POG +
Beal George, sen. do.	(mark)
Beal George, jun. do.	+ PUE
Beal James, Russling Park	(mark)
Beal William, Stannington	(mark)
Beal John, do.	K X
Drabble Ann, Attercliff	◊

Name	Mark
Howden Thomas, Carbrook	9 W
Howden William, do.	2 W
Kent Matthew, Pitfmoor	Pe
Kent Charles, do.	P
Kent Joſhua, do.	P
Ludlam Hannah, and Sons, Cherry-tree Hill	YES
Shemeld John, Attercliff	JOY
Shemeld Luke, Bridgehouſes	NOW
Sorby Jeremiah, Attercliff	
Sowden Joſeph, Bradfield	TOWOFT
Swallow Thomas, Attercliff	
Swinden Samuel, Attercliff	SWINDEN
Thompſon Timohy, do.	T P
Wainwright John, Cherry-tree Hill	ONLY
Walſh Thomas, Attercliff	

SHEARS.

Manufacturers in SHEFFIELD.

Name	Mark
BISHOP George, Brinſworth's Orchard *Wool*	G BISHOP
Butterworth John, Pea Croft; *Wool (omitted among the Edgetool Makers)*	BUTTERWORTH
Gillot Malin, Far-gate; *Wool*	
Green Jane, and Sons, Scotland-ſtreet; do.	GREEN
Green Hannah, & Son, Burgeſs-ſtreet; do.	JOHN GREEN
Greaves Abraham, Pea Croft; *Bookbinder's, Gardener's, Tailor's, Goldſmith's, &c.*	GAMBIA
Law Philip, Carver-ſtreet; *Wool*	P. LAW
Maxfield Thomas, Barker-pool; *Wool*	HOW
Newbould Samuel, Sheffield Moor; *Wool*	NEWBOLD
Siddall Matthew, Broad-lane; *Gardener's and Tailor's*	SIDDAL
Skidmore Simon, Church-lane; do.	UNITY
Weldon William, Colſton Croft; *Wool*	WELDON
Wilde John, Church-lane; do.	WILD

Manufacturers in the NEIGHBOURHOOD.

Name	Mark
Field John, Marſh-lane	
Wilkinſon Paul, Grimeſthorpe	PAUL WILKINSON

SICKLES.

Name	Mark
ATKIN William, and Son, Norton	C
Atkin Joſeph, Himſworth Moor	K A
Booth Jonathan, Woodſeats	
Booth Paul, do.	PBO
Booth John, Ridgway	RW
Booth Joſeph, do.	W
Burrows John, and Joſeph, Marſh-lane	*I B* K I
Cowley John, Moſbro'	W C
Ellis John, Mosbro' Moor	
Field William, Marſh-lane	W. Field
Fox Stephen, Troway	FOX
Havenhead Mark, High-lane	M H
Havenhead Thomas, do.	58
Hutton Joſeph, Ridgway	I H
Hutton George, Moſbro'	I Q K
Keeton John, High-lane	R
Littlewood John, Handley	
Mallender George, Killamarſh	G M
Mullins William, Ford	I R
Rotherham William, Troway	W R
Rotherham Thomas, do.	T R
Slagg Thomas, Ford	B Y
Staniforth and Booth, do.	IOBE RS
Staniforth John, Troway	J S
Staniforth Luke, Moorhole	C A
Staniforth Thomas, Hackenthorpe	I S
Turner Robert, Ridgway	W
Turner William, Plumley	I I
Turner Godfrey, Ridgway	V V
Watts Thomas, Moſbro' Moor	T CHS
Webſter William, Ridgway Moor	

19th Century American Pocketknife Firms

THE FIRST knifemakers to work in the United States usually called themselves "cutlers and surgical instrument makers." They had learned their trade in the Old World, mainly in England, but also in Germany, France, and the Low Countries.

In her book, *History of the Cutlery Industry in the Connecticut Valley* (1955), Martha Taber reports having found a reference to such a cutler working in Pennsylvania in 1698. I have found contemporary ads and listings for several of them in that state in the 1780s. Information about these men is in the chapter on American bowie knives.

Any such skilled artisan would have been able to make a first-class pocketknife, but if he actually did so, it would only be on special order. Even with shipping added in, the commercially-made Sheffield product would be less expensive than his, and of at least equal quality. I have yet to see an 18th century pocketknife that is demonstrably of American make.

The 19th century is altogether a different story. Beginning after the War of 1812 (perhaps even before), a number of Yankee artisans and entrepreneurs, most with Sheffield backgrounds, began to manufacture pocketknives in America.

To drive their wheels and hammers and bellows, these first American pocket cutlers used small waterpowers in the hilly regions of southern New England. To sell their goods, they employed the fabled "Yankee peddlers," and they also contracted with or created wholesale firms in New York City, New Haven, and Boston.

The first pocketknife firms in New England were evidently one-man operations and their names have not come down to us. The first American *manufacturing* cutler whose name we know (as opposed to surgical instrument maker who made knives to order) was Henry Harrington of Southbridge, Mass. He opened his first shop in 1818 and was active until his death in 1876. The firm he founded is still flourishing as Russell Harrington. I have seen razors and bowie knives by Harrington but not yet a pocketknife. To find the first American manufacturers who specialized in pocket cutlery, we must turn to Connecticut.

CONNECTICUT FIRMS

Taber reports that the pocket cutlery industry of Connecticut began before 1800 as a part of the workshop production there of "Yankee notions" to be sold by itinerant peddlers throughout the new nation. These notions included "buttons, spoons, forks, thimbles, tin pans, small brass castings, pocket books, and pocketknives." She found that this production had expanded to factory form by the late 1820s.

The 1840s

The first reasonably firm date we have for pocketknife manufacture in Connecticut is 1841, the approximate date of foundation of LYMAN BRADLEY & COMPANY of Naugatuck. I do not know how long this early factory lasted, but Bradley himself was active both as a distributor and as a manager of other cutlery firms until the 1890s.

Two years later, in 1843, the WATERVILLE MANUFACTURING COMPANY of nearby Waterbury was established. This firm grew to be one of the nation's largest pocketknife producers of the 19th century. Lyman Bradley was one of its managers in its formative years. The Waterville name survived for seven decades, to 1913, under at least three different groups of owners.

GEORGE J. BABCOCK, Pres. and Treas.   WILLIAM H. KENNEY, Sec'y.
ELTON E. HOTCHKISS, Ass't Sec'y.

THE
Waterville Cutlery Company
MANUFACTURERS OF
FINE POCKET CUTLERY,
RAZORS, SHEARS AND SCISSORS.
WATERVILLE, CONN.

1844 saw the creation of the HOLLEY COMPANY in Lakeville, up in the northwest corner of Connecticut. This too grew to be an important firm.

About 1904, the owners of Holley decided not to adopt the machine methods then beginning to dominate the industry. (The first practical automatic grinding machine, the Hemming, was introduced in 1903. Virtually every Hemming machine made is still in use.) Instead they gave up their national distribution and continued to make knives by hand for local sale up into the 1930s.

The remainder of the 1840s saw the establishment of several small pocketknife firms in Connecticut, and one large one. The small firms included SMITH & HOPKINS of Naugatuck (c1848), and also CLARK R. SHELTON and the BIRMINGHAM KNIFE WORKS, both of Derby (c1849). Some of the shears makers in Cornwall Bridge at this time seem also to have made pocketknives.

The large firm was the AMERICAN KNIFE COMPANY of the Reynolds Bridge section of Plymouth Hollow (renamed Thomaston in 1875). This American Knife Company was founded in 1849 and survived until about 1911.

Do not confuse this firm's knives with those of the AMERICAN KNIFE COMPANY of *Winsted*, Connecticut, in business 1919–1955. (Two other Winsted firms of the 1910s and 1920s were BUD BRAND CUTLERY CO. and the CAPITOL KNIFE CO.)

The 1850s

1851 saw the establishment of the UNION KNIFE COMPANY in Naugatuck. This small firm lasted until 1885, and was not related to the later Union Cutlery Company of Olean, New York.

The following year, 1852, THOMPSON & GASCOIGNE opened a knife factory in Winsted. In 1856 it changed hands and was renamed the EMPIRE KNIFE COMPANY. In 1880 the factory was moved to the old Lathrop and Barton table cutlery plant in West Winsted. Empire grew to be a large firm which did a lot of private brand contracting. Charles L. Alvord, Empire's president from about 1890 to 1923 was a leader in the fight for tariff protection for the American cutlery industry. Empire went out of business in 1930.

HUMASON & BECKLEY, of New Britain, was founded in 1853. This firm did a moderate business until 1912 when it was sold to LANDERS FRARY & CLARK. L. F. & C. (founded 1865) was the largest cutlery firm in the world at the turn of the century, but it did not make pocketknives. L., F. & C. turned H. & B. into its pocket cutlery division about 1914, and continued making pocketknives into the 1930s.

In an 1857 Connecticut business directory, I found listings for three pocketknife firms whose knives I have never seen. Perhaps they subcontracted to one of the larger firms, or perhaps they were distributors. Their names were JOHN KAY of New Haven, HAUGH & FRISBIE, also of New Haven, and R. M. HAVEN of Norwich.

1858 saw the establishment of the NORTHFIELD KNIFE COMPANY in Northfield. The first cast iron handled jack knives were made there in 1862. Its UN-X-LD knives were made until 1919. Then the factory was bought by Clark Brothers of Kansas City, who ran it for 10 years. Next a former employee named Gill moved some of the equipment to a nearby site and resumed making "Northfield" knives by hand until about 1960.

The 1860s

In 1863 MILLER BROTHERS commenced operations in Yalesville and Wallingford. They moved to Meriden in 1872. Miller Brothers was an important firm that did much contracting, both private brand and government. Its knives are of exceptional quality. Many have the handle scales secured by tiny brass screws, a Miller Brothers trademark. Any older knife with these screws is a contract knife made by Miller. Miller Brothers got out of the knife business (in favor of steel pens) in 1926. The firm went out of business in 1943.

Both the SOUTHINGTON CUTLERY COMPANY, of Southington (whose pocketknives were distributed by the Connecticut table cutlery giant, Meriden), and the CONNECTICUT CUTLERY COMPANY, of Naugatuck, were established in 1867. Connecticut Cutlery lasted until 1883, Southington until about 1914.

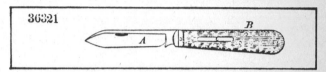

Northfield's 1862 cast iron handle patent.

The 1870s

In 1870, the American Shear Company of Hotchkissville (founded 1853) changed its name to the AMERICAN SHEAR & KNIFE COMPANY and began to make pocketknives. Some of their product was marked H'VILLE (Hotchkissville) KNIFE CO. This firm lasted until 1914.

The NAUGATUCK CUTLERY COMPANY, of Naugatuck, began in 1872 and lasted to 1888. About the same time, the TWITCHELL BROTHERS had a pocketknife plant in Naugatuck. I do not know its dates.

In 1876, James D. Frary of Bridgeport, one of the founders of Landers Frary & Clark, established the FRARY CUTLERY COMPANY. This was the most "high-tech" pocketknife plant of its time. Frary had about a dozen patents and employed more than 500 people mass-producing very cheap but serviceable knives which are now quite rare (the Smithsonian has a fine collection of them).

In 1884, Frary was forced out of business by cut-priced German competition. His son, Harry, continued afterwards in a small way as superintendent of the LaBELLE CUTLERY WORKS in Bridgeport. (See my two-part article in *Knife World*, September–October 1979.)

The 1880s and 1890s

The EXCELSIOR KNIFE COMPANY of Torrington was founded in 1880. It lasted only until 1884, when it was bought out by Northfield.

Another small firm, the THOMASTON KNIFE COMPANY, of Thomaston, began about 1887. It lasted until 1923.

CHALLENGE CUTLERY COMPANY of Bridgeport, was started by the important New York wholesale firm of Wiebusch & Hilger in 1892. It was liquidated at the death of Mr. Wiebusch in 1928.

HATCH CUTLERY COMPANY, of Bridgeport, also began in 1892. It moved to South Milwaukee, Wisconsin, in 1898.

Russell

Finally, around the turn of the century, the BILLINGS & SPENCER tool company, of Hartford, began to manufacture a few novel and expensive styles of knives. One of these was the original "butterfly knife" or "balisong," which was adopted as the national knife of the Philippines. [See *Foreign, Exotic, Primitive and Historical Folding Knives* for pictures and information.]

Up until 1940, Connecticut, as the home of both Remington and Winchester, continued to dominate pocketknife manufacture in the United States. Now, oddly enough, not a single factory pocketknife is made anywhere in the state.

MASSACHUSETTS FIRMS

Throughout the latter part of the 19th century, Massachusetts at least equaled Connecticut in the production of fixed blade knives. Despite this, it never offered serious competition in pocketknives.

A few Massachusetts men before 1850 might have made pocketknives, but no actual knives by them of provable age and origin have yet been found. We earlier met HENRY HARRINGTON of Southbridge (active 1818–1876). I found a reference in a 1922 magazine to a razor supposedly made by a J. LEE, of Medway, circa 1830. The Ames Manufacturing Company, of Chicopee, (1829–1900) seems to have sold the pocketknives with AMES on the tangs, but I suspect these were made on contract for them later in the century.

The Bay State's first documented pocket cutler was AARON BURKINSHAW. He had left Sheffield for Connecticut in 1846. He moved up to Pepperell, Massachusetts, in 1853, and there he worked until 1920.

Shelburne Falls

During the Civil War, LAMSON & GOODNOW, of Shelburne Falls (founded 1844), one of the big three of American table cutlery production (Russell and Meriden were the other two), began to make folding knife/fork and knife/fork/spoon combinations. Some of the Connecticut pocketknife firms made these as well, and all are prized by military knife collectors, though they were never a government issue item.

According to recent research by Cindy Rabb, these combinations are the only folders actually made by Lamson & Goodnow. Later pocketknives with their name or marked SHELBURNE FALLS CUTLERY CO. were made on contract by others, including Waterville and, possibly, Joseph Gardner.

Gardner was the superintendent of the Lamson & Goodnow plant. About 1876 he is reported to have opened a small pocketknife factory nearby. Knives marked GARDNER 1876 probably came from this shop.

In 1875, the famous John RUSSELL Green River Works, originally founded in Greenfield in 1834, but since 1870 located at Turners Falls, began to make pocketknives. They made a full line, but one specialty was their American version of the traditional barlow knife. Within a generation, "Russell" and "barlow" were almost synonymous in many parts of the country.

Russell Barlow, 1914.

Russell pocketknife production was suspended at the time of World War I. Manufacture just of the barlows was resumed in 1924, and continued even after the merger with Harrington in 1933 and the move to Southbridge in 1936. In 1941 Russell barlows were finally dropped.

The J. R. TORREY Razor Company, of Worcester, established in 1858, evidently made some pocketknives late in the 19th century. At least, knives with their stamping are known, and Torrey was certainly equipped to have made them.

A small pocketknife firm was active in Massachusetts around 1880. This was the BEAVER BROOK KNIFE COMPANY. It was in the town of Beaver Brook, but both the company and the town disappeared before the turn of the century. Its knives were usually marked B. B. Knife Co.

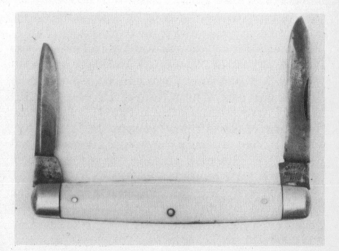

Beaver Brook ivory handled crown pen knife.

Like Connecticut, Massachusetts is now out of the running as far as pocket cutlery goes. A good number of fixed blade knives are still made there, however. Rhode Island is now the only pocketknife state in New England, but all of its firms began in this century.

NEW YORK FIRMS

At least since the War of 1812, New York City has been the center of cutlery wholesaling (and importing) for the United States. Virtually every American knife manufacturer who aspired to a national or world market had either an office or an agent in New York. However, due to the lack of water power, knives were never made on a production basis in the city itself. Like every important 19th century city, New York did boast a number of custom "cutlers and surgical instrument makers."

The 1850s and 1860s

Industry developed in upstate New York a little more slowly than it did in New England. The first recorded upstate knife company grew to be one of the most important. This was the NEW YORK KNIFE COMPANY.

New York Knife was founded in 1852 in Matteawan (since renamed Beacon). In 1856, the young firm was moved across the Hudson to Walden. Almost all of its considerable output was pocketknives, and these were among the finest ever produced anywhere.

About 1880, New York Knife adopted its familiar "Hammer Brand" and arm-and-hammer trademark. In 1928 they adopted the Wallkill River Works brand for a low-priced line of knives. In 1931 New York Knife went out of business. Imperial now owns the Hammer Brand trademark.

Some time about 1860, two pocketknife firms were operating in Bronxville. One was WARD & COMPANY, the other SMITH & CLARK. Both of them seem to have specialized in folding knives with ivory blades. I can find no other information about either firm.

The 1870s

The next important New York state pocketknife firm was the WALDEN KNIFE COMPANY, not far from New York Knife in Walden. Walden was founded in 1870. Like New York Knife, it did a large business in private branded contract knives.

In 1902, Walden was purchased by one of its important customers, the E.C. Simmons Hardware Company, of Saint Louis. In 1923, when Simmons merged with Winchester, the Walden plant was liquidated and the equipment moved to the Winchester plant in New Haven.

1871 saw the establishment of the Co-OPERATIVE KNIFE COMPANY. Though I have seen knives marked Co-O. Knife Company, Walden N.Y., the firm seems to have been located for most of its brief life in Ellenville. It really was a cooperative endeavor, managed jointly by the Sheffield cutlers who started and staffed it.

Co-Operative failed in 1876 and was taken over by Dwight Divine & Sons who renamed it ULSTER KNIFE COMPANY. Ulster is now part of Imperial Schrade.

The CANASTOTA KNIFE COMPANY was set up in the village of Canastota in 1875. It survived there 20 years, until 1895. Canastota knives are especially favored by several advanced collectors of my acquaintance.

The 1880s to 1900

Two small upstate knife companies began late in the 19th century. The CENTRAL CITY KNIFE COMPANY started in Phoenix, N. Y., in 1880. It was renamed PHOENIX KNIFE COMPANY in 1892, and failed in 1916. FAYETTEVILLE KNIFE COMPANY, whose starting date is not known, burned down in 1911.

In 1886, J. B. F. Champlin, formerly a salesman for the New York City importer Friedmann & Lauterjung, started his own jobbing firm in Cattaraugus, N. Y. In 1891, Champlin hired Harvey Nixon Platts away from Northfield to start CATTARAUGUS CUTLERY COMPANY out in the pocketknife manufacturing business (Platts was later a co-founder of W. R. Case & Sons and founder of Western States). Champlin and Platts purchased the equipment of the defunct Beaver Falls Cutlery Company of Pennsylvania.

Cattaraugus was a major firm in the pocketknife line until 1963; it was also strong in fixed blades. After World War II, its main product was plastic handled kitchen knives.

In 1892, Charles SHERWOOD started a small pocketknife plant in Camillus, N. Y. For a few years after 1894 he leased it to Robeson. Then, in 1902, he sold it to the major New York importer, Adolph Kastor & Bros., who renamed it CAMILLUS CUTLERY COMPANY, as it is still called today.

Millard Robeson, a jobber in Elmira since 1879, first produced knives in Sherwood's plant in 1894. In 1898 he opened his own plants in Rochester and Perry.

Robeson died in 1903, but the ROBESON CUTLERY COMPANY continued until 1940. It was reorganized then by Emerson Case and continued manufacturing until 1965. From then until 1977 Robeson was a brand name used on contract knives made for Ontario.

The NAPANOCH KNIFE COMPANY, of Napanoch, started in 1900. Napanoch made extremely high quality knives.

The Winchester Arms Company bought Napanoch in 1919 and moved its equipment to New Haven, Conn., to become the heart of its new pocketknife operation. Most of Napanoch's employees went along to New Haven.

A few of the Napanoch people stayed behind to start HONK FALLS KNIFE COMPANY in the old Napanoch building—it lasted until 1929. In 1931, a man named Cushner bought the Napanoch name from Winchester and revived the old firm in a small way at the old location, where it lasted until 1939.

CARRIER CUTLERY COMPANY (Cronk & Carrier Mfg. Co.) also started in 1900. Located in Elmira, it continued in business until 1921.

NEW JERSEY FIRMS

Booth Brothers

The oldest recorded pocketknife firm in New Jersey was Booth Brothers. It was established in Newark in 1864 by Thomas Booth from Sheffield. In 1867, Booth Brothers exhibited pocketknives at the world exposition in Paris. In 1879, the firm was moved to Boonton, New Jersey, on the Morris Canal.

In dry years, water flow in the canal was not sufficient to power the trip hammers and grinding wheels, so in 1889 Booth Brothers moved again, this time to Stockholm, New Jersey, on the Pequannock River. The site they chose had been used for iron working since the 18th century.

In 1903, the City of Newark bought the Booth Brothers property to add to municipal watershed holdings. The pocketknife firm then moved to Sussex, New Jersey. They went out of business in 1909. [See Edward Lenik, *Booth Brothers Knife Factory*, 1969, North Jersey Highlands Historical Society.]

Heinisch/Wiss/Boker/Valley Forge

New Jersey's principal claim to cutlery fame was for the production of scissors and shears. Newark was the home of Rochus Heinisch, a Swiss emigré who came to the United States in 1825. Heinisch invented the modern style of bent tailor's and dressmaker's shears, as well as the technique of inlaying steel cutting edges into iron shear frames.

In 1847, another Swiss emigré named Jacob Wiss came to Newark and went to work for Heinisch. The following year he started his own scissors firm, also in Newark. In 1914, Jacob Wiss & Sons, by then under the direction of the sons, bought out Heinisch's company. Wiss was already recognized as the pre-eminent scissors firm of the world. In 1969, Wiss acquired Hermann Boker & Co.

H. Boker & Co. is one of the oldest names in American cutlery. The firm was founded in New York City in 1837 by Hermann Boker, a recent arrival from Germany. H. Boker & Co. was mainly a cutlery import firm, but also imported tools and steel.

In 1867, Boker started his own factory, in Solingen, to manufacture knives for the American market—this plant is still one of Germany's leading producers of pocket cutlery. Boker also imported Sheffield cutlery under such trademarks as Manhattan Cutlery Co., John Newton & Co., Regal, and, later, Trenton Cutlery Co.

In 1899, in response to increasing tariffs on imported cutlery, H. Boker & Co., which was still controlled by Hermann Boker's descendants, built a pocketknife factory in Newark. This was called the Valley Forge Cutlery Company. John Goins reports that that Valley Forge was an already existing firm (founded in 1892) which Boker purchased.

In the Valley Forge factory, Boker produced both Boker and Valley Forge knives. It also did a great deal of private brand contracting. One of its biggest customers was the Newark advertising specialty firm Whitehead & Hoag (knives tang-stamped THE W. & H. CO.).

In 1921, Boker sold the Valley Forge plant and moved its U. S. operations to a new complex of buildings in Maplewood, New Jersey. Boker continued to use the Valley Forge trademark until about 1950. Current knives made in the Maplewood plant are marked BOKER/U.S.A.

H. Boker & Co's. gunstock jack knife, junior premium stock knife, and sleeveboard pen knife.

PENNSYLVANIA FIRMS

Herder's

Cutlery has been made in Pennsylvania since the 17th century, but the first recorded *pocketknife* firm in the state began in business in 1847. This was Clarenbach & Herder of Philadelphia, later called L. Herder & Son. Herder's was (and is) a cutlery retailer that in its early days also manufactured scissors and bowie knives. Pocketknives with the Herder's brand are also known, but it is not clear if Herder's made these or just distributed them.

C. F. Wolfertz

The first Pennsylvania firm that definitely made pocketknives was the C. F. Wolfertz Company of Allentown. This firm was organized in 1862. Like many 19th century cutlers working in cities, Wolfertz at first used dog-powered treadmills to power his wheels. This firm made cutlery until the early 1920s when it became just a distributor. In 1944, the firm dropped its cutlery lines, in favor of home furnishings.

Beaver Falls

The Beaver Falls Cutlery Co. was located in Beaver Falls, in the extreme western part of Pennsylvania, and also in the adjoining borough of Rochester; the firm made all types of cutlery. I believe the pocketknife department was in Rochester, because some of the smaller knives are marked only ROCHESTER PA.

The Beaver Falls firm, indeed the whole town, was founded in 1866 by the Harmony Society, a religious sect that began in 1805. The Harmonists had earlier (1825) created the town of Economy, just south of Beaver Falls.

Beaver Falls Cutlery Co. rapidly outgrew the ability of the Harmonists to staff it, so most of the 300 employees were hired employees, rather than Society members. In 1872, after a wage cut, the employees went out on the first strike in the history of the American cutlery industry. The firm brought in 200 Chinese strikebreakers from New Orleans in order to keep running, and the strike was eventually settled.

Beaver Falls went out of business in 1886. In 1891, the remaining tools and equipment were purchased by Cattaraugus.

Shipley

At the 1876 Centennial Exhibition in Philadelphia, one of the many cutlery exhibits was a display of pocket cutlery made at the Coquanoc Works of Howard W. Shipley. The Coquanoc works were located at the northwest corner of Ninth Street and Columbia Avenue, right in Philadelphia.

The Smithsonian has a copy of Shipley's price list circa 1876, evidently given out at the fair. This list includes 192 distinct patterns with from one to five blades. Handle materials included "Oroide" (probably an early composition), cocoa (cocobolo), ebony, bone, buffalo horn, stag, pearl, ivory, and tortoise shell. Despite this evidently extensive output, I have yet to see or hear of a Shipley or Coquanoc pocketknife.

Schatt & Morgan/Queen City

In the early 1890s, J. W. Schatt and C. B. Morgan founded the New York Cutlery Co., an import house in New York City. Schatt had previously worked for Torrey Razor. Morgan had worked first for C. B. Barker, whose Howard Cutlery Company knives were made by Canastota, and then for his brother, Frank Morgan, owner of the Bayonne Knife Co., a New Jersey cutlery importer, in business 1888–1898.

Soon after, Schatt & Morgan decided to open a factory in Gowanda, New York, called the Schatt & Morgan Cutlery Company. In 1896 they sold this plant to Charles Platts and relocated their operations to Titusville, Pennsylvania, the "Queen City" and birthplace of the American petroleum industry. Schatt preferred Gowanda, where he continued to live, and Morgan bought him out in 1911.

In 1922, several Schatt & Morgan supervisory personnel started Queen City Cutlery Company as a sideline. They reportedly used S. & M.'s facilities to make some of their components, and were finally fired for this around 1928. Shortly afterwards, S. & M. went out of business, and the owners of Queen City bought the plant and equipment. In 1945, Queen City changed its name to Queen Cutlery Company, under which name it still operates today.

Tidioute

1897 saw the foundation of a small pocketknife firm called the Tidioute Cutlery Company in Tidioute, Pennsylvania. This firm's claim to fame is that it was purchased in 1902 by the Brown Brothers' Union Razor Company, also of Tidioute. Union Razor was renamed Union Cutlery Company in 1909. When Booth Brothers of Sussex, New Jersey, went out of business in 1909, its tools and equipment were sold to "a firm in Tidioute, Pennsylvania." This was no doubt Union.

Union Cutlery Company moved to Olean, New York, in 1911. It adopted the trademark Ka-Bar in 1923. [See the next chapter for more on this firm, and also for information on C. Platts and Sons of Gowanda, New York, and Eldred, Pennsylvania.]

Case Pocketknives

AMONG collectors of both old and new factory-made pocketknives, W. R. Case & Sons has for about 20 years been the most popular brand. Interest in Case is so widespread that it is the only pocketknife brand where minor differences in marking, and even minor variations within a pattern, can sometimes have as much effect on value as similar variations do in the world of coin collecting. In fact, it would take an entire book to cover the field of Case pocketknives to the satisfaction of advanced collectors.

Luckily for Case fans, such a book exists. It is the *Case Pocket Price Guide* by Jim Sargent and Jim Schleyer. This 288 page 9 x 3¾-inch book went into its third revised edition in 1985. It costs $11 postpaid from the publisher: Knife Nook, Box 243, Burke VA 22015. I use it and recommend it.

For full time knife dealers and advanced Case collectors, the *Case Pocket Price Guide* is essential. However, most people will find all the information they need about Case knives right here in this book.

In the *Pocketknife Brand Chart,* there are 15 Case listings, seven of them for W. R. Case & Sons. These are all the important Case brand variations. When you use these listings with the pocketknife pattern chapters, you will be able to establish the age and current market value of almost every Case knife.

Case Pattern Numbers

A real advantage of using this book for estimating the value of Case knives (and other collectible brands), is that you do not have to know a thing about pattern numbers to look up a knife. Although recent Case knives have the number stamped on the back of the master blade tang, older Case knives generally do not. This often confuses the beginning collector when he tries to use other books.

Even though you do not need pattern numbers to use this book, you will need to know them if you want to get further into Case, or if you want to understand the private language used by Case collectors.

The W. R. Case & Sons pattern numbering system is probably the most rational of any pocketknife brand. However, like the English language, this code has its share of contradictions, ambiguities, and exceptions.

The first digit (disregarding 0) in each pattern number is the handle material code. Knowing this code can help you to spot a knife that has been incorrectly re-handled. A letter prefix in place of the first digit indicates handles of either metal (M, S, T, or W) or else of fancy celluloid (B, BM, G, GS, H, HA, P, R, RM, or Y).

Here is the handle number code:
1 = Walnut.
2 = Smooth black composition.
3 = Smooth yellow composition.
4 = Smooth white composition (rare).
5 = Genuine stag (most Case genuine stag has an orangish color).
6 = Bone stag (jigged bone). Also synthetic bone stag, including "rough black" from the 1940s, and "Delrin" used more recently.
7 = Imitation tortoise shell (rare).
8 = Genuine pearl.
9 = Imitation pearl ("cracked ice").

The second digit in a Case pattern number indicates simply the number of blades in the knife.

The remaining two digits (sometimes three digits, rarely four) refer to a particular "handle die," or shape. A pocketknife shape is called a "handle die" because the liners, which determine the shape, are stamped with a set of steel dies.

Following are the Case handle die codes. An incorrect code on a blade usually indicates that the blade was taken from another knife for repair or replacement. However, in the old days, some of the codes were used on two or three different specialty (or even contract) patterns.

W. R. Case & Sons Handle Die Codes

00 = 4⅝-inch swell-center clasp jack
OR 5½-inch melon tester
01 = 2⅝-inch equal end pen
02 = 3⅜-inch barehead slim jack
03 = 4-inch budding and grafting
OR 3⅝-inch curved jack
04 = 3⅜-inch regular jack
05 = 3¾-inch barlow
06 = 2⅜-inch regular jack
07 = 3½-inch serpentine jack
08 = 3¼-inch swell-center serpentine pen
09 = 3⅜-inch barlow
OR 3¼-inch gunstock budding
10 = 3⅛-inch sleeveboard jack
11 = 4⅜-inch swell-center regular jack
011 = 4-inch pruner

14 = $3\frac{3}{8}$-inch slim jack, cap bolsters

15 = $3\frac{5}{8}$-inch gunstock jack

16 = $3\frac{3}{8}$-inch regular jack

17 = 4-inch curved jack

18 = $3\frac{1}{2}$-inch junior premium stock

19 = $4\frac{1}{8}$-inch slim regular jack

20 = $2\frac{3}{4}$-inch serpentine jack (Peanut)

21 = $3\frac{1}{4}$-inch Wharncliffe pen

23 = $3\frac{5}{8}$-inch slim swell-center jack

24 = 3-inch regular jack

25 = 3-inch swell-center jack

26 = 3-inch dog-leg jack

27 = 3-inch swayback pen (old)

27 = $2\frac{3}{4}$-inch baby premium stock and jack (new)

027 = $2\frac{3}{4}$-inch sleeveboard pen

28 = $3\frac{1}{2}$-inch easy open sleeveboard jack

028 = $3\frac{1}{2}$-inch serpentine jack

29 = $2\frac{1}{2}$-inch curved regular jack

30 = $3\frac{1}{4}$-inch equal-end pen

31 = $3\frac{3}{4}$-inch (approx.) regular jack

32 = $3\frac{5}{8}$-inch gunstock premium stock and jack

33 = $2\frac{5}{8}$-inch square-end baby premium stock, pen, and jack

34 = $3\frac{3}{4}$-inch crown jack

35 = $3\frac{1}{4}$-inch regular jack

36 = $4\frac{1}{8}$-inch equal-end jack

37 = $3\frac{5}{8}$-inch clasp jack (Sod Buster Jr.)

38 = $4\frac{5}{8}$-inch clasp jack (Sod Buster)

39 = $4\frac{3}{4}$-inch pruner

40 = $4\frac{7}{16}$-inch serpentine jack

42 = $2\frac{7}{8}$-inch crown pen

43 = 5-inch daddy barlow

44 = $3\frac{1}{4}$-inch square-end junior premium stock and jack

45 = $3\frac{5}{8}$-inch equal-end jack, cattle, and utility

46 = $4\frac{3}{8}$-inch rigging knife

046 = $3\frac{3}{4}$-inch eureka cattle knife

47 = $3\frac{7}{8}$-inch premium stock and jack

48 = 4-inch (approx.) slim serpentine jack

49 = 4-inch (approx.) serpentine jack

50 = $4\frac{3}{8}$-inch sunfish (Elephant Toenail)

050 = $5\frac{3}{8}$-$5\frac{1}{2}$-inch swell-center hunting knife

0050 = $5\frac{1}{8}$-inch swell-center hunting knife

51 = $5\frac{1}{4}$-inch curved regular jack

051 = $3\frac{7}{8}$-inch fishtail with guard (old)

051 = $3\frac{3}{4}$-inch curved regular jack (new)

52 = $3\frac{3}{4}$-inch curved regular jack take-apart

052 = $3\frac{1}{2}$-inch congress

053 = $2\frac{3}{4}$-inch equal-end pen

54 = $4\frac{1}{8}$-inch heavy trapper

055 = $3\frac{1}{2}$-inch equal-end jack and cattle

056 = 057 = $2\frac{1}{2}$-inch curved regular jack

57 = $3\frac{3}{4}$-inch equal-end office knife

58 = $4\frac{1}{4}$-inch folding hunter

058 = $3\frac{1}{4}$-inch shadow equal-end pen

59 = 5-inch modern folding hunter

059 = $3\frac{1}{4}$-inch equal-end pen

60 = $3\frac{7}{16}$-inch (approx.) equal-end pen

61 = $2\frac{7}{8}$-inch slim equal-end pen
OR $4\frac{3}{8}$-inch switchblade

62 = $3\frac{1}{8}$-inch wide equal-end pen

062 = $3\frac{5}{16}$-inch utility knife

63 = $3\frac{1}{8}$-inch equal-end pen

063 = $3\frac{1}{16}$-inch sleeveboard pen

64 = $3\frac{1}{8}$-inch equal-end pen

65 = $5\frac{1}{4}$-inch clasp folding hunter

66 = $3\frac{1}{8}$-inch junior premium stock

67 = $3\frac{1}{4}$-inch swell-center balloon pen

68 = $3\frac{1}{4}$-inch congress

69 = 3-inch congress

70 = $3\frac{1}{8}$-inch swell-center congress

71 = $3\frac{1}{4}$-inch equal-end pen
OR $5\frac{3}{8}$-inch switchblade

72 = $5\frac{1}{2}$-inch clasp jack (Bulldog, Buffalo)

75 = $4\frac{1}{4}$-inch square-end premium stock and jack

76 = $3\frac{5}{8}$-inch sleeveboard pen

77 = $3\frac{1}{8}$-inch sleeveboard pen

78 = $3\frac{1}{16}$-inch crown pen

79 = $3\frac{1}{8}$-inch (approx.) equal-end pen
OR $3\frac{1}{4}$-inch leg knife

079 = $3\frac{1}{4}$-inch sleeveboard pen

80 = $3\frac{7}{8}$-inch serpentine pen

81 = 3-inch candle-end lobster pen

82 = $2\frac{3}{4}$-inch square-end regular jack

83 = $3\frac{1}{2}$-inch swell-center balloon pen

083 = $3\frac{3}{16}$-inch sleeveboard lobster pen

85 = $3\frac{5}{8}$-inch square-end regular jack

086 = $3\frac{1}{4}$-inch square-end regular jack

87 = $3\frac{1}{2}$-inch gunstock pen

087 = $3\frac{1}{4}$-inch junior premium stock and jack

88 = $4\frac{1}{8}$-inch congress

088 = $3\frac{1}{8}$-inch sleeveboard lobster pen

089 = $3\frac{1}{16}$-inch equal-end lobster pen

90 = 0090 = $3\frac{3}{8}$-inch equal-end utility

090 = $2\frac{1}{4}$-inch lobster pen

91 = $4\frac{1}{2}$-inch sleeveboard pen

92 = 4-inch square-end premium stock and jack

93 = $3\frac{15}{16}$-inch square-end premium stock

093 = 5-inch tickler and fish knife

94 = $4\frac{1}{4}$-inch equal-end jack and cattle
OR $4\frac{1}{4}$-inch canoe cattle

094 = $4\frac{1}{2}$-inch tickler

095 = 5-inch tickler and fish knife

96 = $4\frac{1}{4}$-inch slim square-end equal-end pen

096 = $3\frac{7}{8}$-inch tickler

97 = 5-inch folding hunter (Shark Tooth)

097 = 5-inch leg knife

098 = $5\frac{1}{2}$-inch tickler and fish knife

99 = $4\frac{1}{8}$-inch regular jack

099 = $2\frac{7}{8}$-inch equal-end lobster pen

102 = $2\frac{3}{4}$-inch sleeveboard lobster pen

105 = $3\frac{1}{8}$-inch lobster pen

109 = $3\frac{3}{8}$-inch swell-center serpentine pen

131 = $3\frac{5}{8}$-inch canoe cattle and jack

145 = 4-inch equal-end utility

CASE HISTORY

For nearly a century, members of the Case family, including their many in-laws, have played a prominent role in American cutlery manufacturing and marketing. The clearest presentation I have seen of the family's complex history is the set of family trees and company history charts prepared by Robert Crandall, himself a member of the clan.

Mr. Crandall has very kindly permitted me to include the latest revised versions of his charts in this book. I have supplemented the charts with information drawn from Harvey Platts' excellent book, *The Knife Makers Who Went West*. His book is a history of the Platts family; of the Western Cutlery Company, which the family founded; and of other firms in which members of the family were involved, particularly W. R. Case & Sons, which they helped to establish.

These charts include the summary histories of the following American cutlery firms:

CASE BROTHERS CUTLERY COMPANY
STANDARD KNIFE COMPANY
W. R. CASE & SONS CUTLERY COMPANY
PLATTS CUTLERY COMPANIES
WESTERN (STATES) CUTLERY COMPANY
J. B. F. CHAMPLIN & SON
CATTARAUGUS CUTLERY COMPANY
LITTLE VALLEY KNIFE ASSOCIATION
CRANDALL CUTLERY COMPANY
KINFOLKS
UNION CUTLERY COMPANY
KABAR CUTLERY COMPANY

The charts also include information on the following cutlery firms:

AMERICAN KNIFE COMPANY
NORTHFIELD KNIFE COMPANY
UNION KNIFE WORKS
EUREKA CUTLERY COMPANY
THOMASTON KNIFE COMPANY
REMINGTON CUTLERY DIVISION
FRIEDMANN & LAUTERJUNG
ROBESON CUTLERY COMPANY
BURRELL CUTLERY COMPANY
ALCAS CUTLERY COMPANY
ROBINSON CUTLERY COMPANY

Case Family Tree and
Tree of Knife Companies Surrounding the Case Family

By Robert P. Crandall, 1980 (Revised 1985)
With Supplementary Information from Harvey Platts

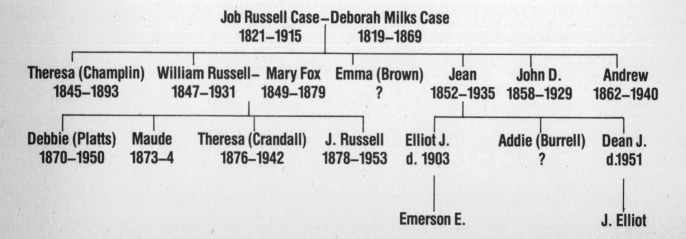

Job Russell Case – Deborah Milks Case
1821–1915 — 1819–1869

Theresa (Champlin) 1845–1893 | William Russell – Mary Fox 1847–1931 — 1849–1879 | Emma (Brown) ? | Jean 1852–1935 | John D. 1858–1929 | Andrew 1862–1940

Debbie (Platts) 1870–1950 | Maude 1873–4 | Theresa (Crandall) 1876–1942 | J. Russell 1878–1953 | Elliot J. d. 1903 | Addie (Burrell) ? | Dean J. d.1951

Emerson E.

J. Elliot

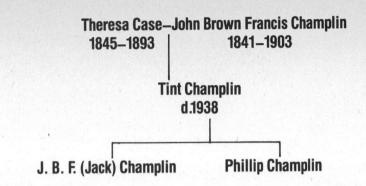

Theresa Case–John Brown Francis Champlin
1845–1893   1841–1903

Tint Champlin
d.1938

J. B. F. (Jack) Champlin   Phillip Champlin

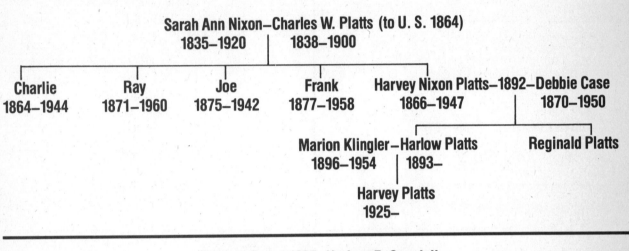

Sarah Ann Nixon–Charles W. Platts (to U. S. 1864)
1835–1920   1838–1900

Charlie   Ray   Joe   Frank   Harvey Nixon Platts–1892–Debbie Case
1864–1944   1871–1960   1875–1942   1877–1958   1866–1947   1870–1950

Marion Klingler–Harlow Platts   Reginald Platts
1896–1954   1893–

Harvey Platts
1925–

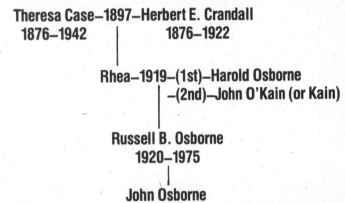

Theresa Case–1897–Herbert E. Crandall
1876–1942   1876–1922

Rhea–1919–(1st)–Harold Osborne
–(2nd)–John O'Kain (or Kain)

Russell B. Osborne
1920–1975

John Osborne

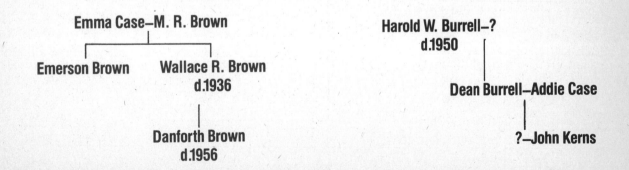

Emma Case–M. R. Brown   Harold W. Burrell–?
d.1950

Emerson Brown   Wallace R. Brown
d.1936

Dean Burrell–Addie Case

Danforth Brown
d.1956

?–John Kerns

Tree of Knife Companies Surrounding the Case Family

Case Bros. & Co. Gowanda NY 1896–1900 Jean and Andrew Case John D. Case 1896–1898 jobber (for C. Platts & Sons) **Case Bros. Cutlery Co.** Little Valley NY 1900–1912 Jean, John D., & Andrew Case Elliot J., & Dean J. Case J. Russell Case manufacturer **Case Bros. Cutlery Co.** Springville NY 1912–1915 Jean & John D. Case manufacturer	**Case Mfg. Co.** **(also J. D. Case)** Little Valley NY 1898?–1899? John D. Case jobber **Standard Knife Co.** Little Valley NY 1901–1903 Elliot J. & Dean J. Case jobber **Case Cutlery Co.** Kane PA 1907–1911 Jean Case (Case Bros. Cut. Co. 2nd plant) manufacturer
W. R. Case & Son Cutlery Co. Little Valley NY 1902–1905 J. Russell Case jobber (for Napanoch) **W. R. Case & Sons Cutlery Co.** Little Valley NY 1904–1905 J. Russell Case, H. N. Platts jobber (for C. Platts' sons) **W. R. Case & Sons Cutlery Co.** Bradford PA 1905–present H. N. Platts left 1911 J. Russell Case d.1953 John O'Kain retired 1971 Russell B. Osborne d.1975 1972–present: Division of American Brands manufacturer	**Alcas Cutlery Co.** Olean NY 1941–present W. R. Case (–1972) and ALCOA manufacturer kitchen knives

American Knife Company
Reynolds Bridge, Plymouth Hollow CT
1849–1911
C. W. Platts, cutler 1864–1872
manufacturer

Northfield Knife Company
Northfield CT
1858–1919
C. W. Platts, Superintendent 1872–1896
H. N., Charlie, Ray, Joe, & Frank Platts
(apprentices)
manufacturer

C. Platts & Sons Cutlery Co.
Gowanda NY
1896–1897
C. W. Platts
H. N., Charlie, Ray, Joe, & Frank Platts
manufacturer

C. Platts & Sons Cutlery Co.
Eldred PA
1897–1900
C. W. Platts (d.1900)
C. Platts' Sons Cutlery Co.
1900–1905
H. N., Charlie, Ray, Joe, & Frank Platts
manufacturer

Platts Bros. Cutlery Co.
Andover NY
1907–1909
Charlie, Ray, Joe, & Frank Platts
manufacturer

Western States Cutlery Co.
Western Cutlery Co.
Boulder & Longmont CO
H. N. Platts d.1947
Harlow & Reginald Platts
Harvey Platts
1911–1920 jobber (for American Shear & Knife,
Valley Forge, Thomaston, W. R. Case & Sons,
Utica, Eureka, Challenge, Clyde)
1920–present, manufacturer
1984 sold to Coleman

Union Knife Works
Union-Endicott NY
c1911–1913
Charlie Platts, Superintendent
Joe Platts, Foreman
manufacturer

Eureka Cutlery Company
Nicholson PA
1911–1915
Charlie Platts, Superintendent c1913
manufacturer

Thomaston Knife Company
Thomaston CT
1887–c1930
Charlie Platts, Manager 1916–c1930
manufacturer

Remington Arms Company
Cutlery Division
Bridgeport CT
1919–1940
Charlie Platts, c1930
manufacturer

Robeson Cutlery Co.
Rochester and Perry NY
c1879–1977
Emerson E. Case president 1940–1965
jobber c1879–1894
manufacturer 1895–c1965
jobber c1965–1977

Robinson Cutlery Co.
Springville NY
1921: founded by J. Russell Case
and George Robinson
c1925–present owned by the Robinson
and Skerker families
manufacturer kitchen knives

Burrell Cutlery Co.
Ellicottville NY
1940–present
Harold W. Burrell 1940–1950
Dean Burrell, Addie Case Burrell, John Kerns
manufacturer (kitchen knives, razors)

Tree of Knife Companies Surrounding the Case Family

Friedmann & Lauterjung
New York NY
c1866–1901
J. B. F. Champlin, salesman 1866–1882
importers

J. B. F. Champlin & Son
Little Valley NY
1882–1886
J. B. F. & Tint Champlin
importing jobber

Cattaraugus Cutlery Co.
Little Valley NY
1886–1963
J. B. F. Champlin d.1903
Tint Champlin (retired 1928, d.1938)
J. B. F. (Jack) and Phillip Champlin
H. N. Platts 1891–1896
C.W., Charlie, Ray, Joe & Frank Platts 1894–1896
W.R., Jean, John D. & Andrew Case 1886–1887
jobber 1886–1891
manufacturer 1891–1963

Little Valley Knife Association
Little Valley NY
1900–1905
Herbert E. Crandall
jobber

Crandall Cutlery Co.
Bradford PA
1905–1912
(sold to W. R. Case & Sons)
Herbert E. Crandall
manufacturer

Kinfolks
also made Jean Case 1928–1948
Little Valley NY
1926–c1951
J. Russell Case & Tint Champlin 1926–8
Jean Case 1928–35, J. Elliot Case
manufacturer

Brown Brothers Mfg. Co.
Brown Brothers Knife Co.
Tidioute PA
c1890–1902
Wallace R. & Emerson Brown
manufacturer and importer

Union Razor Co.
Tidioute PA
1898–1909
Wallace R. Brown
manufacturer

Union Cutlery Co.
Tidioute PA
1909–1912
Wallace R. Brown
manufacturer

Union Cutlery Co.
Olean NY
1912–1951
Wallace R. & Emerson Brown
Danforth Brown
Ka-Bar brand 1923–1951
manufacturer

Kabar Cutlery Co.
Olean NY
1951–present
Danforth Brown d.1956
Kabar brand since 1951
1966–1977 Div. of Cole National
manufacturer
1977–present Alcas Cutlery Co.
jobber

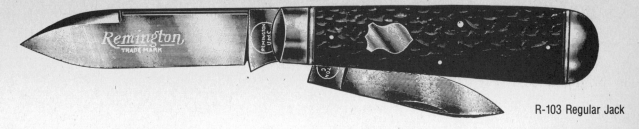

Remington U.M.C. Pocketknives

REMINGTON is one of the most popular brands of pocketknives to collect. Remington knives have a lot going for them, and not just the close association with firearms that they share with Winchester.

First, they are (with certain intentional exceptions) of the highest quality. Remingtons were well made and many of them are very good looking.

Second, Remington pocketknives were made in an incredible variety, more than a thousand patterns altogether. One can specialize in just Remington stock knives or Remington whittlers, for example, and still build up an extensive and varied collection.

Third, though hardly common, Remington pocketknives are readily available to the collector, certainly more so than any of the earlier American brands. Although Remington produced knives for only two decades, they made so many of them in that time that quite a few have managed to survive. Of course, Remingtons in mint condition are plenty scarce, but even these are available, at a price.

Note: The last digit in a Remington pattern number indicates the handle material, and can warn you of an incorrectly re–handled knife. The code: 1–Redwood; 2–Black; 3–Bone Stag; 4–Pearl; 5–PyREMite; 6–Genuine Stag; 7–Ivory or White Bone; 8–Cocobolo; 9–Metal.

Remington Cutlery Chronology

Based on original research by Dennis Ellingsen

November 11, 1918: World War I ends. U.S. government cancels almost all outstanding war contracts.

April 1919: Remington plans cutlery operation. Remington Arms already employs many cutlers who had been put out of work by wartime steel restrictions.

September 1919: Remington begins conversion of Bridgeport, Connecticut, military ammunition complex to modern cutlery plant. It will use machine methods and interchangeable parts. Publication of Remington Cutlery Catalog No. 1 with 150 pages of pocketknives. "Acorn" shield to indicate punch-blade knives.

February 9, 1920: Knife production begins with R-103 regular jack. First R-103s framed for presentation. All Remington cutlery to be sold through hardware wholesalers. All knives to be marked REMINGTON, no private brands. Aggressive consumer and trade advertising program begins.

June 1920: More than 500 dozen Remington pocketknives shipped this month.

May 15, 1921: Remington salesmen blanket the country, taking orders to be filled through hardware jobbers.

July 1921: More than 2,000 retailers in 47 states (not Nevada) are now carrying Remington pocketknives.

October 1921: Pages 151–182 of catalog No. 1 are published; total number of patterns is now over 600. Pre-packaged mixed "assortments" first offered.

March 1922: Remington announces knife production capacity is being doubled.

July 1922: Pages 183–214 of Catalog No. 1 published, containing 100 more patterns. U.S. Trademark 151,481 registered, for Py-REM-ite, Remington's brand of patterned celluloid, in use since 1919.

September 1922: Remington announces first "Bullets," the R–1123 (bone stag) and R–1128 (cocobolo) large trappers (then called "hunting knives"). By 1930 there were to be 12 styles of "Bullets": large, highly finished, outdoorsmen's pocketknives with distinctive Bullet shields. (Some have recently been reissued.)

1923: Remington authorized to make Official Boy Scout Knives, RS–3333 utility knife with Official shield introduced (formerly had acorn SCOUT KNIFE shield).

1925: Publication of Remington Catalog C–5 illustrating 927 patterns of pocketknives. Remington introduces its first six patterns of fixed blade hunting knives with sheaths.

April 1926: Six more sheath knife patterns introduced, retailing for $2–$6 each. Remington knives are now sold in 48 states and more than 60 foreign countries. Two–piece Tillmanns's patent can opener introduced for scout and utility knives (patent issued July 12, 1927).

February 1927: Remington introduces kitchen knives.

August 1930: Second edition of Catalog C–5 published.

February 1931: Remington announces that pocketknife production now exceeds 10,000 knives per day. With a 5½-day work week, that is 2,860,000 per year.

Spring 1933: Remington, in financial difficulty, probably due to numerous hardware wholesaler failures, is acquired by DuPont.

1936: Remington DuPont issues a new catalog. The pocketknife line has been reduced to 307 patterns.

Late 1930s: Introduction of *Remington* straight–line marked assortment knives, many of them contract made.

1939: Remington introduces its first pocketknives with stainless steel blades.

1940: Remington Cutlery Division suffers a $2 million operating loss. In consequence, the division is put up for sale, and is purchased by Pal Blade Company.

Makers of Picture Handle Pocketknives

Celluloid

IN 1872, inventor John Wesley Hyatt introduced celluloid to the manufacturing world. Celluloid, made of cellulose nitrate treated with camphor and alcohol, was the first practical moldable synthetic plastic.

Other moldable materials based on rubber, gutta percha, or shellac had been known for several decades. They all had severe limitations.

These materials were naturally opaque, and all but hard rubber could be made only in black or dark brown. White or red "hard" rubbers were fairly soft, and nearly impossible to keep clean. Also, early hard rubber could not be precisely molded and, what was worse, it smelled bad.

Shellac-based compounds, such as the ones used for daguerreotype cases, were hard but brittle. They could be molded precisely for ornamental use, but they were not suitable for rough use, as on a knife handle.

Celluloid, by contrast, proved to be a nearly ideal synthetic material for decorative practical applications such as handles, buttons, and combs. Its only liabilities were that it is flammable and that it shrinks as it ages. Manufacturers soon learned to minimize shrinkage of finished products by curing or pre-shrinking the celluloid in moderate-temperature ovens for long periods of time before final shaping.

On the plus side, celluloid could be precisely molded. It is hard and shiny, making it easy to keep clean, yet it is not brittle. It can be made in every color of the rainbow, or any combination of colors arranged in any swirled or geometric pattern one desires.

Using these properties, celluloid can be fabricated to simulate most natural materials. Imitation ivory, horn, stag, pearl, amber, agate, tortoise-shell, and even wood were purchased by cutlery firms for knife handles. Most intriguing of all, at least to people a century ago, celluloid can be made perfectly clear.

Picture Handles

It was this magical transparency of celluloid that, in 1879, caught the attention of Reuben and Henry Landis of Canton,

Ohio. They realized that a knife handle made of clear celluloid could cover a picture or inscription on paper, and the whole sandwich would be at least as durable as most other handle materials. The paper could be written or drawn upon, printed or lithographed. It could even be a tiny unmounted photographic print.

The Landises applied for a patent on this idea in July of 1879, and received the patent (number 221,467) on November, 11. While they were waiting for the patent, they licensed two local entrepreneurs who started up rival firms to manufacture knives with the new-style picture handles.

231,467. POCKET-KNIVES. Henry S. Landis and Reuben S. Landis, Canton, Ohio. Filed July 14, 1879.

Claim.—A pocket-knife having marks of ornament or identification beneath transparent cheek-pieces D D, substautially as set forth.

Canton Cutlery and Novelty Cutlery

One of these men was Dr. W. Stuart Carnes, who founded the Canton Cutlery Company on West Tenth Street. The other was the postmaster of Canton, a one-armed Civil War veteran named Major August Vignos.

Like Carnes, Vignos believed that picture handles were a nifty innovation, sure to catch on. However Vignos did not stop there. Paper is so cheap and easy to work with, there was no real reason for any two picture handled knives to be alike. Vignos's new enterprise, the Novelty Cutlery Company at 515 McGregor Ave. (which he later ran as a branch of his Canton Knife Company) would offer its customers any images they liked under the clear handles of their knives.

Customers could, of course, choose from a book of standard designs. However, Vignos encouraged them to submit their own art work or, even better, their own photograph, to be reproduced in miniature under the handle of a knife. In addition, such printed copy as a name and address, a greeting, an ad, or a political slogan could be included under the handles as well.

Marketing

Thus Vignos' Novelty Cutlery Company was entirely a custom or special order business, but one that specialized in nationwide and even international business. No such thing had ever been seen in the cutlery industry before.

In one move, Vignos bypassed the whole elaborate network of national cutlery distributors (most located in New York City), regional hardware wholesalers, and local cutlery and hardware retailers. Only the Novelty factory needed to maintain an inventory, and, except for samples, that inventory was only of parts and unassembled knives.

In assembling a pocketknife, the bolsters and handle scales are first affixed to the liners. Then the handles, springs, and blades are pinned together.

Vignos's unit cost per knife was much higher than usual, because of the required photo-reduction, typesetting, and custom assembly. However, by cutting out most of the middlemen, and eliminating finished inventory, he kept the cost per knife to the consumer competitive with other brands.

Vignos had to market his knives virtually direct from the factory to the retail customer. He realized early that the volume of correspondence this would eventually require might easily bankrupt him; therefore he adopted the idea of local agents, the sales method used by most book publishers at that time.

Any ambitious man or boy with a couple of dollars in capital could become a Novelty Knife agent. Each agent bought an illustrated catalog and, when he could afford it, he supplemented the catalog with samples.

The agent showed the catalog and samples everywhere he went and solicited orders. He answered the customer's questions. He wrote up individual orders to the factory in a standard format, with no instructions left out or garbled. He made sure that the correct pictures and copy were enclosed. In return he took a commission out of the printed list price he charged the customer.

Because they paid the cost of their own catalogs and samples, these agents in effect cost Vignos nothing. Therefore he lined up as many of them as he could. Most of his ads were to recruit agents, not to sell knives.

As a result there were thousands of Novelty agents. They could do as much or as little business as they wanted to, as long as they paid in advance for every knife that they ordered.

With his novel product and his bold marketing plan, August Vignos was a great success. One mark of his success is that he was chosen to be the American juror for the cutlery

exhibits at the 1900 World's Fair in Paris (the fact that he was of French descent and spoke the language did not hurt, of course). Judging from the account of Camille Pagé, the French juror at the Fair, and the first cutlery historian, that was very likely the finest display of cutlery ever held.

Competitors

Another mark of Vignos's success was that his business was copied, more or less exactly, by several competitors. His first rival was his Canton neighbor, Dr. Carnes, with his Canton Cutlery Company.

Like Vignos, Carnes began in 1879. Though never as well known as Vignos, Carnes was also successful. His firm made picture-handled knives until about 1930. Then it changed direction and name (to Car–Van Steel Products) and carried on until 1949.

Potential rivals to the two Canton, Ohio, picture knife firms had to wait until the Landis patent expired before they could jump into the competition. In the meantime, the evidence suggests that, in addition to his army of individual agents, Vignos sold knives through several agencies that did enough business (perhaps as advertising specialty dealers) to demand their own tang stamps. I believe that this accounts for knives with such stampings as INCO (Iowa Novelty Company) of Keota, Iowa, and Novelty Cutlery Co., Brooklyn, New York.

Aerial

The first serious competition to the Ohio firms came from the Jaeger brothers of Duluth, Minnesota. In 1909 they started the Aerial Cutlery Company whose main stock in trade was picture-handled knives. In 1912 they moved their operations to Marinette, Wisconsin.

A 1925 Aerial agent's catalog, reproduced in Tracy Tudor's *Old Knife Book* (1978), shows a wide variety of patterns and an even wider variety of pictures. These include bathing beauties and fashionable ladies, lodge emblems, occupational symbols and scenes, patriotic and political motifs, college banners, cartoon figures, animals, vehicles, ships, buildings, and sample advertisements. Near the end of the catalog is a blank form for ordering personalized knives.

About 1925, the Jaeger Brothers began to transfer their interest from knife manufacturing to the wholesaling of barber and beauty supplies. The transition was gradual, and was not completed until about 1944, when the last picture handled Aerial knives were put into storage.

Thirty years later, several thousand of the stored knives found their way into the collector marketplace. This accounts for the high proportion of Aerials that are now seen in mint condition.

Golden Rule

The next picture knife competitor on the scene was the Golden Rule Cutlery Company of Chicago. This firm began

HOW TO MAKE OUT ORDERS

Agent's Name		Date	19
Agent's Order No.	Remarks		No. of Knife or Article

Name and Address or other matter for right side of Handle.

THE AERIAL CUTLERY MFG. CO., Marinette, Wis.

Designs, Photos or other matter for left side of Handle

Do not neglect to put your name with the date in the heading of each order.

Under the head of "Remarks" place all information relative to blades or designs. Use back of order if space is not large enough.

In the first space representing handle of knife, place the name and address desired on right side of handle. Print or if possible typewrite it to avoid mistakes in spelling.

In second space representing handle of knife, place designs or other matter desired on left side of knife.

Always place your own order number on order with style of knife desired. Make out figures and names as plain as possible.

WARRANTY   Date ....

CANTON CUTLERY CO.,
CANTON, OHIO.
Ⓒ JAN 1st, 1901.

Our Knives are made from the very best material obtainable; blades are forged from best of razor steel and tempered by our own private process. We warrant every blade to be properly tempered and free from flaw.

If any blade should prove defective or break by fair usage within six months from date of purchase, we will repair knife free of charge if the owner will kindly send it to us with this warranty and 5 cents postage for return. We will not be responsible for knives sent by mail unless 8 cents additional is remitted to register. Send stamp for circular and terms to agents.

ADDRESS

The Canton Cutlery Co.

Nos. 1218-20-22-24 W. 10th St.

(P. O. Box 364)   (CANTON, OHIO.)

making picture knives in 1911, and its catalogs and business methods were very similar to those of Novelty and Aerial (1918 catalogs of Golden Rule and Novelty are reproduced in the Fourth Edition of Ferguson's *Romance of Knife Collecting*, 1976). Golden Rule went out of business about 1924.

Lackawanna and Wabash

At least two other pocketknife firms made picture-handled knives. One was the Lackawanna Cutlery Company of Nicholson, Pennsylvania. This firm began as the Eureka Cutlery Company in 1911, changing its name in 1915. I believe that picture knives marked NICHOLSON were also made by this firm. Most Lackawanna picture knives have a diamond shaped gold-flake "tinseloid" border around the picture or inscription. Lackawanna went out of business in 1930.

The other firm was the Wabash Cutlery Company of Terre Haute, Indiana, in business from 1921 to 1935. As with Lackawanna, picture knives were not this firm's main business.

Novelty (Epilogue)

August Vignos died in 1925. He was succeeded as president of Novelty Cutlery Company by his son Alfred. By that time, popular interest in custom picture-handled knives was beginning to decline, but competition among the makers was at its height.

Unlike the others, Novelty proved strong enough to weather the Depression without any change in direction. It even hung on through the war years, although celluloid production in this country ceased in about 1940 (celluloid was replaced by other less flammable and more stable plastics). However, Novelty Cutlery Company found no place in the post-war world. It went out of business in 1948.

Evaluating Picture Handle Knives

To estimate the value of a picture handle knife, first figure the value of an identical shape, brand, and condition of knife with patterned celluloid handles. Then add the value of the image.

PICTURE (and text)	ADD
Family photos, name and address	$0
Local business advertisement; animals	$5–10
Lodge, fraternal, union, or local politics	$10–15
Fashion or bathing beauty / nude (s)	$15/30
Early transportation: car, train, wagon	$20–40
Early transportation: ship, airplane, dirigible	$30–50
Famous person; military or historical scene	$20–40
Nationally advertised product	$25–50
National political campaign or issue	$40–75

Imperial, Ulster and Schrade

THIS CHRONOLOGY is based on information supplied by Henry Baer, Julian Raper, Houston Price, John Goins, and Dennis Ellingsen.

Imperial Knife Company

1916: Brothers Michael and Felix Mirando leave Empire Knife Co., Winsted, Connecticut, to go to Providence, Rhode Island. They start Imperial Knife Co. in a blacksmith shop rented from a cousin for $25 per month.

1917: They deliver their first knives to the Hayward Jewelry Company, Attleboro, Massachusetts. These are cigar cutter "skeletons," knives without handles, to which jewelry firms attach precious metal handles and bails for use as watch fobs [see *Pen Knives*]. These cigar cutters are about 2½ to 2¾ inches long and "tennis racquet" shaped. They have their one blade in the narrow end and a round hole in the wide end, so the end of the blade can clip the end off cigars.

1918: A small space is rented in what is to become the main Imperial plant, on what is now Imperial Place. At first, all of Imperial's output is skeleton knives. Providence is then the center of the jewelry industry.

1919: Dominic Fazzano joins Imperial as a partner.

1921: Imperial has 100 employees and an entire floor in the factory. Imperial begins direct marketing of shadow knives, skeletons to which they affix celluloid handle scales.

1922: Imperial begins the production of bolstered jack and pen knife patterns, using bone stag handles, and also a wide variety of patterned and multi–colored celluloids. Introduction of the IKCO tang stamping.

1936: Imperial introduces an inexpensive line of pocket-knives with sheet metal shell handles. The processes for making these are steadily improved, and receive many patents. Imperial purchases the Hammer Brand trademark of the defunct New York Knife Company for use on the shell-handled knives.

1939: Imperial owns the entire 5–story factory.

1940: Imperial's production surpasses 100,000 knives per day.

1942–1945: Imperial produces millions of knives for the government. A cooperative effort is undertaken with Ulster Knife Co. to make government contract knives under the former Ulster trademark, Kingston.

Ulster Knife Company

1871: Cooperative Knife Company of Walden and later Ellenville, New York, founded.

1876: Cooperative fails. Its plant is purchased by Col. Dwight Divine and renamed Ulster Knife Company.

1941: Albert Baer, who had been with Camillus since 1922, purchases Ulster Knife Company from Dwight Divine & Sons. He is joined by his brother, Henry Baer (Uncle Henry).

1943: Formation with Imperial of Kingston Cutlery Company for cooperative production of Kingston knives for the government.

1945: Kingston forms the Vulcan Safety Razor Company, begins the manufacture of kitchen knives, and acquires Schrade Cutlery Company of Walden, New York, renaming it Schrade–Walden.

1947: Kingston Cutlery Company dissolved. Ulster and Imperial merge to form Imperial Knife Associated Companies under the joint direction of the Baers, the Mirandos, and Fazzano.

George Schrade and Schrade Cutlery Co.

1892–93: George Schrade, an inventor and experimental machinist in New York City, develops and patents an improved switchblade mechanism with a release button in the end of the handle [see *Special Purpose Jack Knives* and *Mechanical Pen Knives*]. He forms the Press Button Knife Company at 137 Center Street with 18 employees. Unable to find enough skilled workers, he sells an interest in Press Button to the Walden Knife Company and moves it to their facilities in Walden, New York.

1903: Schrade sells all of Press Button to Walden (now a subsidiary of E.C. Simmons Hardware Company) but retains his patents.

1904: George Schrade and his two brothers, Louis and William, form Schrade Cutlery Company in Walden to apply the latest machine methods and interchangeable parts to pocket-knife production. Like Walden, Schrade Cutlery Co. does much private brand contract work.

1906–07: George Schrade improves the switchblade by adding a safety slide to make the blade lock open and closed, and by moving the button to the side. These "Safety Push Button Knives" made by Schrade Cut. Co.

1910: George Schrade invents an automatic knife shield inletting machine. He sells his share of Schrade Cut. Co. to his brother Louis so he can travel to market these new machines world-wide.

1911–1916: George Schrade resides in Solingen, Germany. With Wilhelm Weltersbach, he develops the Springer. On his return to the U.S. in, 1916, he introduces the spring-loaded weaver's scissors.

1917: George Schrade introduces the Flylock (patented 1918) which he licenses to Challenge Cutlery Company. Schrade Cutlery Company opens a branch factory at Middletown, New York, under the management of another brother, Joseph Schrade.

1925: George Schrade patents an automatic jigging machine for making bone stag. He forms the George Schrade Knife Company in Bridgeport, Connecticut.

1926: George Schrade patents the Wire Jack.

1928: George Schrade patents an automatic knife handle routing machine. Over the next 15 years, he and his brother Louis patent many improvements in switchblade mechanisms for use by their two firms.

1932: Schrade Cutlery Company closes the Middletown branch factory.

1937: George Schrade patents the pull-button knife.

c1945: Death of George Schrade.

1946: Schrade Cutlery Company purchased by Kingston Cutlery Company and renamed Schrade-Walden.

Imperial Knife Associated Companies
Imperial Schrade

This firm has grown and diversified since 1947. It controls the Richards Brothers factory in Sheffield and the Stag Cutlery Ltd. factory in Ireland. From 1977 to 1982 it owned Rodgers Wostenholm Ltd. of Sheffield. It has marketing organizations in Germany and Canada, and makes Durol kitchen knives in France.

In 1984, the Baer brothers bought the Mirando and Fazzano interests, and now have exclusive ownership. They renamed the company Imperial Schrade Corporation. All Schrade, Imperial, and Ulster pocketknife and hunting knife operations are now located in a large new factory in Ellenville, New York, while all kitchen knives and housewares are made in Providence.

Camillus
Cutlery Company

THIS CHRONOLOGY is based on information supplied by Nilo Miori, Houston Price, John Goins, Dennis Ellingsen, and Alfred Lief.

Adolph Kastor & Brothers

1841: Aaron Kastor leaves Germany for Natchez, Mississippi, thence to New York City and the hardware wholesale business, marketing in the South.

1870: Aaron's 14 year old nephew, Adolph Kastor emigrates to the U.S. from Wattenheim, Germany.

October 1, 1876: Adolph Kastor and his brother Nathan found A. Kastor & Bros. hardware import firm in New York City. Aaron Kastor buys cutlery for them in Europe.

1879: Adolph Kastor takes his first hardware buying trip to Sheffield and London.

1883: Adolph Kastor, returning from Cuba, meets a German pocketknife manufacturer. He buys the man's samples, and the line sells so well he decides to import cutlery exclusively, for sale to jobbers.

1887: Nathan Kastor opens a buying office in Solingen. Adolph and Nathan induce German firms to make American style pocketknife patterns. Brothers Sigmund and August join the firm. Kastor Bros. adopt Clover Brand and a picture of a four-leaf clover, symbolizing the four brothers (registered 1906). They also buy old Sheffield trademarks such as EBRO and XLNT.

Camillus

1894: Charles Sherwood builds a small pocketknife factory in Camillus, New York, west of Syracuse.

1896–98: Sherwood leases his plant to Robeson.

1897: U.S. Tariff Act (Dingley Tariff) nearly doubles prices of imported knives.

1902: Adolph Kastor, needing an American supplier of pocketknives, purchases Sherwood's plant, renames it Camillus Cutlery Company.

1906: Camillus introduces Crossed Swords trademark. Adolph Kastor's son, Alfred B. Kastor, joins the firm.

1914–18: Camillus makes military knives for Canadian, British, and U.S. Navies, the Red Cross, and the Dutch.

1922–23: Albert Baer becomes a representative for Camillus. In 1923 he lands the Sears Roebuck account. Sta–Sharp brand used on knives for Sears.

1924: Camillus establishes Stainless Cutlery Company division to make stainless steel pocketknives.

1927: Adolph Kastor retires, succeeded by Alfred.

1934: Camillus registers Kent trademark, used exclusively on knives for F.W. Woolworth.

1936: Stream Line trademark registered. Other Camillus names include Camco, Syracuse Knife Co., Mumbly Peg, and High Carbon Steel, U.S.A. Hundreds of private contract brands also made. Camillus becomes the leading supplier of private branded knives.

1942–45: Camillus makes millions of knives for the government, creates many important military designs.

1947: Kastor Bros. name dropped in favor of Camillus.

1947–present: Camillus continues to expand and modernize.

Buck Folding Knives

by Vern Taylor

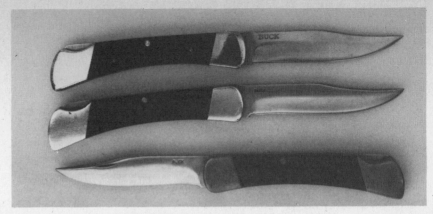

First version Model 110 folding hunters.
Top: Rare etched mark circa 1965: **$100–200**.
Middle: First stamped mark, used before etched mark: **$60–100**.
Bottom: Second stamped mark, used after etched mark: **$50–100**.

Vern Taylor has been a sales representative for Buck since 1967, and he has an extensive collection of Buck knives. For the earlier history of Buck Knives, see the chapter Buck Fixed Blade Knives. *Prices are for knives in excellent unsharpened condition.*

Buck Folding Hunters

IN 1962, Al Buck began work on a new-style lockback folding hunting knife. The Model 110 was the design that would make his knife company world famous and the trade name ''Buck Knife'' just as familiar (and as often misused) as ''Kleenex'' or ''Xerox.''

Although Al Buck popularized the lockback folding hunting knife, he did not invent it. Big lockback knives had been available in this country in the 18th and 19th centuries, and they still had been fairly popular up into the 1930s.

The popularity of big lockbacks had then declined for several reasons: They cost more than sheath knives of the same size; most of them were more fragile than sheath knives; and as pocketknives they were too big for modern pockets, so they were more awkward to carry than small sheath knives. By the early 1960s, there was hardly a single model of lockback folding knife still available on the American market.

What Al Buck did was to rethink the whole idea of the lockback hunting knife. He gave it sleek modern lines. He made it stout and sturdy enough to do almost anything a fixed blade knife could do. He gave it its own belt sheath. This got its bulk out of people's pockets, while making a much more compact and convenient package on the user's belt than any fixed blade sheath knife.

When Al Buck designed the original Buck 110, he saw it as a knife that the average hunter would use for perhaps 2 or 3 weeks a year, much the way they used their sheath knives. However, when the 110 came on the market in late 1963 and early 1964, it was quickly adopted by building tradesmen and many other workmen as an ideal all-around heavy duty work knife.

Because of this heavy everyday use, Buck realized that the design of the 110 had to be beefed up. This led to the first of

four major structural modifications of the 110. Within these four major variations are many minor ones. These are explained in detail in my forthcoming book, *The Buck Knife Story.* Here they are in summary form:

First Version 110

The handle frames of the first 110s were made from die cast brass with recesses for the wood handle slabs. The BUCK marking on some of these earliest knives is stamped along the back of the blade. Etching was briefly used in place of stamping. Other first version knives had BUCK stamped on the ''tang,'' though these earliest 110s do not have a true squared off tang area like most folding knives.

All of the earlier 110s are ½-inch thick through the bolsters. The nail mark is struck and very thin. The spacer between the cap bolsters is a separate piece of steel.

Second Version 110

In the second version of the 110, the spacer between the cap bolsters is integral with the right-hand side of the knife. The brass handles on this version are also castings. Polished areas of the brass consequently show minor porosity.

As with the first version, second version 110s are ½-inch thick. They also have the thin stamped nail mark. Later versions have a wider, machined nail mark.

The earliest of the second version 110s have the BUCK tang stamping. The stamping BUCK/U.S.A. replaced it in 1968; the same is true on the fixed blades.

In the second version, the two sides of the handle were at first designed to be press fit together. One side was cast with projecting studs, the other with matching holes.

This construction did not work well enough, so holes had to be drilled through the bolsters after assembly and brass rivets installed. The very earliest knives of this version lack these rivets.

Finally, the latest knives of the second version have steel rocker pins. All earlier 110s have brass pins.

Third Version 110

The third basic modification of the Buck 110 was to replace the cast brass handles with forged brass. Forged handle parts have none of the porosity evident in the cast ones. Also, overall thickness was increased to 9/16-inch. These brass forgings, made by Revere, were used from 1970 to 1973.

Along with this material and size change was a return to a separate spacer. The earliest third version 110s have a brass spacer. In this 110 design, the end of the spring is seated in the spacer. The steel spring tended to wear down the inside of the brass spacer, which made the spring *seem* weak. In consequence, steel spacers were soon substituted for the brass.

Starting in 1971, the tang stamping of the 110 was changed to three lines: BUCK/110/U.S.A. Later, a third brass rivet was added to the handle slabs.

Fourth Version 110

The fourth and latest version of the Buck 110 involved a complete change in the process used to make the handles. In place of forgings, sintered (powder metal) handles were adopted in 1973. Sintered parts can be made to exact tolerances and require only a minimum of finishing. All fourth version 110s have steel spacers.

In 1983, Buck redesigned and further streamlined the outside appearance of the 110. The handles are now slimmer and all edges and corners are rounded.

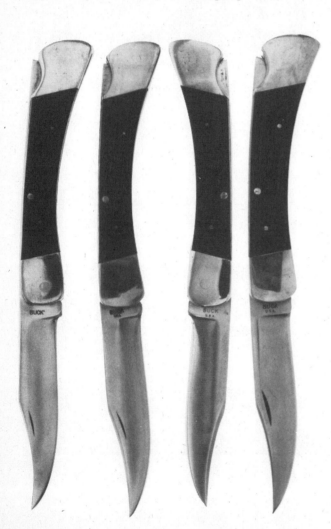

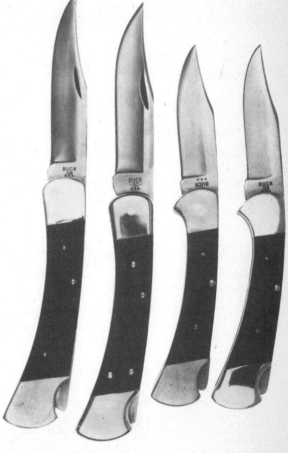

Second and third version Model 110 folding hunters. (Courtesy John Gabrick)
Left: Pre-1968 second version marked BUCK: **$50–75.**
Middle: Two post-1968 second versions marked BUCK/ U.S.A.: **$50–60.** Note narrow nail mark. Example marked on pile side is a variation.
Right: Third version: **$40–50.** Note wide nail mark.

Third and fourth version Model 110s; Model 112s (left to right).
A. 1971–1973 third version 110: **$35–50.** No dots in marking.

B. Current production 110: list price. Four dots, rounded bolsters, additional handle rivet.

C. First style 112 with black micarta handles: **$40–65.**

D. Third version 112 marked BUCK/112/U.S.A., wood handles, no nail mark: **$30–50.**

Dots

In 1978, dots were first added to the tang stamping of the 110. These dots are a code to indicate internal mechanical modifications of the knife. The first was two dots thus: BUCK/·110·/U.S.A. These two dots indicate a change in the profile of the tang which prevents the user from converting the 110 into a gravity knife.

A third dot in the stamping indicates the addition of a bushing in the joint of the knife. This allows nearly friction-free movement of the blade around the pivot pin.

A fourth dot was added when Buck changed blade steel from 440-C to 425-M (Modified). All Buck knives have been converted to 425-M, but only the 110 is marked to indicate the change: BUCK/··110··/U.S.A.

Buck 112

The Buck 112 Ranger, introduced about 1969, is a smaller version of the 110. The first 112s were marked BUCK/U.S.A. in two lines. They had black micarta handles, but the material was soon changed to wood, as on the 110. The sequence of design and technical changes on the 112 matches those on the 110. Buck 112s did not have a nail nick in the blade until 1983.

Contract Pocketknives

In 1966 Buck decided to start offering standard size pocketknives under their own name. The first of these knives, the

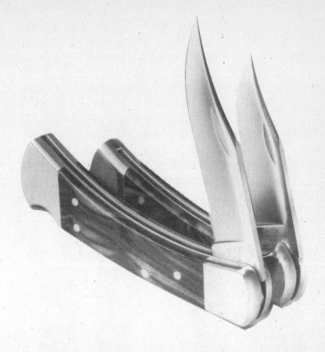

Current production Model 110 and Model 112 folding hunters.

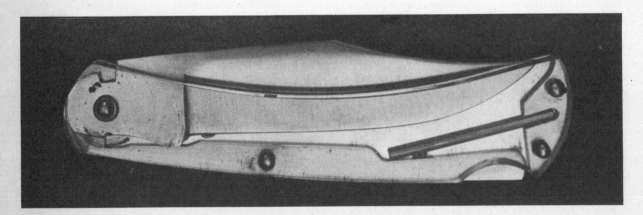

Transparent demonstrator model of current production 110, used by salesmen to show internal mechanism. None have been sold.

Model 301 3⅞-inch three-blade premium stock knife was made on contract by Schrade. Soon the Model 303 Cadet, a 3¼-inch junior stockman, was added to the line, followed by the Model 305 Lancer, a 2⅝-inch premium pen.

Most Schrade-made 301 stock knives are marked BUCK/ U.S.A. on the clip master blade and BUCK on the other two blades. However, most of the earliest ones, which have grooved bolsters, were marked only on the master blade. Most Schrade-made 303s also have all blades marked, but the 305s seem only to have been marked on the master blade.

Buck's contract arrangement with Schrade lasted only about 2 years. Then the contract was switched to Camillus. Camillus made the same three models, and soon added several more.

Camillus-made Buck pocketknives are only marked on the master blade. Most of them incorporate the model number in the tang stamping. Camillus-made 301s are less markedly curved than the Schrades.

Two structural details distinguish Schrade contract from Camillus contract Buck 300-series pocketknives. A small rivet joining bolster to liner is visible only on the Schrades. The brass handle rivets on the Schrades are smaller than on the Camillus knives.

Buck 500 Series

Buck introduced the 500 series of lockbacks and folders in 1975. These are intermediate-sized knives with stainless steel frames.

The first model in the series was the 501 Esquire (now called the Squire), a pocket-sized lockback folder. The earliest 501s have three rivets in the micarta handles. The center one is the rocker pin. On later 501s, the rocker pin is covered by the handles, and only two rivets show.

At first, maroon micarta handles were used on the 500, 501, 503, and 505. Beginning in 1981 this material was phased out in favor of resin filled wood.

Buck 700 and 300 Series Pocketknives

In 1979, Buck began to produce its own newly designed line of pocketknives, the 700 series. These are higher quality than the contract-made 300 series.

In 1980, Buck moved all of its operations to a new and larger plant in El Cajon, California. Then, in 1984, the firm began to tool up to manufacture the 300 series for itself in the new plant, along with all its other knives. This tooling is now complete and all of Buck's contracting with other knife companies has ended.

The 300 series pocketknives made between 1966 and 1985 were the only Buck knives *not* made by Buck in its own plant. Contract-made Buck knives all have shields with the hammer, bolt, and Buck knife pictorial logo.

For more pictures and information, see the chapters *Buck Custom and Limited Edition Knives* and *Buck Fixed Blade Knives*.

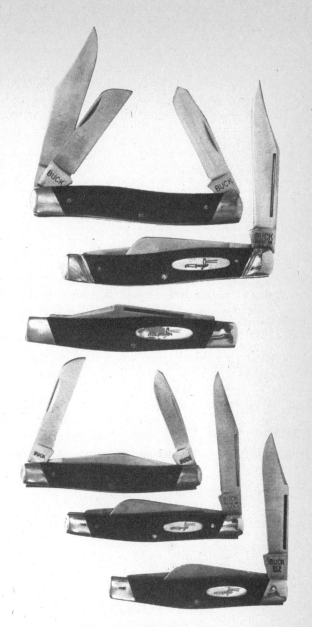

Contract-made Buck 300 series pocketknives (top to bottom).

A. Reverse side of Schrade-made 301 with plain bolsters and all blades marked: **$35–40.**

B. Earliest Schrade-made 301 with grooved bolsters: **$40–55.**

C. Camillus-made 301: **$25–35.**

D. Reverse side of Schrade-made 303 with all blades marked: **$35–40.**

E. Early Camillus-made 303 marked BUCK/MADE IN/ U.S.A.: **$25–30.**

F. Last Camillus-made 303 marked BUCK/303/U.S.A.: **$25.** Note lack of handle rivets.

Jack Knives

The Jack Knife

"JACK KNIFE" is a general term for the simplest form of folding knife. The standard jack knife is single-ended. That is, its blade or blades are hinged at one end of the handle. There are also a few large heavy-duty double-end jack knife patterns. Double-end jack knives have a large blade in each end. These double-ended knives are covered in a separate chapter.

Small knives with blades pivoted at both ends are called "pen knives." Tiny single-ended knives with just a short pen blade are called "quill knives." Although they are constructed like jack knives, quill knives were the original pen-sharpening knives, so they too are classed as pen knives. See the *Introduction to Standard American Folding Knife Patterns* for more detailed definitions of jack knives and pen knives.

In this chapter, I describe the standard jack knife handle

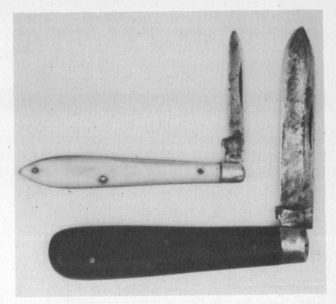

A quill knife compared to a small jack knife.

shapes made or sold in the United States during approximately the last century and a half. Each of these shapes has a descriptive name, and some have several names. In addition, a number of specific combinations of shape, size, blades, bolsters, handle material, or fittings have distinctive "pattern" names.

Within each description of a shape, I mention the named patterns that are made in that shape. For full details and prices on these named patterns, you should refer to the appropriate chapters later in this *Jack Knives* section.

Jack knives made for other markets than the United States, and those made before the middle of the 19th century, are included in *Foreign, Exotic, Primitive, and Historical Folding Knives*. Figural jack knives shaped like shoes or other objects are included in *Advertising and Figural Knives* in the *Pen Knives* section.

Decorated jack knives with silver blades and bolsters are called "fruit knives." They were intended to aid in the dainty

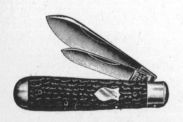

A regular jack, a double-end jack, and a pen knife.

A silver fruit knife.

nibbling of fresh fruit, and were a popular keepsake gift through about the 1920s. All silver fruit knives, regardless of their shape, are covered in their own chapter.

Origins

The origin of the term "jack knife" has been lost in time. It may come from "jack" the sailor, "jack" the common workman, "jack" meaning roughly made, "jack" meaning smaller, or even from "jack" meaning jacket.

In Scotland, a large clasp knife was long called a "jackto-leg," but no one knows where that term comes from, either. Folklore has it that this was a corruption of "Jacques de Liege," supposedly a Flemish cutler named Jacques in or from Liège. I suspect that this explanation has even less substance than the "James Black" bowie knife legend.

Sizes

Jack knives have been made in the widest variety of sizes of any folders. American production jack knives are mainly between 2½ and 5½ inches long closed. This is the size range that concern us here. Big folding bowie knives and dirks have their own chapter. Large European clasp knives are included in *Foreign, Exotic, Primitive, and Historical Folding Knives*. Giant showpiece knives are included in the *Multi-Blades* section. Tiny quill knives and watch fob knives are included in the *Pen Knives* section.

Springs

At its simplest, a folding knife needs only a handle, a blade, and a pivot pin. It does not even need to have a backspring. Jack knives without backsprings are sometimes called "penny knives." Penny knives are included in *Foreign, Exotic, Primitive, and Historical Folding Knives*.

A penny knife.

Bolsters

Because they have blades only at one end, jack knives do not require two sets of bolsters. Jacks with bolsters only at the blade end are called "barehead" or "single bolster" jacks. Bolsters on the "head" end of a jack knife (the non-blade end) are called "cap bolsters." When referring to patterns which never have cap bolsters, such as the barlow, the adjective "barehead" is omitted.

A barehead jack knife.

Some knives without solid bolsters instead have wide round reinforcing washers at the ends of the hinge pins. Pins with such washers are called "birdseye rivets" by collectors.

A farmer's clasp knife with birdseye rivets.

On double-ended knives, the bolsters at the master blade end are called the front bolsters. Those at the opposite end are the rear bolsters. Small knives with no bolsters at all are called "shadow knives."

A shadow knife.

PRICE CHART FOR JACK KNIVES

Base prices for JACK KNIVES of indicated shape with: handles 3¼ to 3¾ inches long; bolsters and cap bolsters; bone stag (jigged bone) or horn handle scales; two blades: master blade plus pen. Excellent unsharpened condition.

NOTE: The following named jack knife patterns have their own separate price lists. BARLOW KNIFE; BOY'S KNIFE; TRAPPER, MUSKRAT, and LARGE TRAPPER; AMERICAN CLASP KNIFE and FOLDING HUNTER; TICKLER (TEXAS TOOTHPICK, POWDER-HORN) and FISH KNIFE; FOLDING DIRK and FOLDING BOWIE; ENGLISH JACK; Special Purpose Jack Knives including: HARNESS, ELECTRICIAN'S, PRUNING, MAIZE, COTTON SAMPLING, RASE, SAILOR'S, PHYSICIAN'S, SMOKER'S, MELON TESTING and SILVER FRUIT KNIVES; also SUNFISH, FARMER'S JACK, and other DOUBLE-END JACK KNIVES.

VALUE RANGE	VERY HIGH	HIGH	MEDIUM	LOW
SHAPE				
EQUAL-END:	$ 90.	$ 60.	$30.	$ 6.
SLIM EQUAL-END:	75.	50.	25.	5.
REGULAR:	100.	65.	35.	6.
SLIM (REGULAR):	90.	55.	25.	5.
SLEEVEBOARD:	90.	50.	30.	6.
JUMBO:	200.	125.	85.	20.
CURVED REGULAR:	115.	85.	40.	10.
CURVED:	110.	65.	40.	10.
CONGRESS:	110.	65.	40.	15.
SWAYBACK:	120.	70.	40.	11.
CROWN:	130.	70.	45.	15.
SWELL-END: (Tear Drop)	125.	70.	40.	12.
SWELL-CENTER: (Small "Coke" Bottle)	150.	100.	50.	15.
BALLOON:	140.	80.	45.	12.
SWELL-CENTER REGULAR:	150.	90.	50.	15.
GUNSTOCK:	185.	125.	75.	25.
PREMIUM:	85.	50.	25.	5.
GUNSTOCK PREMIUM:	110.	60.	25.	6.
SERPENTINE:	110.	65.	35.	6.
SLIM SERPENTINE:	125.	50.	25.	9.
EUREKA:	120.	90.	50.	12.
CANOE or SURVEYOR:	175.	120.	75.	22.
FISHTAIL:	120.	65.	40.	8.
FISH:	160.	100.	50.	12.

PRICE CHART FOR JACK KNIVES

CONSTRUCTION

Easy open notch: **add 10%**

Saber ground or extra heavy master blade: **add 10%**

Single-bladed: **subtract 20%**

Two large blades:
clip and long spey, see Trappers;
spear and screwdriver, see Electrician's Knives;
other combinations: **add 30%**

Three large blades: **add 50%**

Punch as second blade: **add 25%** (see Harness Knives)

Locking blade(s): **add 50%**

Fancy stamped nickel silver bolsters: **add 25%**

Integral one-piece iron bolster-liners: **add 20%**

No bolsters: **subtract 40%**
(with "Birdseye" rivets: **subtract only 25%**)

Barehead (no cap bolsters): **subtract 20%**

SIZE

Under 3¼ inches: **subtract 25%**

Over 3¾ inches: **add 25%**

Over 4½ inches: **add 40%**

(Except Regular, Sleeveboard, and Slim Jacks over 4 inches long: see English Jacks)

HANDLE MATERIALS

Pearl: **add 50%**

Genuine ivory or tortoise shell: **add 35%**

Genuine stag: **add 25%**

Smooth bone: **subtract 10%**

Wood: **subtract 25%**

Fancy celluloid: **add 10%**
(water-fall, Christmas tree, candy stripe, goldstone)

Other patterned or colorful celluloid: **subtract 20%**

Solid color celluloid or composition: **subtract 30%**

Modern plastic: **subtract 50%**

Engraved aluminum: **subtract 20%**

Plain solid brass or bronze: **subtract 20%**

Other solid metal: **subtract 40%**

Pressed hollow sheet metal: **subtract 65%**

Folded flat sheet metal: **subtract 50%**

Embossed, picture, or advertising handles: **add 10–200%** [see *Advertising Knives* chapter, in *Pen Knives* section]

CONDITION

Mint: **add 50%**

Worn: **subtract 50%**

Broken: **subtract 90%**

Equal-End Jacks

The earliest primitive jack knife handle was most likely cylinder shaped. It could have been made from a wooden stick, a bone, or a piece of horn or antler.

The plain cylinder has been pretty much extinct as a handle design for a while now. Most production jack knives of the past century or two are framed with flat metal handle liners. Therefore, the simplest shape you are likely to encounter on a factory-made jack knife is the "equal-end." In the 1920s, firms that favored picturesque names called this shape the "bull-head."

The equal-end handle die, as its name suggests, is equally rounded at both ends. By the way, "handle die" is an old cutler's term for "shape." It probably comes from the specially made steel die or dies used to cut out liners for each particular handle shape from strips of sheet iron, brass, or nickel silver.

There are wide equal-end handles and slender ones. Most equal-end jack knives are built on wide handle frames, as are standard cattle knives, scout utility knives, and tool kit knives. By contrast, most equal-end pen knives are built on narrow frames. However, some older firms made narrow equal-end jacks. Boker blithely called theirs "pen jacks."

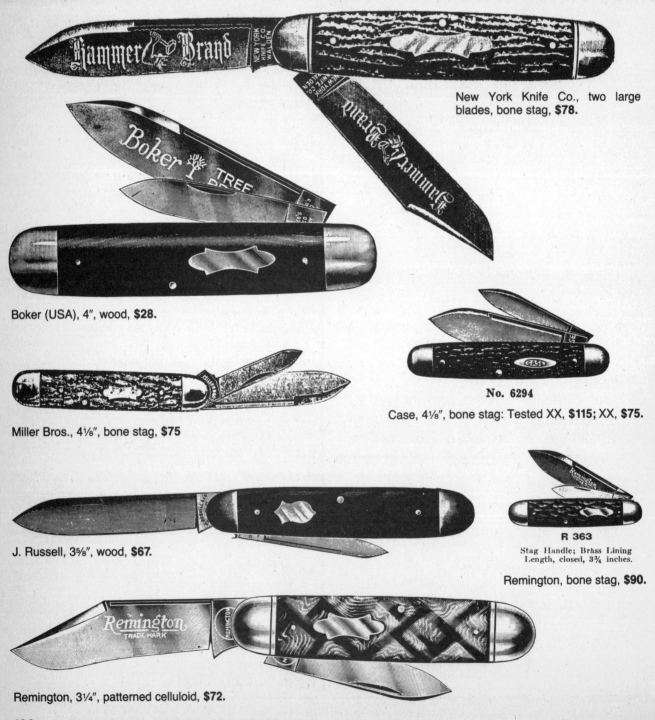

New York Knife Co., two large blades, bone stag, **$78.**

Boker (USA), 4", wood, **$28.**

Miller Bros., 4⅛", bone stag, **$75**

No. 6294

Case, 4⅛", bone stag: Tested XX, **$115;** XX, **$75.**

J. Russell, 3⅝", wood, **$67.**

R 363

Stag Handle; Brass Lining
Length, closed, 3¾ inches.

Remington, bone stag, **$90.**

Remington, 3¼", patterned celluloid, **$72.**

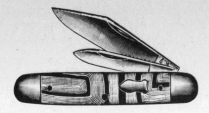

822023

Robeson, 3¼″, patterned celluloid, **$24.**

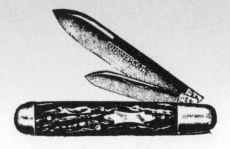

L. F. & C., 4½″, bone stag, **$75.**

No. 2172⅜

Schrade Cut. Co., 3⅝″, wood, **$45.**

Winchester, saber ground blade, 3⅜″,
bone stag, **$100.**

Challenge (U.S.A.), 3¼″, patterned celluloid, **$48.**

No. K2423.

Keen Kutter, 3¼″, bone stag, **$60.**

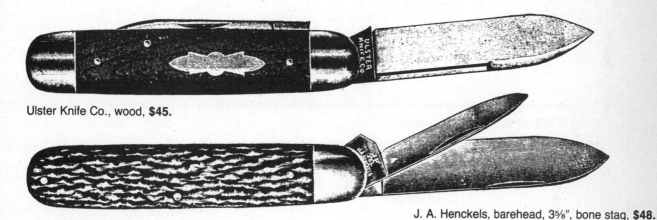

Ulster Knife Co., wood, **$45.**

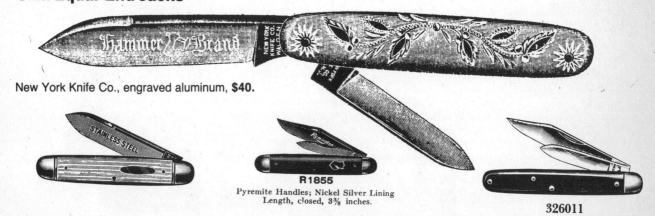

J. A. Henckels, barehead, 3⅝″, bone stag, **$48.**

Slim Equal-End Jacks

New York Knife Co., engraved aluminum, **$40.**

R1855

Pyremite Handles; Nickel Silver Lining
Length, closed, 3⅜ inches.

Schrade Cut. Co., 3⅜″, plain celluloid,
$28.

Remington, 3⅜″, plain celluloid, **$53.**

326011

Robeson, barehead, 3″, plain celluloid,
$13.

Crocus Polish, Brass Lined, "Baby Jack," G. S. Trimmed, Imitation Stag Handle.

Ulster Knife Co., 2¾″, bone
stag, **$35.**

Regular Jacks

Almost as plain as the equal-end is a shape that is called, for want of a better name, the "regular jack." Unlike the equal-end, which has parallel sides, the regular jack is tapered. The blade or blades are at the narrower end. The front bolsters have squared corners. Both Western States and Simmons Hardware Company called this shape the "regular jack" in the 1930s, but most cutlery firms never bothered to give this most common pocketknife shape a name.

Several well-known named patterns are variants of the regular jack. The "electrician's knife" is a regular jack with a spear master blade and a locking screwdriver/wire-stripper blade. Most "barlows" are regular jacks (a few are "sleeveboard jacks") with extra long bolsters, no cap bolsters, and smooth flat bone (or plastic) scales.

The "boy's knife" is a small cheaply made regular jack, usually with just a single spear-point blade and, often, with metal handles. Full-size cheap one-blade regular jacks used to be called the "stabber pattern."

At the opposite extreme from the boy's knife is the "English jack." This term was often applied to large sized (over 4 inches) highly finished regular jacks. Some have locking master blades, and collectors class the larger ones as folding dirks or bowies.

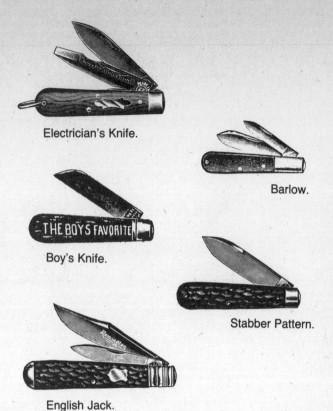

Electrician's Knife.

Barlow.

Boy's Knife.

Stabber Pattern.

English Jack.

One-Blade Barehead Regular Jacks

Ulster Knife Co., 3¾″, wood, **$31.**

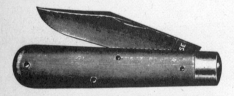

No. 3124½

Case, 3″, plain celluloid: Tested XX, **$35**; XX, **$22.**

ONE LARGE CLIP BLADE, Glazed Finish; Steel Bolster and Lining.

Winchester, 3½″, bone stag, **$64.**

No. 1091

Schrade Cut. Co., 3⅝″, wood, **$31.**

J. Russell, 3⅜″, bone stag, **$64.**

No. K1108.

Keen Kutter, 3⅜″, bone stag, **$42.**

Jos. Rodgers, 3½″, smooth white bone, **$37.**

Barehead Regular Jacks

Ulster Knife Co., one-blade, lockback, wood, **$47.**

J. A. Henckels, bone stag, **$52.**

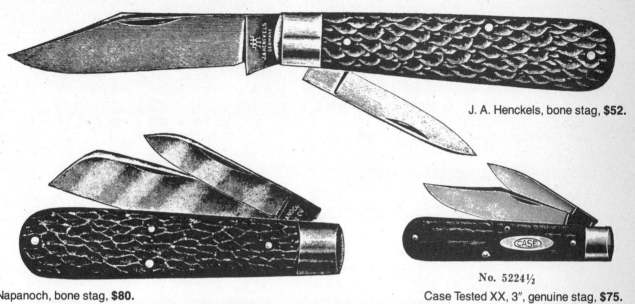

Napanoch, bone stag, **$80.**

No. 5224½
Case Tested XX, 3″, genuine stag, **$75.**

J. Russell, 2 large blades, 3⅝″, wood, **$78.**

Winchester, 3½″, bone stag, **$80.**

J. Russell, 3⅝″, genuine stag, **$100.**

No. 2252⅞
Mill Knife, 3¼ inches long; 2 blades; steel lined; steel bolsters; black inside; glaze finished blades; Ebony handle.

Schrade Cut. Co., wood, **$30.**

Sterling Cut. Co., 3⅜″, bone stag, **$28.**

Remington, patterned celluloid, **$64.**

Regular Jacks (continued)

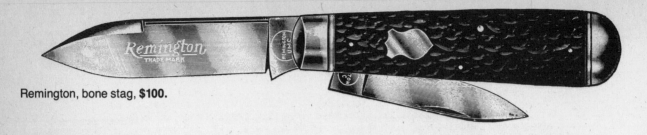

Remington, bone stag, **$100.**

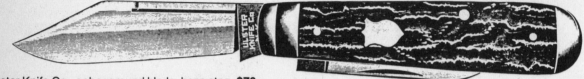

Ulster Knife Co., saber ground blade, bone stag, **$70.**

Ulster Knife Co. (for Bingham), smooth white bone, **$58.**

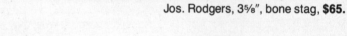

Jos. Rodgers, 3⅝", bone stag, **$65.**

Winchester, 4", bone stag, **$125.**

No. 2269BR

Schrade Cut. Co., 3¼", brass, **$50.**

No. 2266

Schrade Cut. Co., 3¼", pearl, **$100.**

No. 2203¾

Schrade Cut. Co., fancy bolsters, 3½", bone stag, **$80.**

No. 6214½

Case, 3⅜", bone stag: Tested XX, **$100;** XX, **$65.**

H. Boker, plain celluloid, **$25.**

Slim Jacks

The "slim" jack is a narrower version of the regular jack. Many older slim jacks are premium knives. That is, they were made with the best quality materials and workmanship. When new, such premium slim jacks cost more than regular jacks of the same length. However, this does not make them worth any more to collectors now.

The most refined variation of the slim jack is the "physician's" pattern. This pattern is usually about 3½ inches long. The head end is flat and reinforced with a nickel silver cap for crushing powders and pills. A type of "smoker's knife" looks similar to the physician's pattern, but its end is modified as a pipe tamper and cigar box hammer. Some inexpensive slim jacks also have flat head ends, but they are not reinforced.

The most impressive version of the slim jack is the "melon tester," sometimes called the "citrus" pattern or the "sausage knife." Although little wider than a physician's knife, a melon tester is usually about 5 inches long, with one or two proportionally long narrow blades. Some melon testers are "double-end" jacks with a blade in each end, and a few are made in other shapes than the slim jack.

3½" Physician's Knife.

4⅝" Melon Tester.

No. 6285

Case Tested XX, barehead (flat end), 3⅝", bone stag, **$72**. (Rarity of this knife may up to double its value.)

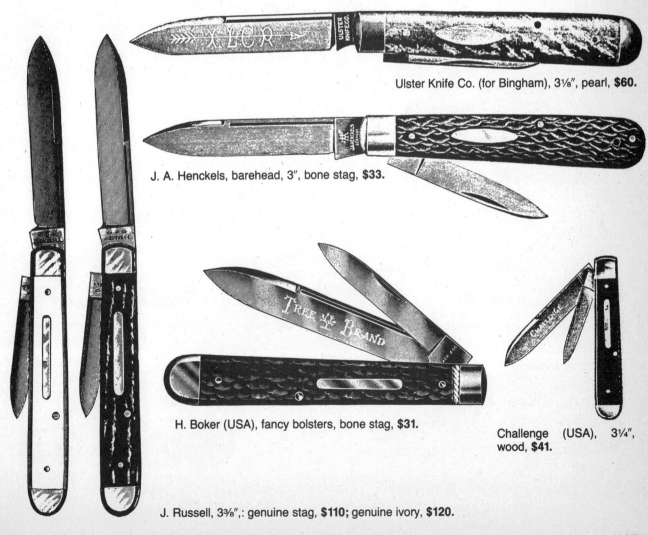

Ulster Knife Co. (for Bingham), 3⅛", pearl, **$60**.

J. A. Henckels, barehead, 3", bone stag, **$33**.

H. Boker (USA), fancy bolsters, bone stag, **$31**.

Challenge (USA), 3¼", wood, **$41**.

J. Russell, 3⅜",: genuine stag, **$110**; genuine ivory, **$120**.

Sleeveboard and Jumbo Jacks

Regular jacks have squared corners at the blade end. Similar tapered knives that are rounded at both ends are usually called "sleeveboard jacks," because they are shaped like the small auxiliary ironing boards once used for pressing shirtsleeves. Unlike regular jacks some sleeveboard jacks have their blades hinged at the wider end.

The most striking sleeveboard jack is the 3⅝ inch long (or longer) and extra heavy "jumbo jack." Besides jumbo jacks, several other types of knives are made on jumbo sleeveboard frames. These include certain cattle knives, double-end jacks (called "jumbo knives"), and big whittlers (called "engineer's knives," and several other names). All of these jumbos are scarce and relatively valuable.

Ulster Knife Co., bone stag, **$50.**

Ulster Knife Co., one blade, barehead, wood, **$30.**

Ulster Knife Co., 2⅞", pearl, **$55.**

Boker (USA), 3", pearl, **$34.**

Keen Kutter, 3⅜", patterned celluloid, **$40.**

622048

Robeson, 2⅞", bone stag, **$22.**

Winchester, 3¼", bone stag, **$90.**

Stiletto (P.H. & S.), 3½", bone stag, **$50.**

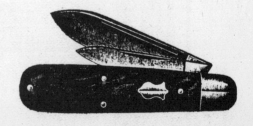

American Shear & Knife Co., barehead, 2⅜", wood, **$23.**

Sleeveboard Jacks (Blades at Wide End)

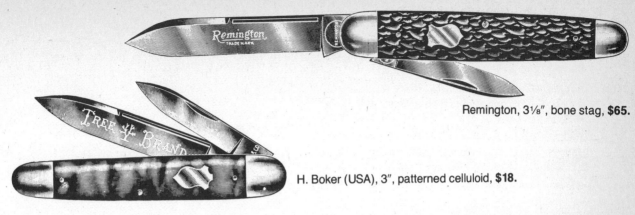

Remington, 3⅛", bone stag, **$65.**

H. Boker (USA), 3", patterned celluloid, **$18.**

Jumbo Jacks

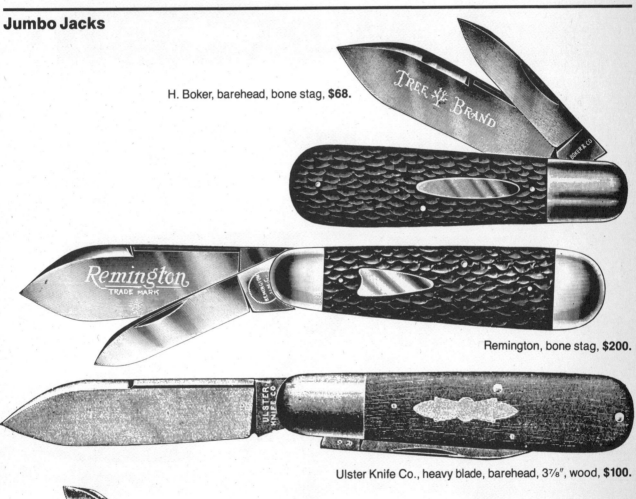

H. Boker, barehead, bone stag, **$68.**

Remington, bone stag, **$200.**

Ulster Knife Co., heavy blade, barehead, 3⅞", wood, **$100.**

222050

626052

Challenge (USA), 3⅞", wood, **$115.**

Robeson, heavy blade, barehead, 3⅞", wood, **$70.**

Robeson, 3¾", bone stag, **$85.**

Curved Regular or Clasp Jacks

Not all regular jacks (boy's knives and barlows included) are straight-sided. Some older ones have an upward curve to the handle. This curve seems to indicate that the regular jack design was based originally on the "clasp knife" (see below for more on clasp knives).

The curved regular jack is mainly a 19th century pattern. However, several 20th century pocketknife firms offered one or two versions of it.

A few curved regular jacks have just the very end of the handle curved. These resemble the 18th century French "crosse" pattern [see *Foreign Exotic, Primitive, and Historical Folding Knives*, Plate I-D].

Curved Regular Barlow.

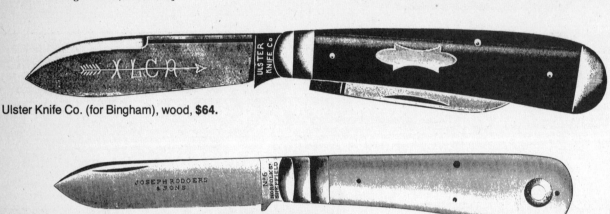

Ulster Knife Co. (for Bingham), wood, **$64**.

Jos. Rodgers, one blade, barehead, 4⅛", smooth white bone, **$61**.

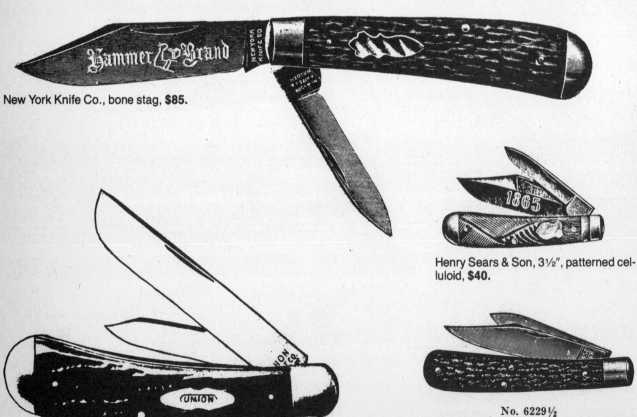

New York Knife Co., bone stag, **$85**.

Union Cut. Co., bone stag, **$115**.

Henry Sears & Son, 3½", patterned celluloid, **$40**.

No. 6229½
Case Tested XX, barehead, 2½", bone stag, **$70**.

Curved Jacks and Congress Jacks

The "curved jack" handle die is similar to the curved regular jack except that the curve goes the other way. The inside of the curve is toward the back or spring side of the knife.

Curved jacks that have all four corners squared and that are equal-ended, or only slightly tapered, are called "congress jacks." The congress shape is ordinarily a pen knife handle die, but some firms, I guess just to be different, made congress jacks as well. All congress knives and just about all curved jacks have sheepfoot master blades.

Small markedly tapering curved jacks with rounded ends were sometimes called "sway-back jacks," although the term "sway-back" also referred to the "swell-center congress," a pen knife pattern. Sway-back jacks were popular in the 19th century but had pretty much gone out of production by 1910.

Medium sized curved jacks (3½ to 4¼ inches long) were often called "New England Whalers." These, and most larger curved jacks, were designed as sailors' rope knives. Also, some firms used curved jack handles for their "pruners." Both pruners and sailors' knives are covered in the *Special Purpose Jack Knives* chapter.

Pruning Knife.

No. 2394½B
Schrade Cut. Co., barehead, 3⁹⁄₁₆", plain celluloid, **$35**.

William Rodgers (J. Clarke), one blade, barehead, buffalo horn, **$25**.

Tacklers   Knife

Ulster Knife Co., two large blades, barehead, wood, **$50**.

NEW ENGLAND WHALER.
Keen Kutter, one saber ground blade, barehead, 3¼", wood, **$34**.

J. Russell, barehead, 3⅝", buffalo horn, **$88**.

Jos. Rodgers, saber ground blade, barehead, 3⅜", genuine stag, **$70**.

No. 6217
Case, barehead, bone stag, 4": Tested XX, **$110**; XX, **$65**.

Congress Jacks

Remington, bone stag, **$110.**

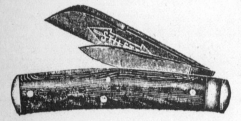

H. Boker, bone stag, **$40.**

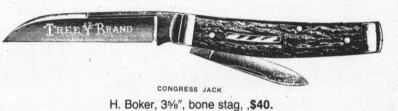

H. Boker, 2¾″, bone stag, **$30.**

Stiletto (P.H.& S.), 3″, patterned celluloid, **$39.**

CONGRESS JACK
H. Boker, 3⅝″, bone stag, , **$40.**

Sway-Back Jacks

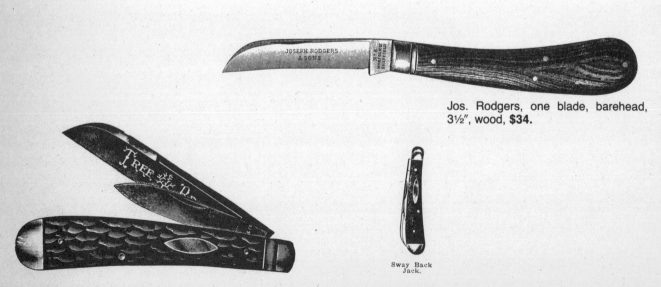

Jos. Rodgers, one blade, barehead, 3½″, wood, **$34.**

Sway Back Jack.

H. Boker, 3″, bone stag, **$30.**

Keen Kutter, 3½″, wood, **$52.**

Crown Jacks

Somewhere between the equal-end jack and the congress jack is the old pattern called the "crown jack" or "coffin" pattern. A crown jack looks like a congress jack that has been straightened out but, since I believe that the crown is the older of the two shapes, it would be more accurate to say that a congress knife is a crown pattern that got bent. In any case, the crown looks more than anything like a slender barrel.

As with the congress, the crown shape was used most often for pen knives. Crown jacks are mainly a 19th century pattern, with only a few having been made more recently. From the little evidence I have seen, they were often made with fancy bolsters.

Crown Pen Knife.

New York Knife Co., fancy bolsters, bone stag, **$88.**

H. Boker, bone stag, **$45.**

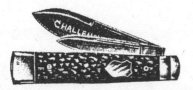

Challenge (USA), 3⅝″, bone stag, **$70.**

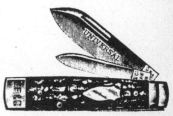

L. F. & C., 3⅞″, bone stag, **$88.**

Swell-End Jacks

Almost as regular as the regular jack, though a little bit fancier, is the shape called the "swell-end jack." Swell-end jacks are somewhat pear shaped, with the blades up at the stem end. Some people call this shape the "tear-drop." The wide end is usually rounded but occasionally pointed.

I find the swell-end jack to be a most attractive shape. It was made in just about every imaginable handle material, including dozens of varieties of multi-colored celluloid. The pattern is pretty much out of production now, and I think that it would be an interesting type to collect.

Harness Knives

Swell-end jacks usually have two blades. The second blade, when present, is most often a pen blade, though sometimes a punch. A swell-end or a regular jack with a spear master blade and a punch blade was sometimes called a "harness knife." Another name for the harness knife is "teamster's knife." Other jack knives with a leather punch blade might reasonably be called harness knives as well. Harness knives are included in the *Special Purpose Jack Knives* chapter.

OUR NEW "PROD-KNIFE"
WITH STIFF HOLLOW SPOON-BIT BLADE
A PERFECT TOOL FOR BORING HOLES IN WOOD, LEATHER, ETC.

Harness or Teamster's Knife.

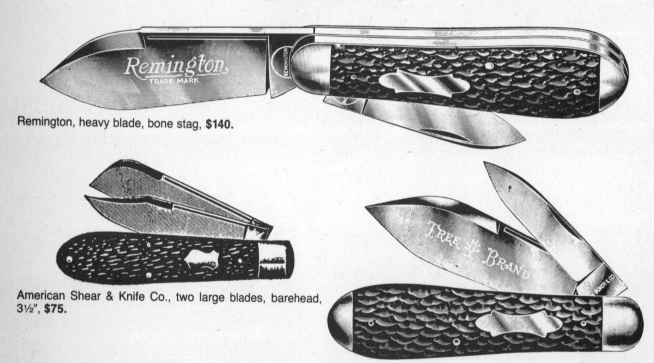

Remington, heavy blade, bone stag, **$140.**

American Shear & Knife Co., two large blades, barehead, 3½", **$75.**

H. Boker (USA), bone stag, **$40.**

J. Russell, barehead, 3¾", wood, **$75.**

Challenge (USA), 3⅞", bone stag, **$85.**

Swell-End Jacks

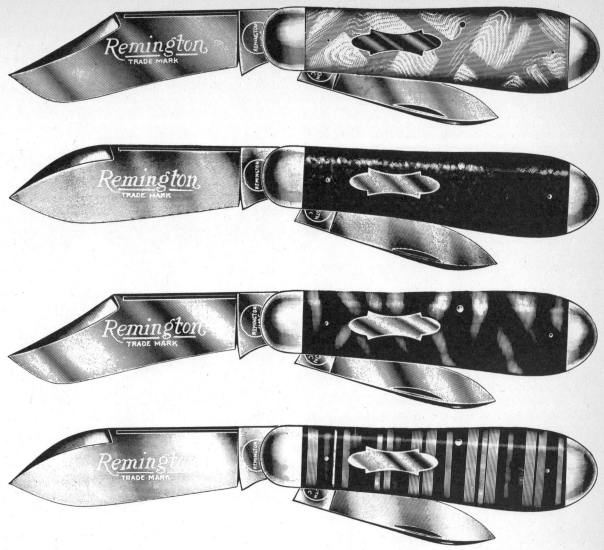

Remingtons, patterned celluloid (pearl gray, English walnut, tortoise shell, brown agate), **$100 each.**

No. 2064P

Jack Knife, 3⅝ inches long; 2 blades; brass lined; nickel silver bolsters, caps and shield; cleaned inside; large blade crocus polished on one side; Smoked Pearl Celluloid handle.

Tortoise Shell Celluloid handle . No. 2064S
Ivory Celluloid handle . . . . No. 2064W
Assorted Celluloid handles . . No. 2064AC

Schrade Cut Co's., patterned celluloid, **$55 each.**

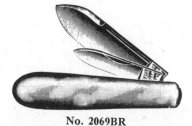

No. 2069BR

Schrade Cut. Co., 3⅝", solid brass, **$55.**

TWO BLADES, 1 Large Clip and 1 Pen; Large Blade Full Polished; Nickel Silver Bolster, Cap, Shield and Lining.

Per Dozen
No. 2098—3⅜ IN.; GREEN CELLU-
LOID HANDLE $18,70

Winchester, patterned celluloid, **$100.**

Easy Openers

Some swell-end jacks, as well as jacks of other shapes, are made with a half-round notch cut into the widest part of the handle. This "easy-open" notch allows one to grasp the end of the main blade with one's finger tips, a boon to people who bite their nails. Jack knives with this notch are called "easy-openers." Some collectors specialize in easy-openers.

The master blade of an easy-opener is generally either a spear-point or a sheepfoot. Small easy-open regular jacks with a sheepfoot master blade and a bail were often given a special name such as Automobile Knife, Navy Knife, or Small Scout Knife. See the *Scout and Utility Knives* chapter for more information on Small Scout Knives.

Swell-End Easy Openers

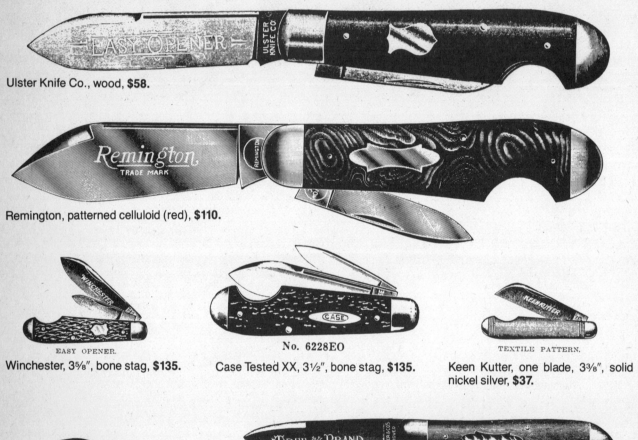

Ulster Knife Co., wood, **$58.**

Remington, patterned celluloid (red), **$110.**

Winchester, 3⅝", bone stag, **$135.**

No. 6228EO

Case Tested XX, 3½", bone stag, **$135.**

TEXTILE PATTERN.

Keen Kutter, one blade, 3⅜", solid nickel silver, **$37.**

H. Boker (USA), 3⅝", wood, **$33.**

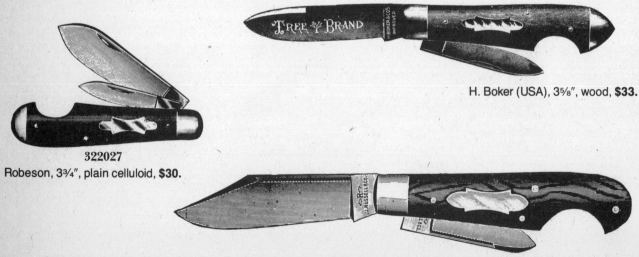

322027

Robeson, 3¾", plain celluloid, **$30.**

J. Russell, barehead, 3¾", wood, **$83.**

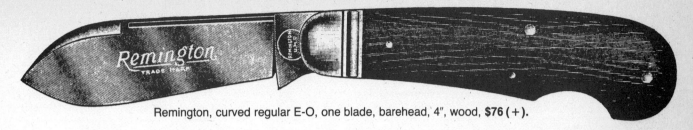

Remington, curved regular E-O, one blade, barehead, 4", wood, **$76 (+).**

J. Russell, regular E-O, 3⅝", bone stag, **$110.**

No. 2423EO

Schrade Cut. Co., slim equal-end E-O, 3⅛", bone stag, **$40.**

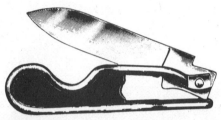

Geo. Schrade, regular E-O, one blade, shadow, 3⅛", solid steel, **$8.** (Wire Jack)

H. Boker, gunstock E-O, 2⅞", bone stag, **$55.**

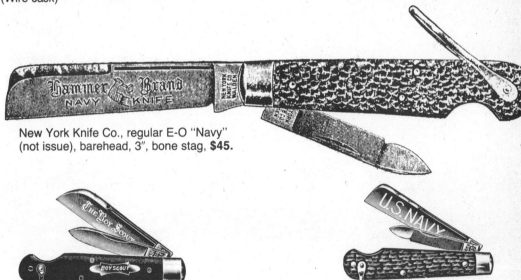

New York Knife Co., regular E-O "Navy" (not issue), barehead, 3", bone stag, **$45.**

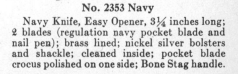

No. S2282½

Easy Opener Boy Scout Knife, 3½ inches long; 2 blades; brass lined; nickel silver bolsters, shield and shackle; cleaned inside; large blade crocus polished on one side; Ebony handle.

No. 2353 Navy

Navy Knife, Easy Opener, 3¼ inches long; 2 blades (regulation navy pocket blade and nail pen); brass lined; nickel silver bolsters and shackle; cleaned inside; pocket blade crocus polished on one side; Bone Stag handle.

Schrade Cut. Co., regular E-O "Small Scout" (not official), barehead, wood, **$43.**

Schrade Cut. Co., regular E-O "Navy" (not issue), barehead, bone stag, **$55.**

Swell-Center Jacks

If you take the swell-end handle die, pinch it in where it is fattest, square the corners at the blade end (or both ends), and then make the handle bulge in the middle like an unfortunate snake who has swallowed a stick sideways, you will come up with what is called the "swell-center" handle die. Often this shape is called the "Coke bottle."

Small swell-center jacks are relatively uncommon. Only a few have been made in the past 70 years, and I do not believe any are being made now.

Before the First World War, the small swell-center jack was a popular standard shape. Wood and smooth bone were the usual handle materials, but more costly ones were used as well.

Some 3½- to 4-inch swell-center jacks were made with a special spear blade that has a false edge along part or all of its back. These knives are called "stabber jacks," and they were the poor man's folding dirk. Stabber jacks would be an interesting specialty to collect. (Recall that the different term "stabber pattern" was once applied to the very cheapest single blade regular jack knives.)

Large swell-center jacks 5 inches long or longer are called "swell-center hunting knives." These are included in the chapter on folding hunters.

A number of firms made long slender swell-center jacks. These generally have a spear master blade. E.C. Simmons called their version with octagon cap bolsters a "gunstock jack," an unfortunate choice since *two* other shapes already had that name (see below).

A few firms made swell-center jacks with a flat cap on the head end. This type of cap is called a "seal cap" because it resembles an old-time wax seal.

3½" Stabber Pattern.

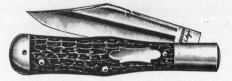

5¼" Swell-Center Hunting Knife.

Ulster Knife Co., fancy bolsters, wood, **$95**.

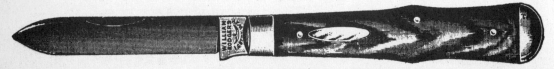

William Rodgers (J. Clarke), one blade, buffalo horn, **$40**.

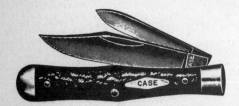

No. 5225½
Case Tested XX, 3", genuine stag, **$140**.

Schrade Cut. Co., fancy bolsters and seal cap, 4", bone stag, **$155**.

Winchester, fancy bolsters, 3¾", bone stag, **$190**.

H. Boker, barehead, 3⅞", bone stag, **$50**.

No. 6213
Case Tested XX, 4", bone stag, **$190**.

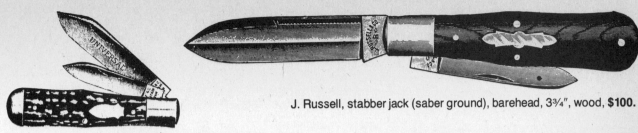

J. Russell, stabber jack (saber ground), barehead, 3¾", wood, **$100.**

L.F.& C., 3¾", bone stag, **$100.**

Remington, stabber jack (saber ground), barehead, bone stag, **$135.**

Ulster (for Bingham), stabber jack (saber ground), barehead, wood, **$66.**

H. Boker, fancy bolsters, bone stag, **$62.**

Robeson, 3½", bone stag, **$50.**

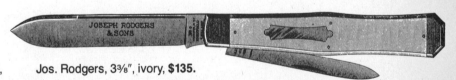

Keen Kutter, fancy bolsters, 3½", bone stag, **$125.**

Jos. Rodgers, 3⅜", ivory, **$135.**

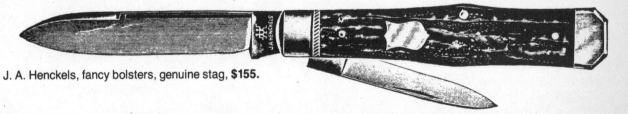

J. A. Henckels, fancy bolsters, genuine stag, **$155.**

Ulster Knife Co., fancy bolsters, bone stag, **$125.**

Balloon Jacks

If you start out to make a swell-center handle but instead of squaring the corners you make both ends round and bulbous like an old-fashioned hot air balloon, you will then have a ''swell-center balloon'' handle die. The swell-center balloon is mainly a pen knife and whittler handle, but some jack knives were made on this frame as well. Balloon whittlers are ordinarily tapered, but balloon jacks are usually equal-ended. The balloon jack was pretty much extinct by the 1920s. It is now a very rare shape.

Swell-center Balloon Whittler.

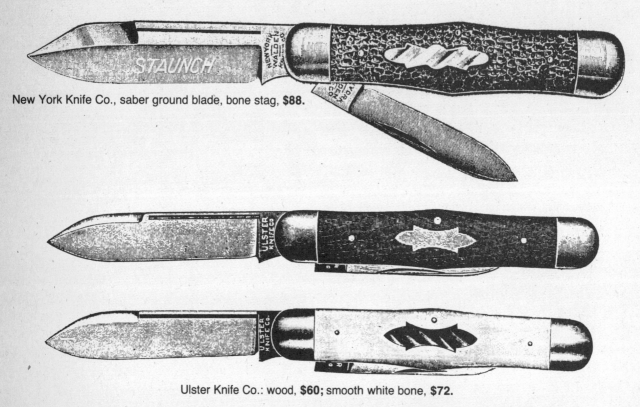

New York Knife Co., saber ground blade, bone stag, **$88.**

Ulster Knife Co.: wood, **$60;** smooth white bone, **$72.**

Remington, 3″, patterned celluloid, **$85.**

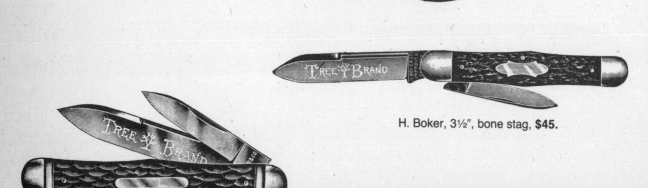

H. Boker, 3½″, bone stag, **$45.**

H. Boker, 2⅞″, bone stag, **$33.**

Swell-Center Regular Jacks

If you take a swell-center jack knife handle and grind off the swell on the bottom or spring side, you will turn it into a "swell-center regular jack" handle. I have only seen a couple of ordinary jack knives made on this handle die. Its main use was in two special patterns, the "heavy trapper" and the "lock knife."

The heavy trapper is one of several varieties of trapper pattern. These are all covered in a separate chapter. All trapper *patterns*, regardless of shape or size, have two full-length blades, a slender clip and a long or "great western" spey.

Most heavy trappers are over 4 inches long. A few firms have also made "large trappers" which are the same shape as heavy trappers, but at least 4½ inches long and nearly twice as massive as the heavy trapper. The best known large trapper is Remington's R1123 Bullet. Large trappers look similar to some clasp knives, from which this shape was derived, and they are often classed as folding hunters by people who collect them. Light-weight trappers are built on the slim serpentine handle die (see below).

The heavy trapper pattern made on the swell-center regular jack handle die has been offered since the 1920s. However, since the mid-19th century, this handle die has been used for lockbacks and folding hunters. These attractive knives usually have a single clip or saber clip blade.

Like the regular jack, the swell-center regular jack is so much a standard shape that it seems never to have been given a distinctive name of its own. The only names I have seen applied to these knives in old catalogs are "lock knife" and "hunting knife." Then, as now, both of these names referred to many other patterns as well.

Case and a few other firms still use swell-center regular jack handles for single-blade lockbacks. Case's most recent version is called the "Cheetah" and has a built-in folding guard, a feature also used on some older "lock knives." All such lock knives and "hunting knives" are included in the *Folding Hunters* chapter.

4⅛" Heavy Trapper.

4½" Large Trapper.

Ulster Knife Co., barehead, wood, **$55.**

Jos. Rodgers, saber ground blade, barehead, 4½", genuine stag, **$125.**

Case Tested XX. 4⅜", bone stag, **$150.**

No. 6211½

Gunstock Jacks

The "real" gunstock jack is similar in shape to the swell-center regular jack. Usually it is smaller, however, and its second blade is a pen blade. Most important, the top of the handle is straight (or nearly so) from the center swell back to the end, giving the handle very much the shape of a rifle stock.

The gunstock jack is a late 19th and early 20th century shape. It is relatively rare, and is very popular among collectors. None have been made commercially since before World War II, but some are now offered as "collectibles" and limited editions.

Gunstock handles were sometimes used on budding knives, which are described in the *Special Purpose Jack Knives* chapter. Unscrupulous dealers sometimes grind the bark spud of these budding knives, and then try to pass them off as gunstock jacks, which are much more valuable. The budding knives are generally single-bladed, while almost all true gunstock jacks have two blades.

Like the slim jack, the gunstock is usually a premium pattern. More often than most jack knives, it was made with luxury handles such as pearl and genuine stag. Some fancy gunstocks have a curved or a "serpentine" shape. Boker even made one with an easy-open notch.

Another shape that is called a "gunstock" looks like the square end "premium" jack (defined below) with a lump in the top of the handles. Winchester called this handle die the "gunstock premium stock." They and several other firms built both stock knives and jack knives on it.

Also, as I mentioned above, the E.C. Simmons Hardware Company called their long slim swell-center jack a "gunstock," I guess because the name sounds sporty.

The first pocketknife shape to be called a "gunstock" was an 18th century version of the curved regular jack. [See *Foreign, Exotic, Primitive, and Historical Folding Knives*, Plate I–D.]

Budding Knife.

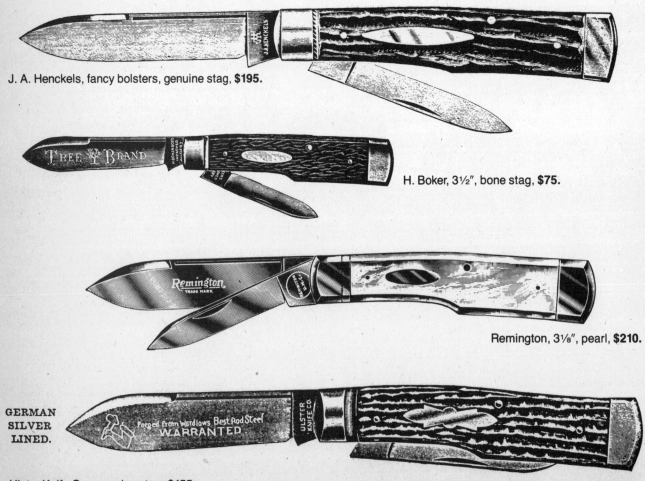

J. A. Henckels, fancy bolsters, genuine stag, **$195.**

H. Boker, 3½", bone stag, **$75.**

Remington, 3⅛", pearl, **$210.**

GERMAN SILVER LINED.

Ulster Knife Co., genuine stag, **$155.**

Serpentine Handles

Several standard jack knife handles dies have more or less of an S-curve shape. Some of these shapes were called "serpentine" (snake-like) by the manufacturers while others were called "curved." However, which particular shape gets which particular name depends on which manufacturer's catalog you look at. I call all of these shapes "serpentine" because the term "curved" is applied to another group of patterns.

In addition to the standard serpentine shapes, some normally straight patterns were sometimes made in serpentine versions. I have seen serpentine gunstocks and serpentine physician's knives. Serpentine equal-ends are classed as premium jacks (see below). Others may exist as well.

Premium Jacks

A premium jack is a two-bladed jack knife built on the same serpentine handle dies as the various three- to five-bladed "premium stock" knives. [See the *Multi-Blades* section for more on premium stock knives.] Premium jacks were probably introduced around the same time as premium stocks, in the 1890s.

The earliest premium jacks were round ended and symmetrical (equal-ended). However, almost all premium jacks made since about 1910, whether round or square ended, are slightly tapered.

The blades of a tapered premium jack are hinged in the wider end. Like premium stocks, all premium jacks (except the early equal-ends) have clip master blades. The second blade is usually a pen, occasionally a punch [See *Harness Knives*] or a spey.

Many current production jack knives are premium jacks because they can be assembled from the same components as the popular premium stock knives. Premium jacks (and all jack knives) are less costly to make than stock knives. Unlike a stock knife, which is a "double-ended" knife, a jack knife has only one blade bearing on each spring. Its blades require no "crinking" (sideways bending) to make them fit together when closed.

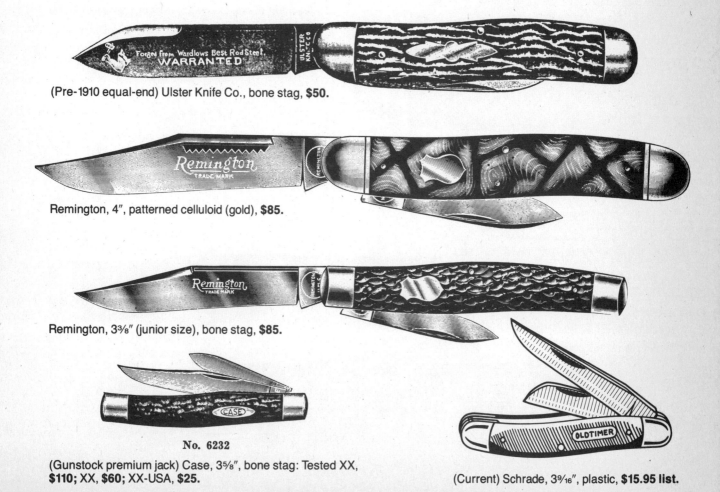

(Pre-1910 equal-end) Ulster Knife Co., bone stag, **$50.**

Remington, 4″, patterned celluloid (gold), **$85.**

Remington, 3⅜″ (junior size), bone stag, **$85.**

No. 6232

(Gunstock premium jack) Case, 3⅝″, bone stag: Tested XX, **$110; XX, $60; XX-USA, $25.**

(Current) Schrade, 3⁹⁄₁₆″, plastic, **$15.95 list.**

Serpentine Jacks

Giving a more pronounced taper to the serpentine handle than is used on the premium jack yields a knife called the "serpentine jack." Small serpentine jacks can have the "head" end (the non-blade end) either round or pointed. Unlike premium jacks, serpentine jacks usually have their blades in the narrower end.

The small (2¾ inches or so) round-ended serpentine jack is now called the "peanut" by collectors. Larger round-ended serpentine jack knives are often called "dog-leg" jacks, as are the much less common Wharncliffe jacks. The Case "Copperhead" (6249) is a serpentine jack with over-sized front bolsters.

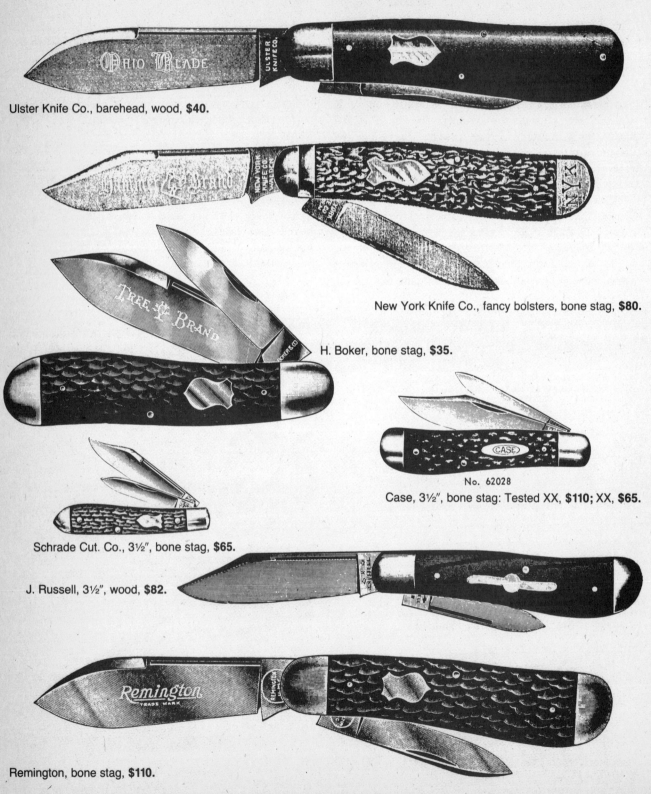

Ulster Knife Co., barehead, wood, **$40.**

New York Knife Co., fancy bolsters, bone stag, **$80.**

H. Boker, bone stag, **$35.**

No. 62028
Case, 3½", bone stag: Tested XX, **$110;** XX, **$65.**

Schrade Cut. Co., 3½", bone stag, **$65.**

J. Russell, 3½", wood, **$82.**

Remington, bone stag, **$110.**

"Peanuts"

Ulster Knife Co.; fancy bolsters, 3⅛", smooth white bone, **$55.**

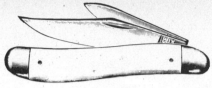

No. 8220
Case Tested XX, 2⅞", pearl, (**$125** + 100% for any *Case* peanut) **$250.**

H. Boker, 2¾", patterned celluloid, **$21.**

Remington, 3", bone stag, **$83.**

"Wharncliffe" Jacks

The most radically tapered serpentine handle die was called the "Wharncliffe" by most manufacturers. Wharncliffe jacks, like premium jacks, have their blades hinged in the wide end of the handle. Some of them are double-end jacks (with a blade in each end); these are called "farmer's jacks."

Lord Wharncliffe was a noble English patron of Joseph Rodgers & Sons of Sheffield in the early 19th century. The true "Wharncliffe Knife," named in his honor, is a pen knife with a Wharncliffe handle *and* a Wharncliffe master blade. By the turn of the century, most any jack knife with just the Wharncliffe handle was called a Wharncliffe jack.

No. 2364¾B
Schrade Cut. Co., 3⁹⁄₁₆", plain celluloid, **$45.**

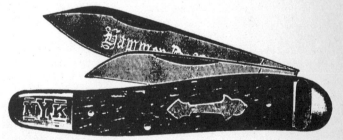

New York Knife Co., two large blades, fancy bolsters, bone stag, **$105.**

Remington, 3⅛", bone stag, **$83.**

Slim Serpentine Jacks

A further refinement of the serpentine shape is one that I follow Schrade Cutlery Company in calling the "slim serpentine jack." Winchester called this shape the "curved jack," which does not do it justice. Queen Cutlery Company calls it the "switch" pattern, and has even offered an easy-opener version of it. Western States called the shape the "jack premier," but then they went and used the term "premier jack" for an equal-end premium jack.

The slim serpentine jack is a relatively large pattern, 3¾ to 4¼ inches long, with a clip master blade. Its blades are hinged at the narrow end. It is slender and graceful, with a slight swell toward the head end.

Often this pattern was made with just the single clip blade. The second blade, when present, was usually a pen.

Many firms have offered 4-inch (or thereabouts) slim serpentine jacks with a clip and a long spey blade, making a slim light-weight trapper. The Case '48s are a recent example. These are covered in the trapper chapter.

Light Trapper.

Napanoch, saber ground blade, barehead, 3¹³/₁₆", bone stag, **$135.**

(Current) Schrade, one blade, lockback, 3⅛", plastic, **$14.95 list.**

Schrade Cut. Co., saber ground blade, 3⅞", bone stag, **$70.**

Winchester, saber ground single blade, 4⅛", bone stag, **$110.**

No. 61048

Case, single blade, barehead, 4", bone stag: Tested XX, **$100**; XX, **$40.**

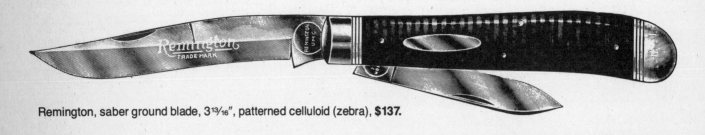

Remington, saber ground blade, 3¹³/₁₆", patterned celluloid (zebra), **$137.**

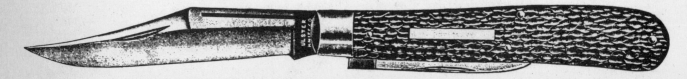

Ulster Knife Co., saber ground blade, barehead, 3⅞", bone stag, **$55.**

Eureka Jacks

The most elegant serpentine jack of all is a shape that Western States called the "Eureka." I much prefer this name to the more descriptive but hopelessly awkward "swell-center serpentine balloon."

The Eureka was primarily a deluxe cattle knife die, but it also was used for jack knives. It is shaped like a dog-leg, except that it has bulbous "balloon" ends and a pointed projection in the middle of the back. It looks better than it sounds, and it is a rare and desirable pattern.

Schrade called this shape the "Norfolk" pattern, and it may indeed have first been made by Joseph Rodgers & Sons, whose plant at No. 6 Norfolk Street in Sheffield was called the Norfolk Works. However, Schrade seems to have copied the shape from Remington, who in turn had copied it from New York Knife Company. Maybe New York Knife had copied it from Rodgers.

New York Knife Co., fancy bolsters, bone stag, **$112.**

Ulster Knife Co., wood, **$72.**

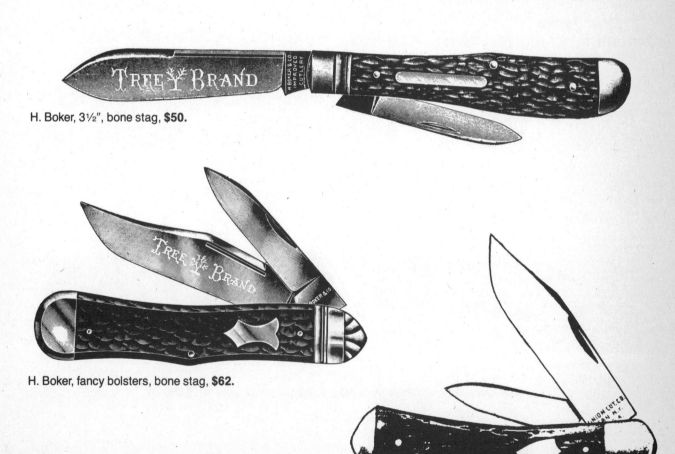

H. Boker, 3½", bone stag, **$50.**

H. Boker, fancy bolsters, bone stag, **$62.**

Union Cut. Co., bone stag, **$120.**

Canoes

Two other deluxe cattle knife handles were also used for jack knives. Neither is serpentine shaped, nor do they resemble any other shape, except perhaps the equal-end.

One is the "canoe" which is shaped like a stubby and unseaworthy canoe. The other is the "swell-center canoe," which was called by Western States the "surveyor" pattern.

H. Boker, fancy bolsters, bone stag, **$95.**

Surveyor Jacks

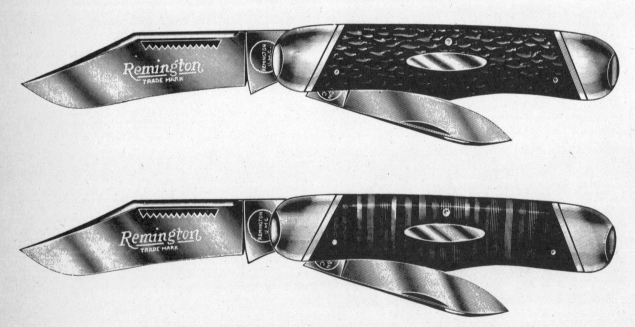

Remingtons, fancy bolsters: bone stag, **$220;** patterned celluloid, **$175.**

Fishtail and Fish Jacks

"Fishtail," like "peanut," is a modern name. The only old name that I have found for this pattern is "Dagger French Pattern" used by Western States in the 1920s. I trust you will agree that "fishtail" is a handier name.

The fishtail is indeed a dagger style handle, and fishtail jacks are often equipped with cross-guards. They most frequently have a single clip blade. In size they range from impractically small on up to folding bowie knife proportions.

The fishtail is related to, and possibly derived from, an older simpler shape sometimes called the "fish jack." Fish jacks I have seen have a convex "head" (it's the "head" of the knife, but it's the tail of the fish that the knife is shaped like), rather than the concave "head" usual on the fishtail.

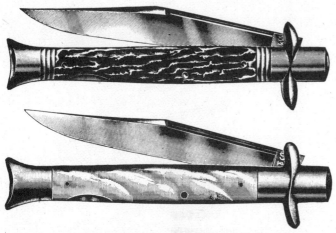

H. Boker (Germany), one blade lockbacks, fancy bolsters: genuine stag, **$75**; pearl, **$90.**

No. 61051

Case Tested XX, one blade, fancy bolsters, 3⅞", bone stag, **$150.**

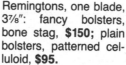

Remingtons, one blade, 3⅞": fancy bolsters, bone stag, **$150**; plain bolsters, patterned celluloid, **$95.**

Fish Jack

New York Knife Co., fancy bolsters, wood, **$100.**

Clasp Knives

A large usually single-bladed jack knife which has an upwardly curved handle that tapers to a point is called a "clasp knife." The clasp knife shape is probably almost as old as the simple cylindrical handle. The term "clasp knife" for a large folder may be even older than the term "jack knife." Regular jacks, swell-ends, swell-centers, serpentines, and probably other shapes as well, seem to have been derived originally from the classic clasp knife.

The first clasp knives were made from the ends of goat or cow horns that were split or slotted to contain the blade. The tip of the horn covered the point of the blade, the blade having been shaped to fit the natural curve of the horn.

Traditional style clasp knives are still made in southern Europe and Mexico. They are often called by their Spanish name, *navaja*. *Navajas* and other foreign clasp knives are described in *Foreign, Exotic, Primitive, and Historical Folding Knives,*

Some contemporary clasp knives with types of handles other than horn still retain the basic horn shape. There are big fat ones like Case Buffaloes and Bulldogs. There are long slender ones called "ticklers" (or "Texas toothpicks" or "powderhorns"). A tickler with a fish scaler added is called a fish knife. Ticklers and fish knives have their own chapter.

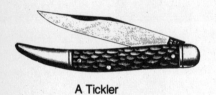

A Tickler

Modern Clasp Knives and Folding Hunters

"Folding hunter" is a broad term that now refers to modern American style clasp knives, large swell-center or "Coke bottle" hunting knives, and large trappers. It also includes various folding lock knives with built-in fixed or folding cross-guards.

Most modern American clasp knives are more streamlined than traditional ones. They have lost their upswept pointed handle ends and retain only enough curve for a comfortable grip.

Big clasp and folding hunting knives are the most popular types of folding knife to collect. They are covered in detail in their own chapter.

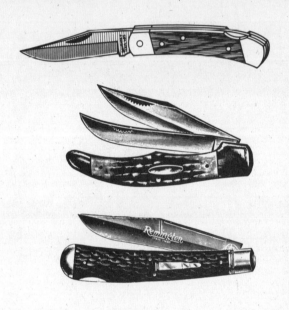

Folding Bowies and Folding Dirks

If you begin at the size of folding hunters (4½ to 5½ inches) and move on up, you enter the realm of the "folding bowie knife" and "folding dirk." Their shapes, sizes, and decoration vary considerably.

Ornate folding bowies and dirks of early to mid-19th century English origin are the most valuable of antique folders. Big fancy English folders in any condition are uncommon. In excellent condition they are extremely rare, and there is avid competition for the best ones among advanced and well-heeled collectors. Folding dirks and bowie knives have their own chapter.

Special Purpose Jack Knives

THE PRECEDING chapters described the various shapes or ''handle dies'' of standard American jack knives. The chapters that follow describe jack knife *patterns* that are built on some of these handle dies and which have special styles of blades designed for specific tasks. These patterns are:

HARNESS KNIVES
ELECTRICIAN'S and **JANITOR'S KNIVES**
PRUNING KNIVES
MAIZE KNIVES and **COTTON SAMPLERS**

BUDDING AND GRAFTING KNIVES
FLORIST'S KNIVES
MELON TESTERS
SAILOR'S ROPE KNIVES
RASE KNIVES or **TIMBER SCRIBERS**
PHYSICIAN'S KNIVES
SPATULA or **PALETTE KNIVES**
CORN KNIVES
BOX KNIVES and **SMOKER'S JACK KNIVES**
SPECIAL SPEY AND VETERINARY KNIVES including **FLEAMS**
SWITCHBLADE JACK KNIVES
SILVER FRUIT KNIVES.

Harness Knives

In the 19th century, a jack knife with a punch blade was often called a ''harness knife'' or a ''teamster's knife.''

In the days when leather harness connected your wheels to your horsepower, a broken strap could be anything from an inconvenience to a disaster. For quick field repairs, a leather punch is essential. The harness knife is the simplest and least expensive pocketknife that includes a punch.

The value of a harness knife is 25% greater than the value of an identical jack knife with an ordinary pen blade as second blade. Compute the value using the *Jack Knives Price Chart,* adding 25% where indicated.

H. Boker, slim equal-end, 3⅛″, bone stag, **$23.**

Remington, premium, patterned celluloid (gold), **$85.**

Ulster Knife Co., regular, barehead, wood, **$49.**

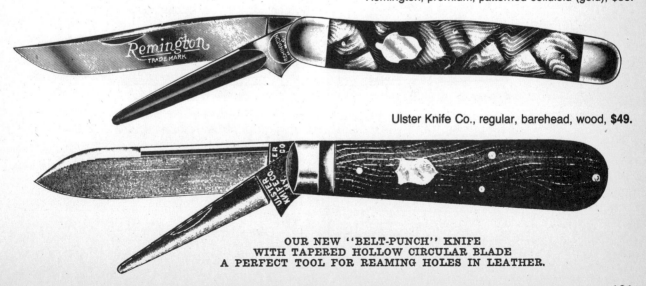

OUR NEW ''BELT-PUNCH'' KNIFE
WITH TAPERED HOLLOW CIRCULAR BLADE
A PERFECT TOOL FOR REAMING HOLES IN LEATHER.

Electrician's Knives

The electrician's knife is identified by the combination of a spear master blade with a locking screwdriver-wire stripper blade. The design is based on military specification TL-29. These knives are often called "TL-29's" and issue examples usually have TL-29 marked on them. "TL" means "Tool for Linemen."

The original TL-29 specification of World War I called for a 3⅝-inch sleeveboard handle with wooden scales. The srewdriver on this first version has oval cut-outs on both sides. Its lock is internal, and is released by depressing the folded main blade.

This version is usually called the Signal Corps knife. According to M. H. Cole, over a quarter million of them were made for the government in 1917–1918. These usually have military markings on the shield. Many more were made for commercial sale.

The revised TL-29 specification of the 1930s calls for a 3¾-inch regular jack, usually with a bail. Its screwdriver has a single cut-out on the back. Its lock is the liner-lock patented by Watson and Chadwick for Cattaraugus on July 3, 1906. The scales are wood, black plastic or, rarely, jigged bone.

Electrician's knives have long been made for civilian as well as military use. A major supplier is Mathias Klein & Sons electrical supply in Chicago. Knives marked M. KLEIN are made for them.

A few variations on the two TL-29 patterns have been offered for sale. Signal Corps size knives with just a screwdriver-wire stripper blade were made in the 1920s. These "Radio Knives" have a back lock.

Another Signal Corps size knife has a blade in each end. Its master blade is sometimes a sheepfoot.

Some firms offered full-sized electrician's knives with a pruner master blade. The hooked blade is used for stripping insulation from heavy cable.

Janitor's Knives

The belt and suspenders man can have both the spearpoint *and* the hawkbill in his electrician's knife, along with the screwdriver blade. Such three-blade belt-anchors are called "janitor's knives."

Base prices of ELECTRICIAN'S KNIVES with wood handles. Excellent unsharpened condition.

Signal Corps style (3⅝" sleeveboard, inside lock):
Very High: **$100.**   Medium: **$40.**
High: **$65.**   Low: **$16.**

Military markings (S.C. U.S.A., TL-29, etc.): **add 25%**
Double-ended: **add 20%**
Screwdriver blade only, back lock: **subtract 25%**
Jigged bone handles: **add 30%**
Composition handles: **subtract 20%**

Modern style (3¾" regular jack, liner lock):
Very High: **$60.**   Medium: **$15.**
High: **$24.**   Low: **$10.**

Military markings (TL-29, USN, US ARMY): **add 25%**
Three blades ("Janitor's"): **add 25%**
Jigged bone handles: **add 30%**
Plastic handles: **subtract 40%**

Mint condition: **add 40%**
Worn: **subtract 60%**
Broken: **subtract 95%**

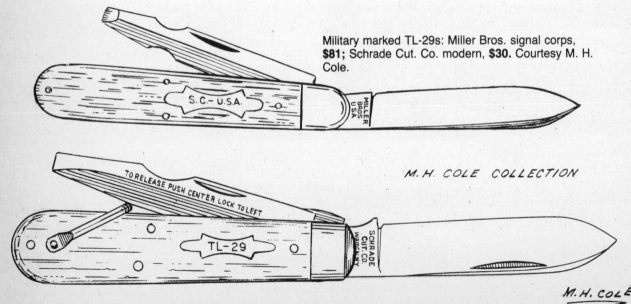

Military marked TL-29s: Miller Bros. signal corps, **$81**; Schrade Cut. Co. modern, **$30**. Courtesy M. H. Cole.

M.H. COLE COLLECTION

M.H. COLE
71

Pruning Knives

Ordinarily, the presence of a hawkbill blade indicates that a knife is a pruning knife. Besides being used to strip electrical insulation, pruning knives are used for cutting such materials as sheet-rock, carpet, linoleum, roofing paper, and string.

In the old days pruning knives were actually used for pruning shrubs and fruit trees. A few eccentric people still use them for this.

Pruning knives are relatively large curved jacks. There is some variation of shape and size among them. The most obvious variation is that some have rounded head ends (the non-blade end), while others have flat heads, usually protected by metal "seal caps."

Most pruning knives are single-bladed. A few have a second blade, usually a pruning saw. The farmer's jack [see *Double-End Jack Knives*] has a pruning blade in one end and a spey or budding blade in the other.

In the 1870s, Wostenholm made a changeable blade pruner that came with a hawkbill blade and a saw, and also sheepfoot and spey blades for grafting. When latched into place, any of the three knife blades (but not the saw) folded, just as in an ordinary jack knife. The end cap was the latch lever.

Hardwoods were the commonest handle materials for pruners. Stag was also favored because its natural curves and rough texture make for a firm grip. Cow horn and bone stag were also used. Most modern hawkbill knives have plastic handles.

Pruning knives, though large and often attractive, are not very popular among collectors. I guess this is because neither orchard work nor hanging sheetrock are considered to be romantic occupations.

Base prices of PRUNING KNIVES with one hawkbill blade, rounded head end; bone stag handle scales; front bolsters. Excellent unsharpened condition.

Very High: **$60.**   Medium: **$20**
High: **$40.**   Low: **$8.**

Brass or nickel silver seal cap: **add 50%**
Steel seal cap (flat end): **add 20%**
Second blade: **add 25%**
No bolsters: **subtract 20%**

Genuine stag handles: **add 50%**
Wood or horn handles: **subtract 20%**
Plastic or composition handles: **subtract 50%**

Mint condition: **add 50%**
Worn: **subtract 60%**
Broken: **subtract 90%**

Geo. Wostenholm, changeable blade, genuine stag, **$300.**
Courtesy Allen Dellenbaugh.

J. Clarke, steel seal cap, 2 blades, 4½″, genuine stag, **$45.**

Remington, 3⅝″, bone stag, **$60.**

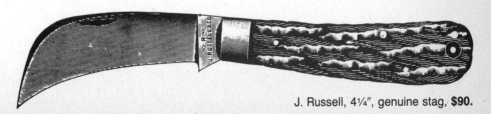

J. Russell, 4¼″, genuine stag, **$90.**

Maize Knives

A close cousin of the pruning knife is the maize or corn-topping knife. Its curved jack handle is the same as some pruner handles, but its short rounded blade is distintive. The very few I have seen had wooden handles. Do not mistake a worn out or broken pruner for a maize knife.

Prices for MAIZE KNIVES in excellent unsharpened condition.

Very High: **$75.**	Mint condition: **add 50%**
High: **$50.**	Worn: **subtract 50%**
Medium: **$30**	Broken: **subtract 90%**
Low: **$12.**	

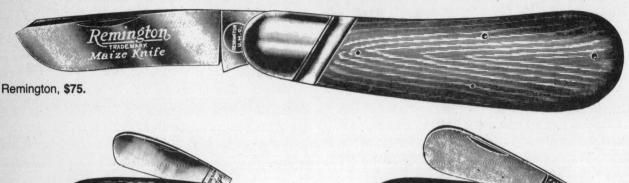

Remington, **$75.**

Robeson, 4", **$30.**   Case Tested XX, 3⅝" or 4", **$75 each.**

Cotton Samplers

Another cousin of the pruning knife is the cotton sampling knife. Cotton samplers were used by cotton buyers for cutting samples out of bales. Maher & Grosh of Ohio advertised them a century ago as folding skinning knives. I imagine they worked just fine.

Like maize knives, cotton samplers have curved jack handles, usually with wooden handle scales. Their blades, however, are distinctive. The straight section next to the tang is blunt.

A few cotton samplers, instead of having this rounded blade, have a broad square-point blade. These are heavy and even wider than rope knife blades, and also may be etched COTTON SAMPLER or COTTON KNIFE.

There is more collector interest in cotton samplers than in pruners or maize knives. They are attractive knives, and rare in excellent condition.

Prices for COTTON SAMPLERS in excellent unsharpened condition.

Very High: **$135.**	Mint condition: **add 50%**
High: **$100.**	Worn: **subtract 50%**
Medium: **$60.**	Broken: **subtract 90%**
Low: **$35.**	

Remington, **$135.**

J. Russell, 4¼", **$135.**

Budding and Grafting Knives

While pruning knives have moved to the city and found new jobs, budding and grafting knives have stayed down on the farm. Perhaps this is why they are seldom recognized by knife collectors.

Grafting, the more general term, is the attachment of living scions (cuttings) from one species or variety of tree, shrub, or vine to the limbs or stump of another species or variety. The stock or host variety may have sturdy branches or hardy and disease-resistant roots, while the grafted variety produces the best fruit or blossoms. Often the grafted variety is a sterile hybrid that produces no seed, and can only be propagated by grafting. Sometimes branches are added to a tree simply to increase its production.

Budding is a specialized type of grafting used on roses and young fruit trees. Individual buds of the desired variety are inserted under the bark of the stock plant.

Patch budding is a technique used on pecan trees. A precise square of bark with a bud in the center is cut from one tree and placed in an identical square hole in the bark of the stock tree. To cut the precise squares, a two-bladed pecan budding knife is used. It has a thick spacer separating the blades.

The blade of a budding and grafting knife, which is often beveled just on one side, cuts off the scions and cuts the incisions in the stock. The spud (or opener or shaft) is used to open the incisions.

On some knives, the spud, which can be fixed or folding, projects from the head end of the knife. This type of spud is made of ivory, bone, or a non-tarnishing metal. It can even be an extension of the handle. On other knives, the spud is a projection on the back of the blade.

Several handle dies were used on budding and grafting knives. The commonest is an equal-end or sleeveboard that has a single blade with a spud on its back. Small swell-end and regular jacks were made both with just a single "budding" or spey-type blade, and also with a folding spud in the opposite end. Small gunstock budding knives have a little clip blade at the narrow end and a fixed spud at the wide end. Budding knives that have the spud integral with the handle have two or three distinctive shapes.

There is now not much collector interest in budding and grafting knives, except among people who collect them to use. Good new ones cost over $20.

Base prices for BUDDING AND GRAFTING KNIVES with: smooth bone or horn handle scales. Excellent unsharpened condition.

VALUE RANGE	VERY HIGH	MED.	LOW
	HIGH			
SHAPE				
EQUAL-END or				
SLEEVEBOARD:	$60.	40.	20.	5.
SWELL-END or				
REGULAR:	80.	50.	25.	6.
Ditto with spud:	100.	65.	35.	10.
GUNSTOCK:	110.	70.	40.	12.
INTEGRAL SPUD:	70.	45.	22.	6.
PECAN (2 BLADES):	200.	100.	45.	20.

HANDLE MATERIAL
Ivory or genuine stag: **add 40%**
Bone stag: **add 20%**
Wood: **subtract 20%**

Plain celluloid: **subtract 25%**
Modern plastic: **subtract 35%**

CONDITION
Mint: **add 30%**
Worn: **subtract 60%**
Broken: **subtract 90%**

Remingtons, plain celluloid: integral spud, 3¾", **$53**; swell-end with spud, **$75**.

Case Tested XX, regular, 3⅜", bone stag, **$96**.

Schrade Cut. Co., sleeveboard, blade with spud, 4", plain celluloid, **$30**.

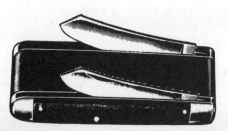
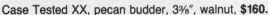

Case Tested XX, pecan budder, 3⅜", walnut, **$160**.

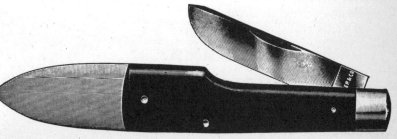

H. Boker, gunstock, plain composition, **$30**.

Florist's Knives

A florist's knife is most readily identified by the inscription " 'Say it with Flowers' " on the white composition handles. There are two types.

Most florist's knives are slim serpentine jacks with a single short sheepfoot or "budding" (spey-type) blade. Usually they have birdseye rivets and a bail.

Double-end florist's knives are equal-ends, usually with a sheepfoot in one end and a "budding" blade in the other. Replacing one of the blades with a V-shaped weed digger turns the knife into a "greenskeeper's knife."

Base prices of FLORIST'S KNIVES with one blade, white composition handles, and birdseye rivets. Excellent unsharpened condition.

Very High: **$65.**　　　Medium: **$15.**
High: **$30.**　　　　　Low: **$5.**
Double-end: **subtract 20%**
Weeding blade ("Greenskeeper's"): **add 25%**
Bolsters: **add 25%**
Mint condition: **add 50%**　Worn: **subtract 60%**
Broken: **subtract 90%**

Remingtons, 3¾": 1 blade, **$65**; 2 blades, bolsters, **$65.**

Schrade Cut. Co., double-end, weeding blade, 4", **$30.**

Melon Testers

A melon tester is a long slim regular jack with a spear master blade. Other names for this pattern are citrus knife and sausage knife. The melon tester is a relatively modern pattern, first offered in the 1930s.

Most melon testers have just the one spear blade. Some also have a long pen blade. A few recent melon testers have a serrated master blade.

Double-end melon testers have also been made. These strange knives may be an odd shape such as an elongated swell-center serpentine. Melon testers are much less valuable than other long folding knives.

Base prices of MELON TESTERS with composition handles; one or two blades. Excellent unsharpened condition.

Very High: **$160.**　　Medium: **$15**
High: **$25.**　　　　　Low: **$5.**

Genuine stag, pearl, or ivory handles: **add 50%**
Bone or bone stag handles: **add 25%**
Advertising on handles does not add to their value.

Mint condition: **add 30%**　Worn: **subtract 60%**
Broken: **subtract 95%**

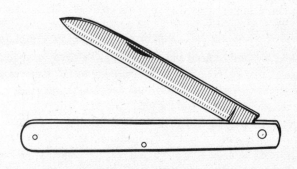
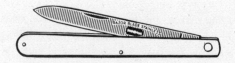

Schrades, 5¾" and 4¹¹⁄₁₆", **$15 each.**

Case Tested XX, double-end, 4¼", bone stag, **$200.**

Sailor's Rope Knives (including Foreign Military)

The ordinary sailor's knife is a curved jack or a curved regular jack with a single sheepfoot or flaring "rope" blade. These special straight-edged blades are used to cut rope cleanly. This is done by laying the rope on a wooden surface and hammering the blade through it with a belaying pin. Between this rough use and the hazards of salt water, it is not surprising that old sailor's knives in good condition are rare.

Ordinary sailor's knives are fairly large, at least 4 inches long closed. They usually have a bail so they can be secured from falling overboard.

Smaller curved jacks with a stout sheepfoot blade are called New England Whalers. I suspect they got their name from being a handy size for working with light harpoon line. Whalers may be drilled for a lanyard, but they have no bail.

I have also seen regular, curved regular, and swell-end jacks, usually with a single clip blade, that were sold and used as rope knives. Values of these and of whalers should be estimated from the *Jack Knives Price Chart*. Add 20% if they have rope company advertising, more (see the examples) for historical inscriptions (beware of fakery!).

Since the late 19th century, some sailor's knives have been made with an auxiliary folding marlinspike. The spike is used in splicing and in fancy knot work.

Some English knives have the spike beside the blade. However, the more usual place in on the back. If the spike locks open (often the bail is the lock release), the knife is a "rigger's knife." If it does not lock, the knife is a "yachtsman's knife." Some recent yachtsman's knives also have a shackle key.

J. Russell, sailor's, 4¼", wood, **$120.**

Schrade Cut. Co., whaler, barehead, 3⁹⁄₁₆", wood, **$31.**

Schrade Cut. Co.: sailor's (above), 4⁷⁄₁₆", "Fibestos," **$65;** yachtsman's (below), 4⅛", bone stag, **$48.**

Base prices for SAILOR'S KNIVES.
Excellent unsharpened condition.

ORDINARY with Wood Handles	RIGGING or YACHTSMAN'S with Composition Handles
Very High: **$120.**	
High: **$65.**	
Medium: **$15.**	Very High: **$65.**
Low: **$5.**	High: **$40.**
	Medium: **$20.**
	Low: **$7.**

Military markings: see picture captions.

HANDLE MATERIAL	CONDITION
Genuine stag: **add 30%**	Mint: **add 50%**
Bone stag: **add 20%**	Worn: **subtract 40%**
Smooth bone or horn: **add 10%**	Broken: **subtract 90%**
Metal: **subtract 20%**	

FOLLOWING PAGES: To show the range of types and values of sailor's knives, I have included photographs of examples from the collection of Melton Ferris. Each of these is an excellent example of its type. Prices are for knives in excellent unsharpened condition.

Sailor's Knives (continued)

ENCORE/T. TURNER & CO./BEST STEEL genuine stag, copper bail: **$125.** Similar Sheffield knife stamped U.S. NAVY on blade, **$250.**

MILLER BROTHERS folder, bone stag, large size: **$250**; small size (1″ shorter, not shown): **$350.**

MILLER BROTHERS gravity, bone stag, U.S. NAVY etched on blade: **$750.** (Gravity knives are illegal to own in most states.)

SCHATT & MORGAN/CUTLERY CO./TITUSVILLE PA. Canadian issue WWI, bone stag: **$175.** Made in the U.S., but only for export.

CAMILLUS/CUTLERY CO./CAMILLUS,N.Y./U.S.A./ /AP-PROVED/ U S C G/1944 Q5 lifeboat knife, wood handles: **$50.** (Similar Kutmaster: **$150.**) Similar knife without Coast Guard approval, **$15.**

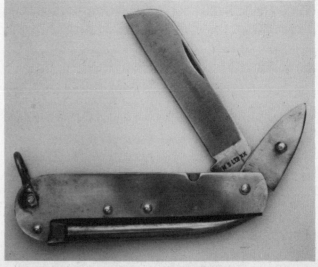

M.S. L℡ XX, all metal, Canadian WWII sailor & aircrew, made by Case "Metal Stampings Limited:" **$100.**

NON • XLL/JOSEPH/ALLEN & SONS/SHEFFIELD, genuine stag, British pre-WWI, **$150.** Other English brands slightly higher.

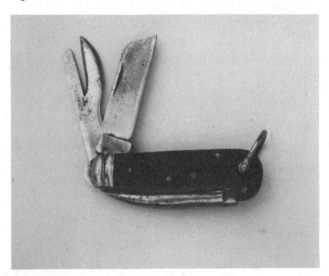

HUMPHREYS/-RADIANT-/SHEFFIELD checkered black composition, British WWII, **$35.** Other English brands somewhat lower.

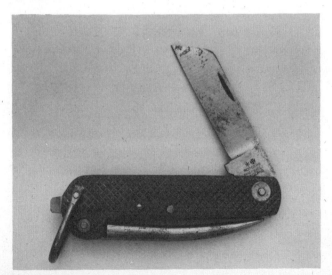

RODGERS/SHEFFIELD/ENGLAND//21306 grey metal, British WWII **$125.**

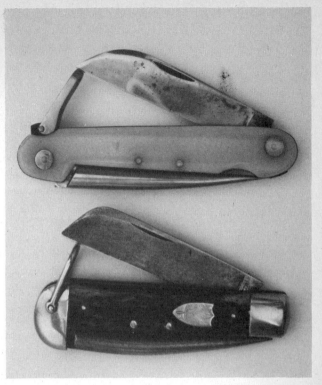

Above—upper:
KA-BAR/REG U.S. PAT. OFF., cream composition riggers knife (with lock spike); made in red (rarest) **$100,** cream (rare) **$50,** black (commonest) **$25.**

Above—lower:
ULSTER/KNIFE/CO. bone yachtsman's knife (no lock on spike) with Official Boy Scout BE PREPARED shield (Sea Scouts) **$250.**

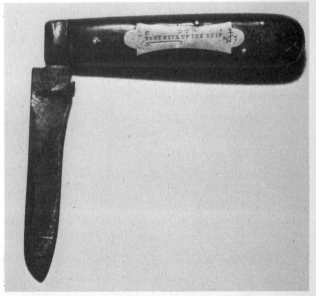

BEST ENGLISH CUTLERY 4-inch regular jack with horn handles, tapered back spring, lanyard hole, long square kick. Pewter shield stamped with an anchor and DON'T GIVE UP THE SHIP. Circa 1815-1830. Value **$250** as is, **$400-600** if excellent. Courtesy Fred B. McDonald.

Rase Knives or Timber Scribers

Although gouge-type blades were almost never used in multi-blades, they were routinely used in jack knives that were specially designed for them. Jack knives with gouge type blades are called timber scribes (or timber scribers). Another name for them is rase knives or race knives, with ''race'' used in the sense of a groove. Rase is pronounced ''raze.''

Rase knives were designed for cutting lines and markings into wood. They are used with a pull stroke, which accounts for the distinctive ''L'' or ''7'' shape of the blade. This bent shape also insures that the ''U'' shaped cutting edge will be safely housed when the blade is folded.

In the old days, the principal use of the rase knife was to scribe ownership and destination markings on wooden barrels and crates. Almost every commodity in the 19th century was shipped in wooden containers, so you can see how important rase knives once were.

Rase knives were also sometimes used for whittling markings off, or e-RASE-ing them. More often, though, a larger tool called a scorp or inshave was used to remove markings so containers could be re-used.

Rase knives were used by carpenters and boat builders to put a permanent mark on wood. On wooden boats, the waterline is sometimes scribed so that it can be readily found when the boat is repainted.

Among the several variations of rase knives, there is even a double edged version which seems to defeat the purpose of having the blade fold. Most rase knives have just the scriber blade, though some have an ordinary spear or clip blade as well.

The commonest rase knife is the version made by New York Knife Company in a choice of either wood or ''Gold-ine'' (bronze) handles. Old bronze or brass handled knives were made for use around salt water.

There are also fixed bladed rase knives, some of them quite elaborate. These were sometimes called cellarman's knives, as they were used in wine cellars.

Base prices of RASE KNIVES with one rase blade and wood handles. Excellent unsharpened condition.

Very High: **$150.** Medium: **$30.**
High: **$40.** Low: **$20.**

Two blades: **add 25%**
Double-ended rase blade: **add 20%**
Fixed blade (''cellarman's''): **add 100%**

Ivory handles: **add 75%**
Genuine stag handles: **add 50%**
Bone or horn handles: **add 25%**
Bronze handles: **add 20%**

Mint condition: **add 60%**
Worn: **subtract 30%**
Broken: **subtract 80%**

New York Knife Co., wood, $40. Wester Bros., double-edge, wood, **$36**.

C.B. Timpson & Tucker, brass, **$180.**

Ulster Knife Co., wood, **$40.**

J. Clarke, two blades, genuine stag, **$57.**

Physician's Knives

The "physician's knife" is the most refined variety of slim regular jack. The standard version is a slender straight-sided knife, usually about 3½ inches long. It has a flat "seal" cap. A rare variant is the serpentine or gunstock version.

Not all physician's knives are jack knives. Another style is a long slim equal-end or sleeveboard "whittler" [see *Pen Knives*].

Years ago, the distinction between the physician, who treated illness with medicines, and the surgeon, who treated by operating, was much sharper than it is now. The *physician's* knife is so called because it is primarily designed for preparing medicines.

The narrow spear master blade was intended for scooping powders from vials, and for loosening powders if they got caked. The flat seal cap, often of coin silver, was used for crushing powders and pills (hence the collector's name for this pattern, the "pill-buster"). The second blade of a pill-buster is sometimes a flexible spatula, used for mixing powders or salves. More often it is a slim pen blade.

Though a physician's knife could be used for emergency surgery, this was *not* its intended function. The one example I have seen that had a scalpel blade was advertised as a *veterinary* knife.

For surgeon's emergency use, folding pocket instruments were made by specialty surgical instrument makers. These little knives have simple two-piece handles, usually of tortoise shell or horn. They have open backs without liners or backsprings.

The physician's knife is a premium pattern. It was made with good handle materials: bone stag, pearl, horn, ivory, celluloid. A few are still made today, but they are for collectors rather than for physicians.

Base prices of PHYSICIAN'S KNIVES with: bone stag handles; spear master blade; pen or coping second blade. Excellent unsharpened condition.

Very High: **$115.**   Medium: **$35.**
High: **$70.**   Low: **$10.**

Scalpel (bistoury) blade: **add 30%**
Spatula blade: **add 10%**
Unusual shape (serpentine, gunstock, etc.): **add 25%**

HANDLE MATERIAL
Pearl: **add 50%**
Ivory, genuine stag, or tortoise shell: **add 35%**
Patterned celluloid: **subtract 20%**
Wood or horn: **subtract 25%**
Plain celluloid: **subtract 30%**

Mint condition: **add 50%**
Worn: **subrtract 50%**
Broken: **subtract 90%**

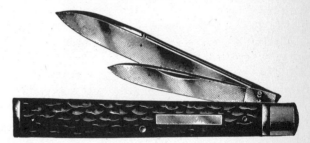

H. Boker, bone stag, **$35.**

Ulster Knife Co., serpentines: bone stag, **$88**; pearl, **$131.**

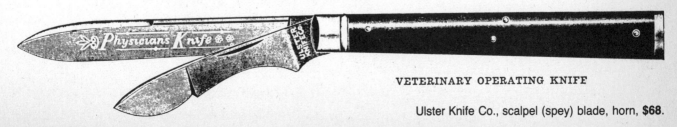

VETERINARY OPERATING KNIFE

Ulster Knife Co., scalpel (spey) blade, horn, **$68.**

Physician's Knives (continued)

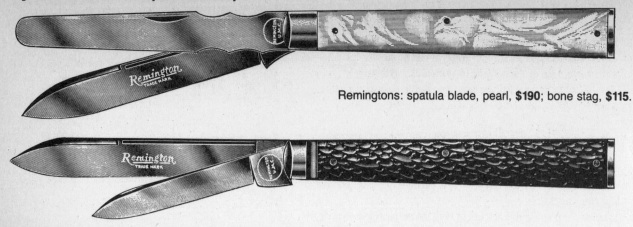

Remingtons: spatula blade, pearl, **$190**; bone stag, **$115**.

Spatula Knives

Some physician's knives have a flexible folding spatula as their second blade. A few cutlery firms used this blade by itself in a smaller folding knife, usually sleeveboard shaped. These, too, were used by physicians, but also by artists as folding palette knives. Most have wooden handles, but a few have fancier handle materials. These seem to have gone out of production by the time of the First World War.

J. Russell: pearl, **$90**; wood, **$60**.

Base prices of SPATULA KNIVES with wooden handles. Excellent condition.

Very High: **$60.**	Pearl handles:
High: **$40.**	**add 50%**
Medium: **$20.**	Ivory handles: **add**
Low: **$15.**	**35%**
Mint condition:	Bone handles: **add**
add 50%	**20%**
Worn: **subtract 50%**	
Broken: **subtract 90%**	

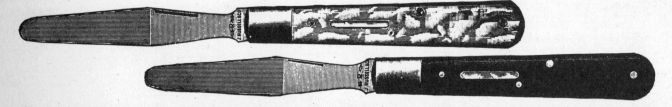

Corn Knives

Corn knives are made for cutting corns off your toes, and that is about all. Their blades are tempered very hard and ground extra thin to cut corns easily, but this makes them too delicate for most other tasks. Corn knives have a characteristic blade shape and many say CORN KNIFE on the handle or the blade.

If you wear fashionably tight shoes, you will eventually need to use a corn remover. Since the 1930s, corn knives have been supplanted by less risky rasps, abrasive materials, and chemical preparations. It is awfully easy to do yourself a serious injury with a razor-sharp corn knife.

Base prices of CORN KNIVES with smooth bone handles marked "Corn Knife;" one blade; no bolsters. Excellent unsharpened condition.

Very High: **$70.**	Medium: **$20.**
High: **$35.**	Low: **$7.**

Bolsters: **add 10%**   Two blades: **add 20%**

Pearl handles: **add 50%**
Ivory handles: **add 35%**
Celluloid handles: **subtract 20%**

Mint condition: **add 50%**
Worn: **subtract 60%**
Broken: **subtract 90%**

Corn Knives (continued)

B.J. Eyre (Wiebusch), celluloid, **$16.**

Ulster Knife Co., celluloid, **$28.**

Box Knives and Smoker's Knives

There are two jack knife patterns that are often confused with the "pill-buster." Like the physician's knife, the "box knife" and the "smoker's knife" both have special purpose metal caps.

The box knife has a little steel hammer head for a cap. Its main blade is a spear. Its second blade is a combination pry-bar and nail puller. Box knives were used for opening and reclosing the small wooden boxes that cigars, chocolate, and cheese used to be sold in. Some box knives advertise one of these products.

Folding box knives are extremely rare. They were used in homes and in fine shops. Most box knives were fixed bladed, and most of the fixed blades were very plain. Folding box knives seem last to have been made in the 1920s.

The smoker's jack knife has the cap modified as a pipe tamper. Like the box knife and the physician's, its main blade is a long spear. Its second blade can be a pen, a pipe reamer, or a cigar punch. More elaborate smoker's knives, are covered in the Multi-Blade section. Some versions of this pattern are still made, usually with metal handles.

Base prices of BOX and SMOKER'S (jack) KNIVES with metal handles, two blades. Excellent unsharpened condition.

	BOX	SMOKER'S
Very High:	$165.	$45.
High:	$125.	$24.
Medium:	$75.	$15.
Low:	$35.	$4.

Pearl handles: **add 60%**
Ivory handles: **add 50%**
Bone handles: **add 20%**
Celluloid handles: **add 10%**

Mint condition: **add 50%**
Worn: **subtract 50%**
Broken: **subtract 85%**

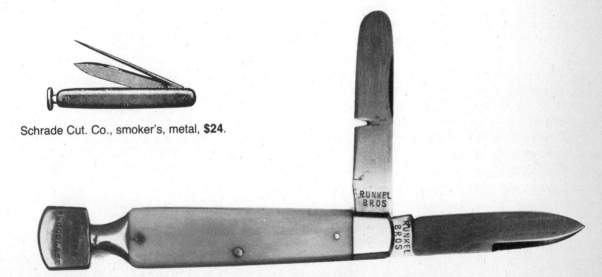

Schrade Cut. Co., smoker's, metal, **$24.**

Runkel Bros. (chocolate; made by Wester), box, ivory, **$113 + advertising**. Courtesy Ed Bruner.

Special Spey and Veterinary Knives

Several special patterns of jack knife were made for use on animals by amateur and professional veterinarians. The commonest sort were spey knives made for spaying or altering young animals.

Special spey knives are regular jacks, curved regular jacks, or serpentine jacks (rarely another shape) with a spey master blade. Most are single bladed, but rarely they have a second blade, a pen or, on some English spey knives, a hawkbill or a sheepfoot.

One American style of the 1930s to 1950s is called a "rooster nutter." This little metal handled curved regular jack has a spey blade and a castrating hook. Though designed for caponizing chicks, the hook is also used on cattle and hogs.

Values: Rooster nutter: **$30.**
    Others: use *Jack Knives Price Chart.*

No. 2000—2⅜" Veterinary Knife. One castrating blade and hook.

Fleams

The fleam is an old style of veterinary knife used for bleeding livestock. When bleeding was thought good medicine for people, it was thought even better for animals. Cattle were often bled on the nose. The point of a fleam blade was placed on the nose, and the back of the blade was struck with a "bloodstick." Automatic spring powered fleams that need no bloodstick were made in the 18th and 19th centuries.

Bleeding did have one legitimate use. It could relieve the painful inflamed feet of foundered horses.

Fleams look like the picture, though sometimes even fancier. Handles are brass, usually with cow horn handle scales. Sometimes the whole handle is horn. Most fleams have three blades, but some have only two. They never have backsprings. Horseman's knives (Multi-Blades) often have a fleam blade.

Values: Three blades, plain: **$75;** fancy, **$125.**
Two blades: **subtract 20%.** More than three:
    add 50%.
Automatic (in fitted case): **$125–200.**

Other Veterinary Knives

One odd veterinary knife is not really a knife at all. It is a little folding saw in a regular jack handle. This "cockspur saw" is used for sawing the spurs off the legs of fighting cocks, to make room for razor-sharp steel spurs or "chicken gaffs."

Values: NOVCO picture handled: **$200.** Unmarked: **$85.**

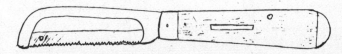

Another odd one is an equal-end double-end jack with two comb-like blades. Some of these have a round shield with a terrier's head, and this reveals their purpose. This is a "dog-stripping" knife, used for grooming kinky-haired mutts.

Values: Remington: **$100.** Case Tested: **$200.**
Spratts (a dog food producer): **$35.**

R4733
DOG STRIPPING KNIFE. Stag Handle; Brass Lined; Mirror Finished Blades; Nickel Silver Trim.
Length, closed, 3¾ inches.

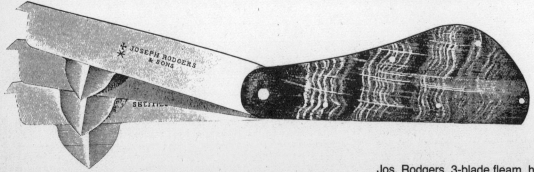

Jos. Rodgers, 3-blade fleam, horn, **$75.**

Switchblade Jack Knives

Switchblade knives have been illegal to own or to sell in this country since 1958. Despite (or because of) this, there is a lot of collector interest in them. I do not recommend buying or keeping them, and you definitely should not mail them.

"Patent Press Button" Lock Back.

THE VICTOR

INVINCIBLE

BUSINESS

Flylock Pattern

Silver Fruit Knives

By Bill Karsten

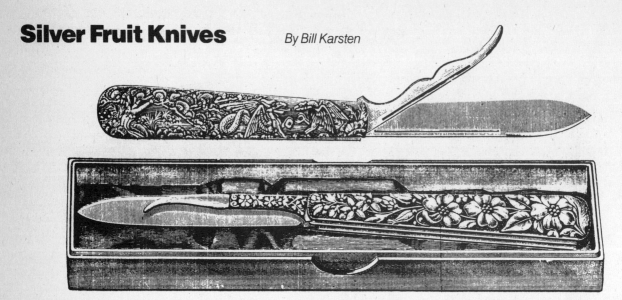

Embossed.

Wallace Brothers American embossed silver plated fruit knives, 1890s.

DECORATED jack knives with silver blades (sometimes silver plated or gold) and silver frames or handles are called "fruit knives." They were intended to aid in the dainty nibbling of fresh fruit and were a popular keepsake gift up through about 1930.

The earliest known folding fruit knives were made in France in the 17th century. They had one silver or gold blade that resisted staining from fruit acids and one steel blade. British knife historian Simon Moore reports that England's King Charles II gave a knife of this type to his mistress, the actress Nell Gwyn. Perhaps this began the fashion of gentlemen presenting dainty fruit knives to ladies.

Another early style of French fruit knife has no backspring. The two blades pivot on a common hinge pin, one blade on each side of the knife. Knives of this type have been called Berge knives at least since the 19th century. Before that, they were called crutch or balance knives. A fine Berge knife, with tortoise shell handles and gold trim, is worth about **$400.**

Earliest French style fruit knife.

French Berge knife. (Courtesy Smithsonian Inst.)

English Fruit Knives

Silver fruit knives were made in England, mainly Sheffield and Birmingham, beginning in the 18th century. The English also made folding silver fruit knife and fork sets for traveling.

Most English silver work is hallmarked—England has had a hallmark system since the 14th century. Official silver assay offices were opened in Sheffield and Birmingham in 1773. Fruit knives made in either place after that date will be marked accordingly. A full hallmark includes the following stamps: city code (a crown for Sheffield, an anchor for Birmingham), sterling mark (a lion passant), year code, maker's initials, and duty stamp (the monarch's profile). Before 1830, sometimes only the sterling mark and duty stamp were used.

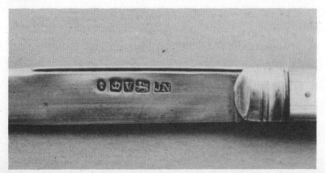

Typical Sheffield hallmark [John Nowill].

Fruit knives of the Georgian period, prior to 1830, are simple in design yet tasteful and elegant. Often the blade is engraved along the back edge. Handle scales are generally thin beveled mother-of-pearl or tortoise shell. Many have a silver shield engraved with the recipient's name or initials. Back springs are chased with a diagonal or, later, a cross-hatch pattern. Some have long ringed bolsters or silver end caps.

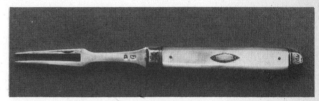

Fork from a Georgian knife and fork set.

Typical Georgian fruit knife.

Georgian fruit knives are the aristocrats of this field. Excellent specimens sell for over **$100,** knife and fork pairs for at least **$200.**

The most valuable Georgian fruit knives have gold blades. Sheffield had no gold assay office until 1904, so these are unmarked. Their Georgian design identifies them. They are worth three to five times as much as their silver counterparts.

Beginning with the reign of William IV (1830–37) and continuing through the Victorian era (1837–1901), English design and decoration changed greatly. Fruit knives were made in more exotic shapes, their pearl, tortoise shell, silver, or ivory handles engraved in various floral or geometric themes. Some of the finest pearl or shell handles were decorated with pin-work: patterns of tiny silver pins painstakingly hand inletted into the scales. Presentation pieces were engraved, usually on the blade, with dates, initials, names, and even brief inscriptions.

Fancy shaped Victorian pearl handled fruit knife.

Georgian and most Victorian fruit knives are single-bladed. Some later ones have a second blade, a slim, curved, unsharpened seed or nut pick. Also, some later knife and fork pairs were made as a single unit, the two parts held together by small lugs which fit into slots.

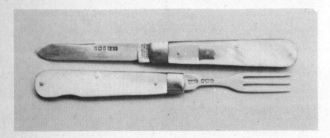

Victorian take-apart fruit knife and fork.

Many English silversmiths made fruit knives. Two whose work is outstanding were George Unite [G.U.] of Birmingham and John Yeomans Cowlishaw [J.Y.C.] of Sheffield. One of the most prolific, whose work is often encountered in the United States, was Thomas Marples [T.M.] of Sheffield.

A number of factors affect the value of Victorian fruit knives. These include the color of the pearl (the more colorful the better), the quality and extent of the engraving or pinwork, the age (a good silver hallmark book is essential for this), the shape and size, the number of blades, and the maker. Most important, a knife that is well proportioned and pleasing to the eye is worth more than a heavy ostentatious piece.

Good quality Victorian examples in excellent condition range in value from **$70** to **$90.** Top quality single knives are worth **$100** to **$150.** Take-apart silver knife and fork sets are worth **$175** and up in excellent condition.

Most 20th century English fruit knives were mass-produced. Decoration was pressed or etched, rather than being cut by hand. Their design and quality are inferior to older ones. This decline heralded the end of the age of fruit knives. Later pieces are worth **$40** to **$60.**

English fruit knife dated 1924.

790—CARVED PEARL HANDLE FRUIT KNIFE; 2¼in. Haft; Sterling Silver Blade . . . . 9/6 each, post free.

795—CARVED PEARL HANDLE FRUIT KNIFE; 3¼in. Haft; Sterling Silver Blade . . . . . . 17/6 each, post free.

Two Sheffield fruit knives from the 1920s.

American Fruit Knives

Except for the brief period 1814–1830, American had no standardized hallmark system like England's. American

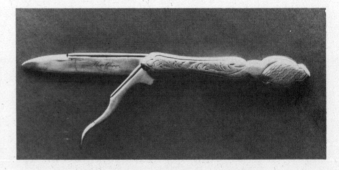

American fruit knife marked COIN.

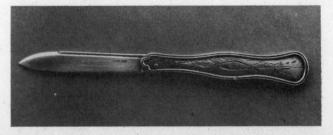

American fruit knife marked STERLING.

silversmiths used all sorts of marks, such as initials, full names, pictorial symbols, simulated hallmarks, fineness designations such as COIN (90% silver) or STERLING (92.5%), or even no mark at all.

There are perhaps 20,000 American silver marks listed in various reference works. Luckily, most American silver fruit knives were made by two firms, Coles and Gorham.

Albert Coles of New York was active from about 1836 to 1880. He produced a large volume of work, much of it for other makers. His mark is in three parts: an eagle, his initials [A.C.] and a man's profile.

Coles's fruit knives are well above average in quality. They feature heavy ornate silver handles. Most have a nut pick. His backsprings are nicely chased in a ladder design.

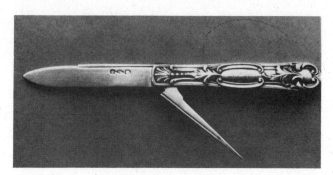

Coles fruit knife.

John Gorham of Providence, Rhode Island, founded one of America's largest silver companies in 1831. It is still very active, though it has not made folding fruit knives in many decades. Gorham's early mark was also in three parts: a letter [G], an anchor, and a lion passant facing left. In 1868, when American substituted the sterling for the coin standard, Gorham turned the lion around to face right. This change can help to date his knives.

Gorham's best fruit knives are perhaps even finer than Coles's. Examples in top condition by either firm are worth **$80** to **$100.** American pieces marked simply COIN or STERLING are less desirable, being worth **$50** to **$70.**

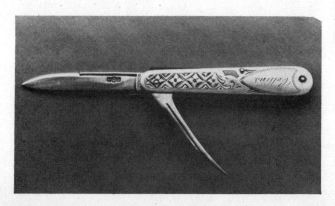

Gorham fruit knife.

Plated Fruit Knives

Silver plated fruit knives are generally unmarked. They range from unattractive to beautiful. If you are not sure whether a knife is silver or plated, *gently* flex the blade a *little* bit. If it feels soft and stays bent, it is silver. (Carefully straighten it back out.) If it feels springy, it is plated. Do not file a knife to do an acid test, or you will destroy much of its value. Plated fruit knives are worth **$30** to **$50** in excellent condition.

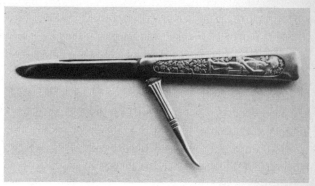

Embossed plated fruit knife with figure of a girl.

The Empire Knife Company of Connecticut made an odd silver plated fruit knife. Its blade and seed pick project from opposite ends of a common tang. The tang is secured in the end of a springy steel handle and the blade unit can be pivoted so that one end or the other is exposed. This item is worth about **$35,** as are most other base metal novelty fruit knives.

Empire plated flop—over fruit knife.

Fruit knives can often be found at antique shops and shows, though some antiques dealers ask excessive prices. English knife dealers bring many fine early examples into this country. A large collection can include 300 or more pieces, all different.

Barlow Knives

A MODERN barlow knife is a regular jack (or rarely a sleeveboard jack) that has extra long bolsters and no cap bolsters. Many pre-1840s barlows were curved regular jacks, as were a handful of more recent ones.

The barlow is a cheap sturdy pattern intended for older boys. The long bolsters are usually iron, and they are most often stamped with a trademark.

Traditional barlow handle scales are smooth flat bone; some are left natural, but most are dyed brown or red. Recent barlows have plastic handles. Older deluxe barlows had jigged bone, stag, or even pearl handles. Some even have fancy stamped bolsters.

There are two basic classes of barlow. One class is standard barlows, which are around 3⅜ inches long closed. The other class is daddy or grand-daddy barlows, usually 5 inches long. The unusual ''baby barlow'' is a low quality knife under 3 inches long.

Both standard and daddy barlows can have clip or spear master blades. Both can be either single-bladed, or else have a pen second blade.

Standard barlows can also have a sheepfoot, a spey, or a ''razor'' master blade. Daddy barlows can have a fish scaler back on the master blade, or have a lock (on single-blades). A few are easy-openers.

The Barlows

The Barlows were a family of cutlers in Sheffield prominent in the 17th and 18th centuries. The first well-known Barlow there was Edward Barlowe, who was elected master of the Cutlers' Guild in 1653.

According to John Goins, the original Barlow of barlow knife fame was Obadiah Barlow, who started in business in 1667. His grandson, John, succeeded him in 1710 and John Junior, of Campo Lane, suceeded John in 1745. In their time, this family seems to have had exclusive use of the word BARLOW *by itself* as a trademark on pocketknives. John Junior, the last of this line of Barlows, died in 1798.

Another branch of the family was represented by Samuel Barlow of Neepsend, near Sheffield. His trademark in 1787 was a sideways 'Z,' a small circle, and a picture of a scimitar. After 1798, he added the word BARLOW to his mark. He worked until the 1830s.

Base prices for BARLOW KNIVES with clip or spear master blade; pen blade; smooth bone, horn, patterned celluloid or wood handles. Excellent unsharpened condition.

VALUE RANGE	VERY HIGH	HIGH	MED.	LOW
SIZE				
DADDY BARLOW:	$165.	110.	65.	20.
STANDARD BARLOW:	75.	50.	30.	6.
BABY BARLOW:	60.	25.	15.	6.

CONSTRUCTION
Curved regular jack shape: **add 50%**
Easy-open notch: **add 10%**
Spey, sheepfoot,or razor master blade: **add 30%**
One blade: **subtract 20%**
Locking blade: **add 65%**
Integral iron bolster–liners: **add 100%**
Fancy stamped bolsters: **add 25%**

HANDLE MATERIAL
Pearl or ivory: **add 100%**
Genuine stag: **add 50%**
Bone stag: **add 25%**
Plain celluloid or composition: **subtract 25%**
All metal: **subtract 60%**
Modern plastic: **subtract 75%**

CONDITION
Mint: **add 60%**   Worn: **subtract 50%**
Broken: **subtract 90%**

Geo. Wostenholm, ENGLAND, 3⅜", brown bone: 1 blade, **$24**; 2 blades, **$30**.

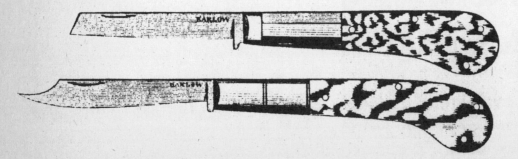

BARLOW (c1816), 3" curved regular barlows, fancy integral bolster-liners, 1 blade, spotted horn, **$180.**

Standard Barlows

Southern Pattern

H. Boker, fancy bolsters, 3⅜", bone stag, **$47.**

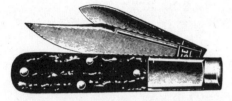

Case Tested XX, fancy bolsters, 3¾",
genuine stag, **$140.**

S.E. Oates, 1 blade, 3⅜", bone,
$24.

Hibbard Spencer Bartlett, razor blade, 3½",
bone, **$39.**

A. Kastor XLNT, 1 blade, 3⅜",
black fiber, **$18.**

Five-Inch Daddy Barlows

Ulster Knife Co. (for W.
Bingham), pearl, **$220.**

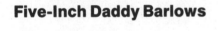

Robeson, 1 blade, bone, **$52.**

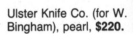

Western States, 1 blade, bone, **$88.**

J. Russells, 1 blade: bone, **$132;** easy-open,
one locking blade, genuine stag, **$360.**

Remingtons, bone; 2 blades, **$165;** 1 locking blade, **$218.**

Boy's Knives

A BOY'S KNIFE is a small (3½-inch or under) regular jack or curved regular jack, ordinarily with a single spear blade. Some have a pen blade as well.

Up into the 1930s, most boy's knives sold for 10 cents or less, so their construction is the cheapest possible. Some even say DIME KNIFE on the handle.

Metal Handles

Integral metal handles make a cheap but sturdy boy's knife. The earliest mass-produced type was the flat "coined" brass handles made in New England and New York in the 1850s and 1860s. These have an elaborate design that includes the manufacturer's name.

In 1862, Samuel Mason of Northfield Knife Company patented the use of cheap "malleable cast iron with a rough or corrugated exterior, in imitation of buckhorn," for jack knife handles. Many iron-handled boy's knives have trademarks (such as Northfield's "UN-X-LD" or Russell's "Boy of America") incorporated into the casting.

Frary Cutlery Company introduced cast tin alloy ("pewter") handled boy's knives around 1880. One style with a blunt-end blade, called the "Our Boy," was for *little* boys. Others were souvenirs of new hit operettas by Gilbert and Sullivan. Cut-rate German cutlery firms copied Frary's methods and continued to use them after forcing him out of business in 1884.

Both the iron and the pewter cast-handled types were eclipsed in the early 20th century by boy's knives with even cheaper pressed mild steel handles. Cheaper yet were knives with one-piece folded sheet steel handles, such as the Allen, patented in 1917, and then Eagle of 1918. Joining these on the market in about 1926 was the "wire jack" invented by George Schrade.

In 1936, Imperial introduced its sheet metal shell-handled construction for inexpensive knives. This and a solid plastic handle made by Colonial are the standard low-priced boy's knives of today.

Besides metal and plastic, boy's knives were handled in wood, horn, and low grade smooth bone. Some came with a shackle and chain for attachment to a belt or to a suspender button.

Most boy's knives are still inexpensive on the collector's market. A variety of these little knives, together with old photos, advertising, and boy's toys, would make a very interesting display.

Base prices for BOY'S KNIVES with: cast or stamped iron or steel handles, or with smooth bone, horn, or wood handle scales; one or two blades. Excellent unsharpened condition.

Very High: **$32.**   Medium: **$12.**
High: **$20.**   Low: **$5.**

"Curved regular" handle: **add 15%**
Easy open notch: **add 10%**
Original shackle and chain: **add 20%**

Bone stag or better: use *Jack Knives Price Chart*
Trademark or adv't in iron handle: **add 50%**
"Coined" brass with trademark: **add 400%**
Tin alloy ("pewter") with design or trademark: **add 100%**
Flat sheet metal: **subtract 20%**
Sheet metal shell: **subtract 35%**
Fiber or plastic: **subtract 50%**
Pictorial advertising: **add 100%**
Mint condition: **add 50%**
Worn: **subtract 60%** Broken: **subtract 90%**

Coined brass handles (H), broken (Civil War relics), **$16 each.**

H. Boker, stamped steel, trademark, **$18.**

J. Russell, 3″ & 3⅜″, wood, **$32.**

Winchester, chain, 3½". wood, **$38.**

Western Cut. Co. (German), curved regular, 3½", stamped steel, trademark, **$9.**

Geo. Wostenholm, 3", stamped steel, trademark, **$30.**

Unmarked (German), chain, 2⅞", stamped steel, adv't, **$9.**

Walter Bros. (German), curved regular, chain, 3¼", adv't, **$10.**

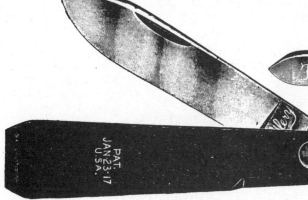

Ulery (Allen patent), sheet steel, **$10.**

H. Boker, 3½", sheet nickel silver, **$10.**

Eagle patent, easy open, 3", sheet steel **$18.**

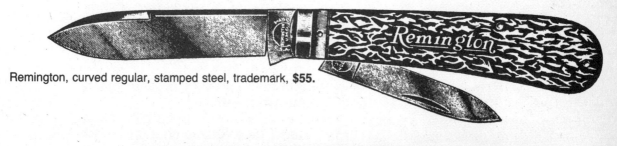

Remington, curved regular, stamped steel, trademark, **$55.**

Geo. Tritch Hdwe. Co. (by Ulster Knife Co.), wood, **$12.**

J. Russell, curved regular, cast iron, trademark, **$55.**

Double-End Jack Knives

ORDINARILY, jack knives have all their blades in one end, while knives with blades in both ends are either pen knives or multi-blades. However, certain patterns of folders with blades in both ends are too large and robust to be called pen knives, while they are too simple, with only two blades, to be called multi-blades. These are the double-end jack knives.

One unusual type is the double-end "melon tester." This long thin knife with a slim spear blade and a pen blade is covered under *Special Purpose Jack Knives.* So is the smaller double-end "florist's knife."

Farmer's Jacks

An even more unusual type of double-end jack is the Wharncliffe shaped "farmer's jack." Its two blades are a pruning blade in the wide end and a spey or budding blade in the narrow end.

Schrade Cut. Co., farmer's, 4⅛", bone stag, **$70.**

H. Boker, farmer's, 3¾", bone stag, **$40.**

Base prices for DOUBLE-END JACK KNIVES of the indicated shapes; over 3½ up to 4⅛ inches long; two large blades; full bolsters; bone stag handles. Excellent unsharpened condition.

NOTE: for MELON TESTERS see *Special Purpose Jack Knives;* for MUSKRATS and DOUBLE-END TRAPPERS see *Trappers.*

VALUE RANGE	VERY HIGH	HIGH	MED.	LOW
SHAPE				
SUNFISH: see chart on next page.				
FARMER'S JACK:	$120.	70.	40.	9.
TEXAS JACK:	140.	85.	40.	10.
DOUBLE-END PREMIUM:	100.	55.	30.	8.
EQUAL-END BULL-HEAD:	130.	60.	30.	10.
JUMBO or BALLOON:	200.	125.	85.	20.
EUREKA or SURVEYOR:	165.	110.	65.	18.
CANOE:	200.	140.	85.	22.

Pen blade: **subtract 20%**
No bolsters: **subtract 10%**
Over 4⅜ inches: **add 50%**
3½ inches or less: **subtract 25%**
  except with pen second blade: see *Pen Knives*

HANDLE MATERIAL
Pearl: **add 60%**
Genuine stag: **add 25%**
Smooth bone, horn, or wood: **subtract 20%**
Fancy celluloid: **add 20%**
  (waterfall, Christmas tree, candy stripe, goldstone)
Other patterned celluloid: **subtract 20%**
Solid metal or solid color celluloid: **subtract 30%**
Sheet metal shell or modern plastic: **subtract 60%**
"OFFICE KNIFE" on handle of equal–end: see *Office Knives* chapter in *Pen Knives* section.
Mint condition: **add 50%**
Worn: **subtract 50%**
Broken: **subtract 85%**

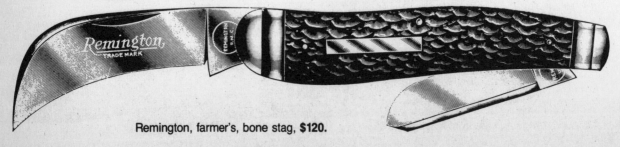

Remington, farmer's, bone stag, **$120.**

Sunfish

Odd as they may seem, the farmer's jack and the melon tester look ordinary compared to the "sunfish" (also called "elephant's toe-nail," "Old English rope knife," and "vest-pocket axe"). Sunfish are massive equal-ends (or rarely swell-centers) at least 3¾ inches long, and usually longer. They are much wider than the "general service knives" described below.

The master blade of a sunfish is a spearpoint nearly the size of a tea plate. The second blade is a "pen" blade that is bigger than many spear blades.

I have seen no evidence that the sunfish is either English or a rope knife. It seems to be a mid- to late 19th century American pattern, perhaps with a hint of Scandinavian influence. Sunfish were most popular in the northern Midwest. They were favored by framing carpenters and by men who strung trolley and telegraph lines. Although a few sunfish are still made, most that turn up pre-date the First World War.

Most sunfish I have seen had bone stag handles—pearl, genuine stag, tortoise shell, wood, and celluloid are rare. Though I have not seen them, I suspect that horn, ivory, and smooth bone handle scales were used on sunfish in the old days. Case's recent elephant toenails have laminated wood handles.

Sunfish are very popular among collectors. Any early one in good condition commands a high price. Pearl handled examples, such as Case. Bros. (made also on contract for Marble's), are particularly valuable.

Base prices for SUNFISH up to 4½ inches long, with: bone stag, smooth bone, or horn handle scales. Excellent unsharpened condition.

Very High: **$250.**   Medium: **$130.**
High: **$175.**   Low: **$45.**

Length over 4½ inches: **add 50%**

HANDLE MATERIAL
Pearl: **add 100%**
Tortoise, ivory, or genuine stag: **add 50%**
Wood or patterned celluloid: **subtract 20%**
Plain celluloid: **subtract 30%**
Laminated wood or plastic: **subtract 80%**

Mint condition: **add 60%**
Worn: **subtract 50%**
Broken: **subtract 85%**

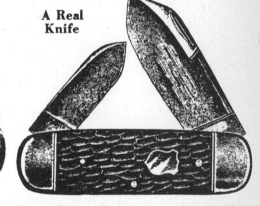

A Real Knife

Hibbard Spencer Bartlett, 4¼", bone stag, **$130.**

Marble's, 3⅞", pearl, **$500.**

Napanoch, bone stag, **$250.**

OLD ENGLISH ROPE KNIFE USED ON SAILING VESSELS
No. 6250
Length closed 4⅜"

Case Tested XX, bone stag, **$250.**

Stock Knife Type Double-End Jacks

With the exception of the sunfish, the farmers' jack, and the double-end melon tester, all double-end jack knives are built on either cattle knife or premium stock knife handle frames (see *Multi-Blades*). In the early years of this century, the names "cattle knife" and "stock knife" were sometimes used for two-bladed knives. Since the 1920s, however, the two names have been used only for knives with three or more blades. Larger two-bladed versions are considered jack knives, no matter if they are single-ended or double-ended. Smaller two-blade double-ended versions (3½ inches long or less) with a pen second blade are pen knives.

The single-ended jack that is based on the premium stock knife is called the "premium jack." The premium jack has several double-ended counterparts. The most impressive of these is the TEXAS JACK or MOOSE.

Texas jacks are big, usually at least 3⅞ inches long. I believe that their size accounts for their "Texas" name, while the large blade out each end must have reminded someone of a bull moose's giant antlers.

The master blade of a Texas Jack is always a wide clip. The second blade is a spear or a long wide spey.

Slender double-end premium jacks with either a slender clip and a spey, or else two clip blades, are considered DOUBLE-END TRAPPERS (see Trappers).

DOUBLE–END PREMIUM JACKS are serpentine (or rarely sleeveboard) knives with a clip blade in one end and a small spey or a pen in the other. Small versions with a pen blade are pen knives.

Schrade Cut. Co., Texas jack, 3½", bone stag, **$64.**

Case Tested XX Texas jacks: genuine stag, 4¼", **$175;** 3⅞", bone stag, **$140.**

Winchester D-E premium jacks, bone stag: 4", **$100;** 3¼", **$75.**

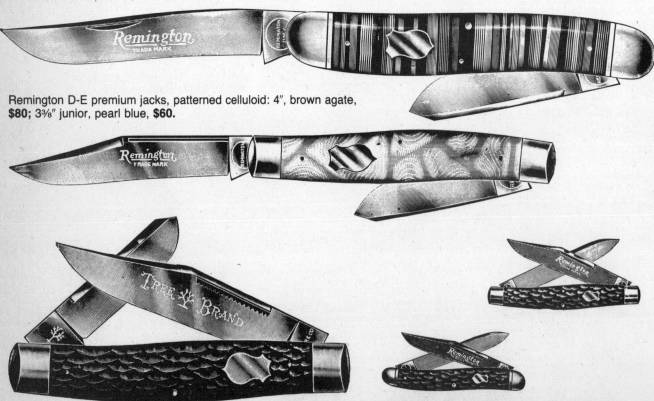

Remington D-E premium jacks, patterned celluloid: 4", brown agate, **$80;** 3⅜" junior, pearl blue, **$60.**

H. Boker, D-E premium jack, bone stag, **$30.**

Remington Texas jacks, bone stag, 3⅞" and 4¼", **$140 each.**

Cattle Knife Type Double-End Jacks

The BULL-HEAD or equal-end double-end jack knife is a two-blade version of the standard cattle knife. These knives have spear or clip master blades. The second blade may be a spey, a sheepfoot, a clip, a punch, or a pen. In 1919, Remington used the term GENERAL SERVICE KNIVES for their 3⅝-inch double-end equal-end jack knives that had pen second blades.

The rarest double-end jack knives are the ones built on fancy cattle knife handle dies. These are the large sleeve-board or JUMBO; the swell-center or BALLOON; the swell-center serpentine or EUREKA; the CANOE; and the SURVEYOR; or swell-center canoe. Most of these were last made in the 1930s.

Winchester balloons, bone stag: 3½", **$150**; 3⅞". **$200**.

Remington, bull-head (oval), 4½", bone stag, **$195**.

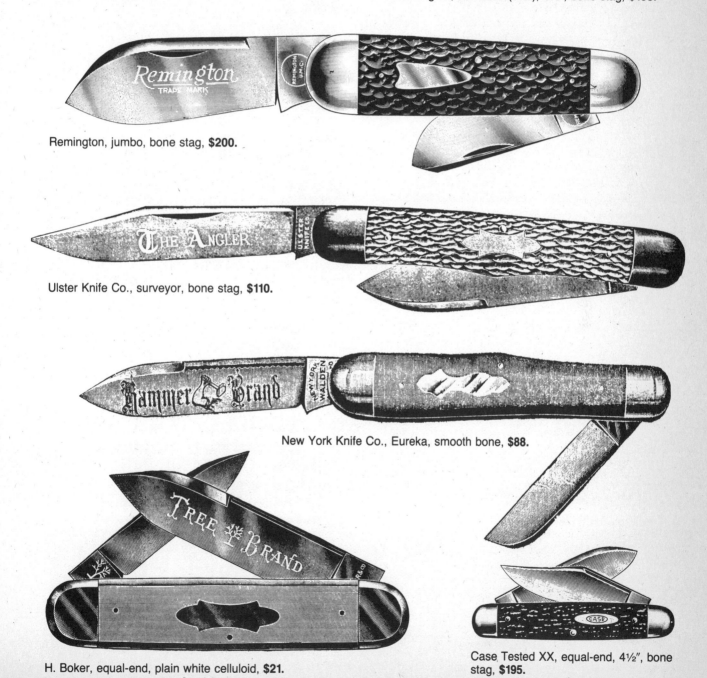

Remington, jumbo, bone stag, **$200**.

Ulster Knife Co., surveyor, bone stag, **$110**.

New York Knife Co., Eureka, smooth bone, **$88**.

H. Boker, equal-end, plain white celluloid, **$21**.

Case Tested XX, equal-end, 4½", bone stag, **$195**.

Ticklers and Fish Knives

THE "TICKLER" is the American clasp knife pattern that looks most like the southern European clasp knife or *navaja*. It is a slender serpentine jack knife with a pointed "head" or non-blade end. Most are 5 inches long closed, or even longer.

Ticklers have several picturesque names. Many collectors, especially Case collectors, call them "Texas toothpicks." Others call them "powder-horns."

In the bad old days in the South, the pattern was called the "nigger chaser" or simply the "chaser." As a large but inexpensive knife, it was favored by young black "sporting" gentlemen for Saturday night wear.

In the same vein, a pearl celluloid handled tickler was described in 1933 as "a beautiful Saturday Evening special, society, or switch knife" by the Chicago hardware wholesaler, Hibbard Spencer Bartlett & Co. Their miniature charm-sized version was called the "pickaninny knife."

The master blade of a tickler is always a clip point, either flat or saber ground. Many ticklers are single bladed. Others have two blades, clip and pen.

A special type of tickler, called a "fish knife," has either a fish-scaler blade back, or else a second blade that combines a fish-scaler and a hook disgorger. For convenience, a few other specialized fishing patterns are included here with these fish knives.

The American-made tickler seems to have been introduced in the 1890s. The high cutlery duties imposed by the Tariff Acts of 1890 and 1897 raised the prices of foreign knives, including clasp knives, and made it possible for American firms to compete with imports. The fish knife version of the tickler seems to date from the 1920s.

Among collectors, ticklers are not nearly as popular as other big American clasp knives. Fish knives are even less popular at present.

Base prices for TICKLERS over 4½ inches long with: bolsters and cap bolsters; bone stag or horn handle scales; flat ground master blade plus pen. Excellent unsharpened condition.

Very High: **$150.**   Medium: **$30.**
High: **$50.**   Low: **$10.**

Saber ground master blade: **add 10%**
Single-blade: **subtract 10%**
Fish scaler back or blade: **subtract 20%**

Fancy stamped bolsters: **add 20%**
Barehead or shadow: **subtract 20%**
Remington with bullet shield (R-1613): **add 500%**

Back lock: **add 50%**
Front "liner lock": **add 20%**

3 to 4½ inches: **subtract 30%**
Under 3 inches: **subtract 40%**

HANDLE MATERIAL
Fancy celluloid: **add 20%**
   (Christmas tree, water-fall, candy stripe, goldstone)
Other patterned or colorful celluloid: **subtract 10%**
Solid color celluloid or composition: **subtract 20%**
Modern plastic: **subtract 50%**
Pressed hollow sheet metal: **subtract 65%**

Mint condition: **add 50%**
Worn: **subtract 50%**
Broken: **subtract 90%**

Winchester, 1 blade, 4¼", bone stag, $95.

Makes a crackerjack carpenter's, mechanic's, teamster's, fisherman's, sportsman's, hunter's or trapper's knife. Ideally suited for sticking, skinning and cleaning game or fish. Substantial enough for heavy work. Has a large comfortable handle affording a firm grip. A real knife for the in or out doors man. Also makes a beautiful Saturday Evening special society or switch knife.

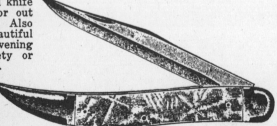

Hibbard, one long substantial clip point blade, Full Mirror Polished on both sides. Super Pearl Indestructible handle, brass lined, fancy nickel silver cap and bolster. Length when closed 5 in., w't per doz. 2 lbs.

C9711Y4 .... each $0.50

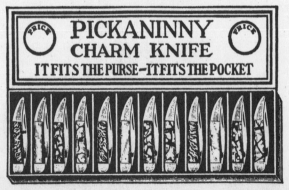

Hibbard Spencer Bartletts, patterned celluloid: saber blade, fancy bolsters, 5", $32; 2½" charm, $15.

Robeson, 5″, 1 blade, candy stripe celluloid, **$32**.

Case, 5″, 1 blade, bone stag: Tested XX, **$135**; XX, **$45**.

Case Tested XX, fishing, 5½″, plain celluloid, **$96**.

Western, fishing, 4 ⅜″, plain celluloid, **$14**.

Western States, "Dox Fish Gaff," 5″, aluminum, **$40**.

Fly Fisherman
Length closed 3⅞″

Fly Fisherman — Nickel silver handle with cutting blade and scissors on one side and pick and file on other side. Screwdriver on one end and bail on other end.

Case Fly Fisherman: Tested XX, **$120**. XX, **$60**.

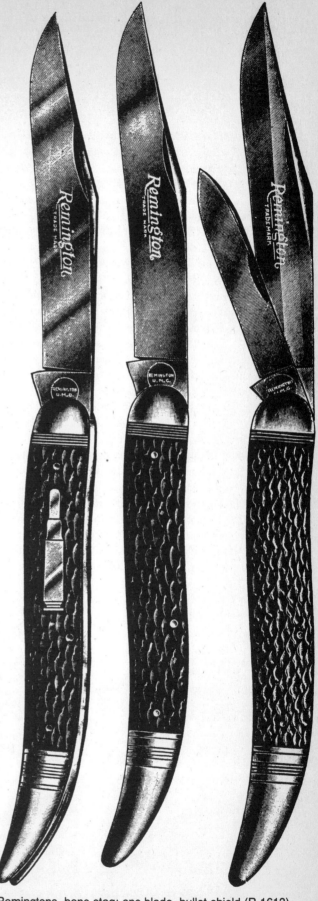

Remingtons, bone stag: one blade, bullet shield (R-1613), **$810**; one blade, **$135**; saber and pen blades, **$165**.

Trappers, Muskrats and Large Trappers

A "TRAPPER" is a jack knife with two specific full length blades. The master blade is a clip point with a very long clip. The second blade is a long spey.

The STANDARD TRAPPER (or HEAVY TRAPPER) is around 4 to 4¼ inches long closed. It is built on the swell-center regular jack handle die.

LIGHT TRAPPERS are built on 3¾-inch or larger slim serpentine handle dies. The light trapper was most likely introduced before the First World War, the standard trapper not until the mid-1920s.

MINI-TRAPPERS are compact trapper style knives, both standard and light-weight, around 3¼ to 3½ inches long closed. They were introduced in the 1970s.

PREMIUM TRAPPERS are built on serpentine premium stock handles, both round-end and square-end. They range from 3⅝ up to 4⅜ inches long.

DOUBLE-END TRAPPERS are similar to premium trappers, only with one blade in each end. A variant of the double-end trapper is the MUSKRAT. It has two identical "muskrat clip" blades, one in each end.

There is intense interest in collecting standard trappers, large trappers, and muskrats. The Trapper Knife Collectors Club has over 300 members. Due to high demand, Case Tested XX *standard* trappers command around **$800-1,000.** They are often counterfeited. For detailed information on Case trappers, see the *Case Pocket Price Guide* described in the Case chapter. Remington bullet-shield equal-end double-end trappers also bring around **$1,000.**

Base prices for TRAPPERS of the indicated style; over 3⅝ inches long; with bone stag handles. Excellent unsharpened condition.

VALUE RANGE	VERY HIGH	HIGH	MED.	LOW
SHAPE				
STANDARD				
TRAPPER:	$175.	100.	45.	15.
Case Tested XX:	$800-1,000. (see text)			
LIGHT TRAPPER:	160.	80.	40.	12.
PREMIUM TRAPPER:	115.	65.	35.	8.
DOUBLE-END				
TRAPPER:	125.	70.	40.	10.
Remington equal-end with bullet shield: **$1,000.**				
MUSKRAT:	160.	85.	45.	12.
(two clip blades)				
LARGE TRAPPER: *see separate chart.*				
"Mini" size (under 3⅝"): **subtract 20%**				

HANDLE MATERIAL

Genuine stag: **add 25%**

Pearl*: **add 50%**

Patterned celluloid*: **add 10%**

Plain celluloid: **subtract 20%**

Modern plastic or laminated wood: **subtract 50%**

Mint condition: **add 50%**

Worn: **subtract 50%**

Broken: **subtract 90%**

*Most Case Tested XXs with these are counterfeits.

R4353

OUTDOORMAN'S KNIFE. Convenient to carry in pocket—has round Nickel Silver Bolsters and full sunk joints. Correct shaped blades for sticking and skinning. Stag Handle, Brass Lined.
Length, closed, 4¼ inches.
Muskrat: Remington, bone stag, **$160.**

R-4593

MUSKRAT KNIFE. Designed from suggestions of Muskrat Trappers. The long, keen, slender lance allows the perfect removal of pelts without perforation, increasing their value. Ideal for skinning all small fur bearing animals. Both blades alike, Mirror Finished. Stag Handle; Brass Lining; Nickel Silver Bolsters.
Length, closed, 3⅞ inches.
Double-End: Remington Bullet, bone stag, **$1,000.**

Standard: Case Tested XX, 4⅛", genuine stag, **$1,000.**

Light: Schrade Cut. Co., 3⅞", bone stag, **$80.**

Premium: Western States "Mountain Man," 4⅜", genuine stag, **$81.**

Double-End: Western States, 3⅞" bone stag, **$70.**

Large Trappers

The LARGE TRAPPER, like the standard trapper, is built on the swell-center regular jack handle die. At 4½ inches, is not much longer than the standard trapper, but it is nearly twice as wide and heavy.

One of the first and best known large trappers was the 6 ½-ounce Remington R-1123 "Old Reliable" with bullet shield, introduced in September, 1922. Similar knives were also introduced by Utica and by Union. In 1928 Western States introduced the 5230, a large trapper with self-guard bolsters and oversized caps.

Remington later introduced a three-quarters scale "large" trapper. This R-1173 "Baby Bullet" is 3 ½ inches long but has the same proportions as the R-1123. The Baby Bullet is much rarer than the larger one.

Prices for LARGE TRAPPERS in excellent
  condition.
Only a few firms made large trappers.
Remington: R-1123 (bone stag): **$400**.
  R-1123 (Rogers bone stag): **$750**.
  R-1128 (cocobolo): **$800**.
  R-1173 (baby, bone stag): **$1,000**.
  Re-issues, (plastic, by Camillus): stainless
  $40.
Utica "Nessmuk" pattern with buffalo head
  shield:bone stag, **$200**; celluloid, **$160**;
  (Utica made H.S.B., Maher & Grosh, Royal
  Brand).
Western States: genuine stag, **$265**; celluloid,
  $200.
Case Tested XX 62100 bone stag: **$400**.
Union/Ka-Bar: genuine stag, **$500**; bone stag,
  $400.
Bowen: **$50**; commemorative for L.L. Bean:
  $85.
Mint condition: **add 50%**
Worn: **subtract: 50%**
Broken: **subtract 90%**

Western States
No. 5230

R 1173

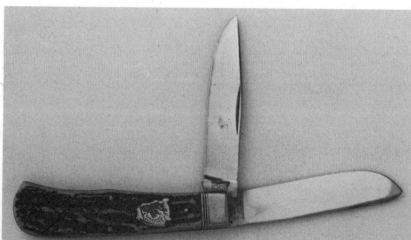

Hibbard Spencer Bartlett & Co., made by Utica. Courtesy of Robert Abel.

R 1123

"OLD RELIABLE." Very popular with Hunters and Trappers throughout the world. One strong heavy gauged blade for sticking and general use, another strong blade for skinning, both blue glazed. Stag Handle, Brass Lined, Nickel Silver bolster, flush square joints, hole in butt end for thong.

Length, closed, 4½ inches.

Folding Hunters and American Clasp Knives

"Folding hunter" is a broad term that includes large swell-center jack knives; various medium to large folding lock knives; and most modern American-style clasp knives.

These types of knives are included in this chapter. The only exceptions are the Marble's Safety Hunting Knives, which are included with the other Marble's knives in the *American Hunting Knives* chapter of the *Fixed Blade Knives* section.

Some collectors use the term "folding hunter" to describe just about all types of large jack knives. They include under this label folding dirks and folding bowie knives, English jacks, daddy barlows, ticklers, and large trappers. These types of knives are all covered in other chapters of this book.

Swell-Center Hunting Knives

Large 5 to 5½ inch swell-center jack knives are called "swell-center hunting knives." These big "Coke bottles" were the standard American folding hunting knives of the late 19th and early 20th centuries.

In the 19th century, swell-center hunting knives were most often handled in ebony, but also in cocobolo, smooth white bone, horn, or stag. Later ones were offered with bone stag, celluloid, or laminated wood. Some 20th century ones have enlarged front bolsters.

Swell-center hunting knives are most often single-bladed, the blade being a heavy saber-ground clip. Some were made with a locking blade, usually a center lock. A few even had a folding guard.

On two-bladed swell-center hunting knives, both blades are normally full length, usually a saber clip and a heavy spear. Some have a saw as a second blade.

Swell-center hunting knives remained popular through the 1940s, though steadily losing ground to fixed blade hunting knives and other large folders. Case had discontinued all but one of their many versions by 1940, and they dropped that one, the C61050 SAB, in 1976. Remington never even made one.

Base prices for SWELL-CENTER HUNTING KNIVES with: bone stag handles; one non-locking blade; bolsters and caps. Excellent unsharpened condition.

Very High: **$400**   Medium: **$135**
High: **$185.**   Low: **$30.**

Two knife blades: **add 10%**
Knife blade and saw blade: **subtract 20%**
Barehead (no cap bolsters): **subtract 15%**
Back lock: **add 65%**   Liner lock: **add 35%**
Folding guard: **add 40%**
   (Marble's: see *American Hunting Knives*)

HANDLE MATERIAL
Pearl or ivory: **add 100%**
Genuine stag or fancy celluloid: **add 50%**
   (water-fall, Christmas tree, candy stripe, goldstone)
Patterned or colorful celluloid: **subtract 10%**
Horn or smooth bone: **subtract 15%**
Wood, plain celluloid, or rubber: **subtract 25%**
Plastic or laminated wood: **subtract 40%**

Mint condition: **add 60%** Worn: **subtract 65%**
Broken: **subtract 90%**

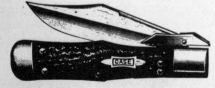
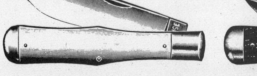

Case Tested XXs; back lock folding guard, 5½", bone stag, **$925**; 5⅛, plain celluloid, **$300**; 5⅜", bone stag, **$400.**

Miller Bros., back lock, 5⅜", bone stag, **$305.**

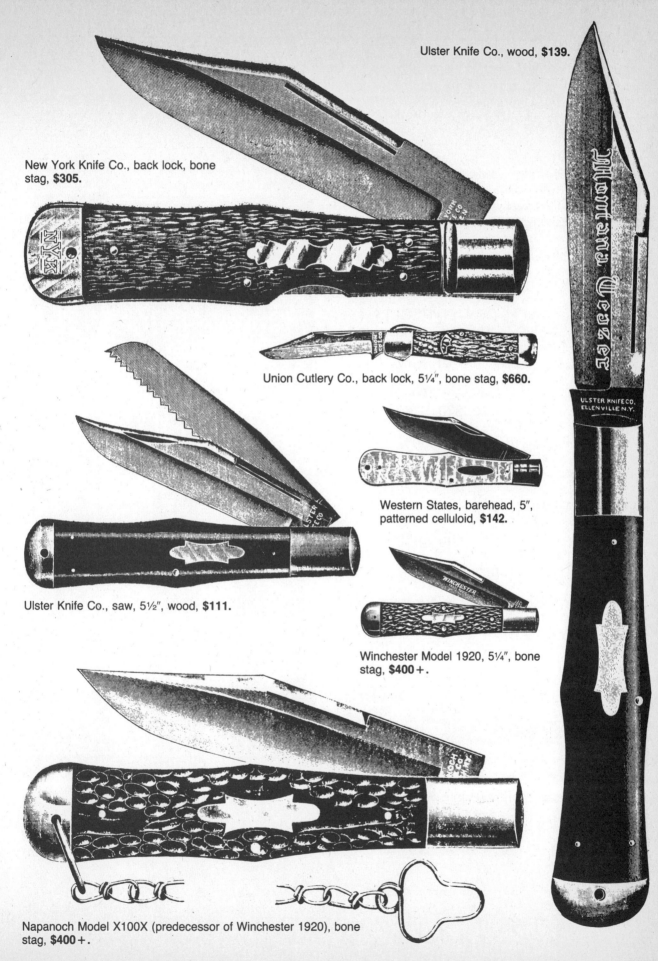

Ulster Knife Co., wood, **$139.**

New York Knife Co., back lock, bone stag, **$305.**

Union Cutlery Co., back lock, 5¼″, bone stag, **$660.**

Western States, barehead, 5″, patterned celluloid, **$142.**

Ulster Knife Co., saw, 5½″, wood, **$111.**

Winchester Model 1920, 5¼″, bone stag, **$400+.**

Napanoch Model X100X (predecessor of Winchester 1920), bone stag, **$400+.**

Swell-Center Regular Hunting and Lock Knives

Since the mid-19th century, the swell-center regular jack handle die has been used for lockback folding hunters. These attractive knives usually have a single clip blade. The only old names I have seen for these knives are "lock knife" and "hunting knife," which both referred to other patterns as well.

In the 1920s and 1930s, Remington and Utica made single-bladed folding hunters on their swell-center regular large trapper handles. More recently, versions of this single-blade style were introduced by Western, and by other firms and individual knifemakers, particularly Jess Horn. Remington has even issued a plastic-handled copy of their original, made for them by Camillus. For more on large trappers, see *Trappers*.

Base prices for SWELL-CENTER REGULAR HUNTING and LOCK KNIVES, standard (narrow) width, with: bone stag handles; one *locking* blade. Excellent unsharpened condition.
Very High: **$250**   Medium: **$70**
High: **$100**   Low: **$20**

Heavy trapper size (wide): **add 150%**
Folding guard: **add 10%**
No lock: use *Jack Knives Price Chart*

HANDLE MATERIAL
Genuine stag: **add 10%**
Cow horn or smooth bone: **subtract 10%**
Wood: **subtract 25%**
Celluloid or plastic: **subtract 40%**

Mint condition: **add 50%** Worn: **subtract 50%**
Broken: **subtract 90%**

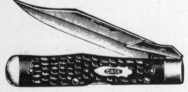

No. 6111½ L
Length closed 4⁷⁄₁₆"

Above—Case Tested XX, narrow, folding guard, bone stag, **$275.**

Right—Remington, wide, genuine stag, **$688.**

Far right—Ulster Knife Co.: narrow, bone stag, **$100;** wide, wood, **$188.**

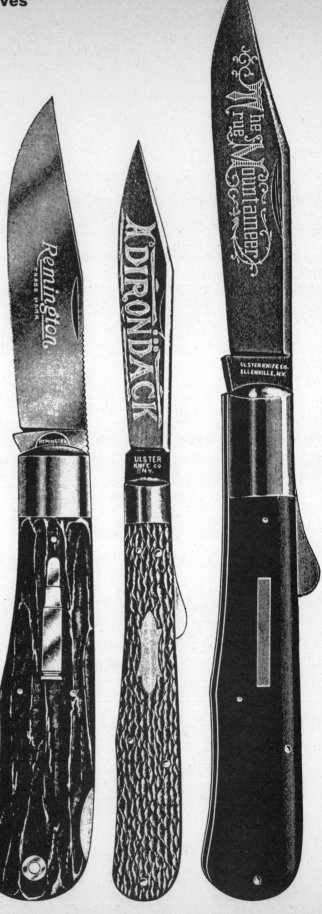

Clasp-Type Folding Hunters

The first clasp knives were made from the ends of cow or goat or sheep horns that were slotted to contain a blade. The blade was shaped to fit the natural curve of the horn so that the tip of the horn covered the point of the blade. Early styles of clasp knives that were used in the United States are shown in *Foreign Exotic, Primitive, and Historical Folding Knives*.

Since the turn of the century, American cutlery firms have made several styles of folding hunter inspired by traditional clasp knives. The plainest and rarest of these clasp-type folding hunters has a simple curve like a curved regular jack. I have heard these knives called "bananas," but I think they deserve a more dignified name.

In the 1920s, Case pioneered swell-center clasp-type folding hunters with the swell on top. These are still a mainstay of the Case line, both the standard width 6265 and the extra-wide single-bladed P172L (Buffalo). Most other firms make similar styles as well, including some that are extra-slim.

Long slender American clasp knives with pointed heads are called "ticklers." A tickler with a fish scaler added is called a "fish knife." Ticklers and fish knives are not classed as folding hunters. They have their own chapter.

Base prices for CLASP-TYPE FOLDING HUNTERS with: one or two blades; bolsters and caps; bone stag or plain or patterned celluloid handles. Excellent unsharpened condition.

VALUE RANGE	VERY HIGH	HIGH	MED.	LOW
SHAPE				
CURVED REGULAR:	$375.	120.	60.	20.
SWELL-CENTERS				
EXTRA-WIDE:	625.	175.	85.	50.
STANDARD:	200.	100.	40.	12.
EXTRA-SLIM:	150.	90.	35.	10.

Remington with Bullet shield: **add 100%**

Genuine pearl or fancy celluloid: **add 50%**
(water-fall, Christmas tree, candy stripe, goldstone)
Genuine stag: **add 25%**
Plastic or laminated wood: **subtract 50%**

Mint condition: **add 50%**   Worn: **subtract 60%**
Broken: **subtract 90%**

Case Tested XX, curved regular, 5¼", bone stag, **$375.**

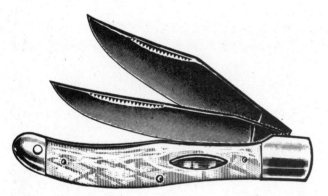

Western, extra-slim, 5¼", patterned celluloid, **$35.**

R1253

HUNTER'S KNIFE, with heavy double sabre clip blade, crocus polished and etched. Stag Handle; Nickel Silver Cap and Bolster. Brass Lined. LOCK BACK. Length, closed, 5¼ inches.

Remington, curved regular, bullet shield, **$750.**

Schrade, standard, 5¼", plastic, **$36 list.**

Western States, extra-wide, 5½", plain celluloid, **$175.**

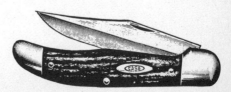

Case Tested XX, standard, 5¼", genuine stag, **$250.**

Modern Folding Hunters

The majority of modern American folding hunters are streamlined versions of the clasp knife. They have lost their upswept pointed handle ends and retain only enough curve for a comfortable grip. I believe that the original version of this modern classic is the Buck 110 Folding Hunter introduced in 1962. The story of this knife is told in the *Buck Folding Knives* chapter.

Since that time, virtually every knife company in the United States has come out with its own interpretations of this design. Gerber even makes a few double-ended versions.

Farmer's Clasp Knife

In 1967 Case introduced a lightweight non-locking version of the modern clasp knife. This 4⅝-inch "Sod Buster" has black composition handles and birdseye rivets. A liner-lock version and a smaller 3⅝-inch "Sod Buster Jr." were introduced in 1970.

At about the same time, several German firms, including J.A. Henckels, R. Herder, and F. Herder, introduced wooden handled versions of this "farmer's clasp knife." Their plastic versions came later.

Base prices for MODERN FOLDING HUNTERS and FARMER'S CLASP KNIVES, with one blade; wood or horn handle scales. Excellent unsharpened condition.

	MODERN FOLDING HUNTER	FARMER'S CLASP KNIFE
Very High:	n/a	n/a
High:	$45.	$21.
Medium:	$25.	$17.
Low:	$5.	$4.

HANDLE MATERIAL
Pearl: **add 100%**
Genuine stag: **add 50%**
Bone stag: **add 25%**
Metal, plastic, or rubber: **subtract 20%**

Mint Condition: **add 50%**   Worn: **subtract 75%**
Broken: **subtract 95%**

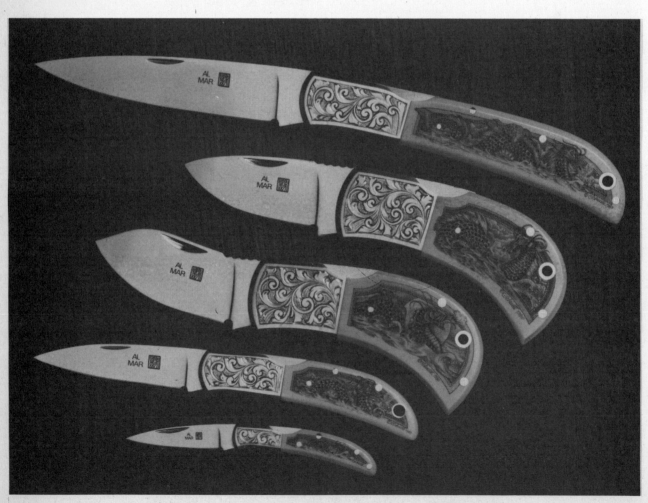

One-of-a-kind set of Al Mar knives, color scrimshaw by Schulte (1980).

SIZE CLOSED - 5 Inches
UNCLE HENRY® BEAR PAW®

SIZE CLOSED - 5 Inches
UNCLE HENRY® PAPA BEAR

SCRIMSHAW BEAR PAW®
LOCKBACK
Size closed - 5 inches. 3½ inch blade

Schrade folding hunting knives, list prices: **$38, $43, $45.**

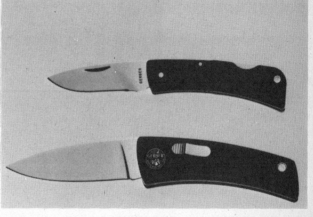

Above—Gerber L-S-T (**$20**) and Bolt Action (**$33**).
Left—Gerber Benchmark Roloxes, list prices: **$105-115.**

Above—Gerber Paul: **$70 list.**

Below—Spyderco "Police Model" Clipit: **$60 list.**

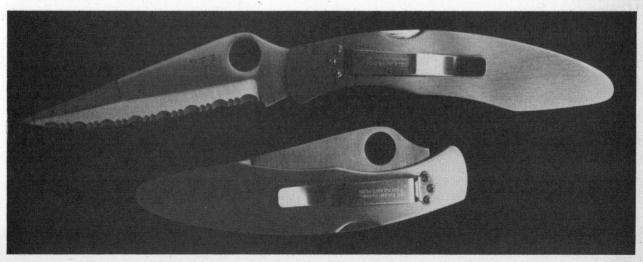

Folding Dirks and Folding Bowie Knives

By Roger Baker and Bernard Levine

THE TERMS "folding dirk" and "folding bowie knife" are used, often interchangeably, to refer to large, well-made, usually ornate jack knives of the mid-19th century that were designed primarily as weapons. Strictly speaking, "folding dirk" refers only to such knives that have double-edged "dirk" or dagger blades. "Folding bowie," the more general term, encompasses larger folding dirks, as well as big folding fighting knives with clip point or spear point blades.

Folding dirks and bowies were the pocketable counterparts of the better known fixed blade bowie knife. Bowie knives leapt to national attention in 1827 and remained in vogue about half a century. The bowie knife and the Colt revolver, introduced in 1837, were the characteristic sidearms of the American frontier. Pundits labeled them America's outstanding contributions to 19th century civilization.

Judging by the relative numbers of surviving examples, the folding bowie may have been just as popular as the less costly fixed blade in the 1830s, the enthusiastic early years of the bowie fad. By the 1850s, the big folders were in eclipse. After the Civil War, only small folding dirks were still available.

Almost all folding dirks and bowie knives are over 4½ inches long closed. They are generally slender, and most have a cross-guard integral with the front bolsters.

Almost every folding dirk and bowie we have seen was made in Sheffield. Most of them were made for sale in the United States. However, those marked with the name of another English city, such as London or Bristol, and most of those with lions in the decorations, were made for sale in England. A German style of folding bowie is described later in this chapter.

Roger Baker has collected folding dirks and bowies for 15 years.

Ornamental appearance was an important consideration in the design of folding dirks and bowies. Therefore they were made in a wide variety of shapes. Another factor in their diversity of shape is that most of these knives were made in the period c1830–1860, before mass production and pattern standardization had taken hold in the cutlery industry.

Not only are the shapes of these big knives varied, so are their decorations. Their bolsters are almost always ornately embossed.

Though the knives themselves were hand-made, their fancy nickel silver bolsters were mass produced. Standard designs were stamped out by specialist firms and sold to all the makers. Some of the original dies used to stamp these fancy mounts still exist, which helps account for a certain amount of inept counterfeiting and questionable repair work.

The design motifs of the mounts are an important factor in estimating the value of a folding dirk or bowie. Bolsters with political or patriotic symbols are worth about 50% to 150% more than similar knives without.

Perhaps the most desirable motif is the "half horse half alligator." This imaginary beast symbolized the "Hunters of Kentucky" in a song of the same name dating from the War of 1812. Equally valuable and even rarer is the bust of Mexican War hero Zachary Taylor.

Bolsters with the American eagle are also popular, as are cross guards with an artillery horse, cannon, and liberty cap. Cross guards with the motto "Liberty and Union" in a banner reflect the sentiments of Daniel Webster's famous "Constitution and Union" speech of 1850. The imperial lion, though a British symbol, is also popular among American collectors, though less so than our own symbols.

Handle materials on folding dirks and bowies are generally of high quality. Genuine stag, ivory, and pearl are the most often encountered. Horn and tortoise shell are more unusual. We have not observed bone or wood handles on them, but some may exist.

Opposite Page:
Folding dirks and small folding bowies, top to bottom. Values approximate.

A: Unmarked, 4¾", ivory handles, **$300.**

B: W(crown)R/THOMAS/BARNES/PATENT/DIRK, 6⅛", ivory handles, **$600.**

C: I*XL//GEORGE/WOSTENHOLM/SHEFFIELD, 5½", LIBERTY & UNION guard, ivory handles, **$500.**

A

B

C

D

E

F

D: SAMUEL C. WRAGG/FURNACE HILL/SHEFFIELD//IM-PROVED PATENT CUTLERY, 5¼", carved pearl handles, worked nickel silver spring cover, **$800.**

E: ARTHUR/LINLEY & CO./SHEFFIELD, 5⅛", two blades, pearl handles, **$1,200.**

F: REGISTERED BY GOVERNMENT/FEBRUARY 9, 1850 №. 2180//LINGARD/PEACROFT/SHEFFIELD, 5¾", two-blade switchblade (press small blade to operate), stag handles, **$1,500.**

(Roger Baker collection)

Makers

In contrast to standard production folding knives, the maker of a folding dirk or bowie is not a major factor in estimating its value, except insofar as the name and blade markings help to date the knife. The earlier circa 1830s knives, which also tend to be larger and more elaborate, are the most valuable. See *Some Clues to Dating and Identifying Knives* and also the *Pocketknife Brand List* for specific information.

From the knives we have seen, the principal firms that made or factored folding dirks and bowies seem to have been Samuel C. Wragg, William and Samuel Butcher, George Wostenholm & Sons, and Robert and Joseph Lingard. Many other Sheffield names are found on these knives as well.

Collecting Folding Dirks and Bowies

The Sheffield folding bowie is fascinating in its historical lore, mechanical workmanship, and elegant beauty. It is frustrating to search for these rare pieces of Americana. It can be devastating to the wallet to acquire one. However, even a single fine example can be considered a respectable collection.

Folding dirks and bowies will never grow to be a popular collecting field simply because there are too few good specimens available to supply a large market. Likewise, there cannot really be a "market price" for a particular type, since almost every one of these knives is different, as is every transaction among the few collectors in the field.

The knives in the photographs illustrate the range of sizes, makers, and decorations that exist. The prices given are estimates only. However, they can serve as a guide to evaluating similar knives. The value of a particular knife is substantially influenced both by its condition and by the condition of the market. The illustrated knives are in as good condition as any that are known.

Be extremely wary of any folding dirk or bowie that has been heavily cleaned or buffed. Their mechanisms are delicate, and many broken ones have been incorrectly restored. Fresh buffing can conceal sloppy repair work. It can also indicate a counterfeit.

Folding bowie and large folding dirks. Values approximate.

Top: SAMUEL C. WRAGG/Nº. 2--/FURNACE HILL SHEFFIELD, 6¼", heavy saber clip blade, wide stag handles, eagle pommel, **$4,000.**

Center: Unmarked, 9", ivory handles with etched panel, **$1,000.**

Bottom: NON-XLL/UNWIN & RODGERS/SHEFFIELD, 8⅛", pearl handles **$2,000.**

(Roger Baker collection)

Above:
Folding bowies. Values approximate.
Top: --MILLS/120 HOLBORN/LONDON, 7″, lion pommel, etched ivory handle, **$4,500.**
Bottom: W(crown)R/GEORGE WOSTENHOLM & SONS/CELEBRATED IMPROVED CUTLERY/ROCKINGHAM WORKS/SHEFFIELD//WARRANTED OF THE BEST QUALITY, 7″, half-horse/half-alligator pommel, ivory handles, **$5,000.**

(Roger Baker collection)

Below:
Folding bowies. Values approximate.
Top: W(crown)R/W. BUTCHER/SHEFFIELD, 7⅛″, horsehead pommel, heavy spear blade, ivory handles, **$3,500.**
Bottom: SNOW/PORTSEA//OF THE BEST QUALITY, 5⅞″, horsehead pommel, saber clip blade, ivory handles, **$3,500.** Portsea is part of Portsmouth, England.

(Roger Baker collection)

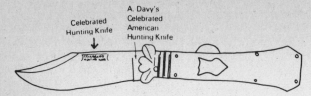

Celebrated Hunting Knife

A. Davy's Celebrated American Hunting Knife

Sheffield folding bowie 6¼″ long closed, marked A. DAVY'S/ CELEBRATED/AMERICAN/HUNTING KNIFE on tang and CELEBRATED HUNTING KNIFE on blade. Cow horn ("English buffalo") handles. 1836–1856. Value **$1,200.** Courtesy Michael Stephen and *Knife World.*

German Style Folding Bowies

German folding ''bowies'' are well made but not nearly as valuable (or as old) as the English knives. The standard style has a blade several inches longer than its handle. Folded it can be used as a handy utility knife, open as a formidable weapon. It must be carried in a sheath.

A knife of this type usually has two locks. A standard back lock keeps the blade open and a button type lock in the front handle keeps it closed.

Case made a knife of this type, as did some of the English firms. The Marble's safety hunting knife was an American improvement on this design (see the Marble's chapter in the *Fixed Blade Knives* section). More recent versions, usually with brass mounts, have been made in India and Pakistan. International copying of knife patterns is as much a part of cutlery history as it is of the cutlery industry today.

See *Foreign Exotic, Primitive, and Historical Folding Knives* for information on other large European jack knives.

German style FOLDING BOWIE KNIVES, value in excellent unsharpened condition, with sheath. Sheath missing: **subtract 20%**
German brand rated V or H: **$150.**
German brand rated M or L: **$75.**
English brand rated V or H: **$200.**
English brand rated M or L: **$100.**
Case No. 551: **$350.**
Indian or Pakistani: **$25.**
Indian or Pakistani with metal blade guard: **$40.**

A

B

German Style Folding Bowies, all sold with sheath.

A: German export circa 1905. 4″ handle, 7″ blade. Ebony handles, folding guard, Medium quality. Value: **$75.**

B: German export by J. A. Henckels circa 1935. 4⅝″ handle, 8⅜″ blade. Stag handle scales, folding guard, High quality. Value: **$150.**

C: Sheffield export by John Clarke & Son, circa 1924. 4″ handle, 8″ blade. Ebony handle scales, no guard, Medium quality. Value: **$100.**

C

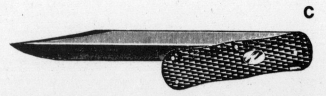

Expanding Bowie Knife. Can be used as a 4″ Blade Locked, Fully Opened as an 8″ Blade Locked.   In Leather Sheath.

English Jacks

"ENGLISH JACK" is a term that was commonly applied to deluxe large-sized (over 4-inch) slim, regular, and sleeve-board jack knives. Premium handle materials, fancy bolsters, and locking master blades are often seen on them.

English jacks most often have a single clip blade. Others have a spear blade, instead. Some have a pen second blade.

Most of the large size jack knives exported from England to the United States from the mid-19th to the early 20th centuries fit this definition. However, the term "English jack" is an American term, and was used equally on large high-grade straight jack knives made in this country.

English jacks are similar in proportion to large "daddy" barlows. I suspect that they appealed to the prosperous southern or western customer who had grown up with barlow knives and liked them, but who wanted and could afford something a little more dressy. For a man who is used to a straight one- or two-blade jack knife, a curved four-blade tobacco knife or three-blade premium stock knife just will not do.

The English jack is less bulky and more pocketable than clasp knives or folding hunters, but its master blade is almost as long as theirs are. In a pinch, a lock-back English jack can serve adequately as a weapon. Very large and ornate English jacks are often classed with folding bowie knives.

Base prices for ENGLISH JACKS 4 to 4½ inches long; plain bolsters; bone stag or fancy celluloid handles; non-locking master blade. Excellent unsharpened condition.

Very High: **$120.**   Medium: **$50.**
High: **$75.**   Low: **$12.**

Locking master blade: **add 25%**
Two blades: **add 20%**
Folding guard: **add 25%**
Fancy stamped nickel silver bolsters: **add 25%**
Very fancy bolsters: see *Folding Dirks and Folding Bowie Knives*
Integral one-piece iron bolster liners: **add 25%** (also see *Foreign, Exotic, . . . Folding Knives*)

Over 4½ inches long closed: **add 25%**
Over 5¼ inches*: **add 40%**
Over 6 inches*: **add 75%**

Pearl handles: **add 50%**
Ivory handles: **add 35%**
Genuine stag or tortoise shell handles: **add 25%**
Wood, fiber, or plain celluloid handles: **subtract 25%**
Plain metal handles: **subtract 40%**

Mint condition: **add 50%**
Worn: **subtract 50%**
Broken: **subtract 85%**
*also see *Folding Dirks* and *Folding Bowie Knives*

H. Boker (USA), 2-blade, bone stag, **$60.**

No. 1863¾

Schrade Cut. Co., 4½", bone stag or candy stripe, **$75.**

Ulster Knife Co., 2-blade, 4⅜", wood, **$68.**

William Rodgers (John Clarke), 4½", genuine stag, **$62.**

English Jacks (continued)

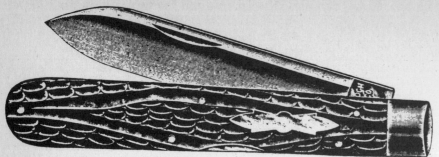

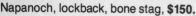

Napanoch, lockback, bone stag, **$150.**

Winchester 2907, 2-blade, 4¼",
bone stag, **$145.**

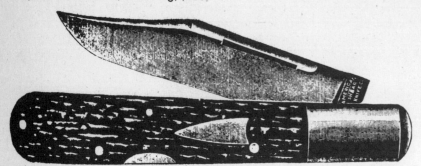

ONE BLADE, Large Spear, Full Polished; Nickel Silver
Bolster, Cap and Shield; Brass Lining.
Per Dozen
No. K1683—4½ IN. STAG HANDLE..............$19.80

Keen Kutter, bone stag, **$75.**

American Shear & Knife Co., lockback, bone stag, **$94.**

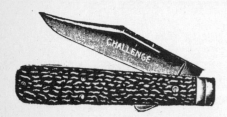

Challenge, lockback, 4½", bone stag,
$95.

R1153	R1343
Nickel Silver Trim	Nickel Silver Trim
Stag Handle; Brass Lining	Stag Handle; Brass Lining
Length, closed, 4⅜ inches.	Length, closed, 4¼ inches.

Remingtons, 2-blade, fancy bolsters, bone stag, **$180 each.**

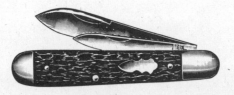

R-1373
One Blade Hunting Knife—with Lock
Back. Stag Handle; Brass Lining; Mir-
ror Finished Blade. Nickel Silver Trim.
Length, closed, 4¼ inches.

L.F.& C., lockback, bone stag, **$94.**

622151

Robeson, 2-blade, bone stag, **$60.**

Remington, lockback, bone stag, **$150.**

HUNTING KNIVES.

We supply hunters, trappers and dealers from all parts of the United States, and offer the very latest and best patterns in this line produced.

No. 10342 J. H. S. & Co. "Hunters and Trappers' Choice," a most excellent knife. The blade when open locks in position, and can not close on the hand.
We call attention to the shape of this blade, made with bowie point, and of the best steel. It will do for either sticking or skinning. 4½ inch stag
handle, solid iron bolster, a big strong knife; a good knife for hunters, stockmen, farmers, etc. Each, 64 cents; per dozen $6 50
Postage on single knife, 5 cents extra.

J. H. Sutcliffe & Co., lockback, bone stag, **$62.**

English Jacks (continued)

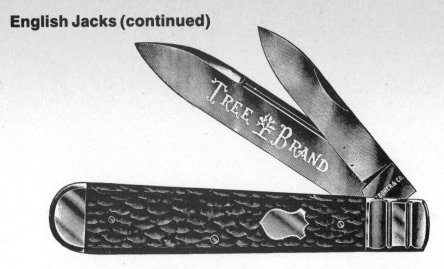

H. Boker, 2-blade, fancy bolsters, bone stag, **$75.**

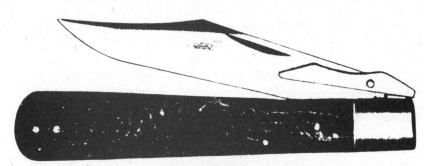

No. 6165 Lg.

Union Cut. Co., lockback, guard, bone stag, **$190.**

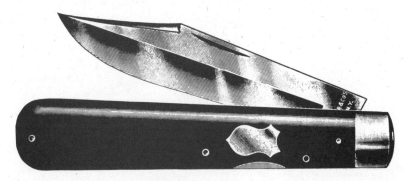

H. Boker (Germany), lockback, black rubber, **$47.**

No. 1134
Brass Lined
Genuine Stag

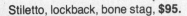
Lock back hunting. One blade, half crocus polished. German silver bolster. Brass lined. Length, 4½ inches.

Stiletto, lockback, bone stag, **$95.**

Ulster Knife Co., lockback, guard, genuine stag, **$145.**

Pen Knives

Pen Knives and Quill Knives

THE TERM "pen knife" now refers to a small folding knife with blades in both ends. Almost invariably, one or more of these blades is a pen blade.

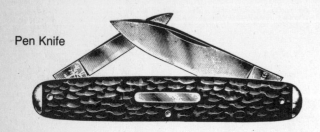

Pen Knife

The pen blade, and the pen knife itself, were originally designed for sharpening quill pens. Quill pens were first used in the early Middle Ages and their use was standard in the western world up until the 19th century. Although steel pens had been made before that time, they did not become common until after 1828, when Josiah Mason began mass-producing them in Birmingham, England.

It is remarkable that quill pens have been gone for well over a century now, but pen blades and pen knives are still very much with us. A sharp little blade still has plenty of uses.

The earliest folding pen knives that I have seen are from the 18th century, when their main use was still sharpening quill pens. I do not know if folding pen knives were used before that time.

Unlike modern "pen knives," which by definition have at least two blades, many of the pen knives from the 18th and 19th centuries in fact have only one blade. Collectors now call little single-bladed folding pen sharpeners "quill knives." These diminutive knives have their own chapter.

Quill Knife

Construction

Double-ended knives, including pen knives, require more labor to make than standard single-ended jack knives. At least one spring in almost every double-ended knife must be adjusted to bear smoothly on two blades. The blades themselves must be "crinked" or bent sideways so that each opposing pair can close into the same slot without one blade banging against the other. (On some modern knives asymmetrical grinding has taken the place of crinking.) In addition, most pen knives are premium quality knives requiring a higher degree of finish than jack knives.

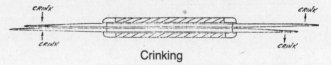

Crinking

For these reasons, pen knives when new have usually cost more than jack knives of comparable size and quality. In fact, most manufacturers a generation and more ago used to charge more for their top-of-the-line pen knives than they did for any of their jack knives, no matter how large.

These relative values do *not* carry over into the collector's market, however. Most collectors find big knives more appealing than small ones, and they will naturally enough pay more for what they like better.

Bolsters and Backs

Pen knives can have full bolsters, tip bolsters, or no bolsters at all. They can have plain liners or liners milled like the edge of a dime. They can have engraved bolsters with plain or engraved handles. They can even have "closed backs."

Full Bolsters

Tip Bolsters

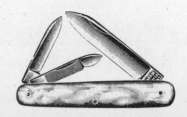

No Bolsters (Shadow)

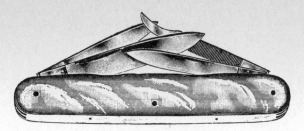

Solid Pearl Back.

On a knife with a closed back, both handle liners are made from one piece of metal that is wrapped around the back-springs. A closed back is always a mark of cheap construction on a jack knife or stock knife. On a pen knife it most often is, also. However, some of the very finest pen knives are made with closed backs.

Joints

A pen knife can have one of three types of joint: common, half-sunk, or sunk. The type of joint is defined by how much the "run ups" or back ends of the blades protrude from the handles when the blades are closed.

The most elegant type of joint is the sunk joint. With sunk joints, the back corners of the blades are completely "sunk" within the handles, so as not to catch on clothing or break up the lines of the handle.

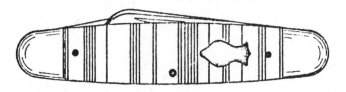

Sunk Joints

Many pen knives with sunk joints need to have little beveled notches cut into the handles beside the nail nicks of the blades, or else the blades could not be opened. Though similar, these notches are not the same as the easy-open notches on some jack knives, since they do not permit the blades to be grasped with the fingertips.

Some large jack knives have over-sized bolsters that cover the run ups of the blades. Though similar in function, this type of reinforced construction is *not* called a sunk joint. Some fancy slim jacks and English jacks do have true sunk joints.

Half-sunk joints, as you may already have guessed, are only half as elegant as sunk joints. The back corners of the blades stick out a little bit, but so do the nail nicks, so notches do not need to be cut in the handles. Half-sunk joints are sturdier than sunk joints.

Half Sunk Joints

Common joints are the least costly of the three types to make, but they are also the sturdiest when the knife is open and in use. In a common joint, the back corners of the blades stick out quite prominently when the blades are closed.

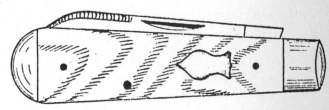

Common Joint

Blades

The spear master blade is standard in most pen knife patterns of the past century and a half. These are the important exceptions: Congress knives have a sheepfoot master blade. Serpentine pens often have a clip master blade; some are Wharncliffe knives with Wharncliffe master blades.

Congress Knife

Pen Knife Handle Materials and Skeleton Knives

Pen knives do not have spey blades, except for some "office knives" which have a spey-type blade intended to serve as an ink-eraser. An office knife is a large equal-end pen knife with white ivory, bone, or celluloid handles; OFFICE KNIFE in fancy letters is usually etched or stamped on the front handle. Office knives have their own chapter in this book.

Many pen knives have a manicure blade, something not ordinarily found in jack knives. Manicure blades have been made in at least half a dozen varieties. Some pen knives with manicure blades also have a little folding scissors.

Pen knives, mainly equal-ends, have been fitted with an incredible variety of mechanisms to assist one in opening the blades. A separate chapter is devoted to these mechanisms.

Ring Opener
Gun Metal Handles

Mother-of-pearl seems to be the commonest handle material on older pen knives. However, it is unusual to find an older pearl-handled pen knife with its handles still intact.

Metal handles of one sort or another are also common on pen knives. The least expensive metal handles are plain nickel silver, aluminum, and "gun metal" (an alloy of copper and tin).

The next step up in cost is decorated metal handles: nickel silver handles decorated with stamping; aluminum with stamping or engraving; and gun metal with color etching, selective plating, or enameling. For more on decorated handles, see page 26 and the chapter on advertising knives.

The fanciest metal handles are covered with silver or gold. Ordinary ones are thin sheets of the precious metal secured to the brass liners of "skeleton knives." Often these thin sheets are engine-turned or have some simple engraving. Cut-rate versions of these flat handles are merely sheet brass that is silver or gold (or even chromium) plated.

The best metal handles are elaborate stampings or investment castings of gold or silver applied by jewelers to "skeleton knives." Such handles may even have jewels or panels of semi-precious stone such as gold-bearing quartz set into them.

A "skeleton knife" is a completely assembled and finished pen knife lacking bolsters and handle covers. Jewelers buy them and dress them up any way they like.

Skeleton with Gold Plated Covers

A few firms have specialized in the manufacture of skeletons. Wostenholm of Sheffield seems to have made a lot of the skeletons for the American market up until around 1910. Miller Brothers and Empire, both of Connecticut, made large numbers early in this century. The Imperial Knife Company got its start in 1916 making skeleton knives for the wholesale jewelry trade in Providence, Rhode Island.

Besides pearl and the various metals, almost any other handle material that you can name has been used on pen knives. Jigged bone and celluloid were common in the first half of this century. Ivory, smooth bone, tortoise shell, and horn were popular in the last century. However, genuine stag and wood are very unusual on pen knives, having been considered more appropriate on larger or coarser knives.

You may sometimes find a pen knife with two different factory-original handles, either pearl and brown bone or black plastic and white plastic. Some of these knives are salesman's samples. Most are sleight-of-hand knives that, with careful manipulation, can be made to appear to "change color."

Lobsters

The main structural division in pen knives is between ordinary spring-back knives and "lobster-spring" knives. A "lobster" knife has its spring or springs (often a single "split" or branched spring) inside the middle of the handle. This allows it to have blades on both top and bottom, as well as at one or both ends. A lobster pen always has its pivot pins set off to the sides of the long axis of the knife.

I do not know for certain why these knives are called "lobsters." I suspect it is because the action of two blades, pivoting at the corners of one end of a knife, is reminiscent of the action of lobster claws.

Lobster spring pen knives were made in a number of standard shapes. Most of these shapes have exotic sounding names, and some have more than one name. Their names, descriptions, and prices are covered in a separate chapter.

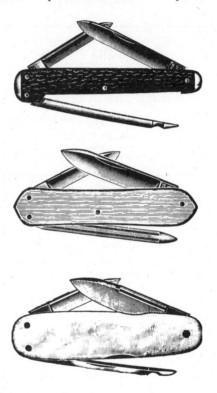

Lobster pen knives are flat and lightly constructed. A wide variety of thicker multi-blade folders have been made that resemble lobsters in that they have blades both top and bottom. These more robust knives are covered in the *Multi-Blades* section.

Multi-Blade

Whittlers

The main structural division in spring-back pen knives is between ordinary pen knives and "whittlers." Most three-blade pen knives of all shapes are constructed as whittlers.

A whittler has two springs. The large thick master blade, at one end of the knife, bears on *both* of the springs. The two thin small blades, at the other end of the knife, each bear on one of the springs.

Years ago, knife manufacturers did not usually distinguish their whittlers from their other pen knives. Today, however, whittlers are a separate and important collecting specialty. Therefore, in this book, all whittlers regardless of shape are described and priced together in one chapter.

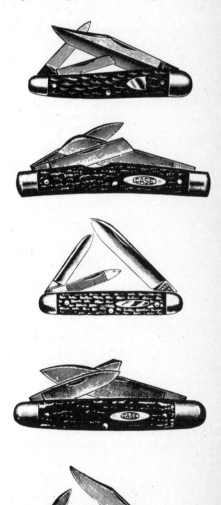

PRICE CHART FOR PEN KNIVES

Base prices for PEN KNIVES of the indicated shape, over 2 ⅞ up to 3 ¾ inches long closed; bone stag (jigged bone) handles; brass or nickel silver liners, nickel silver trim; full bolsters. Excellent unsharpened condition.

NOTE: The following special types of pen knife have their own separate price lists. LOBSTERS, WHITTLERS, QUILL KNIVES, OFFICE and LETTER OPENER KNIVES, ADVERTISING and FIGURAL KNIVES, MECHANICAL PEN KNIVES.

VALUE RANGE	VERY HIGH	HIGH	MEDIUM	LOW
SHAPE				
2-BLADE SENATOR:	$ 60.	$35.	$20.	$ 6.
3-BLADE SENATOR: (not a whittler)	70.	40.	22.	8.
4-BLADE SENATOR:	85.	45.	25.	10.
SLEEVEBOARD:	70.	40.	22.	8.
OVAL or CIGAR:	70.	45.	16.	8.
"GUNSTOCK":	150.	75.	40.	12.
2-BLADE CONGRESS:	75.	40.	20.	9.
4-BLADE CONGRESS:	130.	75.	30.	12.
CROWN or COFFIN: (Barrel-shaped)	65.	26.	20.	9.
MODERN CROWN: (Rectangular)	45.	22.	16.	6.
SWELL-CENTER CONGRESS:	100.	50.	22.	10.
SWELL-CENTER SERPENTINE:	80.	50.	22.	8.
PREMIUM (SEPENTINE):	60.	25.	15.	7.
WHARNCLIFFE:	70.	40.	22.	9.
"DOG-LEG" SERPENTINE:	65.	35.	18.	8.
SWELL-CENTER/BALLOON:	75.	45.	23.	12.

PRICE CHART FOR PEN KNIVES

CONSTRUCTION

Three-bladed whittler: see *Whittlers*
Three blades (not a whittler, not in chart): **add 15%**
Four blades (not shown in chart): **add 35%**
Five or six blades: **add 50%** to 4-blade price
Seven or eight blades: **add 75%** to 4-blade price
Non-standard blade: **add 20%**
(eraser, lance, corn, scissor, ivory, silver, etc.)

Engraved solid gold bolsters: **add 100%**
Engraved sterling silver bolsters: **add 50%**
Fancy stamped nickel silver bolsters: **add 30%**
Contrasting celluloid tip bolsters: **add 25%**
Engraved aluminum bolsters: **add 20%**
Metal tip bolsters: **subtract 10%**
Shadow (no bolsters): **subtract 15%**

Integral one-piece iron bolster-liners: **add 20%**
Milled liners: **add 10%**
File-worked back (original): **add 100%**
Closed back (fancy): **add 100%**
Closed back (plain): **subtract 20%**

SIZE

Over 3 ¾ inches: **add 25%**
(also see *Double-End Jack Knives*)
2 ⅜ to 2 ⅞ inches long: **subtract 20%**
Under 2 ⅜ inches long: **subtract 30%**

HANDLE MATERIALS

Genuine stag: **add 50%**
Pearl or abalone: **add 30%**
Multi-piece pearl or abalone: **add 45%**
Genuine ivory: **add 25%**
Tortoise shell: **add 20%**
Engraving or inlay on pearl, ivory, or tortoise: **add 20%**
Smooth bone or horn: **subtract 10%**
Wood: **subtract 20%**

Fancy celluloid: **add 10%**
(water-fall, Christmas Tree, candy stripe, goldstone)
Other patterned or colorful celluloid: **subtract 10%**
Solid color celluloid or composition: **subtract 30%**
Modern plastic: **subtract 50%**

Pressed hollow sheet steel: **subtract 50%**
Decorated nickel silver or aluminum: **subtract 20%**
Plain nickel silver, aluminum, or gun metal: **subtract 40%**
Advertising or pictorial nickel silver or aluminum: [1]
Color etched or enameled gun metal: [1]
Gold or silver *plated* metal: see next page
Plain sterling silver: **add $8-15.**
Decorated sterling silver: **add $20-35.**
Flat gold covers: **add $20-30.**
Solid gold handles: [2]
Inlaid stones: [2]

[1] see *Advertising* and *Figural Knives*, also see page 26
[2] ask your jeweler

CONDITION

Mint condition: **add 50%**
Worn: **subtract 50%**
Broken: **subtract 90%**

Skeleton Knives With Gold-Filled or Plated Covers

There is little collector interest in these metal handled watch fob knives. (Illustrations from 1925) Value of any style in excellent unsharpened condition:

Very High: $40.　　**Medium: $10.**
High: $20.　　　　**Low: $5.**

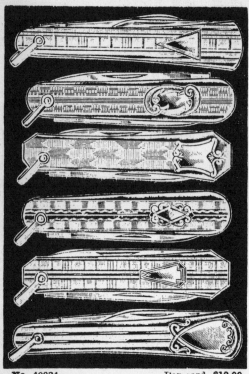

No. 40234.....................Per card, $12.00
6 green gold filled pocket knives, engine turned
on both sides. All have 2 blades.
On fancy display card.
Illustration shows actual size.

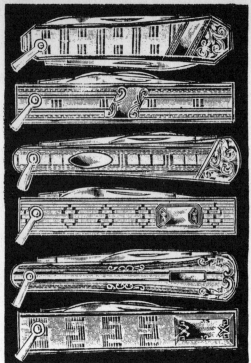

No. 40235.....................Per card, $12.00
6 white gold filled pocket knives, engine turned
on both sides. All have 2 blades.
On fancy display card.
Illustration shows actual size.

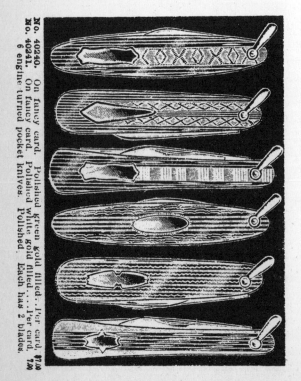

No. 40240. On fancy card. Polished green gold filled....Per card, $7.00
No. 40241. On fancy card. Polished white gold filled...Per card, 7.00
6 engine turned pocket knives. Polished. Each has 2 blades.

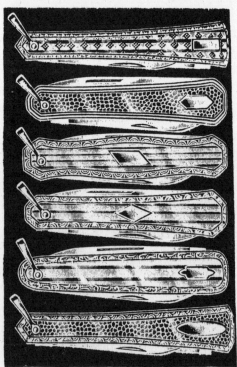

No. 40236.....................Per pad, $12.00
6 green and white combination, pocket knives,
white center, green border. Engine turned
and hammered design, lined backs.
Two have 2 blades and 4 have blade
and file on fancy display pad.
Illustration shows actual size.

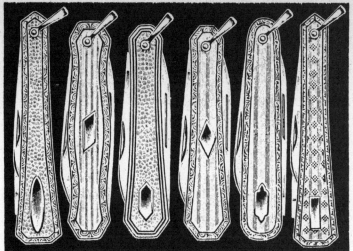

No. 40237. ....Per Pad, $12.00
6 white gold filled pocket knives, satin finish center polished border
and shields. Lined backs. 2 have two blades. 4 have blade
and file. On fancy display pad.
Illustration shows actual size.

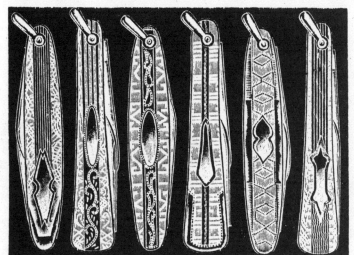

No. 40238. On fancy card........................Per card of six, $11.00
6 polished green gold filled, engine turned pocket knives.
Each has 2 blades.

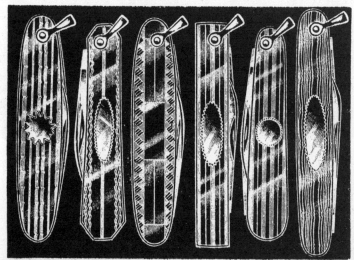

No. 40239. ....Per card, $8.00
6 gold filled pocket knives, three white gold filled and three
polished green gold. Engine turned fronts, plain backs.
On fancy card. Illustration shows actual size.

Senator or Equal-End Pens

Pen knives have been made in a good variety of shapes over the years, though not in as many shapes as have jack knives. Some pen knife shapes are similar to those of jack knives, but the majority are different.

By far the commonest pen knife pattern, the "senator," is similar in shape to the equal-end jack knife. The senator pen is round-ended and symmetrical, like the equal-end jack, but it is proportionally narrower.

Some manufacturers called all of their equal-end pen knives "senators," while others limited this name to knives of intermediate proportions. The latter firms called very narrow equal-end pen knives "regular pens." Very wide or large ones they called "oval" or simply "equal-end."

Senator pens can have two, three, or four blades. Very rarely they have even more. Most three-blade senators are "whittlers."

The master blade of a senator pen is a small spearpoint. The second blade in a two-blade senator is either a pen blade or a nail file. Those three-bladed senators which are not whittlers are the same as the two-bladed ones, only with the addition of a full length blade such as a special manicure, a scissors, a corn blade or, very rarely, a sheepfoot. Most four-bladed senators have a spear, two pens, and a file.

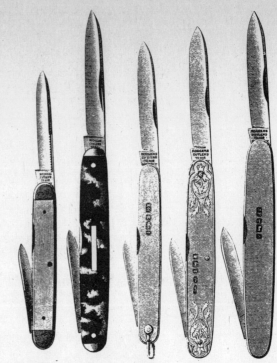

Jos. Rodgers: 2 ¼", ivory, **$30**; tip bolsters, 2 ¾", tortoise shell, **$30**; 2 ⁷⁄₁₆", sterling, **$36**; 2 ¹¹⁄₁₆", embossed sterling, **$48**; 2 ¾", sterling, **$40**.

Robeson, 3", bone stag, **$20**.

Ulster Knife Co., engraved aluminum bolsters: bone stag, **$42**; pearl, **$55**.

No. 7706B

Schrade Cut. Co., fancy bolsters, 2 ⁷⁄₈", pearl, **$45**.

American Shear & Knife Co., 2 ¾", patterned celluloid, **$25**.

Case, tip bolsters, 3 ⁷⁄₁₆", genuine stag: Tested XX, **$81**; XX, **$47**.

H. Boker, 2 ¹³⁄₁₆", pearl with engraving, **$25**.

Senator Pens

TWO BLADES, 1 Large Spear and 1 Pen; Large Blade Full Polished; Nickel Silver Bolsters, Shield and Lining.
Per Dozen
No. 2843—3¾ IN.; STAG HANDLE $20.00

TWO BLADES, 1 Large Spear and 1 Pen; Large Blade Full Polished; Nickel Silver Bolsters, Shield and Lining.
Per Dozen
No. 2053—3¾ IN.; GREEN AND RED CELLULOID HANDLE. $23.00

Winchesters: bone stag, **$60;** Christmas-tree celluloid, **$66.**

H. Boker, shadow, multi-piece pearl, **$25.**

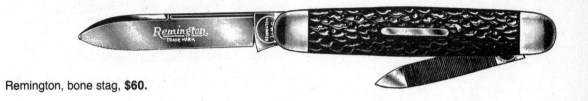

Remington, bone stag, **$60.**

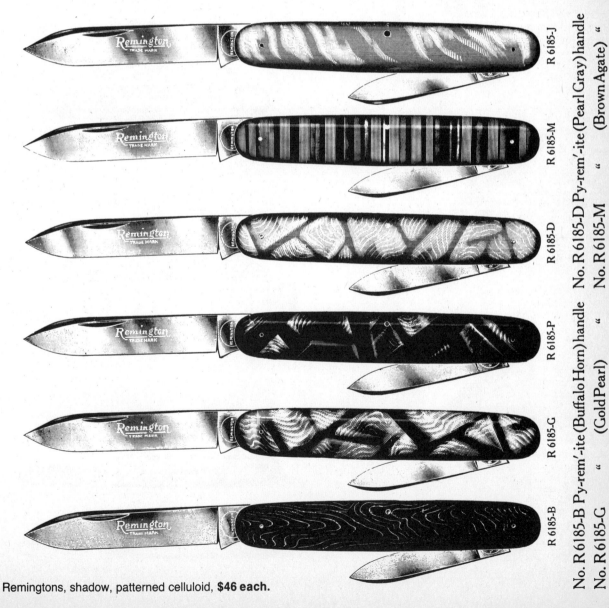

No. R6185-J   R 6185-J
No. R6185-M   R 6185-M
No. R6185-D Py-rem′-ite (Pearl Gray) handle   R 6185-D
"   (Brown Agate)   "
"   (Japanese Pearl)   "

No. R6185-P   R 6185-P
No. R6185-J   "
No. R6185-M Py-rem′-ite (Buffalo Horn) handle   R 6185-B
"   (Gold Pearl)   "
"   (Pearl Blue)   "

No. R6185-B Py-rem′-ite   R 6185-B
No. R6185-C   R 6185-C
No. R6185-P   R 6185-P

Remingtons, shadow, patterned celluloid, **$46 each.**

Three-Blade Senators (not Whittlers)

No. M8423B

Senator pattern, 3⅛ inches long; 3 blades (long manicure file, pen and spear pocket); brass lined; nickel silver bolsters and shield; cleaned inside; spear pocket blade crocus polished on one side; Bone Stag handle.

No. M8424PT

Senator pattern, 3⅛ inches long; 3 blades (long manicure file, pen and spear pocket); brass lined; nickel silver tips and shield; cleaned inside; spear pocket blade crocus polished on one side; Smoked Pearl Celluloid handle.

No. M8426

Senator pattern, 3⅛ inches long; 3 blades; (long manicure file, pen and spear pocket); brass lined; nickel silver shield; cleaned inside; spear pocket blade crocus polished on one side; Mother of Pearl handle.

No. 8704¾BT (*Cut ⅔ size*)

Senator pattern, 2⅞ inches long; 3 blades (flexible manicure file, long clip pocket and pen blades); brass lined; nickel silver tips; cleaned inside; large blade crocus polished on one side; Black Celluloid handle.

Schrade Cut. Co. (from top to bottom): bone stag, **$40**; tip bolsters, patterned celluloid, **$32**; shadow, pearl, **$44**; tip bolsters, plain celluloid, **$25**.

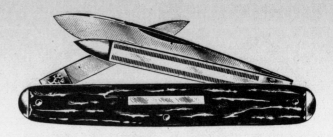

H. Bokers, tip bolsters, milled liners: genuine stag, **$33**; pearl, **$28**.

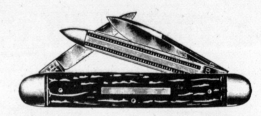

H. Boker, milled liners, 2 ½", genuine stag, **$29**.

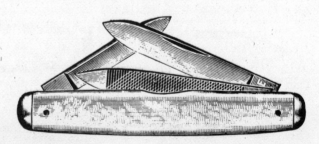

Case, tip bolsters, 3 ⅛", pearl: Tested XX **$82**; XX, **$47**.

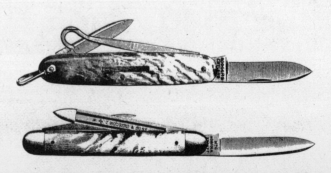

Jos. Rodgers, pearl: shadow, 2 ½", **$27**; 2 ⅝", **$32**.

Four-Blade Senators

Solid Pearl Back

H. Boker, shadow, milled liners, fancy closed back, 2¹¹⁄₁₆″, pearl, **$49**.

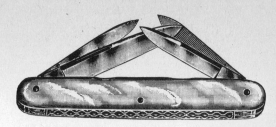

Fire Gilded and Engraved Back

H. Boker, shadow, milled liners, worked back, 2¹¹⁄₁₆″, pearl, **$49**.

H. Boker, milled liners, 2⅞″, genuine stag, **$33**.

No. 6848—Pearl, Brass Lining, Nickel Silver Trimmed, Blue Glazed Blades.

H. Boker, multi-piece pearl, **$36**.

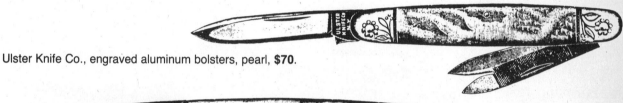

Ulster Knife Co., engraved aluminum bolsters, pearl, **$70**.

Crocus Polish, Full German Silver Mounted, **Bankers Knife**, Pearl Handle.

Ulster Knife Co., eraser master blade, tip bolsters, pearl, **$63**.

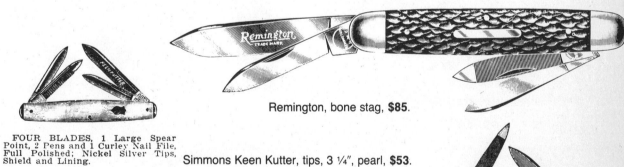

Remington, bone stag, **$85**.

FOUR BLADES, 1 Large Spear Point, 2 Pens and 1 Curley Nail File, Full Polished; Nickel Silver Tips, Shield and Lining.

Simmons Keen Kutter, tips, 3¼″, pearl, **$53**.

Jos. Rodgers, fancy bolsters, 3½″, ivory, **$70**.

No. 9703B
Senator pattern, 2⅞ inches long; 4 blades (flexible manicure file, surgical lance blade, spear pocket and pen blade); brass lined; nickel silver bolsters and shield; cleaned inside; large blade crocus polished on one side; Bone Stag handle.

Schrade Cut. Co., lance blade, 2⅞″, **$43**.

Sleeveboard Pens

A "sleeveboard pen" has round ends like a senator, but its handle tapers. It is shaped like the old sleeveboards once used for ironing shirt-sleeves. Sleeveboard pen knives ordinarily have the master blade in the wider end. Fat heavy-duty sleeveboards are called "jumbo knives." Two-bladed jumbos are covered in the *Double-End Jack Knives* chapter, three-bladed ones under *Whittlers*.

No. 62079½

Case, 3 ¼", bone stag: Tested XX, **$70**; XX, **$40**.

Remington, pearl, **$91**.

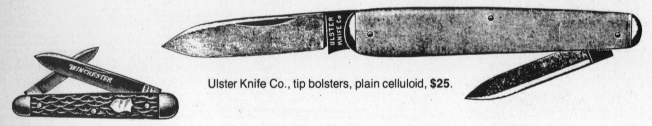

Ulster Knife Co., tip bolsters, plain celluloid, **$25**.

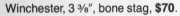

Winchester, 3 ⅜", bone stag, **$70**.

Jos. Rodgers, 3 ¾", ivory, **$50**.

Robeson, tip bolsters, 2 ⅞", plain celluloid, **$11**.

H. Boker, 4 blades, tip bolsters, genuine stag, **$40**.

H. Boker, shadow, 2 ⅜", pearl, **$19**.

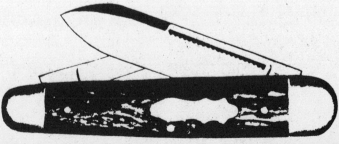

No. 6249.

Schrade Cut. Co., 3 ⅜", patterned celluloid, **$32**.

Union Cut. Co., bone stag, **$70**.

Anglo-Saxon, Milton, Oval, or Cigar Pens

The Anglo-Saxon pattern is a large (sometimes over 4 inches long closed) equal-end or slightly tapering pen knife that has curved sides. Both the senator and the sleeveboard, which are closely related to this oval pattern, have straight sides.

Oval pen knives are usually of premium quality and have sunk joints. Large oval pen knives are very rare. Most of the few 20th century examples that I have seen were whittlers.

H. Boker, tip bolsters, 2 ⅝″, bone stag, **$16**.

Jos. Rodgers, 4 blades, 3 ¼″, pearl, **$79**.

Winchester, 2 ⅝″, pearl, **$73**.

J. Clarke, wood, **$18**.

Cattaraugus, 4 blades, 3 ⅜″, bone stag, **$60**.

Jos. Rodgers, 2 ¼″, tortoise shell, **$38**.

"Gunstock" Pens

There is almost no such thing as a gunstock pen knife. One exception was made by Case, the 3 ½-inch rounded-ended 87 pattern. This is sort of a sleeveboard with a step instead of a ramp. It was offered with pearl handles or stag handles.

Another exception is the gunstock lobster or orange blossom, covered in the lobster chapter. Yet another exception is a sort of double gunstock pen knife made in Sheffield in the 19th century.

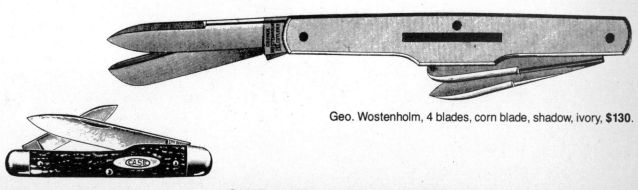

Geo. Wostenholm, 4 blades, corn blade, shadow, ivory, **$130**.

No. 5287   Case Tested XX, 3 ½″, genuine stag, **$225**.

Congress and Tobacco Knives

The "congress" knife is curved like a crescent. It usually has squared corners, though a few have rounded corners. Congress knives can have two, three, four, six, or eight blades. They always have a sheepfoot master blade.

The largest congress knives are from 3½ to over 4 inches long. These large congress knives were often called "tobacco knives," because they were favored for carving bite-sized chews from plugs of chewing tobacco. Larger whittlers of various shapes were also sometimes called tobacco knives. Tobacco knives never have a manicure blade.

It seems that the congress knife appeared on the scene some time in the first third of the last century. It is one of the earliest patterns created specifically for the American market. Knife fanciers have long speculated on the origins of the names "senator" and "congress" for the shapes they refer to, but no solid evidence has yet surfaced.

Not only is the congress a purely American pattern, for most of its history it was a purely southern pattern. Until about a generation ago, you could hardly find one west of the Rockies or very far north of Mason and Dixon's line. English firms and the big northeastern cutlery manufacturers such as Remington and New York Knife Company made congress knives in large numbers, but they mainly distributed them through wholesalers in the Southeast.

An appealing feature to look for on congress knives, one also found on barlows and other patterns made for the southern market, is fancy bolsters. Fancy bolsters are often accompanied by fancy handle materials such as pearl.

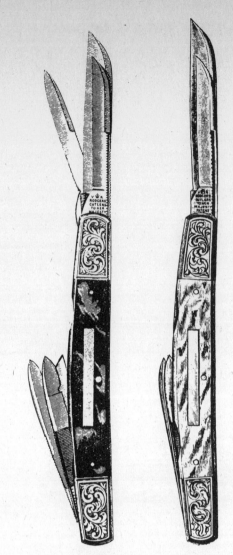

Jos. Rodgers: 6 blades, engraved solid gold bolsters, tortoise shell, **$270**; 4 blades, engraved silver bolsters, pearl, **$147**.

Remington, fancy bolsters, bone stag, **$170**.

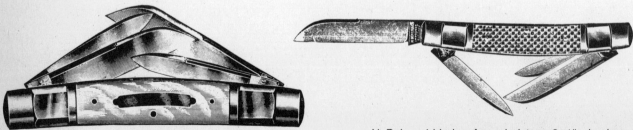

H. Boker, 4 blades, fancy bolsters, pearl, **$50**.

H. Boker, 4 blades, fancy bolsters, 3 ½", checkered bone, **$39**.

Congress and Tobacco Knives

No. 7763

Schrade Cut. Co., 3 ⅞", bone stag, **$50**.

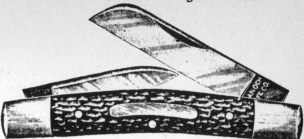

Actual size   No. 2280   *3¼ inches long*

Napanoch Knife Co., bone stag, **$75**.

W.H. Morley, 4 blades, fancy bolsters, 3 ¾", genuine stag, **$73**.

Ulster Knife Co., 4 blades, shadow, pearl, **$83**.

Winchester, 3 ¼", pearl, **$98**.

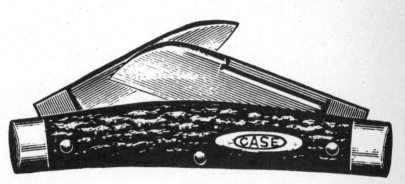

Case Tested XX, 4 ⅛", bone stag, **$94**.

American Shear & Knife Co., bone stag, **$40**.

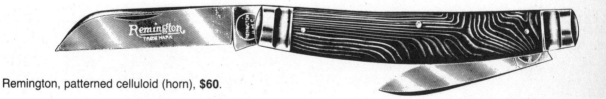

Remington, patterned celluloid (horn), **$60**.

Remington, 4 blades, fancy bolsters, pearl, **$220**.

Crown or Coffin

This scarce 19th century pattern looks more like a slender barrel or cask than it does either a crown or a coffin. More than anything, it looks like a congress knife before it got bent. Indeed, the coffin may be the direct antecedent of the congress pattern, but I doubt that we will ever know for sure. Another possible ancestor of the congress is the English sort of "double gunstock" pen knife mentioned above.

Coffin pen knives are slender and have squared corners and convex sides. They can have two, three, or four blades. I have seen them with horn, ivory, and tortoise shell handles.

A few 20th century firms made pen knives that are nearly rectangular. I have never seen a name for these, but I guess you could call them a modern crown. The Case -78s and the Wallkill River Works closed backs by New York Knife Company are examples.

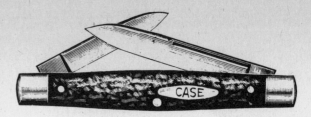

Case, 3″, bone stag: Tested XX, **$65**; XX, **$26**.

H. Boker, genuine stag, **$30**.

Winchester, tip bolsters, 3″, bone stag, **$59**.

Jos. Rodgers, 4 blades, engraved silver bolsters, pearl, **$68**.

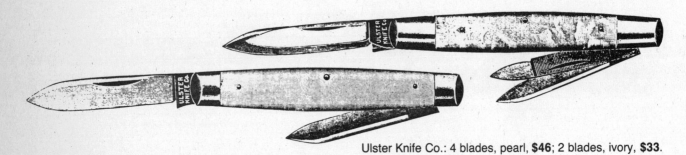

Ulster Knife Co.: 4 blades, pearl, **$46**; 2 blades, ivory, **$33**.

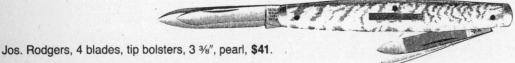

Jos. Rodgers, 4 blades, tip bolsters, 3 ⅜″, pearl, **$41**.

Modern Crown Knives

H. Boker, shadow, fancy (pearl) closed back, 2 ⅜″, multi-piece pearl, **$32**.

H. Boker, tip bolsters, 2 ⅝″, pearl, **$15**.

Swell-Center Congress

The great majority of congress knives have squared corners, while only a few have rounded corners. There exists a curved pattern with rounded corners similar to a round-ended congress, only with a swell in the middle of the back. It is called the "sway-back" or "swell-center congress."

Swell-center congress pen knives are small knives of premium quality. They usually have sunk joints, milled liners, and fancy handles such as pearl or tortoise shell. Older sway-backs are often shadow knives, made without bolsters. Most sway-backs display their kinship to congress knives by having sheepfoot master blades. However, they were also made with clip point and Wharncliffe master blades.

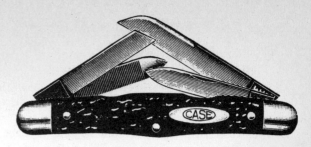

Case Tested XX, 4 blades, bone stag, **$135**.

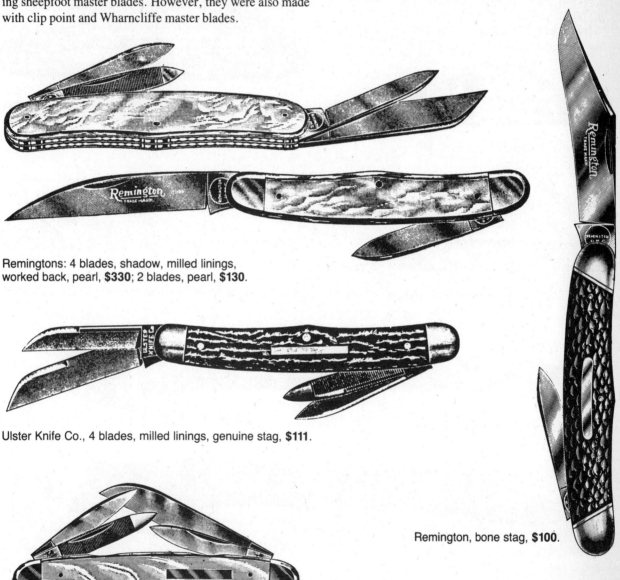

Remingtons: 4 blades, shadow, milled linings, worked back, pearl, **$330**; 2 blades, pearl, **$130**.

Ulster Knife Co., 4 blades, milled linings, genuine stag, **$111**.

Remington, bone stag, **$100**.

H. Boker, 4 blades, pearl, **$38**.

Jos. Rodgers, 2 blades, 3 ¼", horn, **$45**.

Swell-Center Serpentine

This pattern looks superficially similar to the sway-back, the main difference being that the handle is tapered, rather than being equal-ended. It advertises that it is *not* a congress-derived pattern by almost always having a clip or a spear master blade, rather than a sheepfoot.

The swell-center serpentine pen knife is similar in shape to the "Eureka" jack knives and cattle knives. However, it is both slimmer in proportion and smaller.

Like most other pen knife shapes, this one was often used for whittlers. Case's most popular whittler is the 6308 made in this shape, so the firm calls its ordinary two-bladed swell-center serpentine with a clip master blade a "half whittler." Collectors sometimes use the term half-whittler for other pen knives with clip master blades.

Case Tested XX, half whittler, bone stag, **$80**.

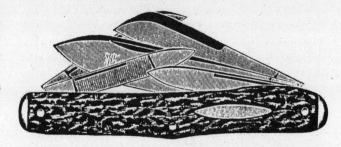

New York Knife Co., 5 blades, tip bolsters, bone stag, **$91**.

H. Boker, fancy bolsters, 2 9/16″, pearl, **$30**.

H. Boker, 4 blades, glove buttoner blade, tip bolsters, 2 3/4″, pearl, **$33**.

Tourist's Knife, G. S. Mounted, Selected Pearl Handle.

Ulster Knife Co., 4 blades, buttoner blade, tip bolsters, 2 11/16″, pearl, **$75**.

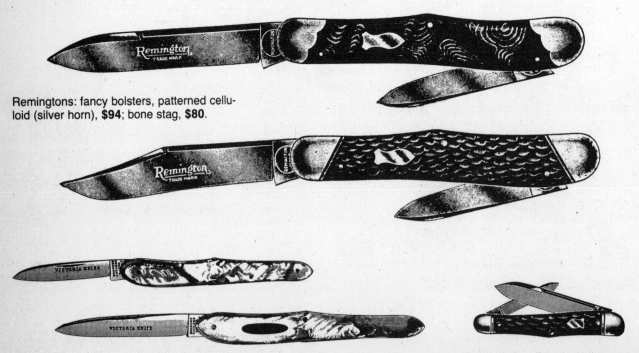

Remingtons: fancy bolsters, patterned celluloid (silver horn), **$94**; bone stag, **$80**.

Jos. Rodgers, 2 blades, shadow, pearl: 2 3/4″, **$44**; 3 1/4″, **$55**.

Schrade Cut. Co., 3 1/4″, bone stag, **$50**.

Serpentine Pen Knives

As with serpentine jacks, the term serpentine pen knives includes all more or less S-curved pen knives, whether tapered or equal-ended. Equal-end (or nearly so) serpentine pen knives are two-blade versions of the junior premium stock knife, so they are often called premium pen knives. Most premium pen knives, like stock knives, have clip master blades. As with stock knives, premium pen knives come in both round-end and square-end versions.

Markedly tapered serpentine pen knives are often called "dog-legs." However, if they have Wharncliffe master blades, they are called Wharncliffe knives.

A Wharncliffe blade has a straight edge like a sheepfoot. However, its back is gently curved and its point is more acute. Lord Wharncliffe, for whom the pattern was named, and who may in fact have designed it, was a noble patron of Joseph Rodgers & Sons of Sheffield some time around 1830.

If the second blade of a double-ended serpentine knife is anything other than a pen blade or a nail file (for example a spey, a spear, or a punch), then the knife is considered a double-end jack knife rather than a pen knife.

Premium Pen Knives

Case, 3 ¼″, bone stag: Tested XX, **$60**; XX, **$25**.

R-7573   **R-7543**

Remingtons, 3 ¼″, tip bolsters, bone stag, **$54 each**.

Remingtons: bone stag, **$60**; tip bolsters, patterned celluloid (gold bronze), **$43**.

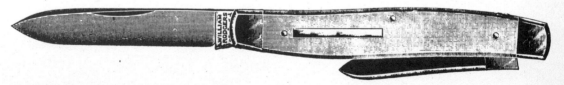

Wm. Rodgers (J. Clarke), smooth white bone, **$14**.

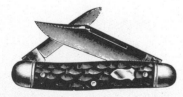

Schrade Cut. Co., 3 ½″, bone stag, **$25**.

Winchester, 3 ¼″, ebony, **$54**.

Robeson, tip bolsters, 3 ¼″, white celluloid, **$9**.

Wharncliffe Knives

Jos. Rodgers: 3″, pearl, **$52**; 4″, genuine stag, **$75**.

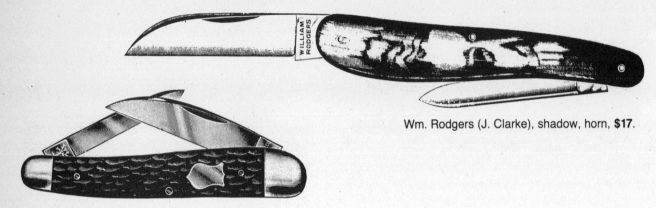

Wm. Rodgers (J. Clarke), shadow, horn, **$17**.

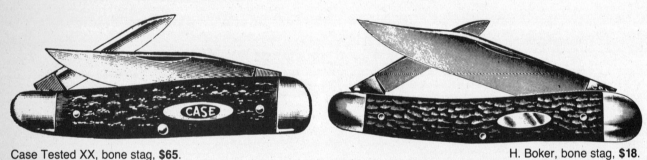

H. Boker, bone stag, **$22**.

"Dog-Leg" Serpentine Pen Knives

Case Tested XX, bone stag, **$65**.

H. Boker, bone stag, **$18**.

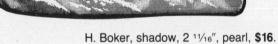

Robeson, 3 ⅜″, bone stag, **$18**.

H. Boker, shadow, 2 ¹¹⁄₁₆″, pearl, **$16**.

Schrade Cut. Co., tip bolsters, 3 ¼″,
bone stag, **$32**.

Schrade Cut. Co., 3 ⁹⁄₁₆″, black celluloid, **$25**.

Winchester, tip bolsters, 3 ⅜″, bone
stag, **$59**.

Swell-Center and Balloon Pens

In the *Jack Knives* chapter, I described the swell-center jack as looking like a snake that had swallowed a short stick sideways. Swell-center pens have this same aspect, with slight pointed bulges top and bottom.

The two basic types of swell-center pen knives are the equal-ended, which are simply called "swell-center," and the tapered, which are called "balloon," or "swell-center balloon." Balloon knives have bulbous rounded ends shaped like hot-air balloons.

Some symmetrical swell-centers have this type of round ends, as well. Others have pointed ends.

Western States called a small swell-center pen with pointed ends the Northfield pattern. This was no doubt a tribute to its founder's early years working for the Northfield Knife Company in Connecticut.

In the 1870s, several American pocketknife firms, including Shipley of Philadelphia, and Holley of Lakeville, Connecticut, called their small round-ended swell-center pens "Jenny Lind" knives. They were honoring the immensely popular concert singer who was known to her American fans as the Swedish Nightingale.

LADIES' OR GENTLEMEN'S KNIFE

No. 2180

2⅞ inches long, pearl handle, German silver lined, two blades, German silver bolster. This is of the very highest quality. There are none better made.

American Shear & Knife Co., **$47**.

H. Boker, pearl, **$30**.

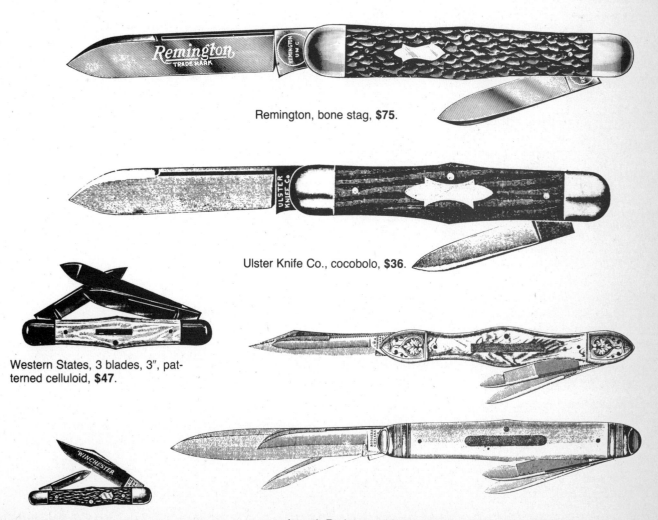

Remington, bone stag, **$75**.

Ulster Knife Co., cocobolo, **$36**.

Western States, 3 blades, 3″, patterned celluloid, **$47**.

Winchester, 3 ⅝″, bone stag, **$75**.

Joseph Rodgers: 4 blades, engraved silver bolsters, 3 ¼″, pearl, **$119**; 5 blades, fancy bolsters, 3 ¾″, ivory, **$185**.

Whittlers

"WHITTLER" is a modern collector's term that refers to a particular type of construction. Any pen knife with this type of construction is considered a whittler, regardless of its shape or handle die.

A whittler is a three-blade pen knife with a large blade in one end and two small cutting blades of equal length in the other end. Whittlers have two springs. Each small blade bears on one of the springs. The large blade is extra thick and it bears on *both* springs. The thick master blade bearing on two springs is the most distinctive feature of a whittler.

The majority of whittlers have a center divider that separates the tangs of the two small blades, and that also separates the two springs for part of their length. This divider can be seen along the back of the knife, where it tapers to nothing just past the center pin.

Other whittlers show no divider at the back. Often the two springs of this type are tapered, and they are not separated at all. The tangs of the two small blades are separated by a very small divider at the end of the knife. An early ancestor of this type of whittler construction is shown in figure 7.1.A. of *Foreign, Exotic, Primitive, and Historical Folding Knives*.

Whittlers range in size from ladies' pen knives under 2 inches long closed, on up to practical woodcarving tools over 4 inches long. Larger whittlers were called "carpenter's knives" by some manufacturers.

Many small knives with "whittler" construction have a manicure blade in place of one of the small cutting blades. These knives are not considered "true" whittlers by some collectors, but a nice one is not out of place in a whittler collection.

The whittler has always been a premium priced knife; a lot of hand-work goes into each one. They were not made by the low price firms, except in Germany around the turn of the century. Even the low priced German ones have high grade mounts and handle material. Most whittlers have brass liners and nickel silver bolsters; some have nickel silver liners. I have only seen a couple of whittlers with iron mounts.

Handle Materials

Handle material on whittlers runs the gamut. Wood, often ebony, seems to have been standard on American-made whittlers in the 19th century, but it is almost unknown after World War I. Ivory and smooth white bone also are common on 19th century whittlers, but almost never found on whittlers made in this century. Green cow horn was a popular early material that continued in use through the 1930s. Aluminum was used by a few firms such as Holley.

Pearl has been the top-of-the-line handle material for whittlers in this century. Even very cheap turn-of-the-century German whittlers usually have pearl handles. In the 19th century, pearl shared the spotlight with tortoise shell. A few pearl whittlers are still being made, usually in limited editions. Genuine stag was also used on whittlers, though much less often than pearl.

In the first half of the 20th century, the standard handles for whittlers were bone stag and celluloid. Celluloid used was mainly its imitative forms: imitation ivory, horn, and wood, plus all the different colors of imitation pearl.

Since whittlers were premium priced knives, gaudy multi-colored celluloids were rarely used on them. However, clear celluloid "picture handles" were fairly common. Smooth black composition has been used widely since the 1920s. Rough black was used in the 1940s, while various synthetics and laminated woods have been used more recently.

Collecting Whittlers

With all their variety, a collection of whittlers can be as narrow or as diverse as you wish. Some big firms, such as Remington and Ulster, made nearly a hundred varieties of whittler. You can collect all types, or just one brand, one shape, one handle material, or whatever you find appealing. Many knife fanciers collect whittlers, and demand for them is strong among brand and handle material collectors as well.

PRICE CHART FOR WHITTLERS

Base prices for WHITTLERS 3¼ to 4 inches long
with: three cutting blades (no manicure blade); full
bolsters; bone stag handles. Excellent unsharpened condition

VALUE RANGE	VERY HIGH	HIGH	MEDIUM	LOW
SHAPE				
EQUAL-END:	$110.	$ 50.	$30.	$10.
SLEEVEBOARD:	115.	60.	35.	12.
JUMBO:	220.	150.	75.	30.
OVAL or CIGAR:	125.¹	75.	45.	16.
CONGRESS:	150.	65.	40.	12.
SWELL-CENTER CONGRESS:	165.	70.	45.	20.
CROWN:	140.	65.	40.	12.
SERPENTINE:	130.	55.	35.	10.
WHARNCLIFFE:	140.	65.	45.	12.
SWELL-CENTER SERPENTINE:	125.	55.	35.	10.
NORFOLK:	225.	85.	55.	18.
SWELL-CENTER BALLOON:	135.	60.	40.	12.
PHYSICIAN'S:	110.	65.	40.	15.

¹ Except Case 5391 (see text)

CONSTRUCTION

Locking master blade: **add 65%**
Saber ground master blade: **add 10%**
Punch blade: **add 20%**
File or manicure blade: **subtract 25%**

Engraved gold bolsters: **add 100%**
Engraved silver bolsters: **add 50%**
Fancy stamped nickel silver bolsters: **add 25%**
Engraved aluminum bolsters: **add 20%**
Tip bolsters or no bolsters: **subtract 20%**

SIZE

Over 4 inches closed: **add 100%**
Under 3¼ inches closed: **subtract 30%**

HANDLE MATERIAL

Pearl: **add 60%**
Genuine ivory or tortoise shell: **add 45%**
Genuine stag: **add 30%**
Smooth bone or horn: **subtract 10%**
Wood: **subtract 20%**
Advertising or picture handles: see *Advertising Knives*, also page 26
Patterned celluloid: **subtract 20%**
Solid color celluloid or composition: **subtract 35%**
Fiber or aluminum: **subtract 40%**
Modern plastic or laminate: **subtract 50%**

CONDITION

Mint: **add 50%**
Worn: **subtract 50%**
Broken: **Subtract 90%**

Equal-End Whittlers

Whittlers have been made in almost every variety of handle shape and size used for standard two- and four-blade pen knives. Ordinary equal-end or senator whittlers are the commonest. However, most of these, especially the smaller ones and the low-priced German ones, have a nail file blade, so they are not "real" whittlers. The master blade in an equal-end whittler is almost always a spear-point.

H. Boker, file blade, fancy bolsters, bone stag, **$28**.

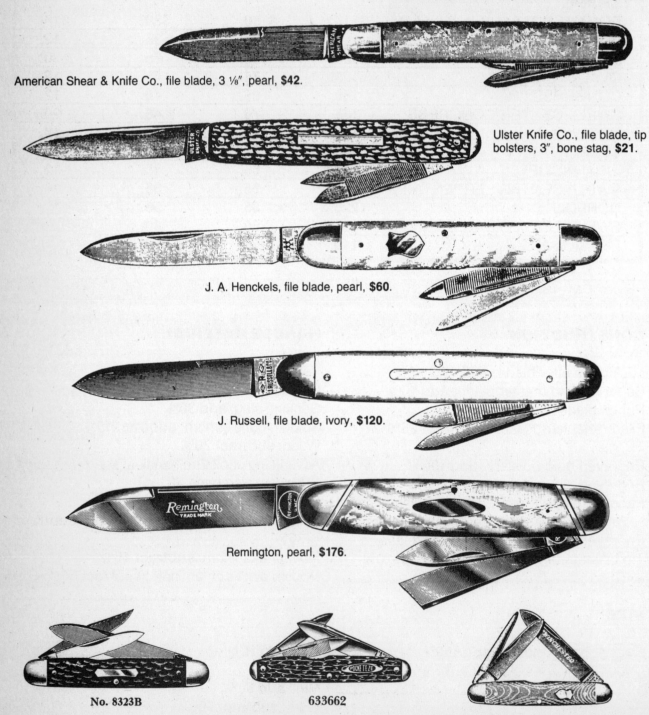

American Shear & Knife Co., file blade, 3 ⅛", pearl, **$42**.

Ulster Knife Co., file blade, tip bolsters, 3", bone stag, **$21**.

J. A. Henckels, file blade, pearl, **$60**.

J. Russell, file blade, ivory, **$120**.

Remington, pearl, **$176**.

No. 8323B

633662

Schrade Cut. Co., 4", bone stag, **$50**.

Robeson, file blade, tip bolsters, 3 ¼", bone stag, **$18**.

Winchester, punch blade, 3 ⅜", patterned celluloid (gray), **$106**.

Sleeveboard Whittlers

Sleeveboard whittlers are also relatively common. The larger of these are true whittling knives, often with a stout clip or saber clip master blade. The two small blades on these heavier sleeveboards are usually a pen blade and sharp pointed coping blade. A few sleeveboard whittlers, mainly from before the First World War, have locking main blades.

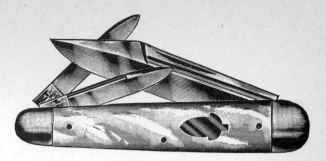

H. Boker, saber blade, 3 3/16″, pearl, **$43**.

No. 32879—3¾″ Carpenter's Knife. Large Clip blade, Pen and Sheepfoot. Brass lined. Nickel silver bolsters. Full polish. Stag handle. Shielded.

Cattaraugus, 3 ¾″, bone stag, **$60**.

H. Boker, lockback, bone stag, **$58**.

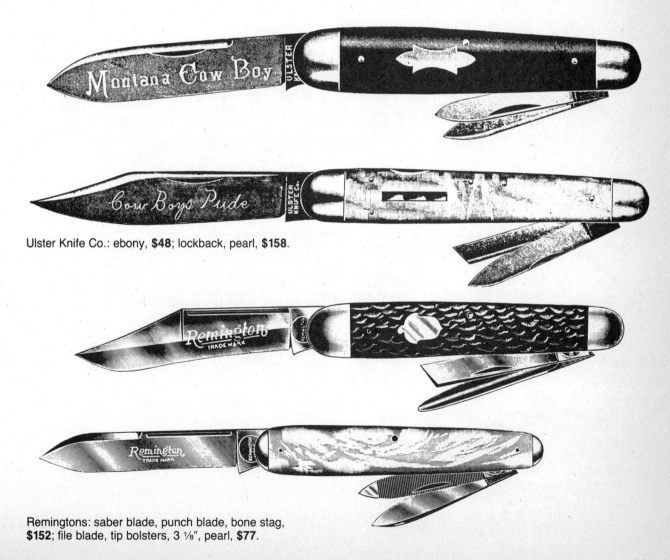

Ulster Knife Co.: ebony, **$48**; lockback, pearl, **$158**.

Remingtons: saber blade, punch blade, bone stag, **$152**; file blade, tip bolsters, 3 ⅛″, pearl, **$77**.

Jumbo Whittlers

Big, fat sleeveboard whittlers are called "jumbos." Jumbo whittlers have been given all sorts of special names. Among these are "engineer's knife" (Western States) and "Swedish pattern electrician's knife" (Boker). All jumbo knives are relatively rare and valuable.

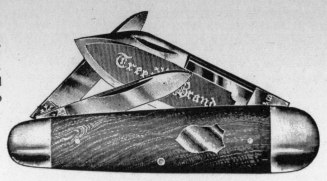

H. Boker, wood, **$60**.

3 Blade, Glazed Etched, Brass Lined, "Engineer's Knife," G. S. Trimmed Ebony Handle.

Ulster Knife Co., wood, **$120**.

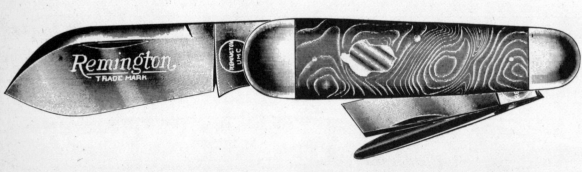

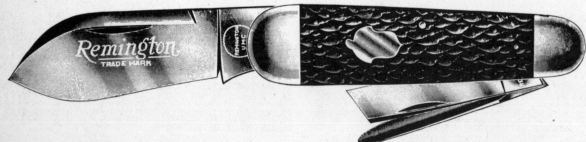

Remingtons, punch blades: patterned celluloid (crimson), **$210**; bone stag, **$265**.

Stiletto (P. H. & S.), 3 ⅝", bone stag, **$150**.

Oval, Cigar, or Anglo-Saxon Whittlers

Oval "cigar" whittlers are quite rare. They are generally premium quality knives with sunk joints and spear master blades.

Perhaps the most valuable Case pen knife is the 5391 4 ½-inch cigar whittler. I have seen this pattern quoted as high as $1,500 to $1,800 in mint condition. Remingtons of the same pattern (7756 and 7766) are quoted at about one-third of this sum.

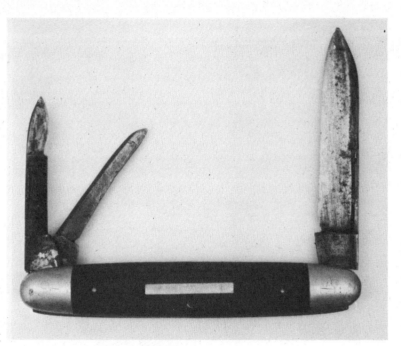

Southington, file blade, wood, **$45**.

J. Clarke, smooth white bone, **$40**.

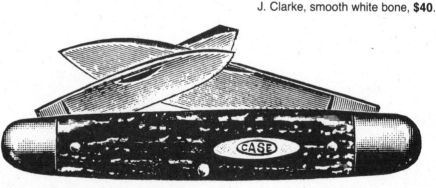

Case Tested XX or Case XX 5391, genuine stag, **$1,000**.

Remington, 4 ⅝", genuine stag, **$325**.

Gunstock Whittlers

The only gunstock whittler I am aware of is the "orange blossom." This is a lobster-spring pattern and is covered in the *Lobster Pen Knives* chapter.

Congress Whittlers and Three-Blade Tobacco Knives

Congress whittlers are relatively rare. They exhibit all the variations in size, handles, and bolsters that other congress knives do. Most smaller congress ''whittlers'' have manicure blades, while larger ''tobacco knives'' with whittler construction do not. Just about all congress and swell-center congress knives have sheepfoot master blades.

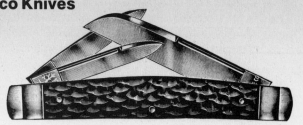

H. Boker, 3 1/16", bone stag, **$28**.

Ulster Knife Co., file blade, pearl, **$78**.

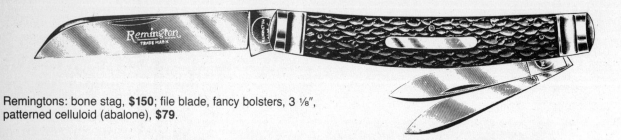

Remingtons: bone stag, **$150**; file blade, fancy bolsters, 3 1/8", patterned celluloid (abalone), **$79**.

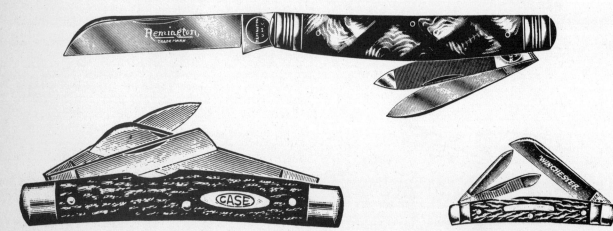

Case Tested XX, 3 1/2", bone stag, **$150**.

Winchester, file blade, 3 1/4", bone stag, **$113**.

Jos. Rodgers: file blade, pearl, $78; genuine stag, $82.

Swell-Center Congress "Whittlers"

Swell-center congress or swayback "whittlers" probably should not be counted as whittlers at all. They are light-weight premium quality knives, and every one of the few I have seen had a manicure blade. However, since they are constructed like whittlers, they are included here for consistency.

Case Tested XX, file blade, 3 ⅛", bone stag, **$100**.

H. Bokers, file blades, 3 1/16": genuine stag, **$35**; pearl, **$43**.

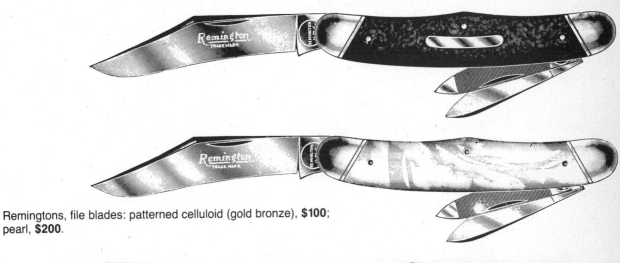

Remingtons, file blades: patterned celluloid (gold bronze), **$100**; pearl, **$200**.

Jos. Rodgers, fancy bolsters, bone stag, **$88**.

Crown Whittlers

I do not recall ever having seen a crown whittler, and I have only seen a few catalog pictures of them. However, 19th century American pocketknife price lists include various sizes of three-blade crown pen knives, and I presume that most of these were whittlers.

Humason & Beckley, file blade, tip bolsters, 3 ¼", pearl, **$62**.

Ulster Knife Co., 3 ⅛", ivory, **$66**.

Serpentine and Wharncliffe Whittlers

Serpentine whittlers are almost as common as sleeve-boards. Heavier serpentines or ''dog-legs'' usually have clip master blades. Slimmer serpentines more often have spear master blades. Some firms made Wharncliffe whittlers, serpentines with a Wharncliffe master blade.

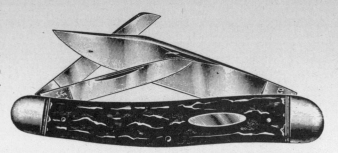

H. Boker, genuine stag, **$46**.

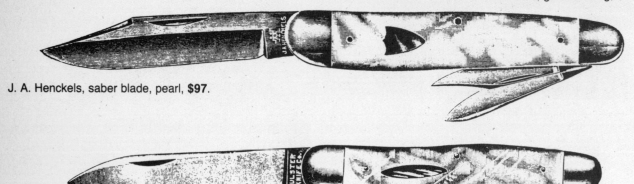

J. A. Henckels, saber blade, pearl, **$97**.

Ulster Knife Co., 3 ³/₁₆″, pearl, **$62**.

No. 8794KT

Schrade Cut. Co.: saber blade, 3 ⁷/₈″, bone stag, **$60**; tip bolsters, 3 ¼″, patterned celluloid (horn), **$35**.

Winchester, punch blade, 3 ¼″, bone stag, **$156**.

Wharncliffe Whittlers

Schrade Cut. Co., 3 ¼″, bone stag, **$65**.

Jos. Rodgers, 3 ³/₁₆″, genuine stag, **$60**.

Ulster Knife Co., file blade, pearl, **$78**.

Swell-Center Serpentine and Norfolk Whittlers

Swell-center serpentine (or serpentine balloon) whittlers were made with both clip point and spear point master blades. Case's -08 handle die is a popular small version of this pattern.

A specific ornate version of the swell-center serpentine whittler is called the Norfolk whittler. These have a distinctive saber clip blade used in no other knife. I have seen examples by Rodgers and by Remington. Some of these have locking main blades.

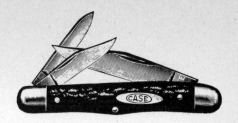

No. 6308
Case Tested XX, 3 ¼", bone stag, **$125**.

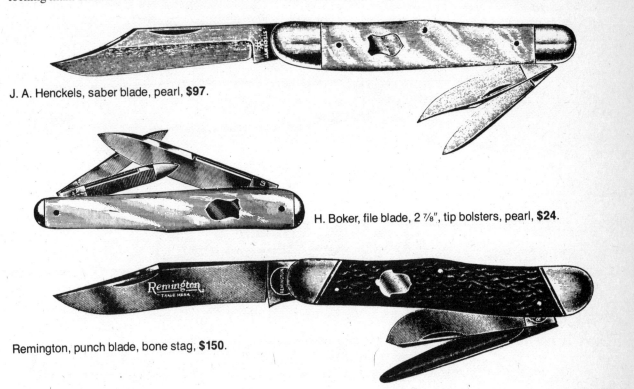

J. A. Henckels, saber blade, pearl, **$97**.

H. Boker, file blade, 2 ⅞", tip bolsters, pearl, **$24**.

Remington, punch blade, bone stag, **$150**.

Norfolk Whittlers

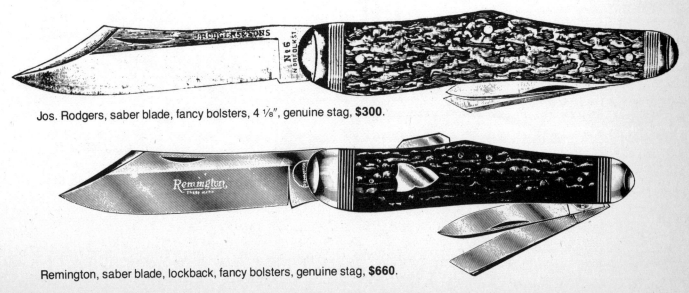

Jos. Rodgers, saber blade, fancy bolsters, 4 ⅛", genuine stag, **$300**.

Remington, saber blade, lockback, fancy bolsters, genuine stag, **$660**.

Swell-Center Whittlers

Swell-center whittlers almost always have balloon ends. Knives with other shaped ends command about a 50% premium. The master blade can be either a spear or a clip. I consider the swell-center balloon whittler to be one of the most attractive pocketknife patterns.

Remington, file blade, tip bolsters, 3″, bone stag, **$57**.

Winchester, 3 ½″, bone stag, **$135**.

Remington, saber blade, punch blade, buffalo horn, **$160**.

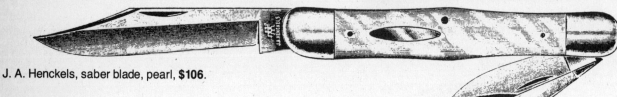

J. A. Henckels, saber blade, pearl, **$106**.

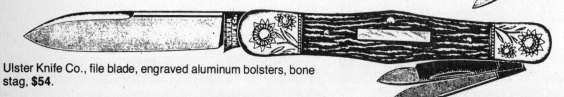

Ulster Knife Co., file blade, engraved aluminum bolsters, bone stag, **$54**.

HAND ENGRAVED

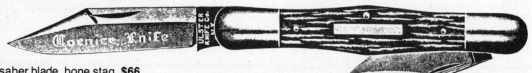

Ulster Knife Co., saber blade, bone stag, **$66**.

Ulster Knife Co., unusual shape, wood, **$72**.

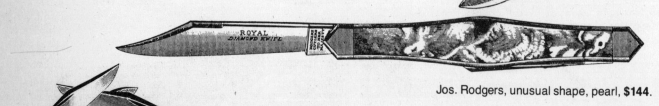

Jos. Rodgers, unusual shape, pearl, **$144**.

No. 6383

Case, 3 ½″, bone stag: Tested XX, **$135**; XX, **$60**.

Three-Blade Physicians' Knives

Long slim whittlers were made in a variety of shapes including equal-end, sleeveboard, and swell-center serpentine. These knives always have long slim spear master blades. They were often listed in old catalogs as physicians' knives. In collections they are usually included with physicians' pattern jack knives or "pill-busters."

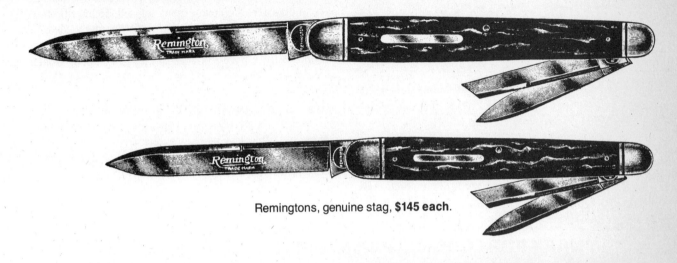

Remingtons, genuine stag, **$145 each**.

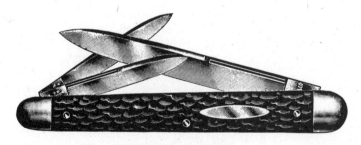

PHYSICIAN'S KNIFE

H. Boker, bone stag, **$40**.

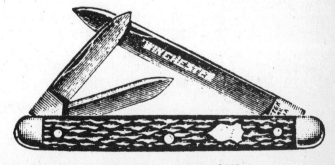

H. Boker, bone stag, **$40**.

Winchester, bone stag, **$110**.

Lobster Pen Knives

AN ORDINARY pen knife, like most folding knives, has its spring or springs in the back, where they are plainly visible. By contrast, a "lobster" pen knife has its spring or springs (often a single "split" or branched spring) inside the middle of the handle.

This hidden central spring allows a lobster to have blades on both top and bottom, as well as at one or both ends.

Because its spring is in the middle, a lobster pen always has its pivot pins set off to the sides of the long axis of the knife.

The action of two blades pivoting at the corners of one end of a lobster pen knife resembles the action of a lobster's claws. I believe this is how the knife got its name.

Lobster pen knives are flat and lightly built. Heavy-duty knives with blades both top and bottom are covered in the *Multi-Blades* section.

Except for a few in the "Sheffield" pattern, lobsters never have full bolsters. Of course many lobsters do have tip bolsters. Bolsters or their absence do not affect the value of a lobster.

Lobsters often have bails so that they can be hung from a watch chain. This too does not affect value, unless a knife that was made with a bail has lost it.

Lobster spring pen knives were made in a number of standard shapes. Most of these shapes have exotic sounding names, and some have more than one name.

Most lobster pen knives have plain or rounded ends. Some have pointed ends. The pointed ones have "candle-end" as part of their names.

PRICE CHART FOR LOBSTER PEN KNIVES

Base prices for LOBSTER PEN KNIVES of any size, with three blades (except where indicated); bone stag (jigged bone) handles; with or without bail. Excellent unsharpened condition.

VALUE RANGE	VERY HIGH	HIGH	MED.	LOW
SHAPE				
2-BL. OVAL or CHARM:	$ 40.	$25.	$15.	$ 7.
3-BLADE OVAL (FROG):	45.	30.	20.	7.
EQUAL-END:	45.	30.	20.	8.
SUNFISH LOBSTER:	50.	35.	20.	8.
DOLPHIN (FISH CANDLE-END):	75.	50.	30.	15.
SERPENTINE (CANDLE-END: (2 Blades)	60.	40.	25.	10.
SLEEVEBOARD:	45.	30.	20.	7.
"SHEFFIELD":	50.	35.	22.	8.
SERPENTINE SLEEVEBOARD:	70.	50.	30.	14.
FANCY SLEEVEBOARD:	100.	60.	40.	18.
GUNSTOCK (3-BLADE):	90.	55.	35.	16.
ORANGE BLOSSOM (4-BLADE GUNSTOCK):	120.	75.	45.	20.

CONSTRUCTION

Four blades (not in chart): **add 20%**
More than four blades: **add 40%**
Two blades (not in chart): **subtract 25%**
Scissors: **add 25%**
Tweezers and pick in handle: **add 25%**

HANDLE MATERIALS

Genuine pearl or ivory: **add 30%**
Multi-piece pearl: **add 35%**
Genuine stag or tortoise shell: **add 25%**
Smooth bone, horn, or wood: **subtract 25%**
Patterned celluloid (except "water-fall"): **subtract 35%**
Plain celluloid: **subtract 50%**
Sterling silver: **add $8-12.**
Plain metal: **subtract 50%**
Advertising or pictorial: see *Advertising Knives*, also page 26
Decorated gold or silver plated: see *Skeleton Knives*

CONDITION

Mint condition: **add 50%**
Original bail missing: **subtract 25%**
Worn: **subtract 50%**
Broken: **subtract 90%**

Oval Lobsters and Charm Knives

The simplest lobster is the two-blade oval. It has a small spear blade on top and a manicure blade on the bottom. A candle-end or pointed two-blade oval lobster is called a "charm knife."

Three-blade oval lobsters have a pen blade facing the spear blade. This style is tapered, but it has curved sides, unlike a sleeveboard, which has straight sides. Another name for this style is the "frog" pattern.

Jos. Rodgers, 2-blade charm, pearl, **$33.**

Ulster Knife Co., 2-blade, pearl, **$33.**

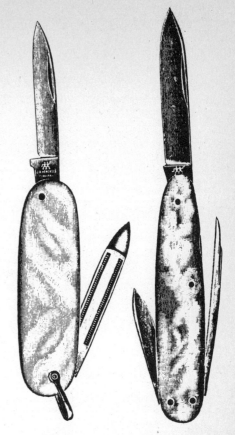

J. A. Henckels, pearl: 2-blade, **$33;** 3 blade, **$39.**

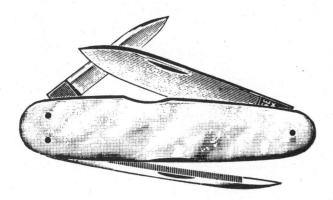

Case Tested XXs, pearl, **$59 each.**

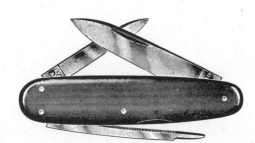

H. Boker, plain gun metal, **$10.**

No. 9736 Shac (*Cut ⅔ size*)

Scissors Knife, Oval Lobster pattern with shackle, 2⅝ inches long; 4 blades (manicure file, pen and spear pocket blades and scissors); nickel silver linings and shackle; cleaned inside; blades full crocus polished; Mother of Pearl handle.
Same, without shackle. . . . . No. 9736

Schrade Cut. Co., scissors, pearl, **$49.**

Equal-End Lobsters

The commonest lobster pen is the equal-end. Some of these are rounded at the ends, like other equal-end knives. Others are oblong, sort of a round-cornered rectangle. A few are quite rectangular, complete with sharp corners. Oblong lobsters are often pinched in slightly top and bottom.

Case Tested XX, 2 blades, scissors, pearl, **$55.**

Ulster Knife Co.: 2 blades, pearl, **$29;** 4 blades, genuine stag, **$45.**

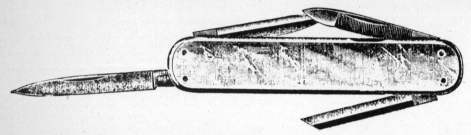

American Shear & Knife Co., 4 blades, pearl, **$47.**

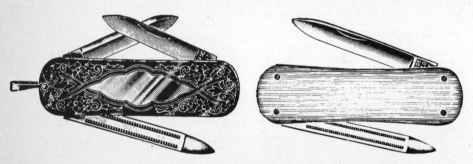

Schrade Cut. Co.: sterling silver, **$38;** 2 blades, patterned celluloid (ivory), **$15.**

J. A. Henckels, pearl, **$39.**

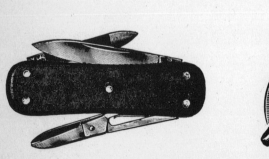

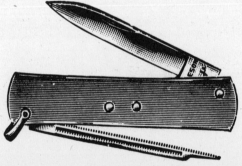

H. Boker, 2 blades, scissors, plain gun metal, **$10.**

Robeson, plain chrome plated, **$8.**

Sunfish Lobsters and Dolphins

Equal-end lobsters with pointed "candle" ends and pinched sides are usually given fish names. Those pinched near one end so that they look like a planarian, the flat-worm beloved of biology teachers, are called "fish candle-end lobsters," or "dolphins." Those pinched in the middle are called "sunfish lobsters." ("Sunfish" alone is the name of a large double-end jack knife, also called "elephant toenail.")

No. 8654GT

Sunfish Lobster pattern, 3 inches long; 3 blades; brass lined; nickel silver tips; cleaned inside; spear blade crocus polished on one side; Green Pearl Celluloid handle.
Cocobola Celluloid handle . . No. 8654CT
Golden Pearl Celluloid handle   No. 8654GPT
Tortoise Shell Celluloid handle   No. 8654ST
Ivory Celluloid handle . . . No. 8654WT
Assorted Celluloid handles . No. 8654ACT

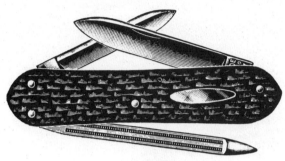

No. 8653

Schrade Cut. Co.: bone stag (above), **$35;** patterned celluloid (upper right), **$23;** pearl (lower right), **$46.**

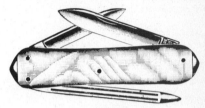

No. 8656T

Sunfish Lobster pattern, 3 inches long; 3 blades; nickel silver lined, with milled edges; nickel silver tips; cleaned inside; blades full crocus polished; Mother of Pearl handle.
With nickel silver shackle   No. 8656TShackle

Dolphins (Fish Candle-End Lobsters)

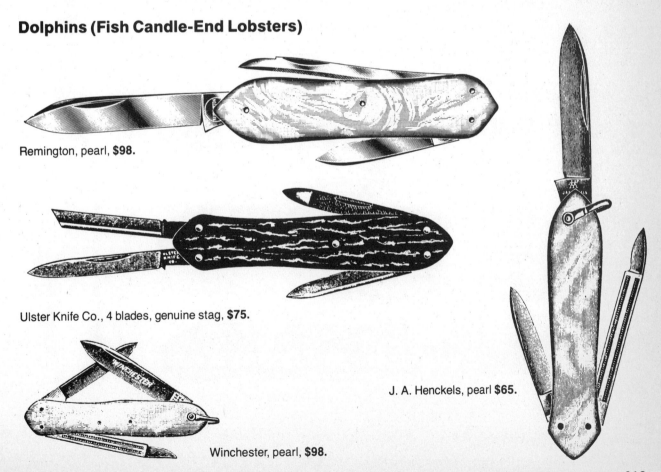

Remington, pearl, **$98.**

Ulster Knife Co., 4 blades, genuine stag, **$75.**

Winchester, pearl, **$98.**

J. A. Henckels, pearl **$65.**

Serpentine Candle-End Lobsters

I have never seen a straight-sided equal-end candle-end lobster, but this S-shaped version is relatively common. Serpentine candle-end lobsters seem always to have only two blades. Round-ended two-blade serpentine lobsters are very unusual, but their value is the same as the candle-ends.

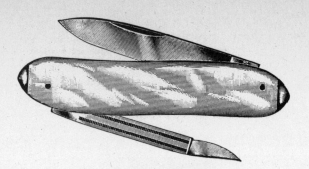

H. Boker, pearl, **$33.**

Winchester, bone stag, **$60.**

Remingtons (from top to bottom): bone stag, **$60**; pearl, **$78**; patterned celluloid (horn, gold bronze), **$51**; plain gun metal, **$30.**

J. A. Henckels, round ends, pearl, **$52.**

Sleeveboard Lobsters

Sleeveboard lobsters, like other sleeveboard knives, are tapered and have straight sides and round ends. I have never seen a sleeveboard with candle ends. Most sleeveboard lobsters have three blades, as on the oval frog pattern, but I have also seen them with both fewer and more. The sleeveboard is one of the commonest lobster patterns.

Keen Kutter, 3″, bone stag, **$30.**

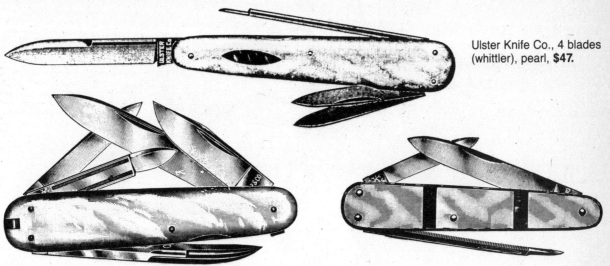

Ulster Knife Co., 4 blades (whittler), pearl, **$47.**

Pick and Tweezer

H. Bokers: 4 blades, scissors, pick and tweezers, pearl, **$49;** multi-piece pearl, **$27.**

Sheffield Pattern Lobsters

One type of sleeveboard lobster has a cut-out most of the length of its back in order to accommodate a large manicure blade as thick as the entire knife. Western States called this style the ''Sheffield pattern,'' which is as good a name as any. These knives sometimes have full bolsters.

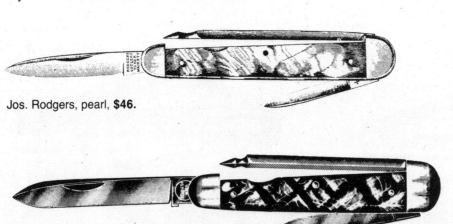

Jos. Rodgers, pearl, **$46.**

Remington, patterned celluloid (gray), **$33.**

J. A. Henckels, pearl, **$46.**

Serpentine and Fancy Sleeveboard Lobsters

Unlike the standard sleeveboard lobster and the Sheffield pattern, both of which are common, the serpentine sleeveboard lobster is very rare. It is also very handsome.

Even handsomer and even rarer is the straight sleeveboard that is pinched in three or four times along the sides. This fancy sleeveboard may once have had a special name, but if so it has gotten lost. Fancy sleeveboard will just have to do.

H. Boker, bone stag, **$30.**

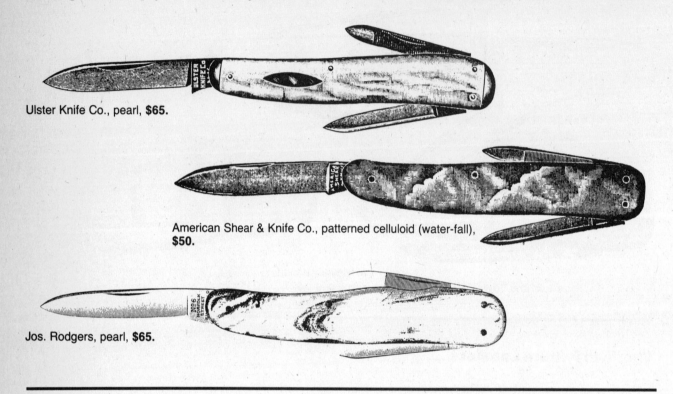

Ulster Knife Co., pearl, **$65.**

American Shear & Knife Co., patterned celluloid (water-fall), **$50.**

Jos. Rodgers, pearl, **$65.**

Fancy Sleeveboard Lobsters

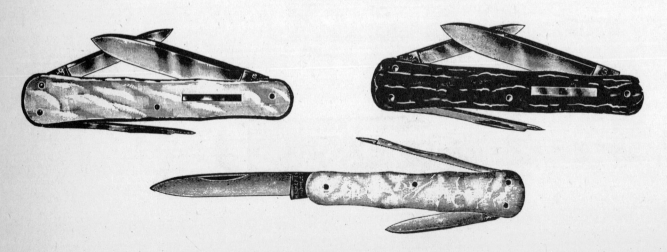

H. Bokers: pearls, **$52 each**: genuine stag, **$50.**

Gunstock Lobsters and Orange Blossoms

To me the most appealing style of lobster is the gunstock, sort of a swell-center sleeveboard. These can have three blades or four. One of the blades is a long manicure blade on the back.

Four-blade gunstock lobsters have a top deck like a whittler. The double-thick spear master blade rides on the full width of the spring at the narrow end. Two small blades ride on the split ends of the spring at the wide end.

This four-blade gunstock lobster whittler is called the "orange blossom." A pearl handled orange blossom was one of the most expensive pocketknives a person could buy in the 1920s and 1930s. Remington's R6454 pearl orange blossom cost nearly 2½ times more than their R1123 large trapper with bullet shield ($8 versus $3.35 in 1925). These relative values of course do not hold in today's collector market.

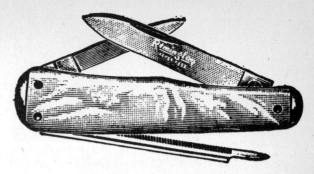

Remington, 3 blades, pearl, **$117.**

Orange Blossoms

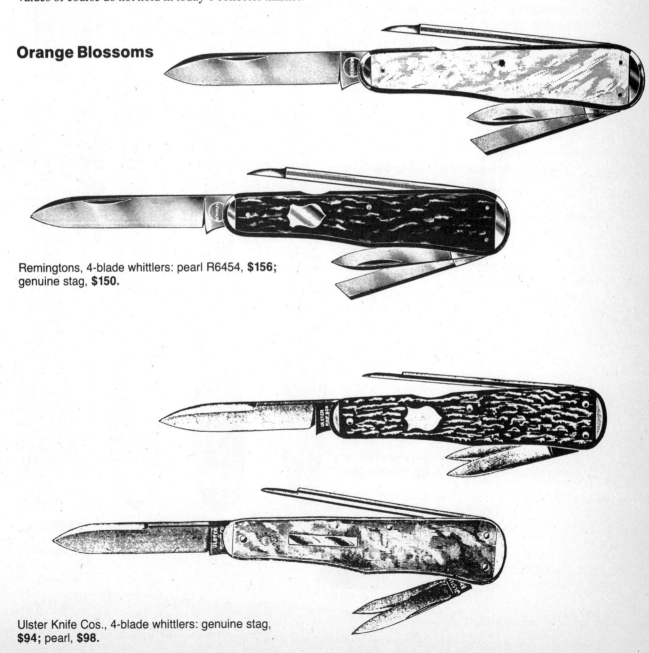

Remingtons, 4-blade whittlers: pearl R6454, **$156;** genuine stag, **$150.**

Ulster Knife Cos., 4-blade whittlers: genuine stag, **$94;** pearl, **$98.**

Quill Knives

QUILL KNIVES are the tiny "pen" knives used in the 18th and early 19th centuries for sharpening quill pens. Some of these were made in the latter part of the 19th century, not for sharpening quills, which had largely gone out of use, but for inclusion as tiny utility knives in fancy manicure and sewing kits.

The distinguishing feature of one-bladed quill knives is that the single tiny blade, usually either a pen blade or a coping blade, but sometimes a clip or a curved bistoury-like (scalpel) blade, is much shorter than the handle. The "head" of the spring ordinarily fills the extra space in the handle.

Single bladed quill knives were made in a variety of shapes, but they are generally around 2 ½ inches long closed and relatively slender. The handles of some older ones have a pointed finial at the head end.

In the latter part of the 19th century, almost all quill knives were single-bladed. A few double-ended ones with two blades were still made, however.

At the time of their greatest popularity, before about 1830, many quill knives were made with two or even more blades. Most of these were double-ended, but some were single-ended like miniature jack knives.

What distinguishes quill knives with more than one blade from other "pen" knives is that no matter how many blades a quill knife has, they are all of the same tiny size. None of them is a larger "master blade."

There was one standard double-ended quill knife pattern that was shaped like a needle case or a miniature cigar. It had eight tiny blades, four in each end, one every 90 degrees. This pattern was also made with two, three, or even four blades in each position, yielding a knife with 16, 24, or 32 tiny blades. These usually have ivory handles and are worth **$200** to **$500**.

Multi-bladed quill knives were not standard *American* patterns, though they were certainly used here. They were made throughout Europe in incredible variety during the 18th and early 19th centuries. Some representative examples of these, along with a selection of older style single bladed quill knives, are shown in part 5 of *Foreign Exotic Primitive and Historical Folding Knives*.

Prices for single-bladed QUILL KNIVES of any shape and with any handle material, in excellent condition.

Plain two-bladed quill knives are shown in c1890s U.S. catalogs, but they are very rare. Value is about the same as single-bladed, or perhaps up to 20% more.

Very High: **$60.**   Medium: **$25.**
High: **$35.**   Low: **$8.**

Worked back: **add 50%**
Engraved or carved handles: **add 35%**

Mint condition: **add 35%**
Worn: **subtract 50%**
Broken: **subtract 90%**

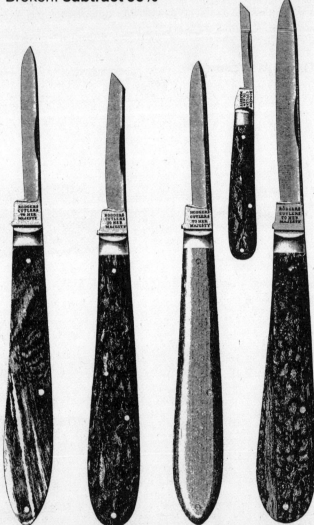

Quill knives by Jos. Rodgers and by Ulster Knife Co., **$35 each.**

Mechanical Pen Knives

Ring Opener

SOME pen knives, mostly equal-ends, have mechanical devices to open the blades. The simplest are blade attachments like Joseph Rodgers ''Pellett'' lifts (**add 10%**). Next simplest are turn-rings or ring openers (**add 20%**). A German firm made flush-mounted cam-locking ring openers in single-ended (photo) and double-ended versions (**add 50%**).

Spring-open knives date back to the 18th century. Some rare 19th century ones had spring-assists to open the blades about 30 degrees when a lever is pressed. I have seen four-blade senators with four levers (**add 100%**).

All push-button and switchblade knives are illegal in interstate commerce. The bottom three (full-size) are Press Buttons circa 1900. The others (half-size) are Schrade Cut's from the 1930s. Both types were invented by George Schrade.

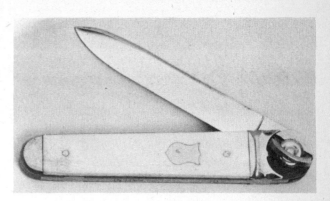

Unmarked German, ivory (courtesy Smithsonian).

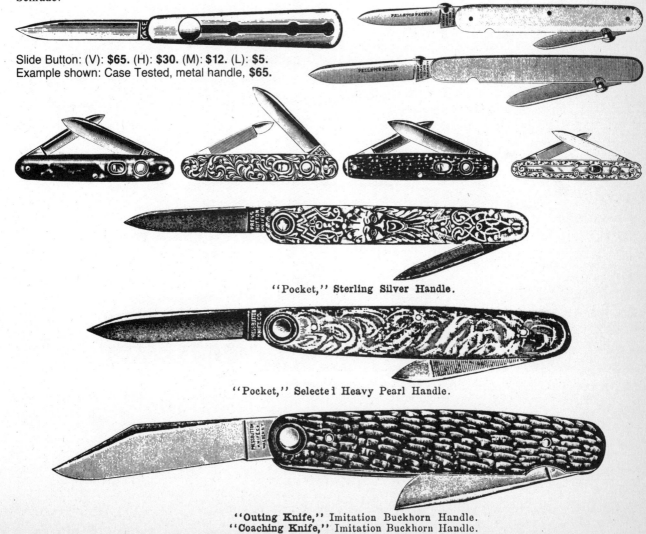

Slide Button: (V): **$65.** (H): **$30.** (M): **$12.** (L): **$5.**
Example shown: Case Tested, metal handle, $65.

''Pocket,'' Sterling Silver Handle.

''Pocket,'' Selected Heavy Pearl Handle.

''Outing Knife,'' Imitation Buckhorn Handle.
''Coaching Knife,'' Imitation Buckhorn Handle.

Office and Letter-Opener Knives

Office Knives

An "office knife" is a relatively large equal-end pen knife that has a spear master blade for opening letters and a spey-type blade intended to serve as an ink eraser. Office knives have white handles. Most 20th century ones have celluloid handles. Older ones have bone or even ivory. OFFICE KNIFE in fancy letters is usually etched or stamped on the front handle.

An office knife is a working knife for a clerical worker. The comparable fixed blade version is the ink eraser shown in the *Industrial Knives* chapter.

Letter-Opener Knives

A letter opener knife is a pocketknife handle with a folding blade in one end, usually a small spear or a spey-type eraser blade. The other end is a fixed letter opener. Most of the letter openers are slender, but some are as wide as the handle. Letter opener knives often have advertising or presentation inscriptions on the handle or on the opener blade.

There is little interest in letter opener knives at this time. Unscrupulous sellers sometimes cut off the letter opener and offer the handle as an ordinary knife. Close inspection will always reveal this foolish trick.

Base prices for OFFICE KNIVES and LETTER-OPENER KNIVES with celluloid handles. Excellent unsharpened condition.

VALUE RANGE	VERY HIGH	HIGH	MED.	LOW
OFFICE KNIFE:	$70.	45.	25.	6.

Ivory handles: **add 40%**
Bone handles: **add 20%**
Office knife without OFFICE KNIFE on handle: **subtract 40%**

	VERY HIGH	HIGH	MED.	LOW
LETTER-OPENER KNIFE:	$35.	20.	8.	2.

Pearl handles: **add 60%**
Decorated metal handles: **add 20%**
Advertising: see *Advertising Knives*

Mint condition: **add 50%**
Worn: **subtract 60%**
Broken: **subtract 90%**

H. Boker, Germany, celluloid, **$25.**

Ulster Knife Co., celluloid, **$45.**

R6175   **R6785**

White Pyremite Handle; Brass Lining   White Pyremite Handle; Brass Lining
Length, closed, 3¾ inches.   Length, closed, 3⅜ inches.

Remingtons: celluloid, **$70 each.**

Case XX 42057 **$45**; Tested XX 4257 **$70.**

422174

Robeson, celluloid, **$25.**

No. O7564W

Schrade Cut. Co., celluloid, **$45.**

No. 07894W

Schrade Cut. Co., celluloid, **$45.**

Office and Letter-Opener Knives

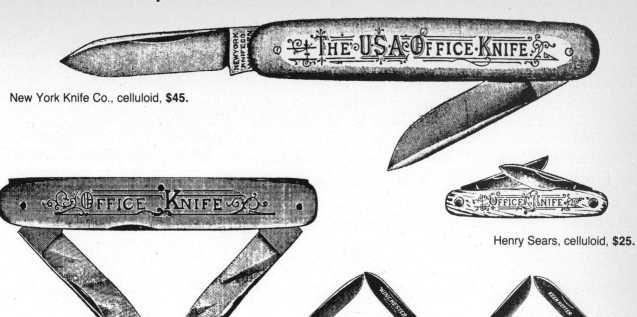

New York Knife Co., celluloid, **$45.**

Henry Sears, celluloid, **$25.**

American Shear & Knife Co., bone, **$55.**

Winchester, celluloid, **$70.**

Keen Kutter, celluloid, **$45.**

RLO 35

RLO 24

Remingtons: celluloid, **$35;** pearl, **$55.**

RLO 44

RLO 70

Remington, pearl, **$55.**

Remington, gold plate, **$40.**

No. L1824M

Schrade Cut. Co., celluloid, **$20.**

John Clarke folding eraser: wood, **$25;** bone, **$35.**

Keen Kutter, black fiber, **$20.**

Advertising Knives

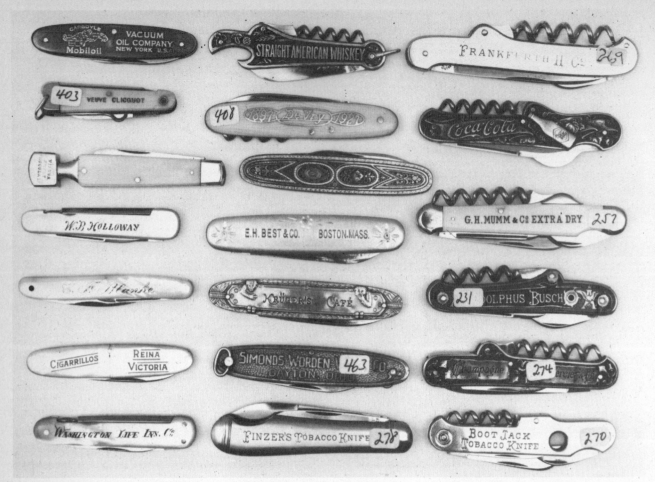

Advertising knives circa 1910-1930, by Wester & Butz of Solingen, except as noted. (Courtesy of Ed Bruner.)

First column, top to bottom:

1. Senator pen, grey gun metal handles with red and silver, for Mobil. **$50.**

2. Lobster pen, Stanhope viewer, ivory handles etched for C. F. Schmidt & Peters Veuve Clicquot champagne. **$85.**

3. Box knife, stamped iron hammer and etched ivory handles for Runkel Bros. Vienna Sweet Chocolate. **$125.**

4. Lobster, etched pearl handles, for W. B. Holloway, Harvard Brewery. **$85.**

5. Serpentine pen, etched pearl handles, for C. F. Blanke. **$65.**

6. Senator pen, etched pearl handles, for Reina Victoria Cigarillos. **$70.**

7. Lobster, etched pearl handles, for Washington Life Insurance. **$65.**

Second column, top to bottom:

8. Fred. Herberz & Co., Solingen, opener knife, embossed brass handles, for "Juarez Straight American Whiskey." Probably a fantasy c1970.

9. Opener knife, inlaid celluloid handles, for De Vry 1897-1927. **$40.**

10. Equal-end pen, toledo scales, for Neckarsulmer Fahrzeugwerke (NSU Automotive Works). **$65.**

11. Schrade Cutlery Co. equal-end pen, stamped and engraved aluminum handles, for Best & Co. Knoxall Textiles. **$35.**

12. Equal-end pen, embossed nickel silver handles with Katzenjammer-type kids, for Kruger's Cafe. **$45.**

13. SWWCO/Made in USA (by Camillus) turn-ring pen, embossed brass handles, for Simonds Worden White Co. **$40.**

14. Easy-open jack, nickel silver handles, FINZER'S TOBACCO KNIFE. **$40.**

Third column, top to bottom:

15. Champagne pattern, nickel silver handles, for Frankfurth & Co. **$35.**

16. Pseudo-champagne pattern, brass handles, "COCA-COLA." Fantasy c1970.

17. Champagne pattern, etched ivory handles, for G. H. Mumm & Co. Extra Dry Veuve Clicquot Champagne. **$125.**

18. N. Kastor, Ohligs, Germany, champagne pattern, enameled and gilt brass handles with Stanhope viewer, for Adolphus Busch. **$200.**

19. Champagne pattern, embossed nickel silver handles with winery scene on reverse, for Mercier & Co., Epernay, Champagne. **$100.**

20. Champagne pattern with cigar cutter, stamped nickel silver handles. BOOT JACK TOBACCO KNIFE. **$55.**

Figural, Character, and Miniature Knives

Cap Lifter

No. 2521—Assorted celluloid handles; lgt., 3¼ ins.; brass lined; nickel silver bolster and patent cap lifter; two blades, clip and pen, half polished;

Figural knives are knives shaped like other objects, or like animals or people. The oldest style, at least 300 years old, is the leg knife. Eighteenth century ones were called "Princess Legs," and are worth at least **$150.** Little 19th century ones (top left) are worth **$40-65.** 20th century American "ballet knives" have a shoe that serves as a cap lifter. They are worth from **$35** (Boker, H. Sears 1865) to **$100** (Remington). Other figurals, such as guns or shoes are worth **$20-50,** depending on quality. Vehicles or nudes can be worth up to **$100.** Modern reproductions (most have brass handles) are worth **$5.**

Character knives (Popeye, Hopalong Cassidy, Buck Rogers, etc.) by Camco (plastic handles) or Imperial (sheet metal handles) are worth up to **$50** in mint condition. New lithographed plastic handled ones by Colonial (marked MADE IN U.S.A.) sell for **$1 each.**

Some miniature knives are functional (bottom left) while others are strictly charms. Value range is from **$3** (below) to **$25,** also depending on quality.

[See *Picture Handle Knife Companies* and page 26.]

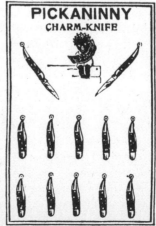

Introduction to Multi-Blades

MULTI-BLADES are folding knives that have a multitude of blades. This multitude can be as small as three and as great as a hundred or more.

At least one of the multitude of blades in a multi-blade is either a special purpose blade, such as a spey blade, or else it is a special implement (other than a nail file or a leather punch, which are sometimes used in three-bladed pen knives). The special implement may be a can or bottle opener, a champagne wire cutter, a hoof pick, a wrench, or even a dinner fork. I have seen 100-bladed showpiece knives in which all 100 blades were different.

Like standard jack knives, multi-blades are usually large and sturdy. Like standard pen knives, multi-blades are almost always double-ended.

There are many standard patterns of multi-blades, most

with their own special names. However, there are no standard named *shapes* for multi-blades, as there are among jack knives and pen knives. Multi-blades are classified by structure and by function.

If someone refers to an equal-end jack or an equal-end pen, his meaning is clear (if it is not clear to you, see the appropriate chapters). However, if he refers to an "equal-end multi-blade," his meaning is *not* clear. He could mean a utility knife or a cattle knife, a sportsman's knife or a bottle opener knife.

For this reason, there is no general multi-blade chapter in this book. Each type of multi-blade is treated separately. These types are listed below. In the types marked with an asterisk (*), there is either so much or so little diversity that the examples shown for those types are priced individually in order to serve as a guide. The other types have price charts.

*Horseman's and Sportsman's Knives.
*Champagne Patterns
* Bottle Opener Knives.
*Smoker's Knives
*Folding Knife-Fork-Spoon Combinations.
Scout and Utility Knives.
*U. S. Military Utility Knives.
Cattle Knives.
Premium Stock and Junior Premium Stock Knives.
*Plier and Wrench Knives.
Tool Kit Knives
*Showpiece and Exposition Knives.

Horseman's and Sportsman's Knives

THESE styles are the original multi-blades. Sometimes they are all called "combination knives." They have been made in an incredible variety of shapes and blade combinations over at least the past 250 years. Older versions are covered under *Foreign, Exotic, Primitive, and Historical Folding Knives.*

Horseman's Knives

A horseman's knife can have anywhere from three on up to over 40 blades. What distinguishes it from other multi-blades, and especially from sportsman's knives, is that it has a hoof pick (sometimes called a stone hook) for cleaning horses' hooves. Also, horseman's knives often have a fleam blade for bleeding foundered horses [see *Special Purpose Jack Knives* for more about fleams].

Most horseman's knives are made in a standard shape. The shape is pinched at the end where the larger blades are hinged, giving a sort of bottle-neck appearance. This shape allows the hoof pick to open 180 degrees. However, as the illustrations show, horseman's knives were also made in other shapes, while the "standard" horseman's shape was also used on some sportsman's knives that have no hoof pick.

An interesting feature of larger standard shaped horse-

man's knives is that they often have a cut-out in the handle, under the stone hook. The inside of the hook usually has teeth opposite the cut-out. This cut-out lets the arm of the hook double as a nut-cracker.

Most horseman's knives sold in this country were made in Sheffield. A few were made in Germany, sometimes of inferior quality. A very few were made in the United States. See the following pages for information on values.

Sportsman's Knives

"Sportsman's knife" is really a catch-all term for the larger and more elaborate multi-blades that do not have a specific application, such as horses. There is probably more variety in sportsman's knives than in any other type. Some are no bigger than pen knives, though loaded with a multitude of blades. Others are big enough for two-handed use. The familiar "Swiss Army" knives are sportsman's knives.

Sportsman's knives are so diverse that their values must be estimated on a knife by knife basis. Brand name has some effect, but is not nearly as significant as on ordinary knives. The main factors are quality, condition, size, number of blades, unusual features, and handle material. The examples I have selected show the range.

Horseman's Knives

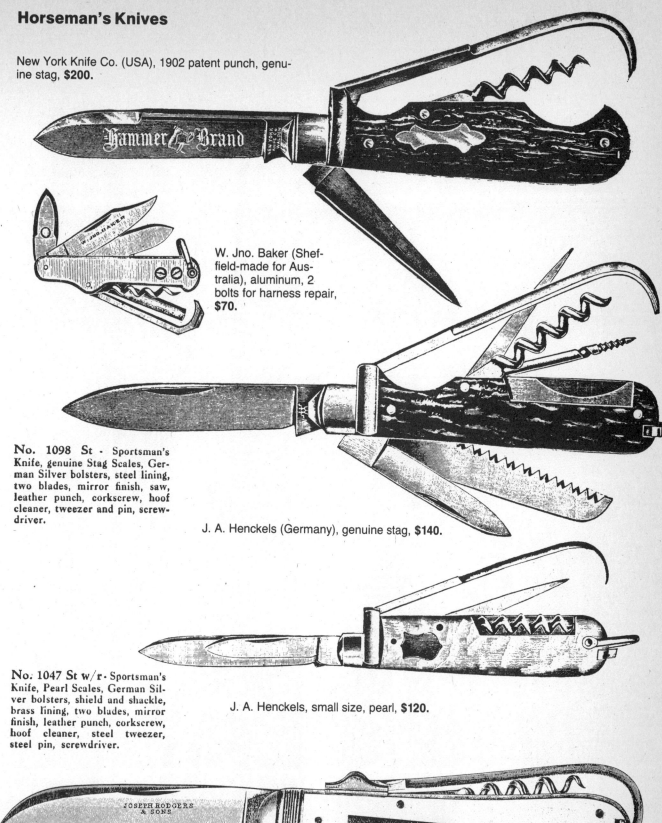

New York Knife Co. (USA), 1902 patent punch, genuine stag, **$200.**

W. Jno. Baker (Sheffield-made for Australia), aluminum, 2 bolts for harness repair, **$70.**

No. 1098 St - Sportsman's Knife, genuine Stag Scales, German Silver bolsters, steel lining, two blades, mirror finish, saw, leather punch, corkscrew, hoof cleaner, tweezer and pin, screwdriver.

J. A. Henckels (Germany), genuine stag, **$140.**

No. 1047 St w/r - Sportsman's Knife, Pearl Scales, German Silver bolsters, shield and shackle, brass lining, two blades, mirror finish, leather punch, corkscrew, hoof cleaner, steel tweezer, steel pin, screwdriver.

J. A. Henckels, small size, pearl, **$120.**

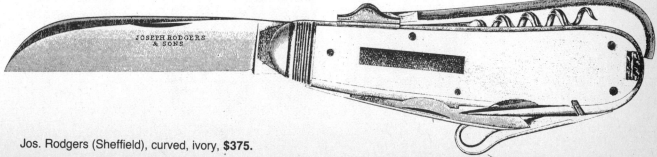

Jos. Rodgers (Sheffield), curved, ivory, **$375.**

Horseman's Knives: Values

Any American-made horseman's knife is worth at least **$150.** Standard shape Sheffield examples with genuine stag handles (the usual material) are worth from **$65** for small ones up to about **$175** for large ones. **Add 50%** for pearl or ivory. **Subtract 20%** for bone or horn, **40%** for metal. Unusual shaped Sheffield examples are worth **50-100% more** than standard ones. German ones are worth **60-85%** of the value of English ones.

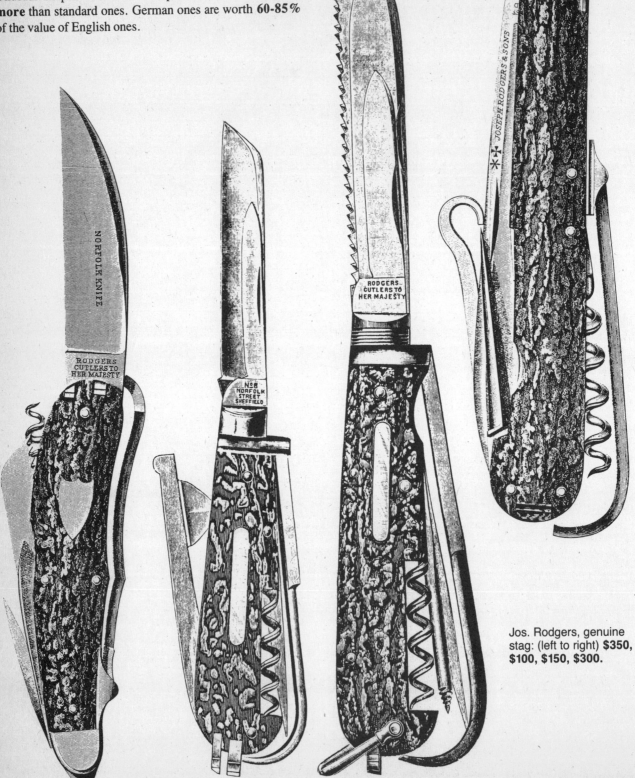

Jos. Rodgers, genuine stag: (left to right) **$350, $100, $150, $300.**

Horseman's and Sportsman's Knives

This Page: Nickel silver handles for use near salt water. Henckels with marlinspikes: 4 blades, **$90;** 7 blades, "compass-joint," **$135.** Baker, 5 blades, compass-joint, **$75.** Rodgers (horseman's), 4½", with shotshell extractor, buttoner, harness mending bolts, British oval-style tin opener, etc., **$175.**

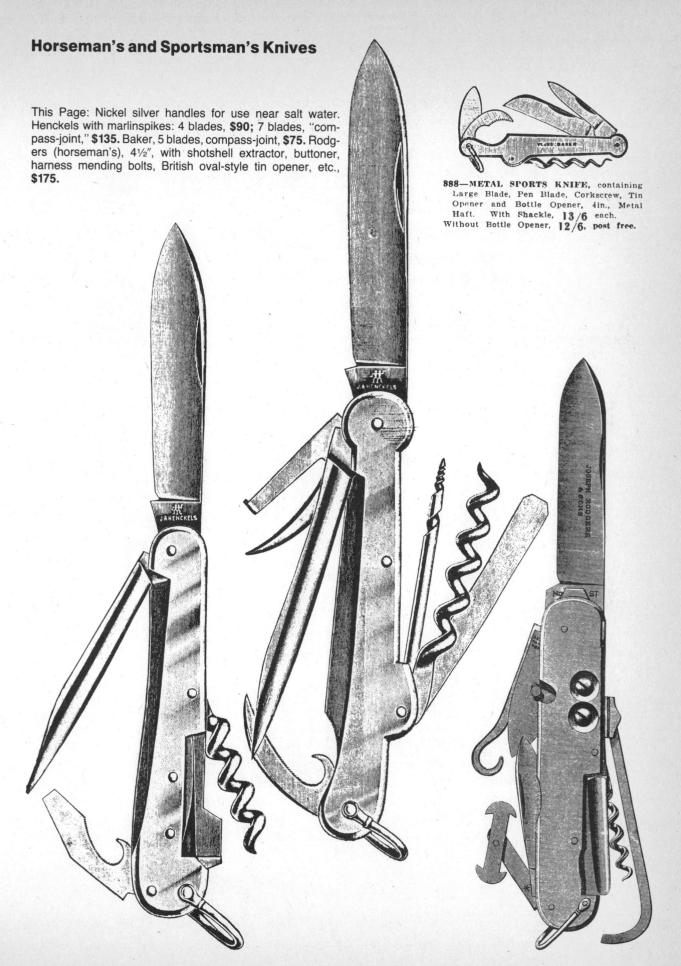

888—METAL SPORTS KNIFE, containing Large Blade, Pen Blade, Corkscrew, Tin Opener and Bottle Opener, 4in., Metal Haft. With Shackle, 13/6 each. Without Bottle Opener, 12/6, post free.

Sportsman's Knives

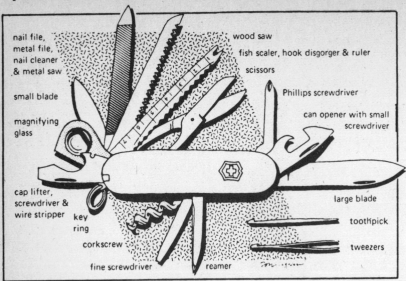

The 'Champion' Victorinox Swiss army officers' knife $40 list.

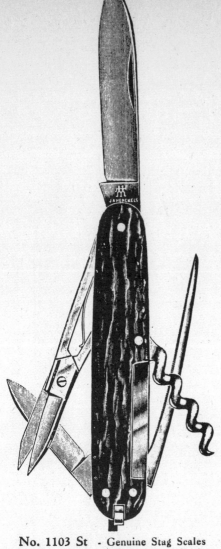

No. 1103 St - Genuine Stag Scales two blades and scissors, mirror finish, nailfile, corkscrew, tweezer and toothpick, German Silver lining, milled.

No. 1103 GM - With genuine Gun Metal Scales.

No. 1103 P - With genuine Pearl Scales.

J. A. Henckels, genuine stag, **$60** (gun metal, **$35**; pearl, **$90**).

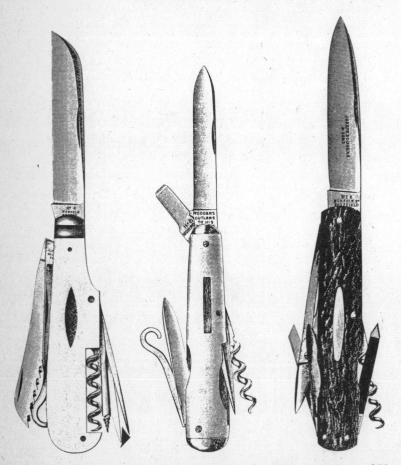

Jos. Rodgers (left to right): 3¼", 8 blades, ivory, **$225**; 3¹/₁₆", ivory, **$90**; 3⁵/₁₆", genuine stag, **$120**; BOTTOM: 3½", genuine stag, **$100**.

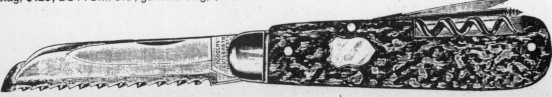

Sportsman's Knives (Deluxe Shadow Combination Knives)

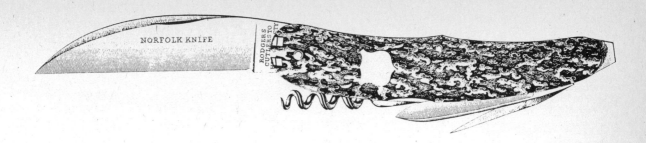

Above: Jos. Rodgers, genuine stag, **$165.**

Below: J. A. Henckels, pearl: 18 blades, **$350;** 6 blades, **$80.**

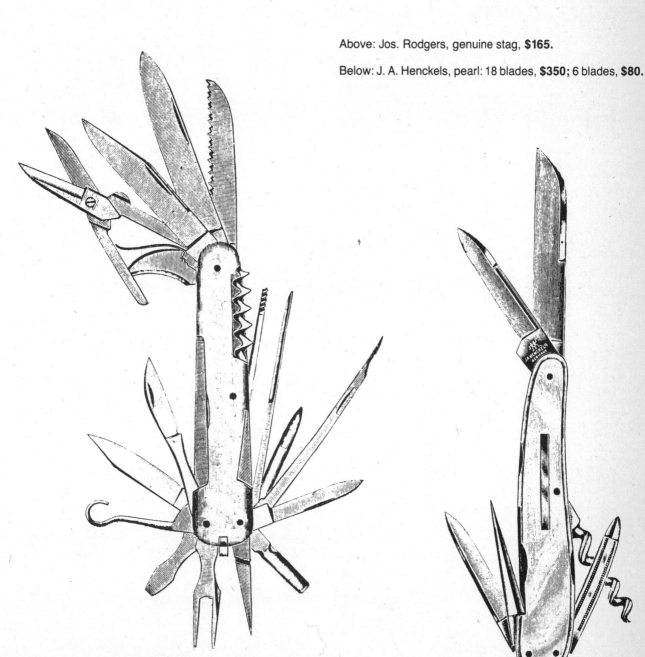

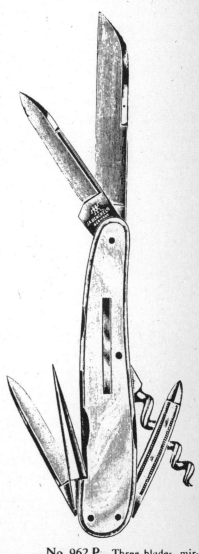

No. 1042 P - Four knife blades, one cuticle knife blade, scissors, saw, wire cutter, screw driver, buttonhook, fork, auger, corkscrew, two leather punchers, bodkin, nailfile, long reamer, all mirror finish, tweezer and tooth-pick, German Silver milled lining.

No. 962 P - Three blades, mirror finish, leather punch, nail-file, corkscrew, German Silver shield and lining, milled.

Champagne Patterns

CHAMPAGNE patterns always have a corkscrew, usually on the back. Older ones (from before about 1925) also have a champagne wire cutter blade. Later versions have a crown cap lifter instead, but are nonetheless called champagne patterns. Note that a "champagne *knife*" is a fixed blade knife with a champagne wire cutter blade only.

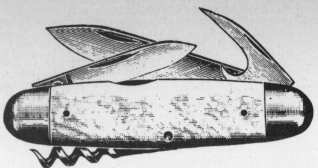

Case Tested XX, pearl, **$200.**

H. Boker, genuine stag, pick and tweezers, **$35.**

H. Boker, nickel silver, cigar clipper, **$15.**

Keen Kutter, 3¼″, pearl, **$55.**

Henry Sears & Son, 3¼″, bone stag, **$30.**

Schrade Cut. Co., patterned celluloid, **$25.**

R-7993
Stag Handle
Length, closed, 3⅜ inches.

Remington, bone stag, **$45.**

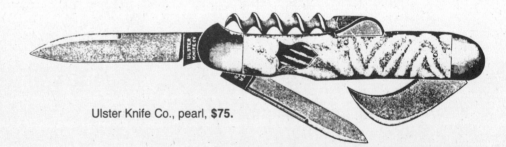

Ulster Knife Co., pearl, **$75.**

R4336
Genuine Stag Handle
Length, closed, 3½ inches.

Remingtons: pearl, **$150**; genuine stag, **$125.**

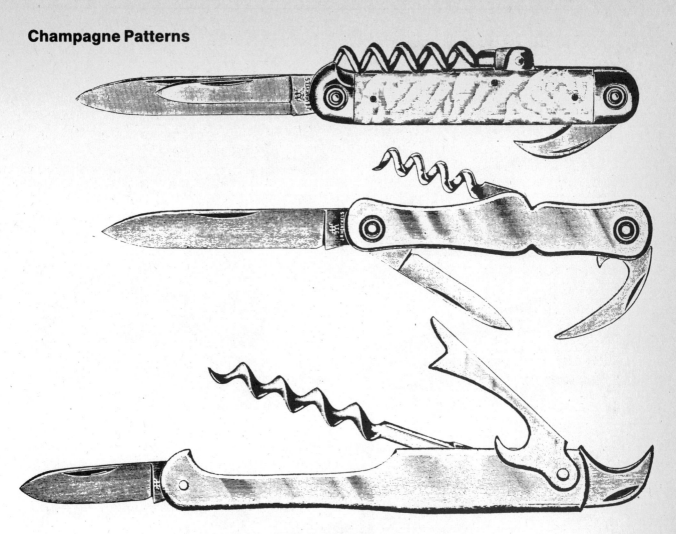

J. A. Henckels (top to bottom): pearl, **$70;** nickel silver,
$25; nickel plated steel (waiter's knife), **$15.**

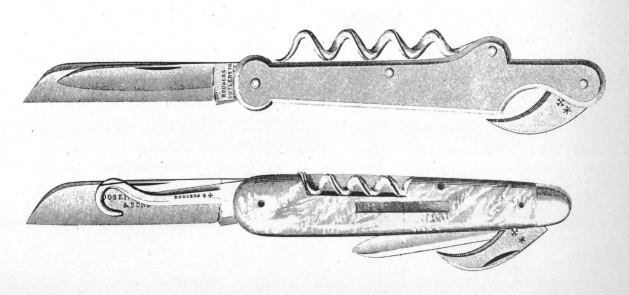

Jos. Rodgers: compass-joint nickel silver, **$25;** pearl, **$60.**

Bottle Opener Knives

A BOTTLE OPENER knife is a pen knife or small jack knife with either a corkscrew in the back or a caplifter built into the handle or one of the blades.

"NAPANOCH" Gentleman's Knife

Napanoch, bone stag, **$80.**

Case Tested XX, metal, **$60.**

Schrade Cut. Co., nickel silver, **$15.**

Stiletto (P. H. & S.), bone stag, **$40.**

American Shear & Knife Co., patterned celluloid (waterfall), **$50.**

Ulster Knife Co., pearl, **$60.**

H. Bokers: embossed nickel silver, **$20;** 3¼″, black and white celluloid, **$25.**

Smoker's Knives

SMOKER'S knives are multi-blades some or all of whose blades are designed for use on pipes or cigars.

The blades or fixtures can include: cigar cutters for clipping off the ends of cigars; long thin cigar punches for opening an airway down the center of a cigar; cigar forks for holding short cigar stubs without burning one's fingers; pipe tampers; and pipe bowl reamers. A simpler style of smoker's knife is included under *Special Purpose Jack Knives*.

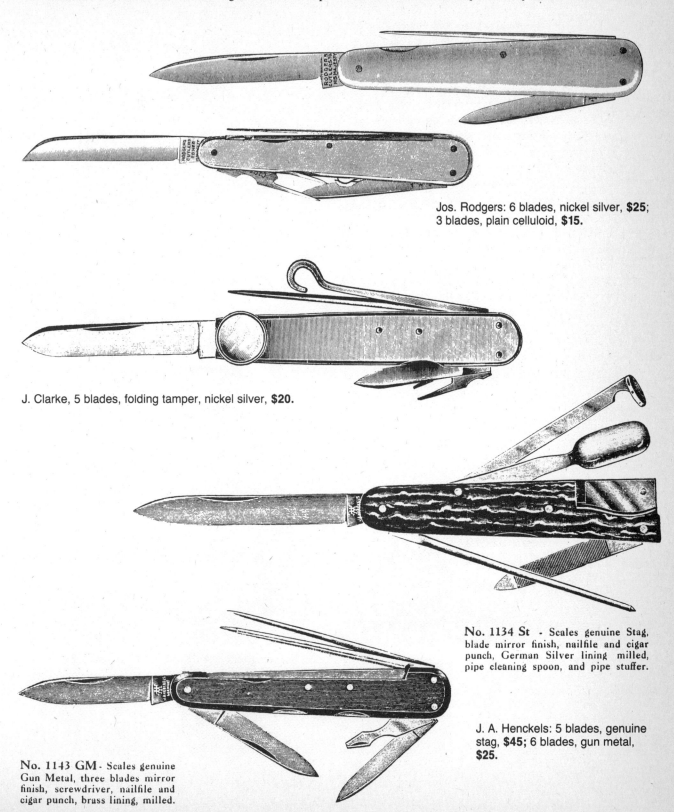

Jos. Rodgers: 6 blades, nickel silver, **$25**; 3 blades, plain celluloid, **$15**.

J. Clarke, 5 blades, folding tamper, nickel silver, **$20**.

No. 1134 St - Scales genuine Stag, blade mirror finish, nailfile and cigar punch, German Silver lining milled, pipe cleaning spoon, and pipe stuffer.

J. A. Henckels: 5 blades, genuine stag, **$45**; 6 blades, gun metal, **$25**.

No. 1143 GM - Scales genuine Gun Metal, three blades mirror finish, screwdriver, nailfile and cigar punch, brass lining, milled.

Folding Knife-Fork-Spoon Combinations

MOST OF THESE eating sets take apart into two or three pieces. In the early 19th century they were called "slot knives," because of the tab and slot mechanism that joins the pieces.

Slot knives with forks seem to have been made for as long as people have eaten with forks, since the late 17th century. I have seen fancy 18th century French examples consisting of a pair of knives slotted together; people ate with pairs of knives before use of the eating fork became popular.

The first American slot knives seem to have been made in the early 1860s. Ames Cutlery Co. of Massachusetts patented one type in 1861. American Knife Co. of Connecticut patented another type in 1862. Lamson & Goodnow made them in this period, as did most of the other American pocketknife companies then in business [see *19th Century American Pocketknife Firms*].

American slot knives were popular with Federal troops going off to the Civil War, though they were never an issue item. All the older ones I have seen had wooden handles, and many had tin-plated blades.

A European style of folding knife and fork set has separate handles for the knife and fork, and for the spoon, if present. These sets were sold with carrying cases. Values per implement: horn, **$10**; ivory, **$30**.

For information on silver-bladed folding knife and fork sets, see *Silver Fruit Knives*. Older styles of "slot knives" are covered in *Foreign Exotic, Primitive, and Historical Folding Knives*.

Combination Folding Knife, Fork and Spoon.

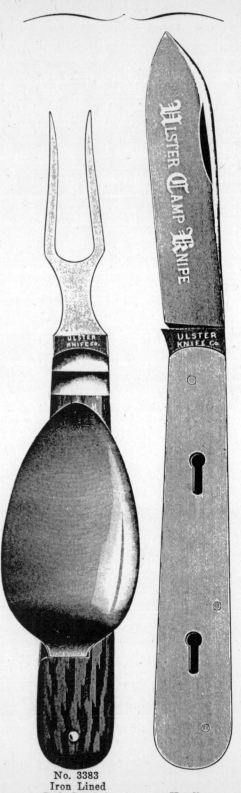

Stiletto (P. H. & S.), fork functions as can-opener, has cap-lifter on side, 4⅜", wood, **$100.**

Ulster Knife Co., wood, **$150.**

No. 3383
Iron Lined
Red Cocobolo
$12 00......

Handles
Per Doz........

Knife-Fork-Spoon Combinations

Curved jack style, bone stag. V: **$250**; H: **$175**; M: **$125**.

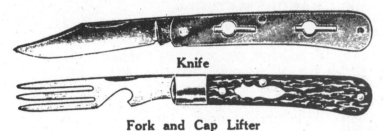

Knife

Fork and Cap Lifter

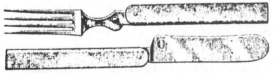

Spoon and Can Opener

Vest Pocket Knife and Fork
WITH IMITATION LEATHER CASE ½ x 1¼ x 4 INCHES.

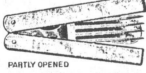

PARTLY OPENED

The most convenient and lightest two-piece set ever devised. It is strong, carefully fitted and beautifully finished in nickel—a pleasing addition to any outfit.

A fork is a necessity on any trip and this knife will save you from dulling your hunting knife when cutting meat on a plate.

No. 60. 3½ ounces; nickel plated; with case; prepaid....................$1.50

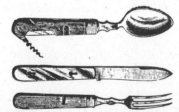

Combination Knife, Fork and Spoon, with small penknife blade in handle of fork and small corkscrew in handle of spoon. Finely finished and all lock together like a large pocket knife.
Price, $2.00 each.

COMBINATION CAMP KNIFE, FORK AND SPOON.

Marble's (German made), **$150.**

European style: wood or horn, **$35;** ivory, **$65.**

No. 3452

Case Tested XX, 3¾″, yellow celluloid, **$225.**

No. Y249K&F _Handles slip apart forming general utility knife and fork combination. Amber composition handles. Size over all 3⅞″.

No. Y349KFS Handles slip apart forming three piece utility set. Amber composition handles. Size over-all 3⅞″.

Western States, either style **$150.**

25—COMBINATION KNIFE, FORK AND SPOON, each detachable for separate use; 3½in. Metal Haft. **5/6** complete, **post free.** With Bottle Opener .. .. **1/6** extra
22—Similar to above, without Spoon, **3/6** each, **post free.**

English style, nickel silver, **$30.**

Utility and Scout Knives

By Dennis Ellingsen and Bernard Levine

Dennis Ellingsen writes for Knife World. *He collects scout and utility knives.*

Utility Knives

THE UTILITY KNIFE is an equal-end multi-blade pattern. The standard utility knife is 3⅝ inches long closed and has two backsprings and a bail. It has four blades: ordinarily a spear master blade, a punch, a can opener, and a screwdriver-caplifter.

There are several uncommon variations on this basic design: There are both smaller and larger sizes. There are a few three-blade versions, lacking one of the tool blades. There are five-blade versions, with the fifth blade a stubby Phillips screwdriver.

There is also a six-bladed version of the utility knife. It has a pen blade in place of the punch on top, and has a corkscrew and punch on the back. In the 1920s, this version was called the picnic knife, or sometimes the army and navy pattern.

The standard four-bladed utility knife seems to have been derived from the equal-end cattle knife some time around 1900. It was an inexpensive home-grown substitute for the multi-bladed horseman's and sportsman's knives long imported from Europe.

Those fancy foreign multi-blade patterns had been popular in this country for generations, but had never been profitably produced here because of high American labor costs. The Tariff Acts of 1890 and 1897 made even the imported horseman's and sportsman's knives prohibitively expensive, so American firms began to offer the utility knife as a substitute.

The six-bladed utility knife, with punch and corkscrew on the back, began as a German response to the American utility pattern. A stripped down and streamlined version of a traditional multi-blade, it too was cheaper to produce than the older styles. Some American firms copied the six-blade, but it was never a big seller here.

Base prices for UTILITY KNIVES (non-official) with four blades; bone stag handles; full bolsters. Excellent unsharpened condition.

Very High: **$100.**	Medium: **$30.**
High: **$50.**	Low: **$12.**

CONSTRUCTION
Five or six blades: **add 15%**
No bolsters: **subtract 15%**
Compass in handle: **add 20%**
Military markings: **add 100%**
Official Scout: see separate chart
Large size (over 4¼ inches): **add 500%**
   (see examples)
Clasp type: **add 100%**

HANDLE MATERIAL
Pearl: **add 100%**
Genuine stag: **add 25%**
Fancy celluloid or picture handles: **add 50%**
   (Flag, waterfall, scouting picture, etc.)
Patterned celluloid: **subtract 10%**
Plain celluloid: **subtract 25%**
Solid metal: **subtract 50%**
Hollow sheet metal shell: **subtract 65%**

Mint condition: **add 50%**
Worn: **subtract 50%**
Broken: **subtract 90%**

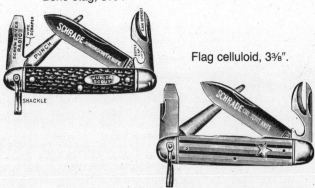

Bone stag, 3⅜".

Flag celluloid, 3⅜".

Schrade Cut. Co., 4-blade utility knives: bone stag, **$50**; flag celluloid, **$75**; pearl, **$100.**

Bone stag, Pres-to-lite key, 3⅝".

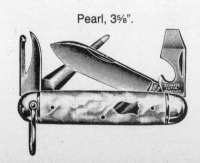

Pearl, 3⅝".

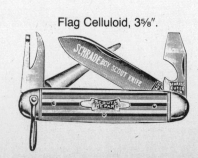

Flag Celluloid, 3⅝".

Six-Blade Utility Knives

HERE'S the Bird for K.P.— the Remington Camp Knife

A *Man's Knife*—Remington Steel, made to the exacting Remington standards of quality and accuracy— with clean cutting edges that stay keen a long time.

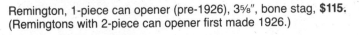

Daniel Peres, sold by Von Lengerke & Antoine, Chicago (1925), no bolsters, 3⅝", plain celluloid, **$22.**

Remington, 1-piece can opener (pre-1926), 3⅝", bone stag, **$115.** (Remingtons with 2-piece can opener first made 1926.)

J.A. Henckels, genuine stag, **$72.** (Note European-style leather punch with eye.)

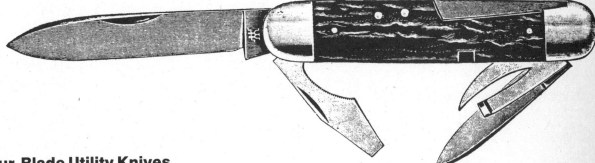

Four-Blade Utility Knives

Miller Bros., 3⅝", patterned celluloid (imitation stag), **$45.**

Napanoch, bone stag, **$100.**

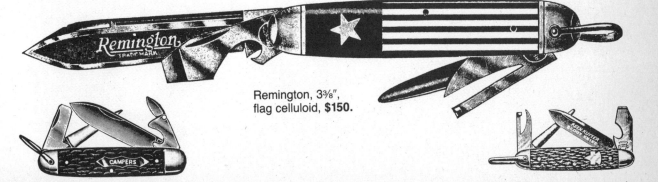

Remington, 3⅜", flag celluloid, **$150.**

Robeson, 3⅝", bone stag, **$30.**

Keen Kutter, 3½", bone stag, **$50.**

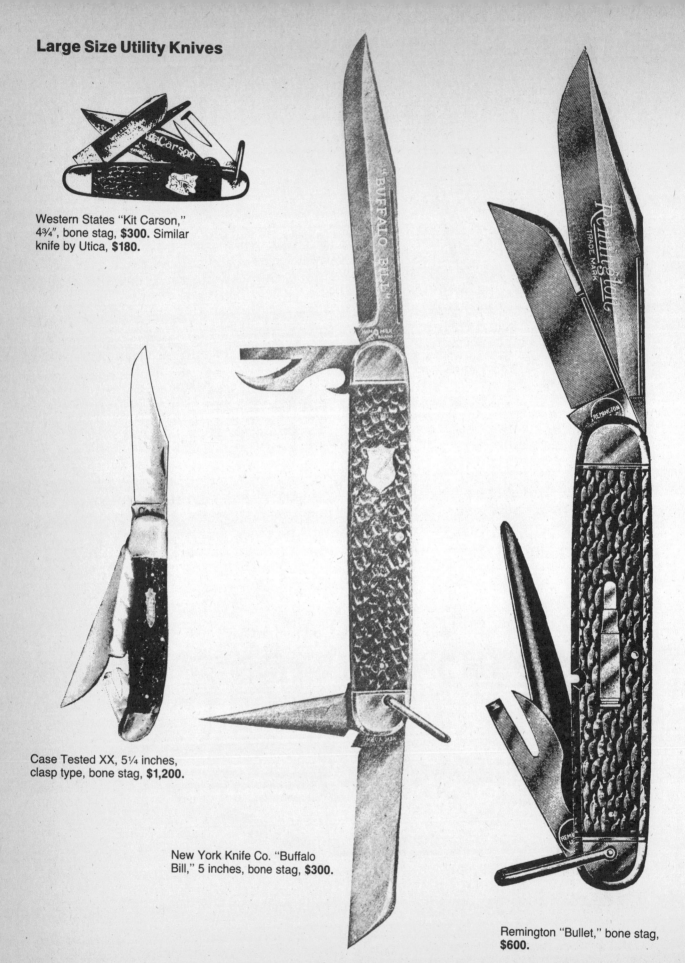

Western States "Kit Carson," 4¾", bone stag, **$300.** Similar knife by Utica, **$180.**

Case Tested XX, 5¼ inches, clasp type, bone stag, **$1,200.**

New York Knife Co. "Buffalo Bill," 5 inches, bone stag, **$300.**

Remington "Bullet," bone stag, **$600.**

Boy Scout Knives

At first the four-bladed utility knife did not really catch on in this country. What brought it to the forefront of popularity here was its designation in 1910 or 1911 as the official style of pocketknife for the Boy Scouts of America. That parent scouting organization was founded in 1910, modeled after the British organization established in 1908.

New York Knife Company was at first the only manufacturer authorized by the Boy Scouts of America to make Official Boy Scout knives. All *Official* Boy Scout folding knives had a special shield. Up until late 1922, while New York Knife still had its Official Scout Knife monopoly, that firm's official shield was a banner with the words BE PREPARED. Also, the blade etch of these knives states that they are official, but the etch is worn off of most surviving specimens.

In those early days of scouting, the utility pattern was not the only style of Official Boy Scout knife offered by New York Knife Company. New York called their utility version the Number 1 Boy Scout. Their Number 2 Boy Scout was an easy-open regular jack with a sheepfoot blade, a pen blade, and a bail. However, the utility pattern quickly eclipsed the smaller jack knife. The Number 2 Boy Scout seems to have become extinct shortly after 1925.

Although New York Knife Company had a monopoly on *Official* scout knives until 1922, just about every one of its rival pocketknife companies made *unofficial* scout knives. Rival firms marked their knives SCOUT KNIFE, CAMP KNIFE, MADE FOR SCOUTS, or even BOY SCOUT.

After World War I, some of New York Knife's competitors lobbied the scouting organization for permission to make official knives. In 1923, Remington, Ulster (Dwight Divine), and Landers Frary & Clark got the okay to make Official utility knives.

L. F. & C. and Remington (and other firms) also made easy-open scout-type jack knives like the New York "Number 2 Boy Scout," but only L. F. & C. made any that were "Official." Even the Remington R-963 with a Boy Scout hat shield was not official. Both New York and L. F. & C. also made unofficial versions, with BOY SCOUT shields instead of the official BE PREPARED.

In the late 1920s, the George Schrade Knife Company was authorized to make Official Boy Scout folding knife-fork-spoon sets using their patented "wire-jack" construction. A complete set of this type with original case is worth about **$45.**

New York Knife Company went out of business in 1931. Soon after, L. F. & C. abandoned pocketknife production. They were replaced on the Official Boy Scout Knife roster by Cattaraugus, who offered a modified utility pattern they called the Whitt-L-Kraft. Cattaraugus ceased pocketknife production early in World War II.

Remington sold its cutlery division to Pal in 1940 and Pal made Official Boy Scout Knives until 1948. They were the first firm to use plastic handles on Official Boy Scout Knives.

After World War II, in 1947 and 1948, Camillus briefly made Official Boy Scout knives. Camillus has long made all the Official Cub Scout knives.

Also after the war, Ulster, Schrade, and Imperial merged to form Imperial Knife Associated Companies. Both the Imperial and the Ulster brand have since appeared on Official Boy Scout utility knives. Very recently, Buck and Camillus have offered Official Boy Scout lockback folding hunters.

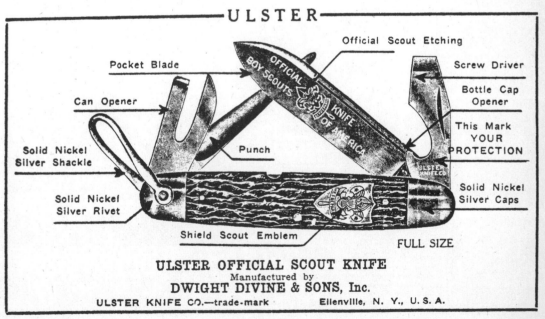

ULSTER

Official Scout Etching
Screw Driver
Bottle Cap Opener
This Mark YOUR PROTECTION
Solid Nickel Silver Caps

Pocket Blade
Can Opener
Punch
Solid Nickel Silver Shackle
Solid Nickel Silver Rivet
Shield Scout Emblem
FULL SIZE

ULSTER OFFICIAL SCOUT KNIFE
Manufactured by
DWIGHT DIVINE & SONS, Inc.
ULSTER KNIFE CO.—trade-mark   Ellenville, N. Y., U. S. A.

$75.

No. 1004. SCOUT KNIFE. Usually the first acquisition of a Scout. Stag handle, large polished cutting blade etched with official emblem, screw driver, can opener and boring tool for leather articles. Equipped so as to be hung on the Scout belt. Prepaid......**$1.00** **Given for 2 subscriptions to BOYS' LIFE.**

No. 1005. SCOUT KNIFE. This also is official and is designed for those Scouts who prefer a two-bladed knife. Ebony handle. One small blade and one large, opening without use of finger nail. Has shackle for hanging on Scout's belt. Prepaid..............**50c** **Given for 1 subscription to BOYS' LIFE.**

ULSTER   HAMMER   REMINGTON

New York Knife Co. pre-1923 Official knives: **$125; $150.**

Approved and licensed by the Boy Scouts of America.

Above, right—After 1921, and up until 1948, each authorized official manufacturer adopted its own distinctive version of the Official Boy Scout shield. This allows one to identify the makers of older Official Scout knives from the shields alone. (Chart from 1929.)

Official Scout, length when closed 3¾ in. large clip point cutting blade highly mirror or crocused polished on front side and etched with official Boy Scout Emblem, combination screw driver and wire scraper blade, combination can opener and crown cap bottle opener and Patent Knurled Genuine Harrison Leather Punch or Gouge Blade. Stag handle, brass lining, nickel silver bolsters, toggle and shield. The shield is stamped with the official Boy Scout Fleur-de-lis Insignia and the words "Be Prepared," w't per doz. 2¾ lbs.

C9744Y4 ....each **$1.50**

New York Knife Co. post-1923 Official knife, **$125.**

No. 64900. Size 3⅝". Ulster Official knife. Also in less expensive knife No. X350ST with bone stag handle. With pearl composition handle, X350 Comp.

Ulster Official knife sold by Western States circa 1941, **$75.**

OFFICIAL BOY SCOUT KNIFE
Stag handle; heavy cutting blade; screw driver; bottle and can opener; punch blade.
No. 1496
   "REMINGTON" $1.50
No. 1502 "ULSTER"   1.50
No. 1585
   "UNIVERSAL"   1.50
WHITT-L-KRAFT KNIFE
Excellent for whittling, carving, cutting and all other handicraft work. Has four blades.
No. 1087 $1.50

No. 1087

Official knives circa 1932.

Cattaraugus **$150.**

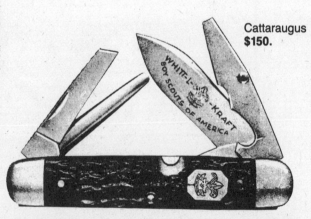

RS 4783

OFFICIAL KNIFE BOY SCOUTS OF AMERICA STAG HANDLE; THREE BLADES, 1 Large Spear, Crocus Polished and Etched with Scout Insignia; 1 Combination Bottle-Opener and Screw Driver, 1 Can Opener, Both Blue Glazed. Nickel Silver Lining, Bolsters and Emblem Shield, Snap-on Nickel Plated Shackle.
Length, closed, 3½ ins.

Remington small 3-blade (1936), **$100.**

No. D2589—Whitt-L-Kraft Knife. 3½" 4 Blades consisting of one large spear point for coarse work, one small blade, with 45 degree offset point for fine work; hollow chisel blade for extra-fine close-in work; and a scraper blade for finishing, which is also a combination can opener, bottle opener and screw driver. Full polish, brass lined, Nickel silver bolsters. Stag handle with shield bearing Scout Insignia. With or without bale.

Remington Boy Scout Knives

$100.

$100.

$150.

$150.

R 3333

$100.

RS3333
OFFICIAL KNIFE

RS 3333
Official Knife
Boy Scouts of America

RC 4523
Official Knife
Boy Scouts (Spanish)

RS 4233
Official Knife
Boy Scouts of America

Top left: pre-1923 non-Official. Above three: c1925 Official. Far left: 1936 Official.

Non-Official circa 1921: bone stag, **$100.**

R 963
R 963 Stag
R 965 Flag Pyremite

Girl Scout and Campfire Girls Knives

Although the Girl Scouts of America were established in 1912, the earliest Official Girl Scout knives we have seen date from the 1920s. The first were by Ulster (Dwight Divine), followed some time after 1927 by Remington. Both firms only made junior sized (3⅜-inch) Girl Scout utility knives with bone stag handles. In the mid 1930s, Remington also made a two-blade equal-end pen Girl Scout knife with a bail.

Later in the 1930s, Utica/Kutmaster began making Official Girl Scout Knives. They made both junior and full-sized versions with clear celluloid over green handles. They also made Featherweight (aluminum framed) two-blade Girl Scout knives with black or green handles. They even made small knives for the Brownie Scouts. These have clear over red celluloid handles.

The Campfire Girls were established in 1911. By 1915, if not earlier, they were having an official knife made by New York Knife Company. It has the motto WOHELO (Work Health Love) on the shield. In the 1920s, Remington also made an Official Campfire Girls knife. Some of these official knives have a manicure blade.

Utica/Kutmaster began to make Campfire knives in the 1930s. These did not have a special WOHELO shield, the only official designation being in the blade etch.

OFFICIAL SCOUT KNIVES. Values in excellent condition.

BOY SCOUTS OF AMERICA
New York Knife Co. 4-blade: **$125.** 2-blade: **$150.**
Remington RS-3333 full size: **$100.** Spanish: **$150.**
Remington RS-4233 junior size 4-blade: **$150.**
Remington RS-4783 junior size 3-blade: **$100.**
Ulster Dwight Divine utility (bone stag): **$75.**
Ulster yachtsman's (Sea Scouts, bone stag): **$250.**
L. F. & C. (Universal) full size: **$75.**
   Junior size: **$150.**   2-blade: **$200.**
Cattaraugus Whitt-L-Kraft: **$150.**
Pal (bone stag): **$75.**   Pal (plastic): **$50.**
Ulster (plastic): **$15.**   Camillus: **$50.**
Imperial (4 blades): **$15.** (5 blades): **$20.**
Kingston (by Ulster & Imperial c1945, metal): **$25.**
Camillus Cub Scout (blue plastic): **$8.**

GIRL SCOUTS OF AMERICA
Ulster Dwight Divine junior size: **$75.**
Remington R-4373 junior size: **$150.**
Remington R-4723 two blades: **$150.**
Utica/Kutmaster full size: **$30.** junior: **$25.**
Utica Featherweight black: **$20.** green: **$20.**
Utica/Kutmaster Brownie knife: **$12.**

CAMPFIRE GIRLS
New York Knife Co.: **$175.** Remington: **$175.**
Utica/Kutmaster: **$20.**

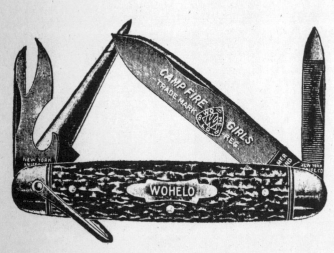

New York Knife Co. Campfire circa 1915, **$175.**

R4373
OFFICIAL KNIFE
GIRL SCOUTS, INC.

R4723
OFFICIAL KNIFE
GIRL SCOUTS, INC.

Remington Official Girl Scouts circa 1936, **$150 each.**

Remington Official Girl Scout circa 1925, **$150.**

U.S. Military Utility Knives

From the introduction of the utility pattern early in this century, cutlery manufacturers advertised one or another version of the four- or six-blade utility knife as an "army and navy" or "military" pattern. No doubt individual servicemen bought lots of these knives, but with only one exception, the government did not issue any multi-blades until World War II.

The one exception was purchased by the Army Medical Department prior to World War I. It was a 3½-inch barehead swell-center regular jack with bone stag handles. It had a corkscrew on the back, a spear master blade marked MED.DEPT./U.S.A. and A.KASTOR & BROS./GERMANY; and a saw blade marked KASTOR over a date—I have seen 11-8-12 and 10-22-14. Value **$125.**

During World War II the government purchased millions of utility knives for issue to soldiers, marines, and Navy hospital corpsmen. Most had the standard four blades (rarely three), bone stag handles, and steel mounts. Some had shields marked with branch initials (U.S.A., M.D.-U.S.N., U.S.N., U.S.M.C.). For these **add 100%** to the value in the Utility Knives price chart. Most had no shield or military markings, so they command no premium.

About 1945, the Army and Marine Corps switched to checkered stainless steel for utility knife handles, though the blades were still carbon steel. By the 1950s, they had switched to stainless blades.

For commandos and mountain troops, beginning in 1942, the Army had Ulster make junior-sized utility knives with an added Phillips screwdriver, either as a fifth blade or welded to the extra-wide bail; also a sheepfoot or spey blade in place of the cap-lifter. Handles were bone stag, mounts steel, bail or shield usually stamped U.S. Value **$125.**

The oddest G.I. folder of the war was the Navy pilot's survival knife. It was 6 inches long, with black painted steel mounts and checkered black plastic handles secured by screws. It had a stout saber-ground clip blade with a liner lock in one end, and a flexible fine-toothed saw in the other. Some had a bail at the saw end. The sheath was canvas. They were made by Colonial Knife Co. and by United Machine Tool Co. of Grand Rapids, Michigan. Value **$40.**

Other military folding knives are found under *Special Purpose Jack Knives* (lineman's and sailor's knives) and under *Cattle Knives*. G.I. folding machetes are included with *U.S. Military Fixed Blade Knives*.

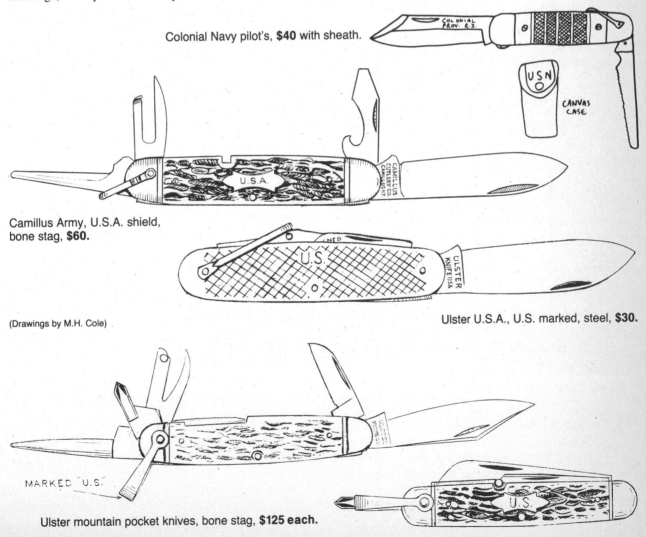

Colonial Navy pilot's, **$40** with sheath.

Camillus Army, U.S.A. shield, bone stag, **$60.**

(Drawings by M.H. Cole)

Ulster U.S.A., U.S. marked, steel, **$30.**

Ulster mountain pocket knives, bone stag, **$125 each.**

Cattle Knives

THE CATTLE KNIFE is a heavy duty three-bladed pocketknife, ordinarily 3⅝ or 3¾ inches long. Some are junior sized, as small as 3¼ inches. Others are as large as 4½ inches (such as the Case 94s). A very few cattle knives have four blades.

As the name suggests, the cattle knife was designed for work on and around livestock. The type seems to have been introduced in about the 1870s.

The standard cattle knife has the same round-ended equal-end shape as the equal-end jack, and was probably derived from that common jack knife shape. At least 90% of cattle knives are standard equal-ends, but a few have been made in other shapes. These include:

the "premier" or serpentine;
the "Eureka," or swell-center serpentine;
the "balloon" or straight swell-center;
the "jumbo" or heavy sleeveboard;
the "canoe," which looks like its namesake;
the "surveyor," sort of a swell-center canoe.

Two-bladed versions of these knives are found in *Jack Knives* and in *Double-End Jack Knives*.

The master blade of a cattle knife is most often a spear blade, though many, including most Case cattle knives, have clip master blades. A few have sheepfoot master blades. The second blade is usually a spey, while the third can be a sheepfoot, a pen, or a punch.

An uncommon version of the cattle knife is the three-spring, with a separate spring for each blade. Most of these are swell-center serpentine "Eurekas."

The "premier" or equal-end serpentine cattle knife was the ancestor of the more slender premium stock knife, introduced in the 1890s. Premier cattle knives have spear master blades while stock knives have clip master blades. Some transitional cattle knives are slender like stock knives but have spear master blades.

In the First World War, both Camillus and Simmons Hardware sold 4¼-inch wood handled equal-end cattle knives to the Army Signal Corps. In World War II, Camillus made a bone handled equal-end cattle knife as a "utility knife" for the Army Air Corps.

Plain celluloid and bone stag are the most common handle materials on cattle knives; fancy ones were made with patterned celluloid, or sometimes even pearl. Neither wood nor genuine stag handles seem to have been used on cattle knives after about 1930.

Cattle knives are not especially popular among pattern collectors. I guess the standard ones are too plain, while the fancy ones are too rare. Fancy, odd-shaped, and three-spring cattle knives would be interesting types to collect if you are patient.

Base prices for CATTLE KNIVES with: over 3⅜ up to 3¹⁵/₁₆-inch standard equal-end handles; bone stag or patterned celluloid handle scales; three blades. Excellent unsharpened condition.

Very high **$110.**   Medium: **$30.**
High: **$60.**   Low: **$12.**

CONSTRUCTION

Premier (serpentine): **add 20%**
Eureka (swell-center serpentine): **add 35%**
Balloon (straight swell-center): **add 30%**
Jumbo (heavy sleeveboard): **add 150%**
Canoe: **add 200%**
Surveyor (swell-center canoe): **add 30%**

Three springs: **add 25%**
Four blades: **add 100%**
No bolsters: **subtract 10%**

4 inches and over: **add 50%**
Junior size, 3⅜ inches or under: **subtract 20%**
Military issue: **add 50%**

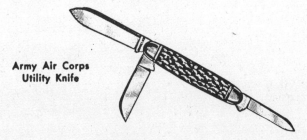

Army Air Corps
Utility Knife

Camillus, bone stag, military issue, **$45.**

HANDLE MATERIAL

Pearl: **add 60%**
Genuine stag: **add 50%**
Wood handles: **subtract 20%**
Solid metal or plain celluloid: **subtract 30%**
Modern plastic: **subtract 50%**
Metal shell handles: **subtract 65%**

CONDITION

Mint condition: **add 50%**
Worn: **subtract 60%**
Broken: **subtract 95%**

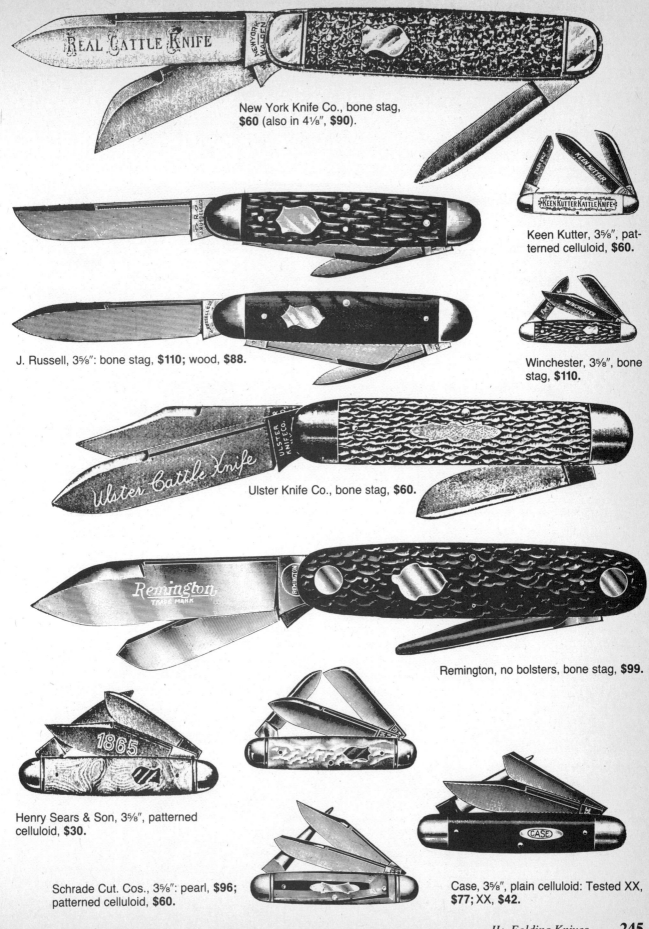

New York Knife Co., bone stag,
$60 (also in 4⅛", $90).

Keen Kutter, 3⅝", pat-
terned celluloid, $60.

J. Russell, 3⅝": bone stag, $110; wood, $88.

Winchester, 3⅝", bone
stag, $110.

Ulster Knife Co., bone stag, $60.

Remington, no bolsters, bone stag, $99.

Henry Sears & Son, 3⅝", patterned
celluloid, $30.

Schrade Cut. Cos., 3⅝": pearl, $96;
patterned celluloid, $60.

Case, 3⅝", plain celluloid: Tested XX,
$77; XX, $42.

Cattle Knives (Four Blades)

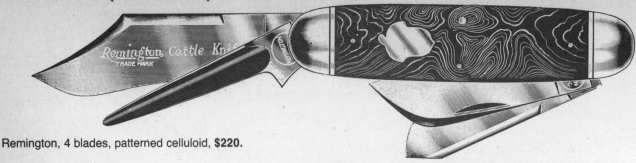

Remington, 4 blades, patterned celluloid, **$220.**

Ulster Knife Co., 4 blades, bone stag, **$120.**

Schrade Cut. Co., 4 blades, 3⅝", bone stag, **$120.**

Case, 4 blades, 3⁷⁄₁₆", bone stag: Tested XX, **$220;** XX, **$120.**

Cattle Knives (Junior Size)

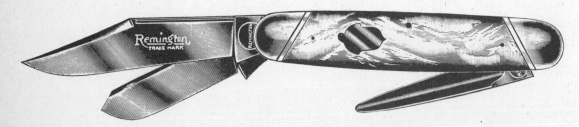

Remington, pearl, **$141.**

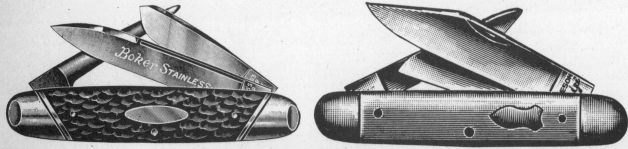

H. Boker, bone stag, **$24.**

Robeson, plain celluloid, **$17.**

Cattle Knives (Fancy and Three-Spring)

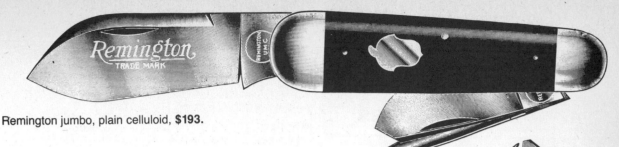

Remington jumbo, plain celluloid, **$193.**

Winchester balloon, 3⅝",
patterned celluloid, **$143.**

Schrade Cut. Co. balloon, 3½", bone stag, **$78.**

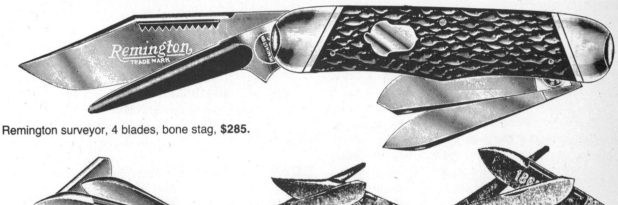

Remington surveyor, 4 blades, bone stag, **$285.**

Case Tested XX canoe ("gunboat"),
4¼", genuine stag, **$745.**

Each blade on separate spring.　　　Each blade on separate spring.

Henry Sears & Son, 3-springs: surveyor, 3⁷⁄₁₆", patterned celluloid, **$49;**
Eureka, 3⅝", bone stag, **$51.**

Remington, 3 spring, patterned celluloid (gold pearl), **$138.**

Winchester premiers: 3¼" patterned celluloid, 3" bone stag, **$106 each.**

Landers Frary & Clark Eureka, 3⅝",
bone stag, **$81.**

Premium Stock Knives

THE PREMIUM STOCK KNIFE is a serpentine shaped double-end pocketknife that ordinarily has two springs and three blades. Some stock knives have four blades, and a few have five. Five-bladed stock knives have three springs. Any stock knife under 3½ inches long is called a "Junior Premium Stock Knife."

The premium stock pattern was introduced about 1890 as a less bulky and more dressy version of the cattle knife. The stock knife was designed as a rancher's pattern, so it was at first marketed mainly in the West.

The master blade of a stock knife is always some type of clip point. The second blade is usually a spey, for castrating young animals or for skinning. The remaining blade or blades can be a pen, a sheepfoot, or a harness punch.

Stock knives are made in two basic shapes, square end and round end. Simmons Hardware Company called round-ended stock knives the "Vaquero" pattern. Schrade Cutlery Company called square-ended ones the "Texas" pattern. I don't use these names, but you can, if you want to impress people. Heavily curved round-ended stock knives are called "hump-back premium stocks." Square-ended stock knives with a center "swell" on top are called "gunstock premium stocks."

On older stock knives, the most common handle material is jigged bone. Next is celluloid. Genuine stag is uncommon, though a few firms such as Case and Henckels favored it. Pearl handled stock knives, called "stockman's Sunday dress knives," are rare.

Wood handles were first used on premium stock knives in the 1960s. Ivory and smooth bone seem never to have been used, and horn only rarely. Metal handles were tried by a few firms but they were not popular. Most modern stock knives have plastic handles.

Until the late 1940s, even the plainest stock knives were considered "premium" or high-priced knives. By then manufacturers had compared the stock knife to other three-bladed patterns, and realized that it requires much less skilled hand fitting than any whittler, while it is more attractive and less bulky than the cattle knife. In consequence, in the past 40 years the stock knife and junior stock have become the standard (or only) three-blade patterns of most pocketknife firms.

Up until the 1920s, two-bladed serpentine knives were sometimes called premium stock knives. Since that time they have been called Texas jacks if they are large and double-ended (see *Double-End Jacks*), premium pen knives if they are small and double-ended (see *Pen Knives*), or premium jacks if they are single-ended (see *Jack Knives*).

Older stock knives are starting to become popular among collectors. Some stock knife collectors limit themselves just to pearl handles, just to certain brands, or just to four- and five-blade examples. Since most older stock knives are of high quality, they are also of interest to the brand specialist.

If you want to collect modern factory folding knives, rather than antiques, premium stock knives are a good choice, since many brands and variants are still made. However, do *not* expect a collection of modern factory stock knives purchased at retail to be a profitable investment in your lifetime.

Base prices for PREMIUM STOCK KNIVES with: 3½–4 inch handles; bone stag (jigged bone) handle scales; three blades. Excellent unsharpened condition.

Very High: **$120.**   Medium: **$35.**
High: **$75.**   Low: **$16.**

CONSTRUCTION

Humpback shape: **add 50%**
Gunstock shape: **add 10%**
Four blades: **add 50%**
Five blades: **add 450%**
Long (Great Western) spey blade: **add 20%**
Locking master or punch blade: **add 20%**

Over 4 inches long: **add 30%**
3½ inches or less: see *Junior Premium Stock Knives*

HANDLE MATERIAL

Pearl: **add 60%**
Genuine stag: **add 35%**
Cow horn: **subtract 20%**
Patterned celluloid: **subtract 20%**
Solid color celluloid: **subtract 30%**
Solid metal or wood: **subtract 35%**
Modern plastic: **subtract 50%**

CONDITION

Mint: **add 50%**
Worn: **subtract 50%**
Broken: **subtract 90%**

No. 341 STOCK AND CASTRATING OR SPAYING KNIFE

Stock Knife, 3 Blades—$1.50
Weight, 3½ ounces

Cut shows exact size and style of knife. 60,000 sold in three years Retails in far west at $2.00.

Has long bowie point blade, small blade, and the sheep foot "tobacco" or scribing blade—all are very thin and as carefully made and tempered as a $2 razor. Don't bone them still thinner and expect them to cut wood.

This knife is our best seller and it ought to be, for it is the best knife for the money ever made.

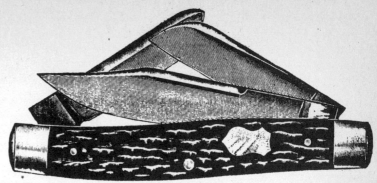

American Shear & Knife Co., bone stag, **$75.**

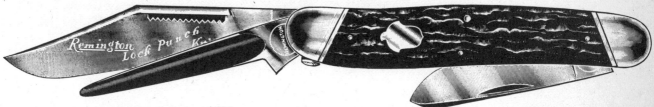

Remington, lock punch, genuine stag, **$195.**

No. X6374. Over-all size 3⅞". Bone stag handles. Also made with punch blade in place of sheepfoot, No. X6374P.

Western States, $75.

Keen Kutter, gunstock, 3¾", bone stag, **$83.**

533750
Solid nickle silver handle
Length closed 4 in.

Robeson, **$23.**

Schrade, 4", plastic, **$24** list.

Miller Bros., 3⅞", bone stag, **$75.**

Landers Frary & Clark, gunstock, patterned celluloid (horn), **$66.**

H. Boker, long spey, bone stag, **$42.**

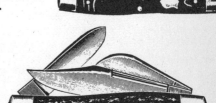

Case, 4⁵⁄₁₆", bone stag: Tested XX, **$156**; XX, **$98.**

Premium Stock Knives (Sunday Dress; 4 and 5 Blades)

Cutlered by Master Cutlers—All Blades Full Crocus Polished, Punch Blade Blued and Crocus Polished, Back Springs Crocus Polished, Full Milled Nickel Silver Linings, Linings Full Burnished and Polished, Clip Blade Etched

Remington, pearl, **$192.**

3 Blade, Crocus Polish, Etched, Full German Silver Mounted, **Ranch Knife**, Pearl Handle.

Ulster Knife Co., **$120.**

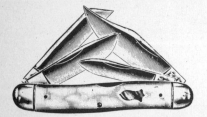

Schrade Cut. Co., 4 blades, 4″, pearl, **$180.**

Winchester, 4 blades, 4″, patterned celluloid (green), **$144.**

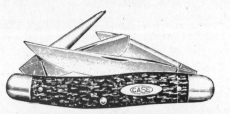

Case Tested XX, 4 blades, bone stag, **$180.**

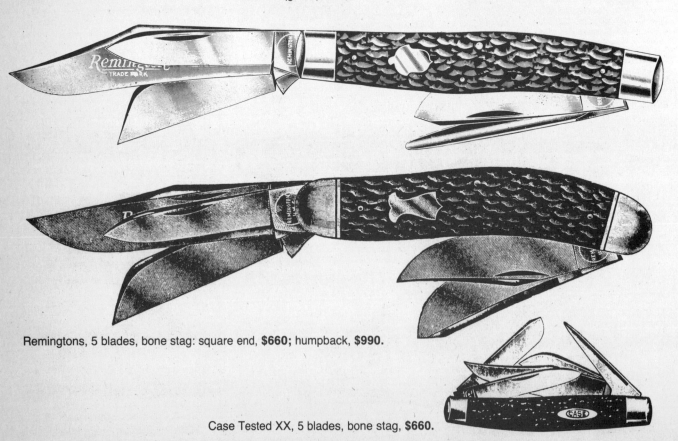

Remingtons, 5 blades, bone stag: square end, **$660;** humpback, **$990.**

Case Tested XX, 5 blades, bone stag, **$660.**

Junior Premium Stock Knives

Junior premium stock knives are small versions of premium stock knives. They are not really big enough for frequent work on animals, but how many owners of junior or even full size stock knives actually use them on livestock?

The first junior stock knives, in the 1910s, were 3⅜ inches long. Most are still around that size, but more recently many have been made in smaller sizes, some as small as 2½ inches.

The traditional small three-bladed knife is the whittler, but a junior stock knife of the same size and comparable quality takes so much less labor to make that it can be sold for 2/3 or even 1/2 the price. For this reason, junior stock knives have almost entirely replaced whittlers in modern pocketknife lines.

There is not much variation in junior stockmen; long spey blades were not used in them, nor have I seen one with more than three blades.

One odd junior stock variant is the Remington R-100 series of "Dollar Knives." These have one-piece closed-back frames with integral bolsters.

Junior stock knives are not very popular among pattern collectors, probably because of their small size. Older ones are of interest to brand collectors.

Base prices for JUNIOR PREMIUM STOCK KNIVES with: 3-3½-inch handles; full bolsters; bone stag or horn handle scales; three cutting blades. Excellent unsharpened condition.

Very High: **$100.**   Medium: **$21.**
High: **$50.**   Low: **$9.**

Punch blade: **add 20%**
Tip bolsters or no bolsters: **subtract 20%**

Over 3½ inches: see *Premium Stock Knives*
Under 3 inches: **subtract 35%**

HANDLE MATERIAL
Pearl: **add 50%**
Genuine stag: **add 30%**
Patterned celluloid: **subtract 20%**
Solid color celluloid: **subtract 30%**
Solid metal or wood: **subtract 35%**
Modern plastic: **subtract 50%**
Hollow sheet metal: **subtract 65%**

Mint: **add 50%**
Worn: **subtract 50%**
Broken: **subtract 95%**

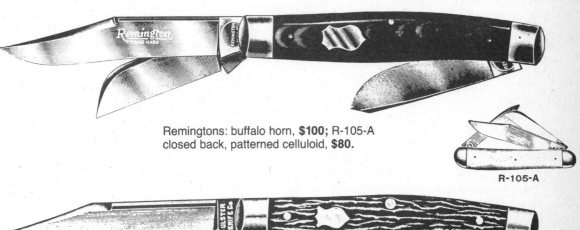

Remingtons: buffalo horn, **$100;** R-105-A closed back, patterned celluloid, **$80.**

R-105-A

LIGHT "OUTING KNIFE" WITH BELT-PUNCH BLADE.

Ulster Knife Co., punch, bone stag, **$60.**

Schrade, 2¾", plastic, **$15 list.**

Winchester, 3¼", red celluloid, **$70.**

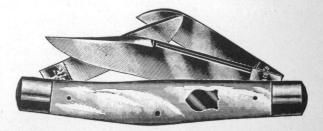

H. Boker, pearl, **$32.**

Plier and Wrench Knives

H.H.H. ad from 1910 Thomas Mfg. Co. catalog.

AMERICAN PLIER KNIVES

By Houston Price
Publisher and Editor of Knife World.

PLIER KNIVES are multi-blades about the size and shape of an equal-end cattle knife (3½-4¼ inches long). They incorporate a small but functional pliers either as a separate blade or as a part of the handle.

Lewis Patent

The American plier knife most often found is the "HHH" made by the Oscar Barnett Tool Company of Newark, New Jersey. These knives are based on U.S. Patent No. 662,005 issued to James C. Lewis of Tracy, California, on November 20, 1900. Most have "Trade HHH Mark" etched on the blade or stamped on the plier handle.

Barnett went out of business in about 1915. In the 15 years that HHH knives were produced, many hardware wholesale houses distributed them, as did such national retail mail order firms as Sears Roebuck and the Thomas Manufacturing Company of Ohio. In consequence, these knives can be found all over the country, though rarely in good condition.

HHH knives have brown jigged bone handles. They have a spear master blade and a punch. One end of the center liner projects for use as a screwdriver. The pliers incorporates a wire cutter, and the end of its handle doubles as a hoof pick.

HHH knives were made with a variety of markings. Some have an O. BARNETT TOOL CO. tang stamping, while others have J. C. LEWIS PAT. NOV. 20, 1900. Some have two patent numbers stamped on the side of the plier handle (the second is 606,547 from June 28, 1898).

Original retail price for the HHH knife ranged from 92¢ in the Sears big book up to $2.75 in the 1910 Thomas catalog. Current value is about **$50** for a knife in worn condition with no blades broken, and about **$200** for an excellent unsharpened example.

Undy Patent

Less common than the HHH is the Valley Forge plier knife patented by Charles Undy of Newark, New Jersey, on September 11, 1923. A 1925 Von Lengerke & Antoine retail catalog offered it as a "'Radio' Knife."

This plier knife has brown jigged bone handles, a spear master blade, and a screwdriver wire-stripper blade. The spring-loaded pliers folds into the handle.

Most of these knives are tang stamped VALLEY FORGE CUTLERY CO., NEWARK N.J. U.S.A. Some are stamped H. BOKER & CO'S IMPROVED CUTLERY, U.S.A. Boker had owned Valley Forge since 1899. Boker/Valley Forge also made this knife on contract for Case, and I have seen examples with three different Case stampings. All the knives have PAT APPL'D FOR stamped into one handle.

THE "RADIO" KNIFE

The handiest little tool for the radio fan or all around repair man. American made. Of finest quality crucible steel throughout. Pliers are 2⅞ inches, handy size and built for service—note wire cutter. Blade 2¾ in. Wire scraper and screw driver are most convenient. Stag handle, brass lined. Nickel silver shield, and bolsters. Weight, 4 oz.

C6836 Price, each ....$2.00 net

1925 V.L. & A. ad. (Courtesy of Frank Gamble)

When new, this knife sold at retail for about $2. Current value ranges from **$150** to **$300**, though unusual stampings may go even higher.

Morley

This imported plier knife was made for and sold by an American firm. Marked W. H. MORLEY & SONS/GERMANY, it was imported by Adolph Kastor & Bros. of New York, owners since 1902 of Camillus Cutlery Co.

This knife, too, has brown jigged bone handles. The blades are spear and pen. The plier handle has a screwdriver tip, and is held shut by the bail.

This knife probably dates from the mid-1920s. It is worth **$200–250** in excellent condition.

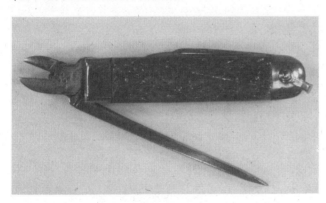

Morley plier knife.

Heilrath Patent

This rarest of the plier knives also has the simplest mechanism. It was patented May 23, 1905 (No. 790,432), by Christian Heilrath of Sacramento, Calif. He transferred his patent to G. M. Parkinson, who manufactured the knives under the name PLI-R-NIF.

The PLI-R-NIF measures 4¼ inches closed. Its appearance is that of two single blade knives, each with a spring whose end is shaped into one jaw of the pliers. The two parts are joined by the pivot of the pliers. Friction between the two nickel silver inner liners keeps the pliers shut when not in use.

The few known PLI-R-NIFs have a spear master blade. The second blade is either a screwdriver or a punch. The punch's handle has an easy-open notch. Handle scales I have seen are aluminum, and one of them has stamped advertising.

The usual marking is PLI-R-NIF/WARRANTED/SAN FRANCISCO in large letters on one liner. PAT'D MAY 23, '05, may be stamped on the master blade tang or on one of the handles.

The offices of Parkinson's PLI-R-NIF Co. were in San Francisco until the 1906 earthquake and fire. Afterwards they were across the Bay in Berkeley, at 2700 Dana St. Distribution was limited, probably just to the West Coast. Current value is **$250–350.**

Heilrath PLI-R-NIF.

I have seen U.S. patent drawings of other plier knives, such as a bicyclist's version by John Watts of Sheffield from 1897, and a changeable blade model by Frederik Nielsen of California from 1925. I have never seen or heard of specimens of those knives, but if they do exist, their value would be about **$150–250.**

WRENCH KNIVES

Toward the close of World War I, Cattaraugus introduced a multi-blade with a built-in wrench. It has brown jigged bone handles. Its mechanism was patented March 5, 1918 (No. 1,258,396), by Tint Champlin, son of the firm's founder, J.B.F. Champlin.

This wrench is a sliding alligator or bulldog type. The master blade is a screwdriver wire-stripper; the other is a

---

1,258,396. COMBINED KNIFE AND WRENCH. TINT CHAMPLIN, Little Valley, N. Y. Filed Mar. 8, 1917. Serial No. 153,241. (Cl. 81—130.)

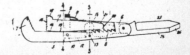

March 5, 1918, plier knife patent.

punch. Most are marked PATENT APPLIED FOR. Value is **$200–250.**

That first Cattaraugus wrench knife was only made for a short time. About 1920, the firm replaced it with two knives that have standard crescent wrenches at one end. The 1-W

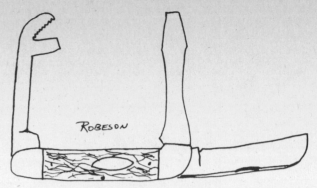
Robeson automobilist's knife.

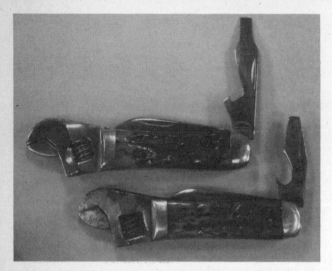
1920s (top) and 1930s Cattaraugus 3-Ws.

has a spear blade and punch. The 3-W has a spear blade and a screwdriver cap-lifter, of which two variations are known. These are worth about **$200** each in excellent condition.

Also in the 1920s, Aerial Cutlery Co. offered a picture handled knife with an alligator wrench built into one end. The example shown has pearl handles, which are probably

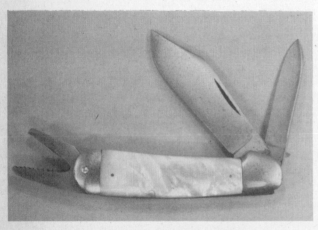
Aerial D399 "Alligator Special."

not original. A picture handled example is worth about **$150** in excellent condition.

In the same period, Robeson offered an automobilist's knife with a sheepfoot master blade, a large screwdriver, and a folding alligator wrench. One of these is worth about **$80.**

Imports

More recently, both plier and wrench knives have been made in France, Germany, Italy, and Japan for export to the United States. The French knives are of the highest quality and are worth **$75–100.** German and Italian ones are worth **$35–75** depending on quality. Japanese ones are worth **$20–40.**

Dynamite Knives

Closely related to plier and wrench knives is the large variety of multi-bladed crimping knives made especially for miners, road builders, and others who work with explosives. The example shown here, made in Germany for the Koehler Mfg. Co. of Marlborough, Mass., is typical. Value of older examples in excellent condition ranges from **$75** to **$150.**

Koehler Mfg. Co. dynamite knife.

Tool Kit Knives

SINCE THE 18th century, if not earlier, specialty cutlers have contrived to include more and more tools in handy sized multi-blade knives. Of course the more tools that are included, the more delicate each one has to be. This is why so many older multi-blades have broken blades: they did not stand up to heavy use.

As an alternate way to get a lot of tools into a small knife handle, some cutlers made tool-kit knives. A tool kit knife is an ordinary sized jack knife handle that resides in a fold-up kit with an assortment of sturdy blades and tools. At least they are sturdier than the tools in one-piece multi-blades.

The tools with a tool kit knife include, at a minimum, knife blade, file, saw, and screwdriver. Often there are several types and sizes of each of these, and also gimlet, punch, chisel, ruler, can and bottle openers, cork pullers, and even a small hammer.

The tool kit handle has an opening in one end for attaching the tools. Sometimes there is a second opening in one side of the handle for attaching the gimlet or cork puller. All but the highest quality tool kit handles have a permanent spear blade in the end opposite the opening, rather than a detached knife blade.

In the best tool kits, each tool pushes straight into the handle opening and locks rigidly in place. This prevents tools from shutting on your fingers. Modern knife-axe hunting knife sets and 18th century changeable blade carving knives use the same mechanism.

Cheaper kits do not have this feature. They have a fixed pivot pin in the open end of the handle, while each tool has a hooked tang. The tang is hooked on to the pin, and the tool is pivoted into place. Tools in this type of knife usually do not lock. [see *Pruning Knives* for another type of changeable blade mechanism.]

Base prices for TOOL KIT KNIVES with: original leather or plastic cases; bone stag or picture handles; all original tools. In excellent condition.

Very High: $450.	Medium: **$150.**
High: $250.	Low: **$60.**

Large set with 2 handles: **add 50%**
Wood handles: **subtract 20%**
Celluloid or composition handles: **subtract 35%**
Pressed sheet metal handles: **subtract 50%**

Mint condition: **add 50%**
Worn or 1–2 tools missing: **subtract 50%**
Case missing: **subtract 40%**

Odd parts of Very High value tool kit knives have some value. A single Napanoch handle or blade might be worth **$50-100** to a collector trying to fill in an incomplete kit. Advertise.

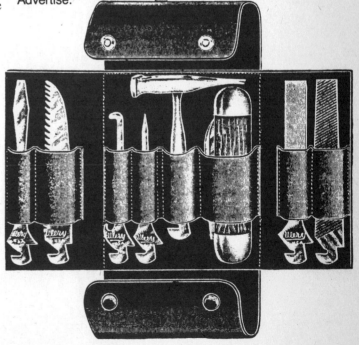

Napanoch, bone stag handles, **$400.**

Ulery, wood handles, **$120.**

Showpiece and Exposition Knives

THESE are one-of-a-kind or, rarely, limited production knives. They were made to serve as the center-piece of a store or exposition display case. Most are either very large, very ornate, or both.

Every showpiece knife should be evaluated on its individual merits. Big elaborate ones with 20 or more blades can be worth from **$2,000** to over **$100,000**; giant jack knives and pen knives are worth from **$300** to **$3,000**.

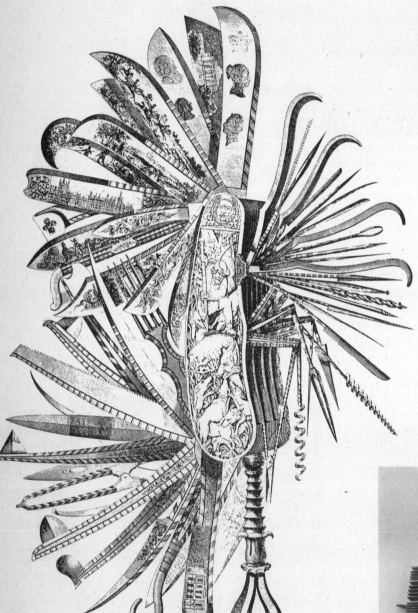

Ivory handled showpiece knife made for Martin L. Bradford of Boston c1850. Courtesy National Knife Museum. Approximate value, **$20,000**.

(Phil Pankiewicz photo)

The Joseph Rodgers Norfolk Sportsman's Knife, mid-19th century. Handle length, 14½ inches. Total height open on stand, 38 inches. Approximate value, **$125,000**.

5½" Bohemian showpiece knife c1900, carved ivory handles. Value **$2,500**.

(Wiebusch Collection, Smithsonian Inst.)

Folding Medical Instruments

IN THE 19th century, folding pocket instruments were made for surgeon's emergency use. They are distinguished by small size, unlined flat handles (usually tortoise-shell or horn), open backs, and extremely fine finish. Many are double-ended, almost all have blade stops at 180°, and many lock open. A very few have spring backs with locks.

The illustrations are from a c1874 catalog of Tiemann & Co., New York (Courtesy of George Sarris). Values indicated are for examples in excellent condition with any legible maker's mark. **Subtract 25%** for unmarked examples. A complete matching cased set is worth at least **20%** more than the sum of its parts.

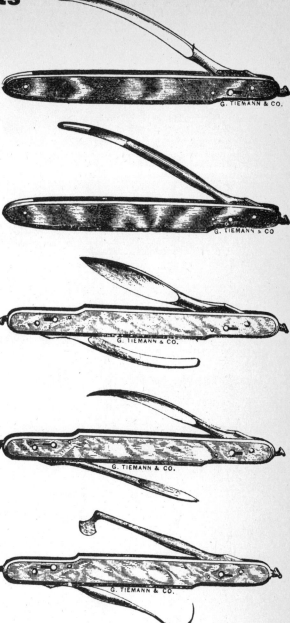

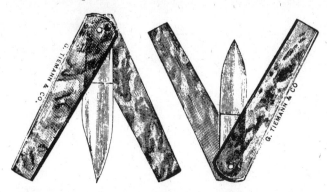

Thumb Lancet. Used for phlebotomy or blood-letting. Bleeding was a popular cure-all up until about 1870. This style of folding thumb lancet was introduced in the 17th century and was in common use throughout America during much of our history. Value, **$40.**

FIG. 176. Four Bladed Spring-catch Pocket Instrument.

1 Scalpel, 1 Finger Knife, 1 curved probe-pointed Bistourie.
1 curved sharp-pointed Bistourie.

Spring Catch Pocket Instruments. 2 blades (not shown), **$75**; 4 blades, **$125.**

Slide Catch Pocket Instruments. 1 blade, **$35.** 2 blades, **$50.** Examples shown, top to bottom: curved probe-pointed bistoury; Cooper's hernia knife; scalpel and probe-pointed bistoury; sharp-pointed bistoury and tenotome; gum lancet and tenaculum (hook).

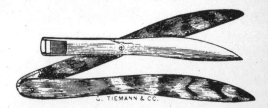

Seton Needle. Used for setaceum, introducing a silk string under the skin to induce the formation of pus, an even more drastic treatment than bleeding. Value, **$75.** Larger versions included in pocketknives were used to inoculate cattle against blackleg.

Commemorative and Limited Edition Knives

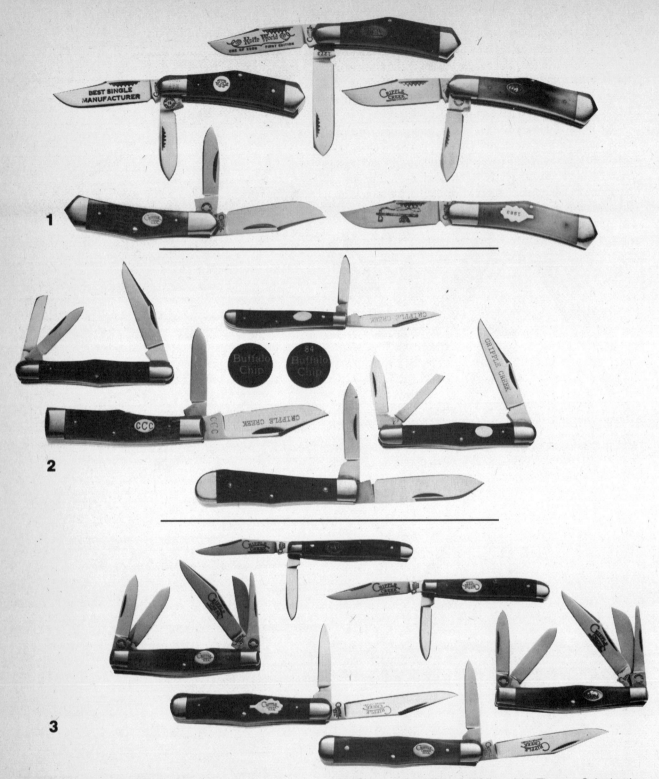

2—1981 knives and prototypes include:
Far Left: swell center balloon whittler with no shield.
Far right: whittler with shield and blade etch.
Top: peanut with plain shield.
Lower left: gunstock jack with CCC shield.
Bottom: jack with no shield.
   An offer of $1,000 for this group was turned down in 1983.

3—Some early 1981 and 1982 models. The two Coke bottles (bottom) retailed for $30 and are now trading for **$125.** The five-blade knives are worth **$150** for the buffalo shield and **$250** for the "CRIPPLE CREEK" shield. Any mint knife with this shield is worth at least **$150.**

1 (Opposite page)—This Cripple Creek design is based on a pattern from the 1920s. Each knife has a distinctive shield, stamping, or etch. Original retail was $40–50. Current value is in parentheses.
Top center: 1982 *Knife World* 1st Edition ($100–200).
Top left: Northeast Cutlery Collectors Association (NCCA) 1982 award knife (**$125**).
Bottom left: 1981 "CRIPPLE CREEK" shield (**$200**).
Top right: 1981 buffalo shield (**$150**).
Bottom right: 1983 "Hawk" with oak leaf shield (**$75–90**).

Cripple Creek U.S.A. Benchmade Collectible Knives

By Houston Price
Editor and Publisher of Knife World

BRAND NAMES such as Remington, Winchester, Case, and New York Knife Company have long held special significance for pocketknife collectors. Finding the high quality knives made years ago by these famous firms is a constant challenge. Almost all of them are highly valued, so finding one at a reasonable price means you have a real treasure to keep, or else the makings of a quick profit.

Cripple Creek is a new name, but already you can add it to that elite list. In a few short years, Bob Cargill's limited edition brand has earned recognition and respect, as well as a dedicated following of serious collectors.

There are several good reasons for the rapid rise in popularity and collector value of Cripple Creek Knives. First, both the patterns and the quality of workmanship of these American made knives is reminiscent of knives from the U.S. cutlery industry's "golden years," the 1920s and 1930s.

Second, a very limited number of knives has been made since the brand's introduction in 1981, and production will continue to be limited in the future. Cripple Creek knives are benchmade one at a time. The company's founder, custom knifemaker Bob Cargill of Lockport, Illinois, works on every knife from the time the design is conceived until production is complete. In fact, until his son, Barry, entered the business in 1984, Cargill performed all the tasks of a one-man factory. Even with modest growth, he intends to maintain this personal involvement and limited production.

Third, Cargill has used an effective dating system on his Cripple Creek knives so that it is easy to pinpoint when any knife was made. It is also easy to learn the total production of each pattern. Most Cripple Creeks were made in special limited editions, often for knife clubs, with total quantity marked accordingly. Those not so marked can be identified from Cargill's own production records.

Identification of a Cripple Creek knife requires noting four features: pattern, handle material, shield, and stamping. Cargill's patterns are traditional, so they can be identified from the folding knife pattern section of this book.

Cripple Creek handle materials are bone, genuine stag, and mother of pearl. Few pearl Cripple Creeks have been made, and those few are much in demand. Most of the knives have bone handles, with the "honey" and the "strawberry" colored being the most popular.

Cripple Creek's standard shield is an oval embossed with a three-legged buffalo, modeled after the one on some 1937-D nickels. Bob Cargill lost a leg in an accident several years ago, and this misfortune combined with his wry good humor inspired his brand name and his trademark.

Cargill has used the crippled buffalo shield since late 1981. Before then, he sold a few Cripple Creeks without shields. Others had a flat oval shield stamped with the CRIPPLE CREEK brand name. A wise collector would never pass up a knife with this "Cripple Creek" shield.

The small blade of each Cripple Creek knife is tang stamped with the company name in a circle. Knives made in 1981 have no date marking, but after that the last two digits of the production year have been added to the circle stamping. Most of 1982 was devoted to producing the 2,000 *Knife World* 1st Edition knives. Only about 40 other knives of different patterns were made that year, and any of these would be a rare find.

Several local area knife collecting clubs have chosen a Cripple Creek as an annual club knife. Club knives are made in very limited quantities and are usually sold only to club members. Some collectors join local clubs all over the country, by mail, in order to be able to purchase club knives. Also a few businesses have commissioned Cripple Creek limited editions to commemorate special occasions. All these special limited editions are rare and desirable to collectors.

Recently, several of the Cutlery World chain of stores have begun to stock a selection of current Cripple Creek knives. You'll not find it difficult to recognize a Cripple Creek. Its distinctive pattern and workmanship will beckon with a whisper of bygone years. A quick check of the handle, shield, and stamping could easily tell you that you have found a pocket-sized treasure

All illustrated Cripple Creek knives are from the Vanderveen collection. Photos by Weyer of Toledo.

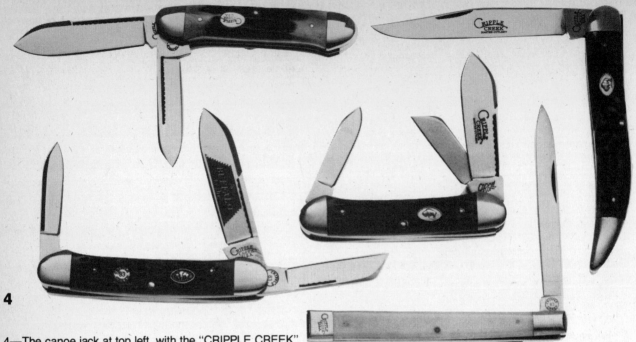

4

4—The canoe jack at top left, with the "CRIPPLE CREEK" shield, is the real sleeper here. Originally retailed for $35, it recently sold for **$400.** The others are 1983 models valued between **$65** and **$85.**

5

5—Unusual knives based on old-time patterns. In 1981, fifty "Sachem" knives (top right) were sold for $100 each. They now bring up to **$250.** The rest are 1983 and 1984 models.

CRIPPLE CREEK KNIFE PRODUCTION: 1981–1984

Standard patterns called "10 Little Indians" (LI-1-LI-10).

Handle	Shield	Description
LI-1 Dog Leg Jack		
1981		
24 Honey bone	Cripple Creek	
24 Honey bone	Buffalo	
24 Stag	Buffalo	
2 Pearl	Buffalo	
1 Pearl	Buffalo	3 Blade
1 Honey bone	K.W. in Oval	Knife World prototype
1982		
1 Stag	Buffalo	File worked springs
2000 Honey Bone	Knife World	1st Edition
1983		
1 Stag	Buffalo	Clip and skinner blades
8 Stag	Buffalo	
1 Strawberry bone	Buffalo	
1 Honey bone	Oak Leaf	
100 White bone	Oak Leaf	
LI-2 Canoe		
1981		
1 Honey bone	Cripple Creek	3 Blades
2 Pearl	Buffalo	2 Blades
12 Misc. bone	Cripple Creek	Varied blades
1 Honey bone	Cripple Creek	2 Blades
1982		
1 Pearl	Buffalo	3 Blades
1983		
6 Honey bone	Buffalo	1 Blade each end
1 Honey bone	Buffalo	2 Blade half-canoe
1984		
1 Pearl	Buffalo	3 Blades
4 Stag	Buffalo	3 Blades
3 Honey bone	Buffalo	3 Blades
3 Strawberry bone	Buffalo	3 Blades
LI-3 Peanut		
1981		
3 Honey bone	Cripple Creek	
12 Stag	Cripple Creek	
24 Stag	Buffalo	
12 Honey bone	Buffalo	
1983		
26 Honey bone	Buffalo	
LI-4 Coke Bottle		
1981		
24 Honey bone	Cripple Creek	
27 Special bone	Oak Leaf	
48 Stag	Buffalo	
1982		
1 Honey bone	Buffalo	1 Blade
LI-5 Stockman (old style-blades have 81 stamp)		
1981		
24 Honey bone	Cripple Creek	3 Blades
12 Stag	Cripple Creek	3 Blades
12 Honey bone	Buffalo	3 Blades
24 Stag	Buffalo	3 Blades
1 Honey bone	Cripple Creek	5 Blades
12 Stag	Cripple Creek	5 Blades
1982		
6 Stag	Buffalo	5 Blades
1 Honey bone	Buffalo	5 Blades
1983		
1 Pearl	Buffalo	3 Blades
1 Honey bone	Buffalo	5 Blades
LI-5 Stockman (new style slant bolsters)		
1982		
1 Stag	AECA	AECA Club knife proto.
7 Honey bone	Buffalo	3 Blades
1983		
80 Stag	AECA	AECA Club knife-2 blades
1 Honey bone	Buffalo	2 Blades
10 Honey bone	Buffalo	3 Blades
10 Strawberry bone	Buffalo	3 Blades
8 Stag	Buffalo	3 Blades
1 Stag	Buffalo	Whittler blades
1 Honey bone	Buffalo	Whittler blades
LI-6 Whittler		
1981		
6 Honey bone	Cripple Creek	
12 Honey bone	Buffalo	
24 Stag	Buffalo	
1983		
3 Pearl	Buffalo	
LI-7 Trapper		
1981		
7 Stag	Buffalo	
1982		
50 Stag	Buffalo	
80 Stag	AECA	AECA Club knife
1983		
2 Stag	Buffalo	
3 Pearl	Buffalo	
LI-8 Muskrat		
1981		
8 Stag	Buffalo	
1982		
50 Stag	Buffalo	

Handle	No Shield Bolster stamping	Description
LI-9 Barlow		
1981		
10 Honey bone	Wounded Knee	1 and 2 Blades
4 Honey bone	Wounded knee	Prototype set of 4
1982		
1 Honey bone	Wounded Knee	
1200 Honey bone	Wounded Knee	300 serialized sets
1983		
4 stag	Wounded Knee	1 Blade
150 Honey bone	Fort	Fort City club knife-2 blades
26 Stag	Wounded Knee	
8 Honey bone	Wounded Knee	
9 Strawberry bone	Wounded Knee	
2 Honey bone	Wounded Knee	3 Blades
1984		
61 Stag	Cripple Creek	
27 Honey bone	Cripple Creek	
23 Strawberry bone	Cripple Creek	
12 Smooth white bone	Cripple Creek	
1 Smooth honey bone	Cripple Creek	
1 Black-lip pearl	Engraved	Prototype
100 Black-lip pearl	Engraved	AECA 1984 show knife
200 Smooth red bone	Cripple Creek	"Blood Brothers" set
200 Smooth white bone	Cripple Creek	"Blood Brothers" set
30 Smooth white bone	Cripple Creek	Nutmeg State Club Knife
59 Smooth white bone	Cripple Creek	Firestone 20 year knife

Handle	Shield	Description
LI-10 Buffalo Skinner		
1981		
8 Honey bone	Buffalo	
2 Pearl	Buffalo	
1982		
15 Honey bone	Buffalo	1 Blade
4 Stag	Buffalo	1 Blade
5 Honey bone	Buffalo	2 Blades
1 Stag	Buffalo	2 Blades
1983		
48 Honey bone	Buffalo	1 Blade
25 Strawberry bone	Buffalo	1 Blade
13 Honey bone	Buffalo	2 Blades-small etch
25 Honey bone	Buffalo	2 Blades-large etch

In addition to the LI series, several Cripple Creek special patterns have been made as follows:

Handle	Shield	Description
1981		
6 Honey bone	C.C.C.	Misc. prototypes
50 Stag	Buffalo	Large coke bottle
1 Honey bone	C.C.C.	Gunstock
1 Red bone	Cripple Creek	Gunstock
1982		
2 Honey bone	Buffalo	2 Blade "Sunfish"
1 Pearl	Buffalo	Moose
1 Metal	none	Leg Knife
1 Honey bone	Buffalo	5 Blade sowbelly-proto.
1983		
56 Stag	Buffalo	Allegheny Knife Club-sm. trapper
26 Stag	Buffalo	Small trapper
9 Honey bone	Buffalo	Small trapper
9 Strawberry bone	Buffalo	Small trapper
1 Pearl	Buffalo	Small trapper
1 Honey bone	Buffalo	1 Blade small trapper
1 Honey bone	Buffalo	3 Blade whittler
10 Honey bone	Buffalo-1983	2nd anniversary knife
2 Stag	Buffalo	Gunstock
1 Smooth white bone	None	Large physician knife
100 Honey bone	Buffalo	Gunstock-Sachem 2
100 Smooth White bone	Oak Leaf-1983	Blade etched "Hawk"
2 Stag	Buffalo	Copperhead
1 Honey bone	Buffalo	Copperhead
1 Strawberry bone	Buffalo	Copperhead
1 Stag	Buffalo	2 Blade sowbelly
2 Honey bone	Buffalo	3 Blade sowbelly
2 Honey bone	Buffalo	5 Blade sowbelly
1 Pearl	Buffalo	Gunstock
1 Stag	Buffalo	Gunstock
1 Honey bone	Buffalo	Gunstock
1 Strawberry bone	Buffalo	Gunstock
1984		
52 Stag	AECA	AECA 5th anniv.-toothpick
48 stag	Buffalo	Toothpick
1 Honey bone	Buffalo	Toothpick- 2 shields
1 Pearl	Buffalo	Toothpick
50 Honey bone	Buffalo-1984	3rd anniversary knife
1 Stag	Buffalo	2 Blade jack
80 Stag	AECA	AECA club knife
100 Honey bone	Buffalo	"Northwest Logger" 3 blade sowbelly
38 Stag	Buffalo	5 Blade sowbelly
60 Honey bone	Buffalo	5 Blade sowbelly
53 Strawberry bone	Buffalo	5 Blade sowbelly
2 Honey bone	Buffalo	3 Blade sowbelly
1 Pearl	Buffalo	5 Blade sowbelly
4 Smooth bone	Buffalo	2 Blade sowbelly protos.

Commemorative and Limited Edition Knives

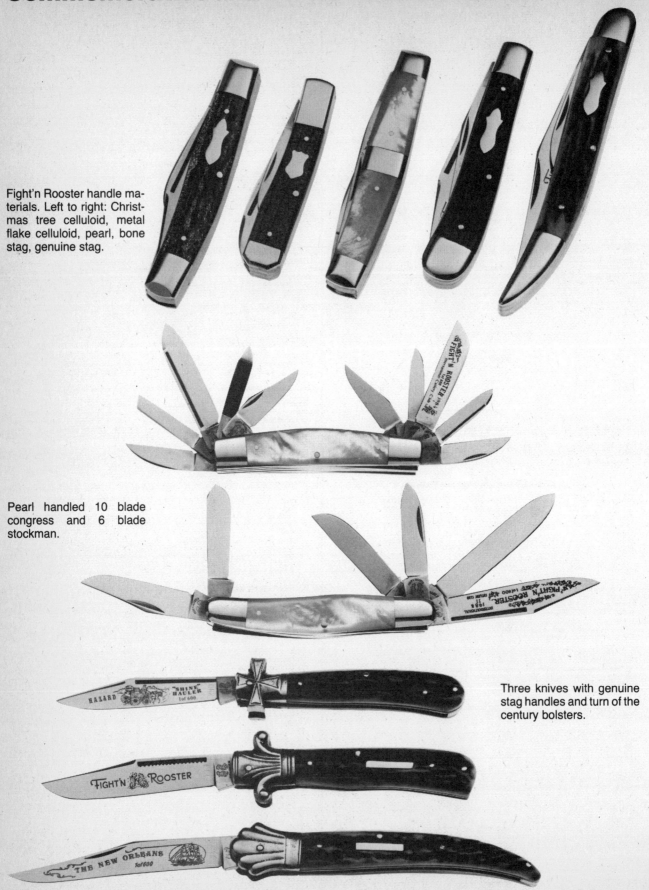

Fight'n Rooster handle materials. Left to right: Christmas tree celluloid, metal flake celluloid, pearl, bone stag, genuine stag.

Pearl handled 10 blade congress and 6 blade stockman.

Three knives with genuine stag handles and turn of the century bolsters.

Fight'n Rooster Fine Limited Production Knives

By Houston Price
Editor and Publisher of Knife World

IN THE EARLY 1970s, Frank Buster, a knife-swapping country store proprietor, recognized that finding old knives at reasonable prices was becoming increasingly difficult. Traveling from his middle Tennessee home town of Lebanon, he sought out cutlery manufacturers willing to make him limited quantities of discontinued traditional patterns of pocketknives that he could sell to his fellow collectors.

Buster learned that most knife factories are geared to producing knives by the tens of thousands. They lacked the flexibility essential for limited production runs, and they would not consider using old-time methods, or old parts and patterns, either.

Finally Buster located a small factory in Solingen, Germany, that was willing to cooperate with him on a few short-run patterns. In 1976 this factory produced the first knives with Frank Buster's FIGHT'N ROOSTER tang stamping of a pair of fighting cocks.

Since that beginning barely a decade ago, hundreds of patterns and variations of Fight'n Rooster knives have been offered to the knife collecting fraternity. Some fans of these knives even carry and use them.

Each of the Fight'n Rooster variations is strictly limited in production. Ordinarily, 300 knives of each style are made, featuring three or four different handle materials. Mother-of-pearl has been a favorite with collectors.

These regular production Fight'n Roosters are offered through dealers at knife shows and by mail. In addition to them, Buster has produced over a hundred different limited edition club knives. Production of these has varied from 100 pieces for smaller clubs, on up to 600 for the largest.

Fight'n Rooster knives are made in traditional styles, but Frank Buster has come up with several new variations on old themes. He has offered canoe whittlers, lockback whittlers, and multi-bladed stock knives. He has offered many knives with six or eight or even 12 blades. He has also offered a few multi-bladed display knives, including one with 100 blades. A few Fight'n Rooster knives feature genuine old fancy bolsters found in the factory storerooms.

A noteworthy feature of Buster's revival of traditional patterns has been his re-introduction of fancy patterned celluloid handles. His was the first contemporary knife firm to revive such traditional materials as "butter-and-molasses," "gold flake," and "Christmas tree."

Up until the early 1940s, when the American production of celluloid was halted, this was a popular handle material used by all of the large knife companies. A few years ago, Buster found the last celluloid factory in Germany. He bought enough of this old-style plastic to last his knife factory several years. In 1984 the celluloid factory went out of business.

Because he is himself a collector of knives, Frank Buster has been careful to tailor the production of Fight'n Rooster knives to the needs and desires of collectors. He has kept quality high and production strictly limited. He has completely catalogued every pattern produced, including year, quantity, and description. He has made Fight'n Rooster a name that will be long remembered.

Photos by Weyer of Toledo, courtesy of Frank Buster Cutlery Company, Box 936, Lebanon TN 37087

Unusual expressions of traditional patterns are typical of Fight'n Rooster knives.

Buck Custom and Limited Edition Knives*

By Vern Taylor

Buck Custom Knives

IN 1981, a few of the most skilled workmen at the Buck Knives plant, under the direct supervision of Chuck Buck, began the production of limited quantities of hand-made and custom knives. There are three categories of Buck Custom knives:

1. Standard Buck patterns with custom handles and highly polished blades.

---

*NOTE: See the Buck Knives chapters in the *Brand History* section and the *Fixed Blades* section for the story of regular production Buck knives.

2. Special patterns of Buck Custom Knives as shown in the Buck Custom catalog, available from Buck dealers.
3. Custom knives made to the customer's specifications, either singly or in limited runs.

Except for slip-joint pocketknives with custom handles, all knives in these three custom categories have a special tang stamp: BUCK/CUSTOM/U.S.A. Knives in the second and third categories, except for prototypes, also have a serial number.

The accompanying chart shows the limited run custom knives from category 3 made so far. In addition to the knives listed in the chart, Buck's custom department has made over 1,000 custom knives for individual customers, and nearly 2,000 customized production knives.

NAME	MADE FOR	QUANTITY	ORIGINAL PRICE	SERIAL NUMBERS
BUCK BOWIE	Cutlery World	100	$600.	1–100
HARLEY BOWIE	Harley Davidson	3,000	300.	1–3,000
SILVER DAGGER	Cutlery World	100	650.	1–100
GERONIMO DAGGER	Providence Mint	1,000	450.	1–2,000[1]
GERONIMO DAGGER	Mainly Buck employees	300	N/A	none
3/PC SKINNER SET	New W. Auto	40+	N/A	1–40

[1]Numbered by customer

Engraved silver-mounted custom dagger for Cutlery World: **$600-700.**

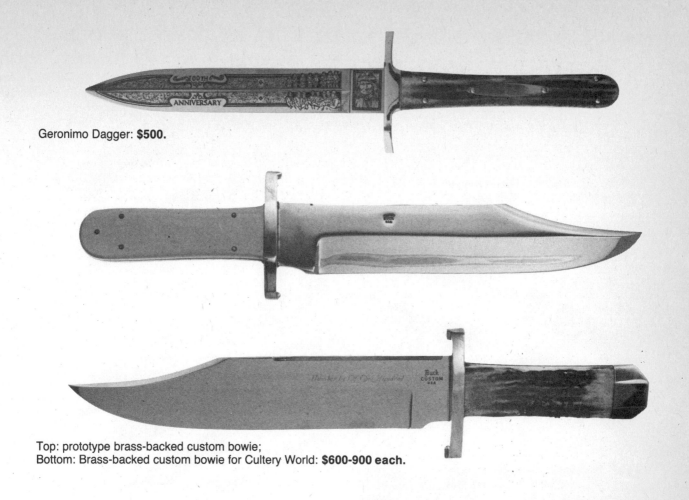

Geronimo Dagger: **$500.**

Top: prototype brass-backed custom bowie;
Bottom: Brass-backed custom bowie for Cultery World: **$600-900 each.**

D-Guard and Mountain Man custom bowies: **$350-400 each.**

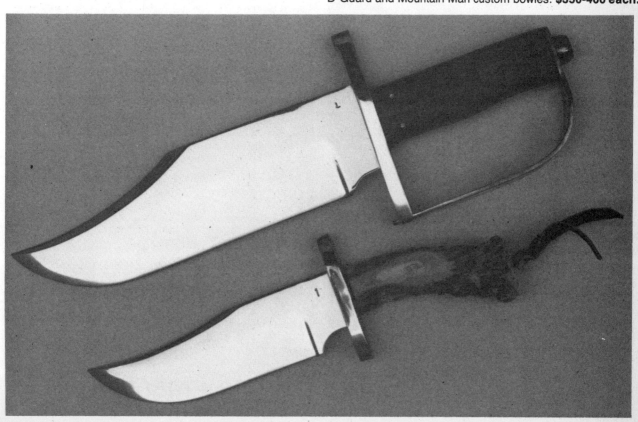

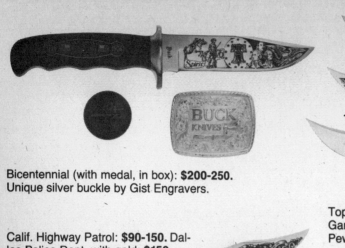

Bicentennial (with medal, in box): **$200-250.**
Unique silver buckle by Gist Engravers.

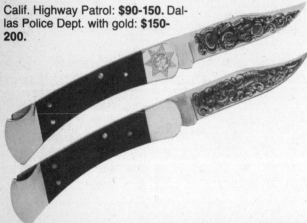

Calif. Highway Patrol: **$90-150.** Dallas Police Dept. with gold: **$150-200.**

Top to Bottom:
Gander; Deer Scene;
Pewter Handle Deer: **$80-100 each.**

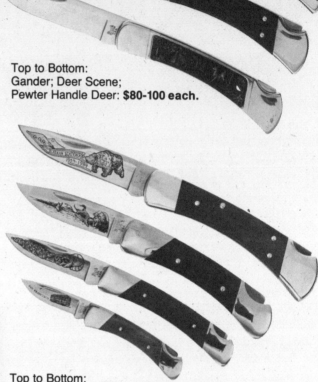

Top to Bottom:
Alaska Statehood: **$100-120.** Ducks in Flight II: **$80-100.**
Buck Bandit: **$70-100.** Cable Car: **$75-90.**

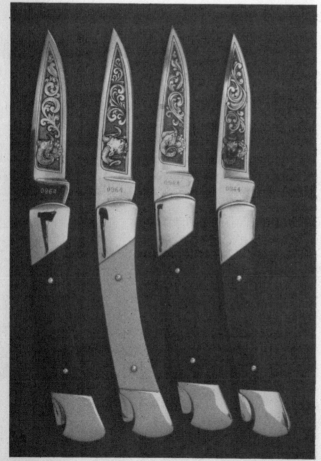

Grand Slam: **$450/set.**

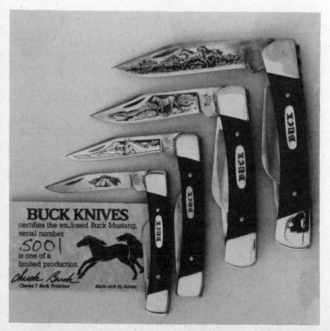

Pony, Yearling, Colt, Mustang (not sold as a set): **$45-85 each.** All four with matching numbers: **$350-450.**

Buck Limited Edition Knives

Since 1976, Buck has offered its customers specially etched, stamped, or engraved limited edition knives. These knives were sold through Buck's regular retail dealers, rather than through knife collecting publications or shows. This chart shows all of the Buck limited editions issued through mid-1985.

BUCK LIMITED EDITION PRODUCTION KNIVES

YEAR	NAME	STYLE	QUANTITY PRODUCED	SERIAL NUMBERS	ISSUE PRICE
1976	Bicentennial (N)	Unique Pattern	7,600	0001-7600	$200.
1977	Aurum Set	110/112/501/ 401/402	app. 500	none	$500.
1978	Etched Colt	703	5,500	0001-5500	$65.
1979	Etched Yearling (N)	709	5,500	0001-5550	$47.
1979	Etched Mustang (N)	701	5,500	0001-5500	$68.
1980	Etched Pony (N)	705	5,500	0001-5500	$45.
1981	San Diego Police Dept.	110	Open end	SDPD Badge No. with gold	$125. $175.
1982	Calif. Highway Patrol[9]	110	10,000	1-10,000	$125.
1982	Dallas Police Dept.	110	Open End	DPD Badge No. with gold	$125. $175.
1982	Sterling Edition Set	110/112/500/501/ 503/505	200 projected	By order	$2,500.
1982	Grand Slam (N)	Four 501s	2,500	001-2500	$450.
1982	Buck Bandit[2]	501	250	All marked 1 of 250	$70.
1983	California Firefighters	110	Open end	none	$125.
1983	Gander[1]	110	1,000	001-1000	$100.
1983	Ducks Unlimited	119 w/spl.hdl.	100	1-100	N/A
1983	Ducks in Flight I[3]	500	2,000	001-2000	$90.
1984	West Virginia Turkey[4]	110	1,000	001-1,000	$80.
1984	Mastodon 110[5] (N)	110 ivory	500	01-500	$395.
1984	Sabretooth[5] (N)	501 ivory	500	001-500	$250.
1984	Ducks in Flight II[3]	500	1,500	001-1500	$90.
1984	White Water	112	2,500	001-2500	$80.
1984	Deer Scene[6]	110	1,500	001-1500	$90.
1984	Pewter Handle Eagle[7]	110	50	*	$100.
1984	Pewter Handle Deer[7]	110	1,500 to date	*	$100.
1984	Colt Firearms[10]	500	350 to date	1-350	N/A
1984	Apple Blossom[11]	110	100	1-100	$100.
1984	Elk Scene[6]	110	2,000	1-2,000	$100.
1985	Alaska Statehood[8]	110 w/426 blade wine wood hdl.	250	1-250	$100.
1985	Alaska Statehood[9]	110 w/426 blade black fibron hdl.	500	1-500	$100.
1985	Cable Car[9]	505	250	001-250	$65.
1985	Ducks Unlimited	110/505	4,000	Not complete	N/A
1985	Fighting Bucks[1]	110	500	1-500	$100.
1985	Fighting Bucks	110	200	none	$100.

Made for:
[1]Gander Mountain
[2]Smokey Mountain Knife Works
[3]Sears
[4]Blue Ridge
[5]Remington Cutlery
[6]J.C. Penney
[7]Great American Buckle Co.
[8]Cutlery World
[9]Available to Buck dealers
[10]Colt Firearms Co.
[11]Old Dominion Sports

*Serial numbers done outside the Buck factory.
(N) Available by mail from Remington Cutlery, 60 Main St., Bridgeport CT 06602

Knife Club Limited Edition Knives

By Bill Karsten and Bernard Levine

Bill Karsten writes for Knife World

A POPULAR class of limited edition knives is annual club knives issued by local and national knife collecting organizations. Most local club knives are very limited in quantity. Some of the earlier national club knives were very limited also. As the national organizations have grown, so too have the sizes of their editions. Club knives are sold both to enhance the clubs' treasuries and to allow members to have ''something special.''

As a rule, newly issued club knives are sold only to club members. However, all clubs allow collectors in distant places to join and then purchase knives by mail. An up-to-date list of knife clubs with contact names and addresses is published every month in *Knife World* magazine.

Price Trends

Back in January through March of 1981, Bill Karsten wrote a series of articles for *Knife World* on club knives and their price changes thus far. I asked him to select some of that information and bring the prices up to date, in order to show the price trends in the more active issues.

He informed mc that interest in older NKCA club knives has remained fairly strong, although prices have fallen off a little. Interest is also strong in Gem Capital club knives. Gem Capital knives are unusual because each one has a little gem stone set in the handles.

However, he observed that the *resale* market in most other club knives seems to have grown weak. *New* club issues still seem to be selling, although quantities of many have been cut back from past years.

I suspect that the reason for this weak resale market is that there are now so very many different club knives that it would be a major undertaking to start a collection of them from scratch. If you are interested in knives from a particular club, your best bet would be to attend a meeting or show sponsored by that club, or else to write to the club and advertise in its newsletter.

NKCA
National Knife Collectors Association, formerly NKC&DA [National Knife Collectors & Dealers Association].

ISSUE	QUANTITY	DESCRIPTION	PRICES: ISSUE	1981	CURRENT
1. 1975.	1,200	Klaas stag oval whittler	$12.00	$600.00	$475.00
2. 1976.	3,000	Case white composition whittler	$15.00	$150.00	$145.00
3. 1977.	5,000	Klaas stag canoe cattle knife	$17.50	$100.00	$75.00
4. 1978.	6,000	Rodgers-Wostenholm bone canoe cattle knife	$18.25	$55.00	$65.00
5. 1979.	10,000	Case stag 1-blade "trapper"	$22.00	$55.00	$60.00
6. 1980.	12,000	Klaas stag "gunstock" cattle	$21.75		$45.00
7. 1981.	12,000	Queen stag equal-end cattle	$24.50		$40.00
8. 1982.	10,000	Schrade stag trapper	$25.50		$60.00
9. 1983.	6,000	Case bone lockback hunter	$45.00		$100.00
10.1984	unltd.*	Bertram 1-blade lockback	$38.00		$50.00
11.1985.	unltd.*	Case 6240 bone light trapper	$40.00		
		Full set 1975–1985: **$1,200–1,400.**			

*Unlimited = size of issue limited to number of orders received by January 15 of the issue year.

GEM CAPITAL KNIFE CLUB, Franklin, North Carolina.

ISSUE	QUANTITY	DESCRIPTION	PRICES: ISSUE	1981	CURRENT
1. 1980.	150	Fight'n Rooster pearl powderhorn with two rubies	$41.	$200.	$225.
2. 1981.	250	Fight'n Rooster pearl 5-blade stockman with two sapphires	$52.		$125.
3. 1982.	300	Fight'n Rooster pearl 4-blade canoe with two emeralds	$52.		$80.
4. 1983.	300	Fight'n Rooster pearl muskrat with two garnets	$52.		$85.
5. 1984.	200	Fight'n Rooster black pearl equal-end jack with one diamond	$65.		$125.

BAY AREA KNIFE COLLECTORS ASSOCIATION, San Jose, California.
(This club's knives are custom knives, mainly by maker members. Information furnished by Ray and Carol Clark.)

ISSUE	QUANTITY	DESCRIPTION	PRICES: ISSUE	CURRENT
1. 1980.	52	Sornberger rosewood trout/bird, sheath	$70.00	$125.00
2. 1981.	50	Centofante FL2 folder, micarta	$155.00	$250.00
3. 1982.	33	Terrill rosewood semi-skinner, sheath	$85.00	$110.00
4. 1983.	50	Corrado folder, coin silver	$83.00	$150.00
5. 1984.	25	Gamble rosewood trailing point, sheath	$75.00	$95.00
6. 1985.	25	Norton cocobolo drop point, sheath	$85.00	$95.00
		(A complete set 1980–1984 was recently offered for **$650.**)		

OREGON KNIFE COLLECTORS ASSOCIATION, Eugene-Springfield, Oregon.
(Information furnished by Dennis Ellingsen.)

ISSUE	QUANTITY	DESCRIPTION	PRICES: ISSUE	CURRENT
1. 1979.	200	Case 21051 LSSP lockback	$20.00	$50.00
2. 1980.	200	Gerber 250 Sp Silver Knight, stag	$27.50	$50.00
3. 1981.	100	Gerber LST, white micarta	$30.00	$40.00
4. 1982	50	Corrado one-blade, Sherwood engraved	$60.00	$100.00
5. 1983.	50	Gerber/Paul, beaver scrimshaw	$55.00	$125.00
6. 1984.	50	Gerber Touché, beaver scrimshaw	$30.00	$75.00
7. 1985.	50	Gerber FSII, beaver scrimshaw	$40.00	——

GOLDEN CIRCLE KNIFE CLUB, Jackson, Tennessee
(Information furnished by the club.)

ISSUE	QUANTITY	DESCRIPTION	PRICES: ISSUE	1981	CURRENT
1. 1978.	300	Klaas stag serpentine whittler	$18.50	$75.00	$100.00
2. 1979.	300	Klaas stag 4-blade sleeveboard	$30.00	$50.00	$90.00
3. 1980.	500	Klaas white equal-end whittler	$30.00		$50.00
4. 1981.	500	Col. Coon stag muskrat	$30.00		$50.00
4-A. 1981 Founder's Knife	200	Col. Coon white bone muskrat	$35.00		$50.00
5. 1982.	500	Case 6265 SAB red bone fol. hunt.	$35.00		$50.00
6. 1983.	300	Case 4254 white comp. trapper	$30.00		$40.00
6-A. 1983 5th Anniv Knife	150	Case 2254 black comp. trapper	$30.00		$65.00
7. 1984.	50	Col. Coon stag trapper	$40.00		$100.00

THE KNIFE COLLECTORS CLUB, INC., 1705 Highway 71 North, Springdale AR 72764.
(Information furnished by A. G. Russell, president. Prices indicated are his current resale prices, which he estimates to be 20-30% *above* current market.)

CM-1. Kentucky Rifle Premium Stock by Schrade. 1971 issue: **$12** (CM-1B).
CM-2. Grandaddy Barlow by Camillus. 1973 issue: **$20** (CM-2B).
CM-3. Luger Pistol "Wharncliffe" Jack by Puma. 1974 issue: **$34.95** (CM-3B).
CM-4. .22LR Baby Barlow, Ivory, by Bertram. 1975 issue: **$18** (CM-4B).
CM-5. .44 Magnum Whittler by Bertram. 1977 issue: **$39.95** (CM-5B).
CM-6. Straight Arrow "Coffin" Jack by Bertram. Issue: **$34.95** (CM-6B).
CM-7. .45 Long Colt Hunter by Bertram. Issue: **$34.95** (CM-7B).
CM-8. .219 Zipper Barlow by Bertram. Issue: **$34.95** (CM-8B).
CM-9. .300 Savage "Canoe" by Bertram. Issue: **$34.95** (CM-9B).

CURRENT PRICES		VARIETY / DECORATION / SERIAL NUMBER RANGE:					
MODEL	TOTAL QUANTITY	A. PLAIN 301-1000	B. PLAIN 1001-TOP	M. MONOGRAM (none)	E. ETCHED 26-300	EE. ETCHED & ENGRAVED 26-300	P. GOLD ENGRAVED & ETCHED 1-25
CM-1	12,000	$150.	$ 95.	N/A	$295.	$395.	$2,995.
CM-2	12,000	95.	60.	N/A	N/A	395.[1]	2,995.[2]
CM-3	3,700	145.	145.	N/A	250.	345.	2,495.
CM-4	1,800	225.	225.	$225.	295.	355.	1,525.
CM-5	1,200	285.	285.	285.	295.	325.	2,495.
CM-6	2,500	175.	175.	175.	325.	455.	2,495.
CM-7	2,800	215.	215.	215.	365.	425.	2,245.
CM-8	2,200	185.	185.	185.	295.	325.	1,995.
CM-9	3,000	100.	100.	100.	175.	295.	2,295.

[1] Numbers 18-200.   [2] Numbers 1-18.

Foreign Exotic, Primitive and Historical Folding Knives

Introduction

IN THIS SECTION, I describe the basic types of folding knives used in Europe and Asia in the past several hundred years. Until this century, folding knives were far more common in Europe than in Asia, while they were virtually unknown in Africa and Oceania. Older Asian folders differ in detail from European ones, but they are similar to them in basic design. Therefore I have divided knives in this section primarily by type, not by geographic region.

Many of the older types of European folding knives included in this section were used by North American settlers from the earliest colonial days up into the 19th century. However, none of these types, so far as I can determine, was regularly offered for sale in this country after about 1860.

Of course in the last decade or two, cutlery traditions throughout the world have been changing radically. Modern versions of some exotic knives, such as the Opinel penny knife, have recently carved themselves a niche in the American market.

Although the older foreign styles lost favor in 19th century America, most of the standard American patterns that replaced them trace their own ancestry to those older types, particularly to the penny knife, the quill knife, and the Navaja, or Spanish clasp knife. Information on this evolution is included in the various pattern chapters.

Some of the old patterns are still made and sold in the Old World. However, most foreign countries and cutlery producing districts have developed their own modern patterns, just as we have here. Since these modern "exotic" patterns occasionally turn up on the collector market in the United States, I have included a sampling of them in this section, as well.

1. Penny Knives

"Penny knife" is a modern adaptation of an old term for the simplest sort of jack knife. A penny knife consists of a more or less cylindrical one-piece handle, a blade, and a pivot pin. Often the hinged end of the handle is reinforced by a sheet metal ferrule that functions like the bolsters on a spring-back knife. Most penny knives are quite plain, but some exhibit fancy turning, or even ornate figural carving.

The basic design of the penny knife seems to go back at least 1,000 years, and quite possibly more than 2,000. The design seems to be indigenous both to Europe and to Asia. It is still made on both continents.

Penny knives were used in the American Colonies in the 17th and early 18th centuries. By the latter part of the 18th century, however, American demand for folders was almost entirely for spring-back knives.

Many of the older penny knives that turn up in this country today were brought here by tourists or immigrants in this century, or else late in the last one. Even the oldest ones found here only rarely can be proven to have been used here in Colonial times. This is because antiques dealers were importing them for collectors even a century and more ago, much as they do now. Dated archaeological sites and period paintings are the only sure sources of information on "authentic" Colonial knives.

Other Spring-less Folding Knives

Not all knives made without springs are "penny knives." Many early pruners and clasp knives have no springs. More important, most 19th century and earlier folding medical instruments have no backsprings, either.

The distinguishing marks of old folding medical instruments are: small size, flat profile, two-piece handles (usually tortoise-shell) with the back completely open, birdseye rivets instead of bolsters, and extremely fine finish. Like knives, but unlike razors, most have some sort of blade stop at 180 degrees. 19th century folding medical instruments are sometimes double-ended and they often have a locking mechanism.

English medical bistoury, circa 1815. Value **$35.**

1.3. Europe. Leg shaped Penny Knife.

Made in all sizes. Example shown is 4½ inches long closed. Horn handle with brass ferrule. Slim leaf shaped blade. Middle Ages to early 20th century. Example shown circa 19th century. Value about **$35.** Higher quality examples worth two to ten times as much. Courtesy Bill Karsten.

1.1 Western Europe (probably Germany). Penny Knife.

About 4 inches long closed. Turned wooden handle with iron ferrule. Blade marked A.SCHMID . . . 19th century. Value about **$40.** Courtesy Don Euing.

Knives with one-word or pictorial marks usually date from c1800 or earlier (**add 100%**). Knives marked on the back side of the blade are usually from Spain.

1.4. Western Europe (Holland?). Ornate Penny Knife.

About 10 inches long closed. Turned wooden handle. Iron ferrule. Circa early 18th century. Value about **$300.** Under 6 inches closed, **subtract 50%;** under 4 inches, **subtract 75%.** Courtesy Smithsonian Institution, Wiebusch Collection.

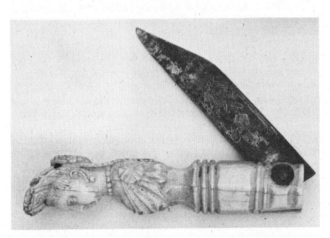

1.2. Western Europe (France?). Figural Penny Knife.

About 3½ inches long closed. Carved bone handle. Example shown has birdseye rivet and gilt design on blade (not typical). Circa late 18th century. Value about **$250.** Value depends on quality of work, also condition. Courtesy Smithsonian Institution, Wiebusch Collection.

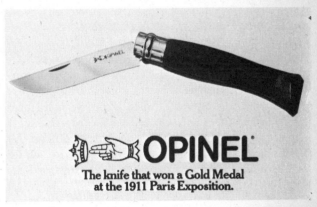

1.5. France. Modern Penny Knife.

This style made from 1¾ inches closed up to 11 inches closed. Wooden handle. Iron ferrule. On larger sizes, ferrule rotates to lock the blade. Made by Opinel of Cognin, Savoie, since about 1890. Value **$4–10** in standard sizes, **$50** for 11-inch giant. Courtesy Gutmann Cutlery Co.

1.6. Japan. Penny Knife. (Not illustrated)

About 3½ inches long closed. Handle of wood or steel (steel handle with maker's marks). Blade of thin steel plate laminated to iron, ground on one side only. Blade stop on tang. 19th–20th centuries. Value **$5–10.**

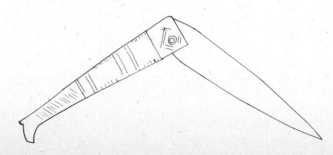

1.7. China. Penny Knife (or Razor).

About 3½ inches long closed. Handle of wood or light green cow horn. Thin steel blade, usually with curved back and relatively straight edge. 19th–20th centuries. Examples shown 20th century with wood handles, sheet iron ferrules. Bottom one has heavy blade like a razor. Value **$5–10.**

2. Other Foreign Jack Knives

2.1. France and England. Straight Jack Knives.

3½ to 8 inches long closed. See plates I & II for descriptions and pattern names of French knives. Distinctive features *may* include: prominent rosette-type rivets on French knives; fancy worked bolsters integral with liners on English knives; tang shaped to fill the "square and clean" joint; thin flat handles; wood and horn, when used, sawed "on the bias" to display their grain; tiny nail mark; superb workmanship. 17th to early 19th centuries.

PLATE I. 18TH CENTURY FRENCH FOLDING COUTEAUX (KNIVES).
from Perret, *The Art of the Cutler*, 1771.

A. (Fig. 26), "*Couteau Eustache Dubois*," the commonest pattern at the time, consists of a blade with stop, a wooden handle, and a single pin. Value about **$75.**

This pattern and the next were mass-produced in factories. The others, with springs, were hand-made.

B. (Fig. 27), "*Couteau à la Capucine*," consists of a blade, a handle of sheep horn, and two pins: a hinge pin and a stop pin. The blade slot is cut with a saw to the depth of the dotted line. Value about **$100.**

C. (Fig. 28), "*Couteau à bec de Corbin*" (crow's beak knife), consists of a blade, a spring, two handle slabs, and three pins. This "ancient" style was no longer in production in 1771, because the pointed handle (which served as a punch) made holes in pockets. Value about **$100.**

Note the square tang which exactly fills the joint in all three positions. This "square and clean joint" was common practice on 18th century French and English spring-back knives.

D. (Fig. 29), "*Couteau à la Charoloise*" or "*Couteau à crosse*" (*la crosse* = gunstock), so-called because of the roundness at the end of the handle. This pattern supplanted the *bec de Corbin* and has the same construction. Value about **$100** for a plain example.

E. (Fig. 30), "*Couteau à poincon*" (punch knife), a double-ended spring knife with stag handles. Note that the French punch blade has an eye so that it can be used for stitching harness and as a seton for inoculating cattle. Value about **$125.** (A more recent version is called a *Laguiole*. Value **$40.**)

F. (Fig. 31), Gunstock knife with a cork-pulling hook, rosewood handles cut obliquely to reveal the grain. Value about **$200,** because of the cork-puller.

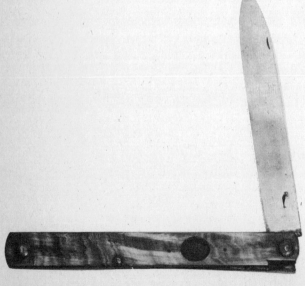

2.1.1. Example shown (left) 7 inches long closed. Probably French. Lock back, horn handles, rosette-type rivets, shield missing (may have been gold), pictorial touch mark of a scimitar (unidentified). Value **$200.** Courtesy Smithsonian Institution, Wiebusch Collection.

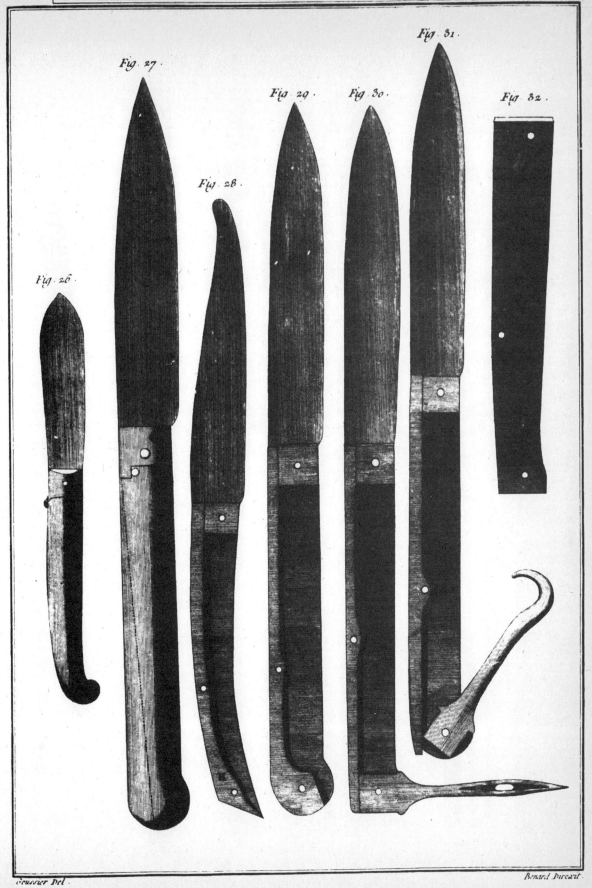

Fig. 26. Fig. 27. Fig. 28. Fig. 29. Fig. 30. Fig. 31. Fig. 32.

Goussier Del.

Benard Direxit.

II: Folding Knives   **273**

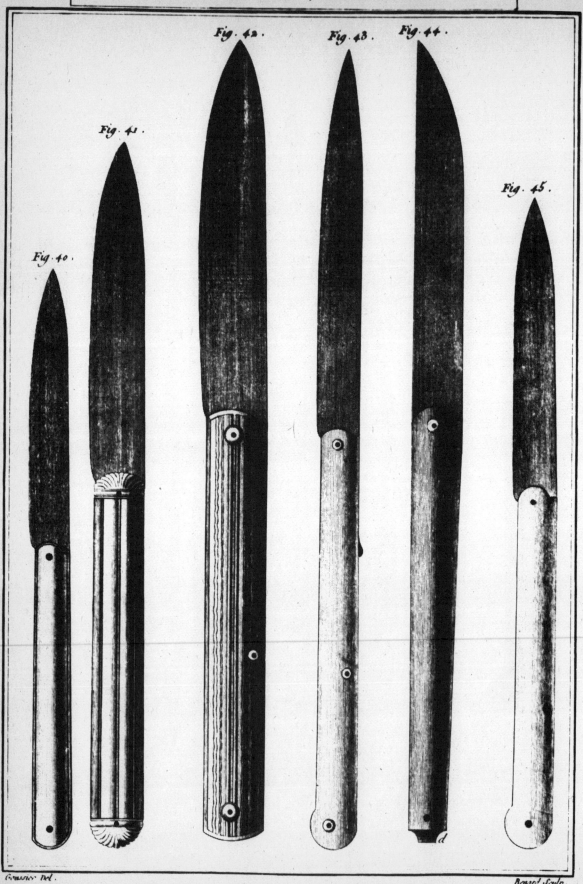

back. Value range **$150** (plain) to **$350** (fancy). I anticipate that as collectors become more aware of these knives, their value should increase. See the section on late 18th century Sheffield markings to identify makers marks. Courtesy EAIA.

PLATE II. 18TH CENTURY FRENCH JACK KNIVES WITH SPRINGS.

from Perret, *The Art of the Cutler*, 1771.

A. (Fig. 40), *"Couteau à grimace"* with ivory handles decorated with a simple groove around the perimeter. Value about **$150.**

B. (Fig. 41), *"Couteau à la Militaire"* with tortoise shell handles decorated with three grooves and "Tartar" style bolsters. Value about **$250.**

C. (Fig. 42), *"Couteau à mouche"* or *"Ramponeau"* mounted with rosette-type rivets and decorated with grooves and hatching. Value about **$200.** (*Mouche* literally means "fly," the insect, but figuratively it can mean any prominent spot, such as a bull's-eye or rosette.)

D. (Fig. 43), *"Couteau à pompe"* or *"Passepartout,"* a slender lockback with smooth rounded ivory handles. Value about **$150.**

E. (Fig. 44), *"Couteau à bayonette & à mouche,"* a folding plug bayonet with a round tapering handle. The hinge rivet has double-strength rosettes, while the butt rivet is filed smooth. The projection (d) of the spring is shaped as a screwdriver. Value about **$450.**

F. (Fig. 45), *"Couteau à tête de compas"* (compass-joint knife), with smooth rounded ivory handles, flush rivets, and flush rounded joint. Value about **$125.**

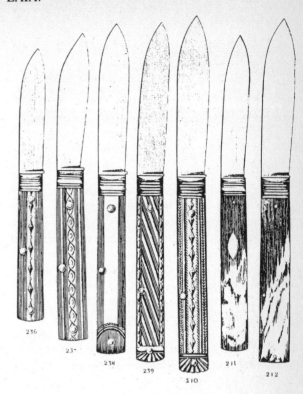

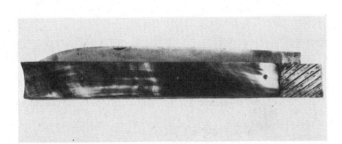

2.1.2. England. Straight Jack Knife.

6 inches long closed. Cut steel gadroon bolsters integral with liners, horn handles, square and clean joint. Tang stamped WATKINSON (Jonathan Watkinson, Silver Street, Sheffield, c1787). Value **$225.**

2.1.3. Straight Jack Knives. Illustrations from an 1816 Sheffield catalog (Smith's Key) of cutlery and tools available for export to the United States. Handles of carved pearl or ivory, bone, horn, wood, and tortoise shell (245). 244 and 247 are "spotted knives" with clear horn handles spotted to resemble tortoise. "Brass shoulders" may mean "white" brass or nickel silver, invented in 1810. 247 and 248 are lockbacks. Similar knives also offered with corkscrew on

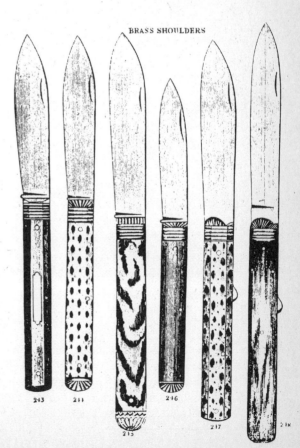

BRASS SHOULDERS

2.2. France. Corsican ''Vendetta'' Knife.

A folding version of the Mediterranean dagger.

5 to 10 inches long closed. Iron mounts including long self-guard bolsters. Bone handles etched with traditional decorations including a black woman in profile. Semi-lock blade (has no lock release), usually with Thiers maker's mark, often etched in Italian, ''Corsican Vendetta,'' on the front and either ''Death to Enemies'' or ''May My Wound be Fatal'' on the back. 19th–20th centuries.

Example shown 8 inches long closed, marked VERITABLE FARGE. Early 20th century. Value $70. Courtesy Bill Spivey. Recent examples with plated bolsters, **subtract 50%**.

2.3. Germany. Folding Hunting Knives.

Folding versions of the *Jagdmesser*.

2.3.2. 5 inches long closed. Stag handles, steel mounts. Locking blade, saw, corkscrew. Early 20th century. Value **$100.**

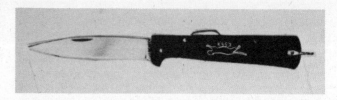

2.3.3. 4¼ inches long closed. One piece black lacquered steel handle, center lock. Marked K55K and MERCATOR. Black Cat Knife made by Kauffmann. 20th century. Value about **$10.** Courtesy Gutmann Cutlery. Japanese copy, **subtract 50%**.

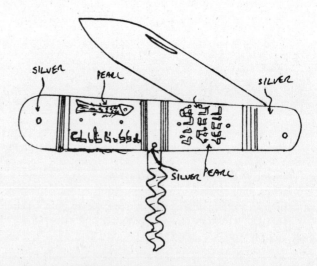

2.4. Germany. Sabbath Knife (?).

5½ inches long closed. Silver handles with engraved pearl panels. Inscribed in Hebrew, ''Honor the Sabbath; The Way of Hillel.'' Some have corkscrew on back. Example shown has unmarked blade. Some are marked Solingen. Circa late 19th century. Value **$250.** Courtesy Harvey Reisberg and *Knife World*.

2.3.1. 5 inches long closed. Stag handles, nickel silver mounts. Heavy blade with front lock. Made by Henckels. Some have corkscrew on back. Circa 1930s. Example shown has damascus blade with gilt oak leaves. Value **$1,200.** Plain blade version, value **$500.** These were briefly exported to the United States.

2.5. Sweden. Jack Knife.

3⅝ inches long closed. Brass frame and screws, hollow black plastic handles, made by EKA: Eskilstuna Knivfabriks Aktiebolag. 20th century. Value **$10.**

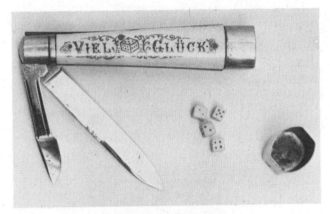

2.6. Austria or Germany. Dice Knife.

4 inches long closed. Spear and manicure blades. Removable plated dice cup containing bone dice, bone handles etched in German "Lots of Luck." Circa 1900. Some were exported to the U. S. Value **$150.** Courtesy Smithsonian Institution, Wiebusch Collection.

3. Clasp Knives

A traditional clasp knife is a large single-bladed jack knife with an upwardly curved handle that tapers to a point. Clasp knife handles are curved and pointed because they were originally made from the solid ends of goat, sheep, or cow horns that were split or slotted to contain the blade. The tip of the horn covers the point of the blade, the blade having been shaped to fit the natural curve of the horn.

Traditional style clasp knives are still made in southern Europe and in Mexico. They are often called by their Spanish name, *navaja*.

3.1. Western Europe. Clasp Knife.

About 7 inches long closed. One-piece cow horn handle (end cap missing). Iron ferrule. Clipped leaf-shaped blade with pictorial touchmarks. Probably 18th or early 19th century. Value about **$100.** Courtesy Smithsonian Institution.

The true leaf-shaped blade may be the earliest pocketknife blade type of all, as it is the easiest to forge. However, horn-handled clasp knives with leaf-shaped blades are still made today in Spain, for example by an old outfit called Bofil in Vich, Catalonia. Value of these is about **$5.**

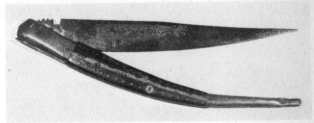

3.2. Spain. Navaja (Clasp Knife).

5 to 10 inches long closed. Handles usually horn. Brass or iron bolsters. Often decorated with pin-work and engraving. Ratcheting blade lock. 18th–20th centuries. Example shown, early 20th century. Value **$40.** Courtesy Eiler Cook.

Larger and finer examples, value up to **$150.** Plain crude examples made recently in Mexico, value **$5.**

3.3. Western Europe. "Rattler" Clasp Knives.

6 to 12 inches long closed. Horn, wood, or stag handles. Clip blade. Iron mounts, cap bolster in the form of rattlesnake rattles. 18th to 19th centuries. These "rattlers" (my name for them) seem to have been made especially for the North American (U.S. and Mexico) market. Examples shown courtesy Smithsonian Institution. (See next page for descriptions.)

3.3.A.

3.3.B.

Foreign Exotic, Primitive and Historical Folding Knives

3.3.A. (See previous page, top.) 8¼ inches long closed, northern European, early 19th century, collected in North Carolina. Value **$450.**

3.3.B. (See previous page, bottom) 10½ inches long closed, probably Spanish, 19th century. Brass back on blade (this is the only type of old knife I have seen with a brass back on the blade. It is likely the source of the modern legend that the first bowie knives had brass backs). Value **$250.**

3.5. Western Europe. Figural Clasp Knife.
   About 5 inches long closed. Blade stop on end of tang (as on many surgical instruments); also hole for ring. No spring. One-piece engraved bone handle. Probably 19th century. Value **$150.** Courtesy Smithsonian Institution, Wiebusch Collection.

3.4. England. Clasp Knife.
   3 to 12 inches long closed. Bone handles, long iron bolsters, usually integral with liners. Late 17th to early 19th centuries. A popular style in the American colonies, often found in archaeological sites. Example shown 4¼ inches long closed. Value at least **$250.** Over 5½ inches long, **add 100%.** See the section on late 18th century Sheffield markings for more information. Courtesy Smithsonian Institution.

3.6. Austria. Clasp Knife.
   4 to 5 inches long closed. Standard pocketknife construction, but decoration indicates it was made for Eastern Europe. Example shown, 4 inches long. Nickel silver and horn. 19th century. Value **$75–100.** Courtesy Smithsonian Institution, Wiebusch Collection.

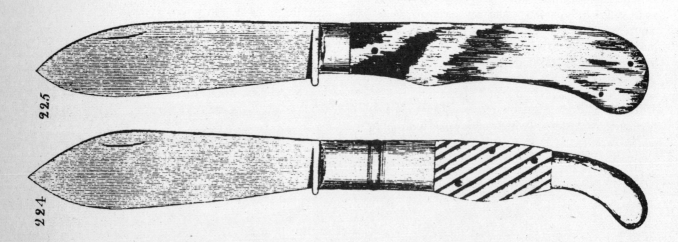

3.4.1. England. Clasp Knives.
   Illustrations from Smith's Key, 1816. These patterns then offered in ¼-inch increments from 3 inches to 5½ inches long closed. Handles are either cow horn or diagonally grooved bone. Value at least **$250.** Courtesy EAIA.

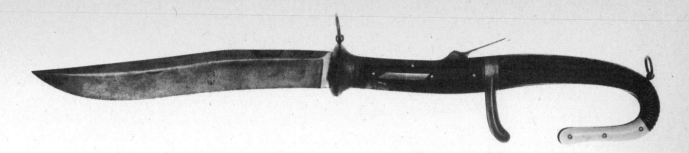

3.7. Western Europe. Fancy Clasp Knives.

Very large ornate folders. Possibly made as weapons or tools, but probably made for collectors.

3.7.1. France. (Above) 9½ inches long closed. Iron mounts. Two-handed grip of tortoise shell, stag, and ivory. Lock release lever. Two rings. 19th century. Value **$1,000.** Courtesy Robert Soares and Hugh Hayes.

3.7.2. Western Europe (Below) (the one marked example I have seen, marked ARNOLD/NAMUR, was Belgian). 9 inches long closed. Switchblade, with external thumb-release trigger that hooks over back of blade. Stag or ivory handle. Steel mounts, trigger, and guard. 19th century. Example shown has etched blade and bolsters. Value **$1,000.** Courtesy Smithsonian Institution, Wiebusch Collection. (Illegal to own in most states.)

3.8. Germany and Austria. Deerfoot Clasp Knife.

4½ to 6 inches long closed. Lockback with folding or fixed guard, nickel silver mounts, deerfoot handle. Late 19th and 20th centuries. Example shown from a 1910 catalog. Value in excellent condition **$75.** Some were exported to the U.S.

LOCK-BACK

3.9. Germany and Austria. Clasp Knife.

4½ to 6 inches long closed. Lockback, usually with two blades, corkscrew. Steel bolsters, stag or bone stag handles. Late 19th and early 20th centuries. Example shown from a 1914 catalog. Value in excellent condition **$100.** Some were exported to the U.S.

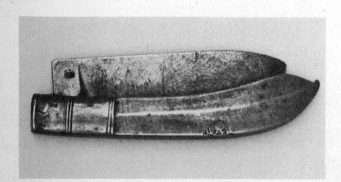

3.10. China. Clasp Knife.

About 3½ inches long closed. Brass handle shaped like seed pod. Brass spring. Brass blade inlaid with steel cutting edge. Circa 1900. Value **$50.** Courtesy James B. Lile.

4.1. Western Europe (Spain?). Early Pruner.

About 5 inches long closed. Example shown has carved one-piece wooden handle with decorative pins, no backspring. Blade stop on end of tang. 18th century. Value about **$85.** Courtesy Smithsonian Institution, Wiebusch Collection.

Undecorated versions with wood or horn handle made into this century in Spain and Latin America. Value **$5–25,** depending on quality.

4.2. Italy (Maniago). Lockback Pruner.

About 6 inches long closed. Horn handles. Well made. Probably 18th century. Value **$100.** Smaller size, poorer quality, **Subtract 50–80%.**

5. Quill Knives

See the *Quill Knives* chapter for more information on these tiny knives used for sharpening quill pens.

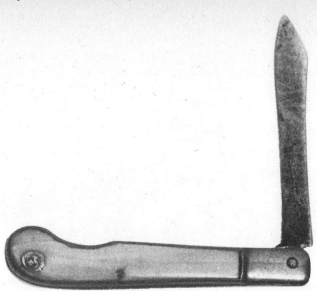

5.1. England. Quill Knife.

About 2½ inches long closed. Example shown 2⅜ inches. Integral bolsters and liners, indicating English work. Ivory handles. Flaring clip blade and pictorial touchmarks (unidentified) indicate early to mid-18th century. Dagger mark may be that of London cutlers' guild. Value **$90.** Courtesy Smithsonian Institution, Wiebusch Collection.

5.2. England. Double-ended Quill Knives.

From Smith's Key, 1816, courtesy EAIA.

5.2.1. Double-ended quill knife. About 4 inches long closed. One of many popular shapes. Value about **$90.**

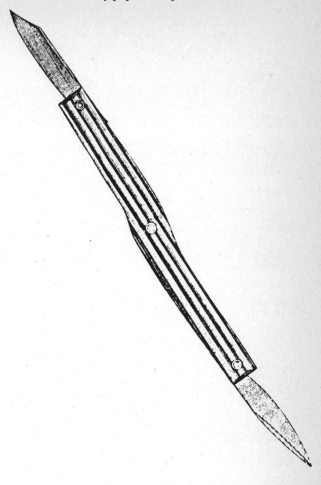

5.2.2. Four-bladed quill knives. 2½ to 3 inches long closed. Three of many varieties. No. 427 is an early congress pattern. Value **$75** (plain) to **$225** (fancy).

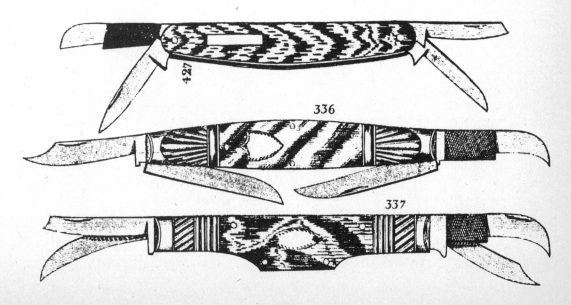

Foreign Exotic, Primitive and Historical Folding Knives

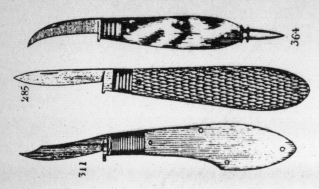

PLATE III. English Quill Knives from Smith's Key, 1816. 2½ to 3 inches long closed. Made in a variety of shapes, handle materials, and decoration. Value **$35** (plain) to **$125** (fancy). Courtesy EAIA.

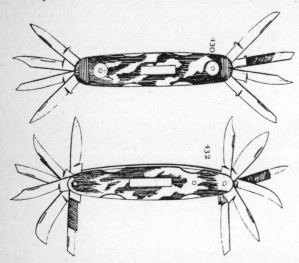

5.2.3. Double-ended double-sided quill knives. Note that these are not lobsters, though lobsters were made at that time. Blades in multiples of four. Value **$100** to **$250,** depending on decoration and number of blades.

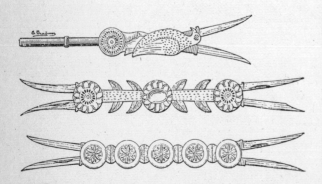

5.3. France. Multi-bladed Quill Knives.

About 3 inches long closed. Carved ivory or pearl handles, early 19th century, **$175 each.**

6. Balance Knives

A "balance knife" or "crutch knife," both names used in 18th century France, is a double sided knife with two (usually) or four blades. The tang of each blade appears "split," though they were formed by folding around a mandrel. The blades are pivoted on a common pin with their tangs interleaved. Thus the "run-up" of one blade serves to stop the opposite blade in its open position.

This end view of a four-blade Indian coir knife shows how the arrangement works.

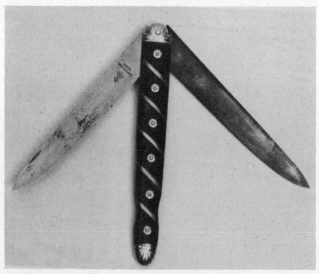

6.1. France. Balance Knife (or Berge Knife).

About 4 inches long closed. Tortoise shell or pearl handles with gold or silver trim. One gold and one silver blade, or one silver and one damascus steel. 18th-19th centuries ("Berge knife" is a 19th century term for these). Example shown 19th century by Cardeilhac of Paris, silver and damascus blades, gold trim. Value **$400.** Courtesy Smithsonian Institution, Wiebusch Collection. [See *Silver Fruit Knives* for more information.]

Foreign Exotic, Primitive and Historical Folding Knives

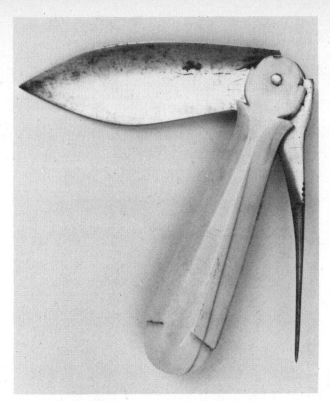

6.2. India or Ceylon. Two-bladed Coir Knife.

About 3¼ inches long closed. Deeply hollow ground steel blade, steel pick. Pick is blunt on recent examples. Both blades usually have an engraved silver panel inlaid along the back. Ivory or wood one-piece handle. Most shaped as shown, but I have seen one shaped like a regular jack. Reportedly a rug weaver's knife. Coir is a material used for rug warp. 18th-20th centuries. Value: ivory **$120**, wood **$50**. Recent example, **subtract 25%**.

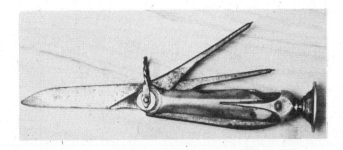

6.3. India or Ceylon. Four-bladed Coir (?) Knife.

About 4 inches long closed. Similar to 6.2, but with addition of brass seal-type base (copper bail probably not original). Blades flat on facing surfaces. Picks may function as dividers. Ivory handle. 18th-19th centuries. Value **$150**.

7. Multi-Blades

Multi-blades have been around at least since the middle of the 18th century. This is a sampling of older styles.

(Overleaf)
7.1. 18th Century French Multi-Blades.
From Perret, *The Art of the Cutler*, 1771.

7.1.A (Fig. 43), Three-bladed single-spring traveler's knife, structurally a predecessor of the whittler. The spacer (44) affixed to the spring (45) separates the two small blades, a harness punch and a cork-puller hook. Value **$250**. With pen blade (*canif*) in place of hook, value **$175**.

7.1.B. (Fig. 46), Six-bladed three-spring amateur gardener's knife. It has two handle scales and two interior liners (47). Crinking, blade adjustment, and position of nail marks are critical for smooth working. Value **$350**.

7.2. England. Multi-Blades.
From Smith's Key, 1816, courtesy EAIA.

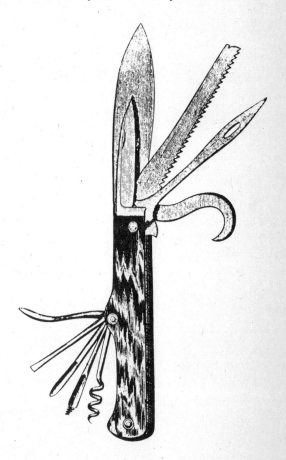

7.2.1. About 4 inches long closed. Multi-blade with tortoise, horn, or stag handles. Ten blades, as shown, value **$500**. Six blades, similar shape, value **$300**. Four blades, value **$175**.

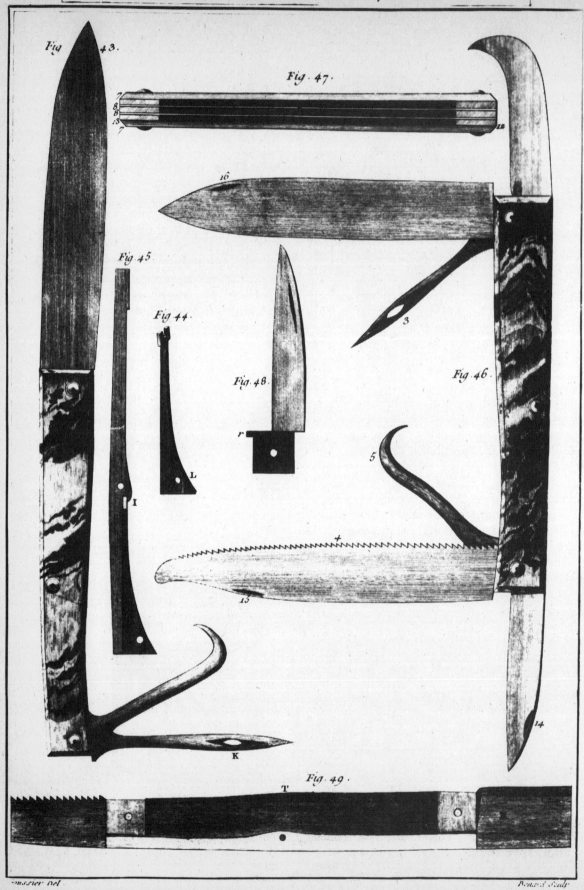

SPORTSMEN KNIVES

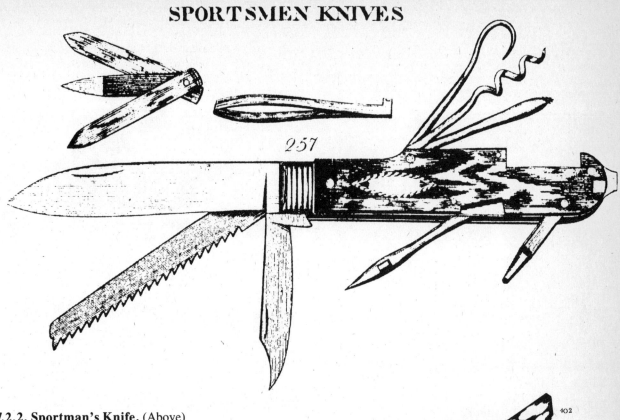

7.2.2. Sportman's Knife. (Above)

About 3⅝ inches long closed. Eight blades plus lancet and tweezers in tortoise or ivory handles. Value **$450.**

7.2.4. Snuff Box Knife.

About 3 inches long closed. Two to four blades. Hinged or rotating snuff box lid. Tortoise, pearl, or ivory handles. Value **$150–300.**

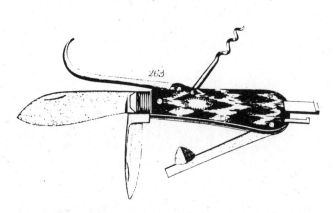

7.2.3. Horseman's Knife.

About 3¼ inches long closed. Note fleam blade and hoof pick. Value **$350.** Similar knife with two or three small blades hinged inside the hoof pick, value **$1,500.** I have seen a *functional* 42-bladed knife of this type and size, its silver fruit blade hallmarked 1790. It was in near-mint condition. Value **$3,500.**

184—BAKER'S SIX. Specially designed for use among stock.   Six Blades, Finest Quality and Finish, in Stag Haft. Size 3½in. (as illustration), **21/-**; larger size, 4in. Haft, **24/-** each, **post free.**

(See next page)

7.3. Australia. Station and Farmers Knives.

3½ and 4 inches long closed. Equal-end handle die. Four, five, or six blades. Fancy bolsters. Bone stag handles. Made in Sheffield. Value, 3½-inch: four-blade, **$50;** five-blade, **$100;** six-blade, **$125.** 4-inch, **add 25%.** Special speying knife: four-blade with four identical hawkbill blades, value **$75.** From a 1924 W. Jno. Baker, Sydney, catalog.

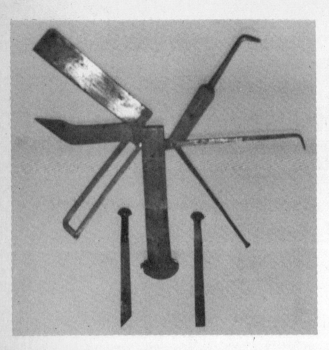

7.4. China (?). Multi-Blade.

Brass handle. Includes cutting blades, saw, forceps, probes. Reportedly used by Chinese army surgeons. 20th century. Value about **$150.** Courtesy Frank Phelps and *Knife World*.

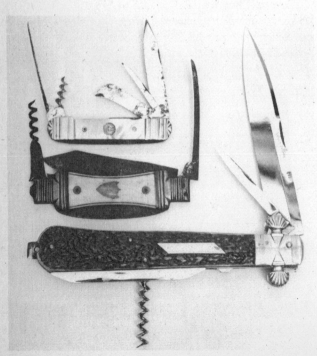

7.5. Austria. Bar-backed Multi-Blades.

2¾ to 6 inches long closed. Various patterns with a heavy steel bar covering the backsprings. I do not know the bar's purpose. Value **$60–150.** Courtesy Smithsonian Institution, Wiebusch Collection.

7.6. Bavaria. Take-apart Knife and Fork Kits.

Courtesy Smithsonian Institution, Wiebusch Collection.

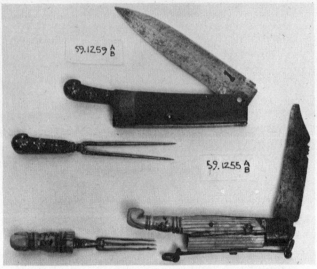

7.6.1. 4-5 inches long closed. Decorated bone, ivory, horn, or wood handles. Locking knife blade. Removable fork. 18th-19th centuries. Value **$150.**

7.6.2. 7 inches overall closed. Springless folding knife with horn or wood handles. Removable fork and two skewers. Tin alloy decorations. 18th-19th centuries. Value **$200.**

7.7. England. Slot Knife.

4 to 5 inches long closed. Take-apart knife and fork combination. Fork part may have spoon in opposite end. Handles of plain horn or wood, or fancy carved ivory or pearl. 18th–19th centuries. Example shown from Smith's Key, 1816, courtesy EAIA. Value **$150** (plain) to **$350** (fancy). For small silver-bladed versions, see *Silver Fruit Knives*.

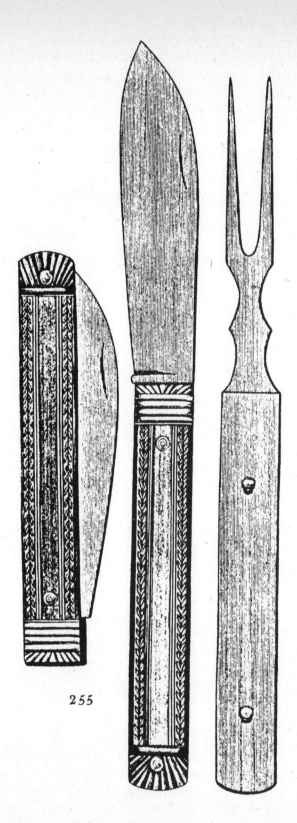

255

8. Secret Knives

The term "secret knife" (translation of the 18th century French *couteau a secret*), does not refer to any particular shape or style. Rather, it refers to any knife that contains a hidden mechanical contrivance, such as a locking or unlocking mechanism, or else hidden extra blades.

I consider secret knives to be one of the most fascinating areas of knife collecting. Quite a variety of them was made from the 17th through the early 19th centuries. Some simpler designs were made more recently. All types of early secret knives are rare.

8.1. Spain (?). Concealed Blade Secret Knife.

About 4 inches long closed. Penny knife type with one-piece horn handle. Blade stop is in fact part of the small blade, which is nested into the back of the hollow large blade. Circa 19th century. Value **$200.** Courtesy Lawrence Bireline and *Knife World*.

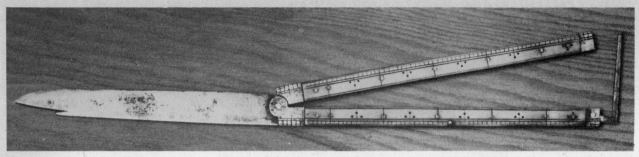

8.2. France. Ruler Secret Knife.

About 6¾ inches long closed. Steel mounts, ivory scales with engraved markings. Looks and works like a folding rule. Open length of rule is one French royal foot (= 13 English inches) divided into 12 French inches (*pouces*) which in turn are divided into twelfths of an inch (*lignes*). To open blade without opening ruler, flip up L-shaped steel cover (right) which exposes nail nick. 18th century. Value **$450.**

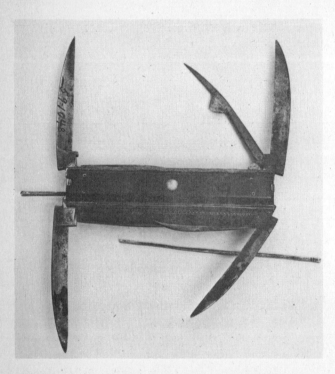

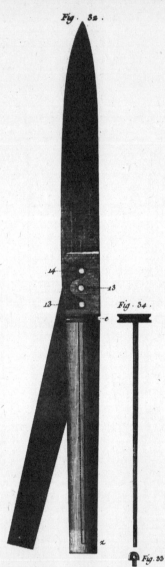

8.3. France (?). Multi-Bladed Secret Knife.

5½ inches long closed; nearly 1 inch wide and 1 inch thick. Wood handles, iron mounts. Made in two sections, each with four blades, two on top and two on the bottom. Blades cannot be opened until tapered square-cross-sectioned rods which block the springs are pushed out with one of the picks hidden in the handle scales. Nest of six saw blades pivoted between the two sections. To open the saw blades, use a pick to press a serrated spot on one of the center liners. This releases a latch at one end of the handle and allows the two sections to pivot at the other end. Some French single-bladed secret knives use a similar pivot mechanism. 18th century. Value about **$2,000.** Courtesy Smithsonian Institution, Wiebusch Collection.

8.4. France. Pivot-handle Secret Knife-Bayonet.

About 5 inches long closed. Three stout pins set in blade tang. Center is pivot pin that joins blade to handles. Other two pins are stop pins, one protruding on each side, to stop handles in open and closed positions. Sliding bolster with long pin inside one handle (Fig. 34) engages eye (Fig. 33) in other handle to lock knife either open or closed, and to prevent use by anyone who does not know the "secret." 18th and 19th centuries. Example shown from Perret, *The Art of the Cutler*, 1771, has handles tapered to allow knife to be used as plug bayonet. Value about **$750.**

Foreign Exotic, Primitive and Historical Folding Knives

An audacious American recieved a patent for the exact same mechanism on April 29, 1890.

426,445. POCKET-KNIFE. AXEL F. HASSELSTROM, Hermosa, (Dak. Ter.,) S. D. Filed July 27, 1889. Serial No. 318,919. (No model.)

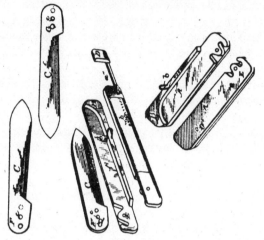

Claim.—The improved knife herein described and shown, consisting of the handles pivoted together and provided on their inner sides concentrically with their pivot with semicircular recesses, one of the handles being further provided with a longitudinal slot and a transverse opening, the blade mounted on the pivot of the handles and provided on its opposite faces and on opposite sides of its pivot with lateral lugs engaging the semicircular recesses in the handles, the spring B, secured to one of the handles, the staple projecting from said spring through the transverse opening in the handle, the removable tip on the end of the said handle, and the spring secured to said tip, adapted to enter the longitudinal slot in the handle, and provided at its free end with a lateral bend adapted to pass through the staple and engage the inner side of the same, as specified.

For an improved modern version, see Barry Wood high-tech folders in *Contemporary, Custom and Hand-Made Folding Knives.*

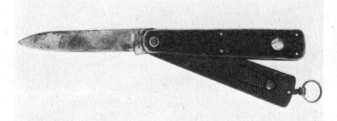

8.5. Germany. Pivot-liner Secret Knife.

About 4 inches long closed. Similar mechanism to 8.4., except inner wrap-around-back liner pivots inside outer wrap-around-end liner. Button in handle releases inner liner. Jigged bone handles. "WERWOLF No. 100" trademark. Circa 1900. Value **$150.** Some made for export to the United States.

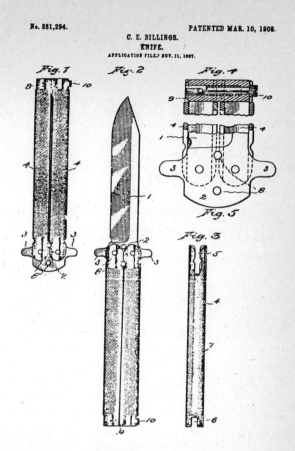

No. 881,294.   PATENTED MAR. 10, 1908.
C. E. BILLINGS.
KNIFE.
APPLICATION FILED NOV. 11, 1907.

8.6. Philippines. Balisong (Butterfly Knife).

2 to 8 inches long closed. Similar to 8.4., except half handles are side by side, rather than back to back. Also latch mechanism is at end, not internal.

This knife appears originally to have been an American invention. The mechanism was patented by Charles E. Billings of Billings and Spencer, Hartford, Connecticut, in 1908. Knives made by that firm (with nickel-plated knurled steel handles) were probably brought to the Philippines by American soldiers. Because it has no backspring, the balisong can be made using relatively primitive technology. Soon it was adopted as the national folding knife of the islands. Today, examples are made in California, Japan, and Italy, as well as in the Philippines. Courtesy William Lipes and *Knife World.*

Values: Original Billings & Spencer **$500**; Philippine made **$25**; Japanese or Italian made **$20** to **$50**; California made, by Balisong, Inc., **$150** to **$250**. American version by Neft Safety Knife of New Jersey, c1930s, value **$75.**

8.6.1. Current all-steel Japanese export balisong, courtesy Gutmann Cutlery Company. Value **$24.**

II: Folding Knives   **289**

Custom and Hand-Made Folding Knives

Introduction

WORKING with collectors Bill and Joanna Spivey, whose main interest is custom folding knives, I have divided this chapter into four parts. Within each part, the knives are arranged alphabetically by maker.

The first part covers **plain and practical hand-made folders.** These appeal equally to the collector and to the discriminating user.

The second part includes **"high-tech" folders.** These are knives, some odd, some practical, whose most obvious feature is the technology of construction, or of the mechanism for opening or locking the blade.

The third part is **decorated folders.** These exquisite knives appeal mainly to collectors. They incorporate exotic blade and handle materials, extraordinary fit and finish, and special decorative treatment such as file work, pin work, etching, engraving, or scrimshaw.

The fourth part is **damascus steel folders.** Damascus steel is made up of many layers of alternating hard and mild steels laminated together by repeated folding and forge welding. It is favored for its strength, its edge-holding ability, and, most of all, for its dramatic appearance. Some damascus folders have only damascus blades, but many have damascus fittings as well.

Most of the hand-made knives that are ilustrated here were selected by the makers themselves. Prices were supplied by the makers.

About 10 percent of the pictures are from my files, and some of these are of knives by makers no longer working. Their knives are still available on the resale market, so I have included them as well.

I estimated the value of the hand-made knives in my file photos with the help of several collectors and of a leading dealer, Nate Posner, owner of the San Francisco Gun Exchange. I also consulted the sales catalogs of most of the custom knife dealers listed in the back of this book.

1. PLAIN AND PRACTICAL FOLDERS

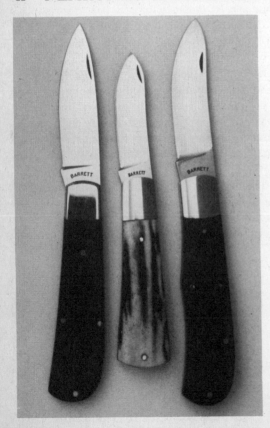

Jack Barrett, three slip-joint folders, hardwoods, stag, **$250 each.** (Courtesy B. & J. Spivey)

J. R. Atkinson, four interframe folders, **$325 each.** (Weyer photo)

1. PLAIN AND PRACTICAL FOLDERS

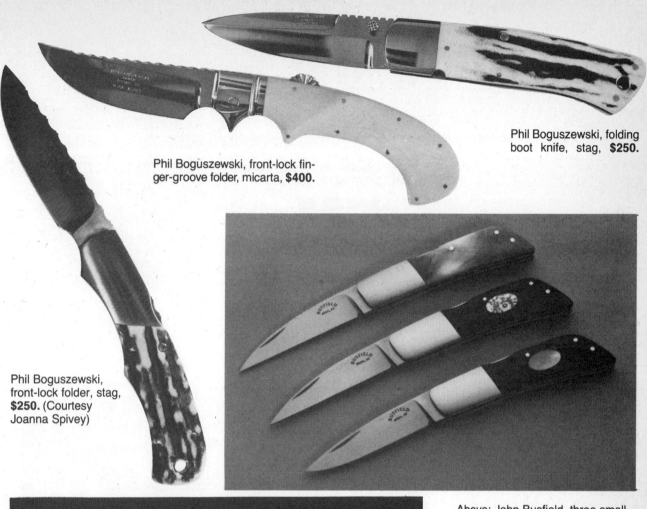

Phil Boguszewski, folding boot knife, stag, **$250.**

Phil Boguszewski, front-lock finger-groove folder, micarta, **$400.**

Phil Boguszewski, front-lock folder, stag, **$250.** (Courtesy Joanna Spivey)

Above: John Busfield, three small front-lock folders, integral stainless bolster/liners: black pearl, filework, **$275;** hardwood, inlay, **$225.** (Lenz photo)

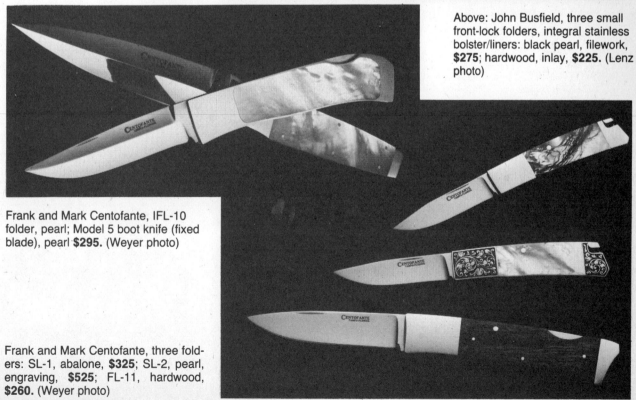

Frank and Mark Centofante, IFL-10 folder, pearl; Model 5 boot knife (fixed blade), pearl **$295.** (Weyer photo)

Frank and Mark Centofante, three folders: SL-1, abalone, **$325;** SL-2, pearl, engraving, **$525;** FL-11, hardwood, **$260.** (Weyer photo)

1. PLAIN AND PRACTICAL FOLDERS

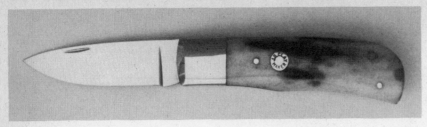

J. D. Clay, slip-joint folder, stag, **$175.** (Courtesy B. & J. Spivey)

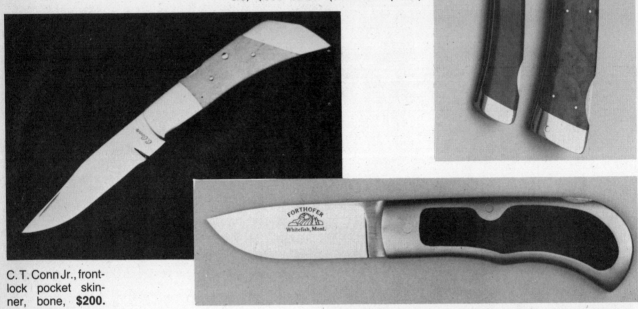

T. M. Dowell, integral bolster/liner folders, **$850 each.** (Gladstone photo)

C. T. Conn Jr., front-lock pocket skinner, bone, **$200.**

Pete Forthofer, stainless interframe lockback folder, pink ivory wood, **$275.**

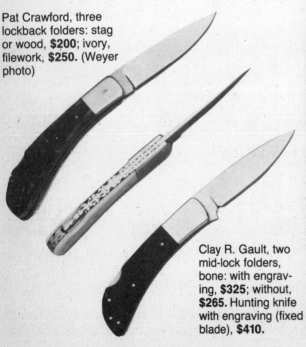

Pat Crawford, three lockback folders: stag or wood, **$200**; ivory, filework, **$250.** (Weyer photo)

Clay R. Gault, two mid-lock folders, bone: with engraving, **$325**; without, **$265.** Hunting knife with engraving (fixed blade), **$410.**

1. PLAIN AND PRACTICAL FOLDERS

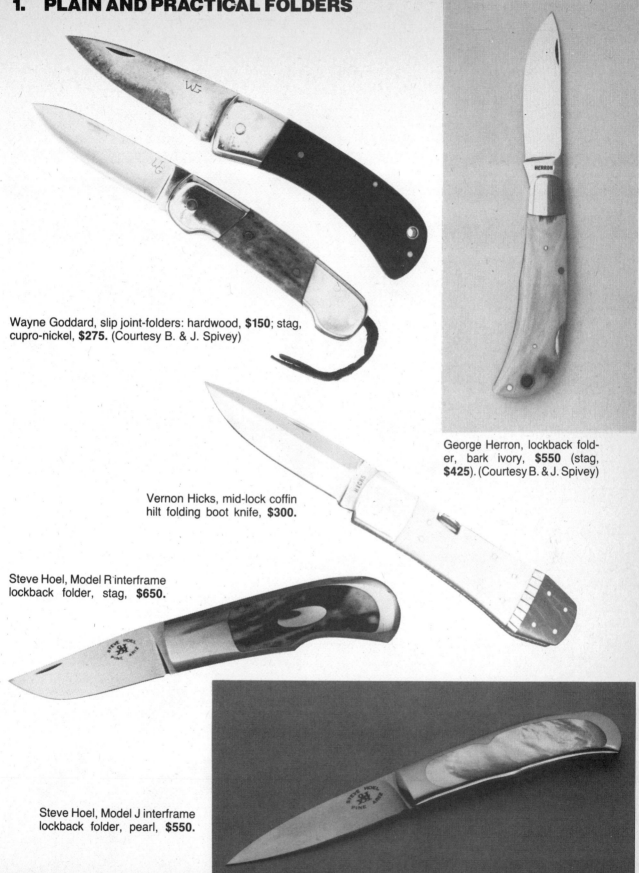

Wayne Goddard, slip joint-folders: hardwood, **$150**; stag, cupro-nickel, **$275.** (Courtesy B. & J. Spivey)

George Herron, lockback folder, bark ivory, **$550** (stag, **$425**). (Courtesy B. & J. Spivey)

Vernon Hicks, mid-lock coffin hilt folding boot knife, **$300.**

Steve Hoel, Model R interframe lockback folder, stag, **$650.**

Steve Hoel, Model J interframe lockback folder, pearl, **$550.**

1. PLAIN AND PRACTICAL FOLDERS

Jess Horn, interframe lockback folders: Lady Boot, **$660**; ISPH, **$610**; IDPH, **$610**; Tiny, **$580**.

Jess Horn, lockback folders: BHL, **$350**; MHL, **$340**; LHL, **$330**; Baby, **$330**.

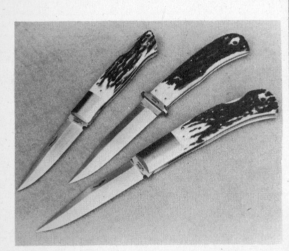

Above: Jess Horn, lockback folders: SHLM, **$395**; FBK, **$470**; DHL, **$395**.

Left: Jess Horn, lockback folding boot knives: SF, **$465**; LF, **$475**. Integral guard boot knife (fixed blade, center), **$875**. (A. Horn photos)

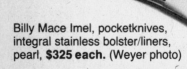

Billy Mace Imel, pocketknives, integral stainless bolster/liners, pearl, **$325 each.** (Weyer photo)

Billy Mace Imel, pocketknives, stainless, 2⅞″, 3¼″, or 4″, **$200**. Engraving by Ray Viramontez extra. (Weyer photo)

1. PLAIN AND PRACTICAL FOLDERS

Ronald B. Johnson, three lockback folders: **$150**, **$190**, **$250**. (Weyer photo)

Ron Lake, Gentleman's Lockback, ivory, toothpick, **$1,800.**

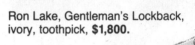

Frank Lampson, Model 143 two-blade lockback folder, **$400.**

Frank Lampson, Model 20 lockback folder, pearl, **$300.**

Ron Little, slip-joint, folder, micarta, **$450.** (Courtesy B. & J. Spivey)

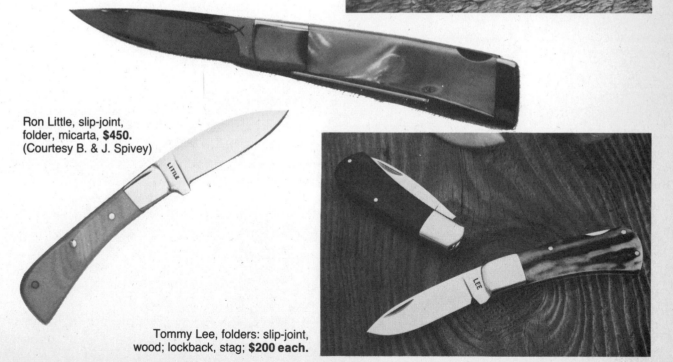

Tommy Lee, folders: slip-joint, wood; lockback, stag; **$200 each.**

1. PLAIN AND PRACTICAL FOLDERS

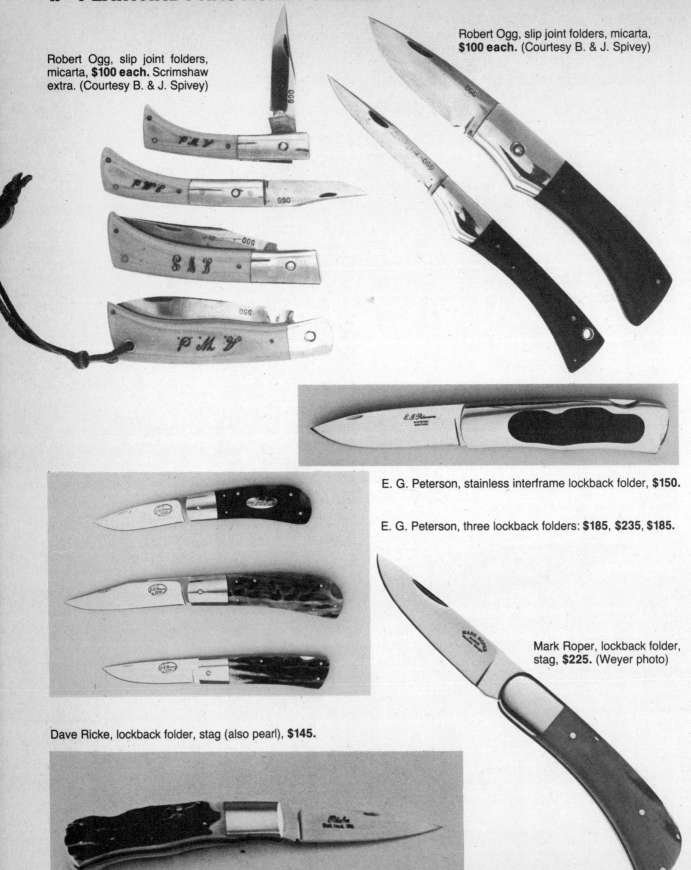

Robert Ogg, slip joint folders, micarta, **$100 each.** Scrimshaw extra. (Courtesy B. & J. Spivey)

Robert Ogg, slip joint folders, micarta, **$100 each.** (Courtesy B. & J. Spivey)

E. G. Peterson, stainless interframe lockback folder, **$150.**

E. G. Peterson, three lockback folders: **$185**, **$235**, **$185.**

Mark Roper, lockback folder, stag, **$225.** (Weyer photo)

Dave Ricke, lockback folder, stag (also pearl), **$145.**

1. PLAIN AND PRACTICAL FOLDERS

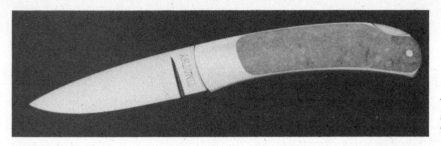

David Taylor, lockback folder, stag, **$175** (Scadlock photo)

TIMOTHY (Timothy Wright), hard aluminum interframe lockback folder, fossil walrus ivory, **$360.**

TRO (T. R. Overeynder), three front-lock folders, stainless frames: Model 3, Dahl sheep horn, **$355**; Model 4, oosic, **$330**; Model 1, stag, damascus steel made by Bill Buckner, **$425.** (Weyer photo)

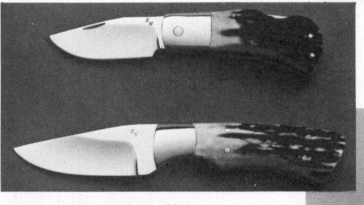

Ken Ward, lockback folder, stag, **$200**; hunter, stag (fixed blade), **$160.** (Weyer photo)

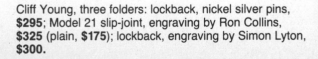

Cliff Young, three folders: lockback, nickel silver pins, **$295**; Model 21 slip-joint, engraving by Ron Collins, **$325** (plain, **$175**); lockback, engraving by Simon Lyton, **$300.**

2. HIGH-TECH FOLDERS

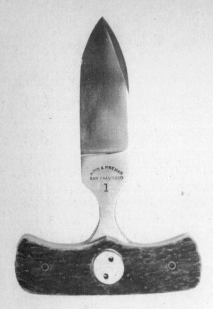

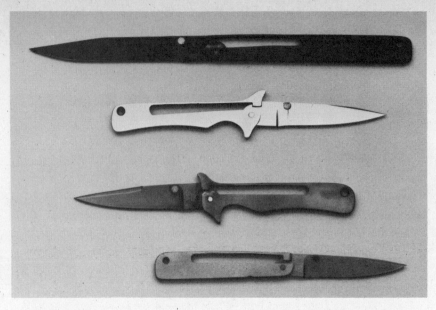

Francis Boyd and Ken Fireman, push dagger that folds into straight knife, patent lock, stag, **$500.** (Tikker photo)

Pat Crawford, one-piece handle locking folders: top three, **$150 each,** bottom, **$125.** (Ruby photo)

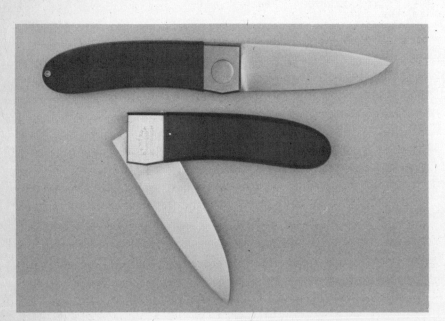

D. E. Henry, patented button-lock folders, hardwood, **$2,200 each.** (Courtesy S. F. Gun Exchange)

Vernon Hicks, lever lock folder, hardwood, **$300.**

T. M. Dowell, Funny Folder, flat-ground hand-rubbed blade, micarta, **$225.** Shown with original flip-flop folder, **$5.** (Courtesy B. & J. Spivey and Colonial Knife Co.)

2. HIGH-TECH FOLDERS

Bob Hayes, two-part side-folding knife, stainless, **$1,200–1,500.**

Bob Hayes, side-lock folder, ivory, **$2,200–2,600.**

Bob Hayes, side-lock folder, checkered ebony, **$2,500.**

Bob Hayes, side-lock folder, pearl, **$2,500–3,000.**

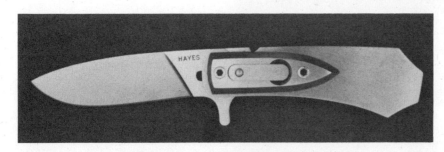

Bob Hayes, side-lock folder, stainless, **$2,000–2,500.**

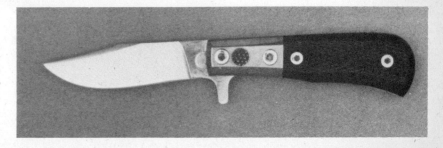

Bob Hayes, button-lock folder, **$2,000–2,500.**

(Hayes knives courtesy Steven Weiss, Wolf Schulz, and S. F. Gun Exchange)

2. HIGH-TECH FOLDERS

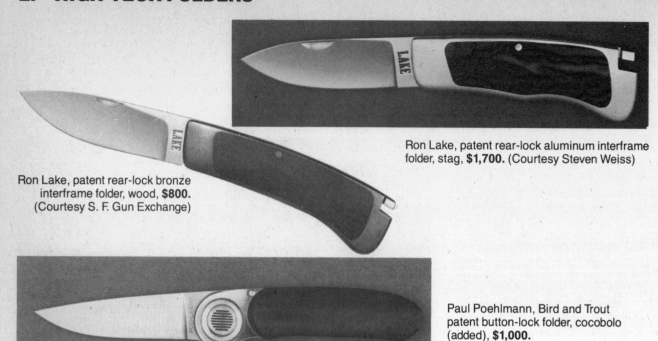

Ron Lake, patent rear-lock aluminum interframe folder, stag, **$1,700.** (Courtesy Steven Weiss)

Ron Lake, patent rear-lock bronze interframe folder, wood, **$800.** (Courtesy S. F. Gun Exchange)

Paul Poehlmann, Bird and Trout patent button-lock folder, cocobolo (added), **$1,000.**

Paul Poehlmann, Model 0312 patent button-lock folder, stainless, **$1,000.** (Courtesy Wolf Schulz)

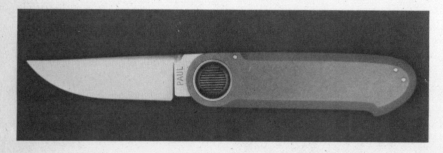

Paul Poehlmann, 1st Edition patent button-lock folding caper, chrome anodized aluminum alloy, **$1,200.** (Courtesy Wolf Schulz)

Scott Sawby and Steve Mullin, button-lock folders, hardwood, filework, **$275 each.**

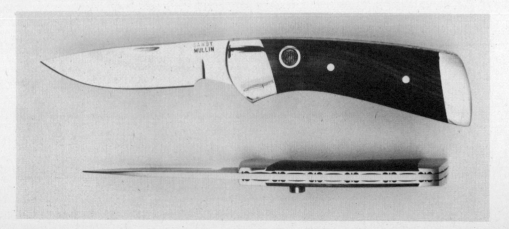

2. HIGH-TECH FOLDERS

Scott W. Sawby, button-lock folder, stag, **$310;** liner-lock folder, jigged bone, **$300.**

Barry Wood, patent rotating folder, ivory, **$500–600.** Adam Funmaker scrimshaw extra. (Courtesy Steven Weiss)

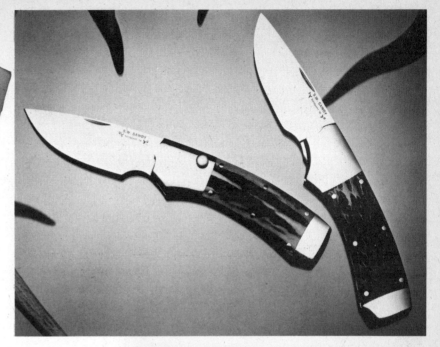

Barry Wood, patent rotating folder, stag, **$500–600.**

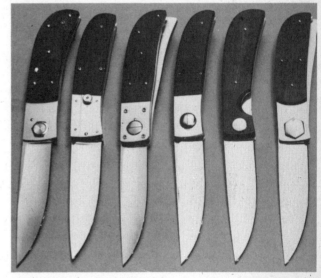

Michael Walker, set of six matching knives with six different lock mechanisms, **$3,000/set.** (Courtesy Wolf Schulz)

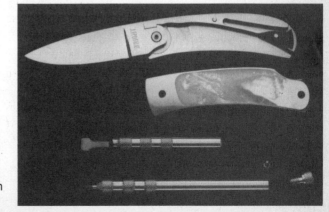

Timothy Wright, aluminum-bronze interframe take-apart folder, pearl, titanium screws, brass tools, **$660;** shown with handle off.

3. DECORATED FOLDERS

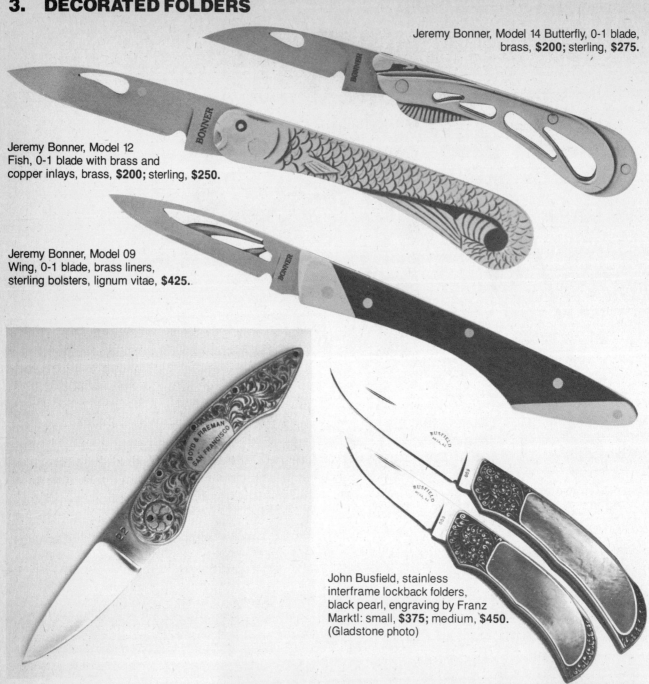

Jeremy Bonner, Model 14 Butterfly, 0-1 blade, brass, **$200**; sterling, **$275**.

Jeremy Bonner, Model 12 Fish, 0-1 blade with brass and copper inlays, brass, **$200**; sterling, **$250**.

Jeremy Bonner, Model 09 Wing, 0-1 blade, brass liners, sterling bolsters, lignum vitae, **$425**.

John Busfield, stainless interframe lockback folders, black pearl, engraving by Franz Marktl: small, **$375**; medium, **$450**. (Gladstone photo)

Above: Francis Boyd and Ken Fireman, patent button-lock folder, fully engraved, **$250**. (Tikker photo)

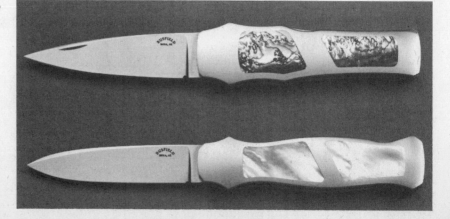

Right: John Busfield, stainless interframe lockback folding sgian dubh and dagger, abalone and pearl, **$475** and **$500**. (Weyer photo)

3. DECORATED FOLDERS

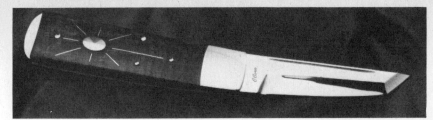

C. T. Conn Jr., Palace Guard front-lock folding tanto, hardwood, inlays, **$350.**

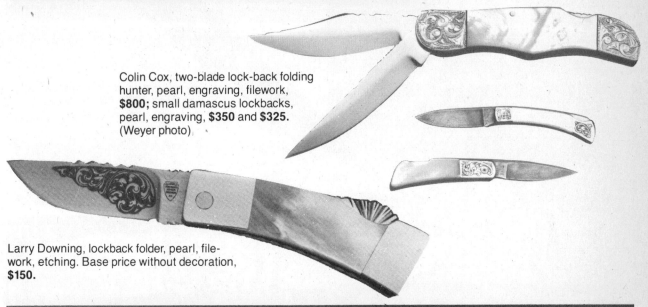

Colin Cox, two-blade lock-back folding hunter, pearl, engraving, filework, **$800;** small damascus lockbacks, pearl, engraving, **$350** and **$325.** (Weyer photo)

Larry Downing, lockback folder, pearl, filework, etching. Base price without decoration, **$150.**

H. H. Frank, lockback folder, ivory, silver, engraving, **$2,500–3,000.**

H. H. Frank, lockback folder, ivory, gold, engraving, toothpick, **$4,000.**

H. H. Frank, lockback folder, ivory, gold, engraving, gold inlay, bluing, **$10,000–12,000.** (Frank knives courtesy Steven Weiss).

3. DECORATED FOLDERS

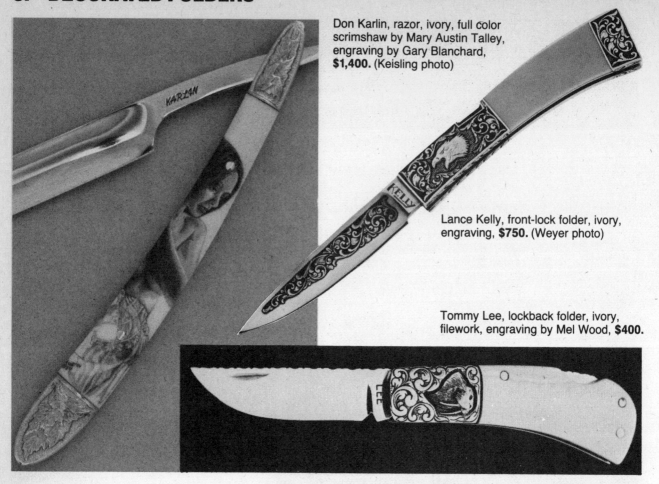

Don Karlin, razor, ivory, full color scrimshaw by Mary Austin Talley, engraving by Gary Blanchard, **$1,400.** (Keisling photo)

Lance Kelly, front-lock folder, ivory, engraving, **$750.** (Weyer photo)

Tommy Lee, lockback folder, ivory, filework, engraving by Mel Wood, **$400.**

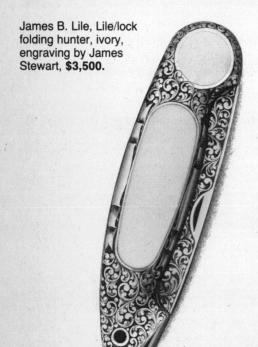

James B. Lile, Lile/lock folding hunter, ivory, engraving by James Stewart, **$3,500.**

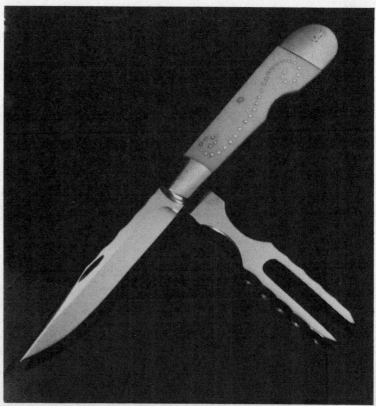

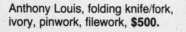

Anthony Louis, folding knife/fork, ivory, pinwork, filework, **$500.**

3. DECORATED FOLDERS

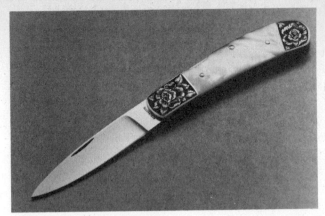

Harvey McBurnette, front-lock folder, pearl, engraving, **$425.**

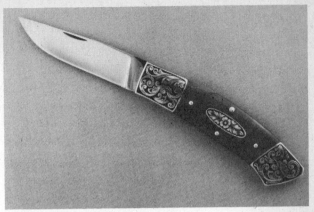

Harvey McBurnette, front-lock folder, pink ivory wood, engraving, **$405.**

Harvey McBurnette, front-lock folding fighter, ivory, engraving, **$750.**

Harvey McBurnette, front-lock folding knife and fork, pearl, engraving, **$950/set.**

Steve Mullin, mid-lock folders: two blade, pearl, engraved, **$600;** one blade, jigged bone, engraved, **$285.**

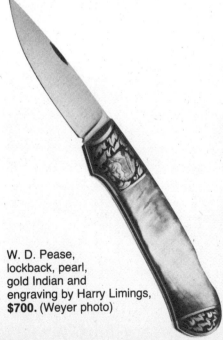

W. D. Pease, lockback, pearl, gold Indian and engraving by Harry Limings, **$700.** (Weyer photo)

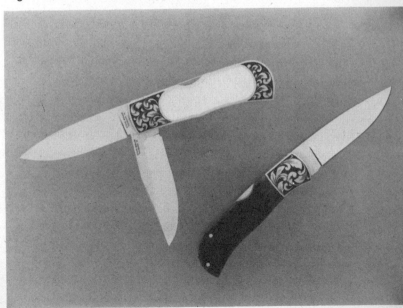

3. DECORATED FOLDERS

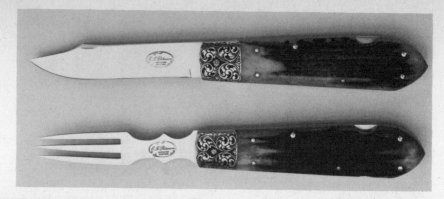

E. G. Peterson, lockback folding knife and fork, stag, engraving, **$500/set.**

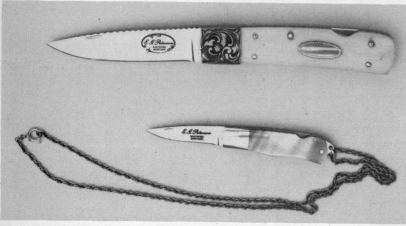

E. G. Peterson, lockback folder, ivory, engraving, filework, **$250;** miniature lockback, pearl, **$150** with silver neck chain.

Jim Serven, interframe folding San Francisco-style knife, pearl, abalone, **$850.** (Weyer photo)

TRO (T. R. Overeynder), Model 6 front-lock folding dagger, hippo ivory, engraving and gold wire inlay by Ron Smith, **$2,500.** (Chase photo)

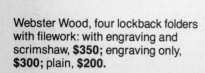

Webster Wood, four lockback folders with filework: with engraving and scrimshaw, **$350;** engraving only, **$300;** plain, **$200.**

3. DECORATED FOLDERS

Michael Walker, seven Walker's Lockers folding tantos, titanium bolsters (except 2nd and 6th with mokume bolsters and damascus blades), fossil walrus ivory (1 & 6), pearl (2 & 5), oxhorn, stag, African blackwood, engraving and scrimshaw by Patricia Walker; **$275** to **$650.** (Bradley photo)

Michael Walker, folding sgian dubhs, African blackwood, engraving and carving by Patricia Walker; **$600** large, **$400** small. (Bradley photo)

Michael Walker, Walker's Lockers, fossil walrus ivory, engraving by Patricia Walker; **$575** large, **$425** small.

Michael Walker, a medley of knives, engraving and scrimshaw by Patricia Walker; **$100** to **$2,500.**

4. DAMASCUS FOLDERS

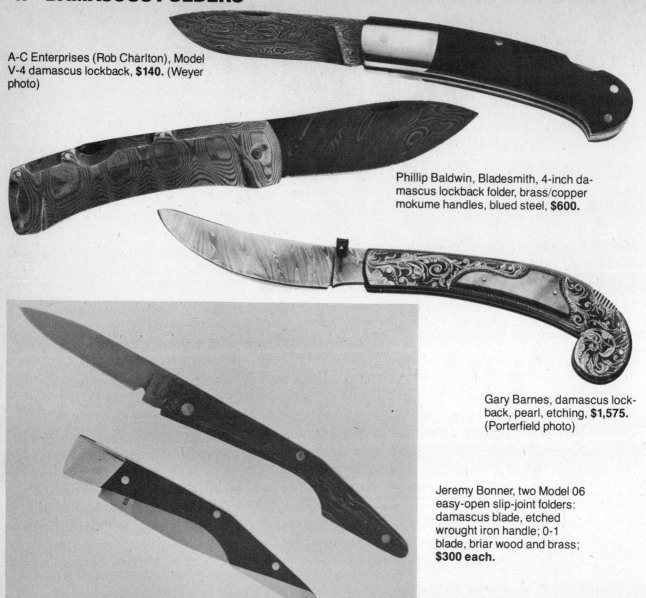

A-C Enterprises (Rob Charlton), Model V-4 damascus lockback, **$140.** (Weyer photo)

Phillip Baldwin, Bladesmith, 4-inch damascus lockback folder, brass/copper mokume handles, blued steel, **$600.**

Gary Barnes, damascus lockback, pearl, etching, **$1,575.** (Porterfield photo)

Jeremy Bonner, two Model 06 easy-open slip-joint folders: damascus blade, etched wrought iron handle; 0-1 blade, briar wood and brass; **$300 each.**

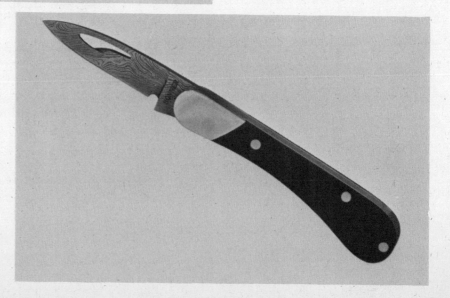

Jeremy Bonner, Model 08 damascus folder, brass, cocobolo, sterling bolsters, **$425.**

4. DAMASCUS FOLDERS

Bob Cargill, all damascus folder with integral front lock, mastodon ivory, **$1,000.** (*Knife World* 1984 Writer's Award Knife)

Jack W. Crain, damascus front-lock folder, pearl, **$1,500** with display box.

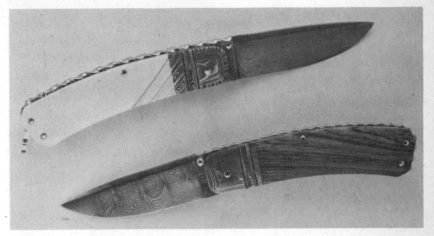

Right: Barry Davis, damascus folders, nickel damascus bolsters, filework: ivory with silver lanyard ring, **$850;** cocobolo **$750.** Below: Barry Davis, damascus folders, worked backs.

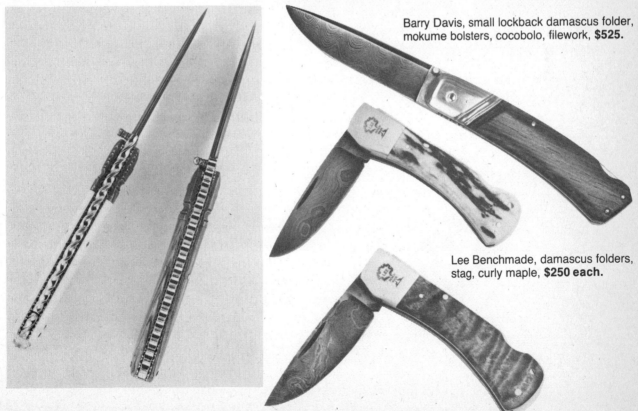

Barry Davis, small lockback damascus folder, mokume bolsters, cocobolo, filework, **$525.**

Lee Benchmade, damascus folders, stag, curly maple, **$250 each.**

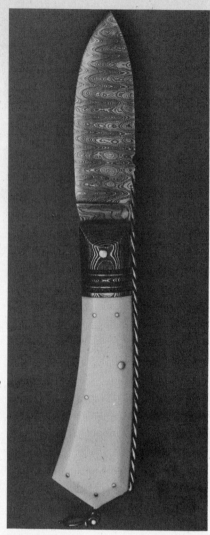

Left: James A. Schmidt, worked backs. Right: James A. Schmidt, damascus lockback folder, ring release, ivory, filework, **$2,400.** (Weyer photos)

James A. Schmidt, all damascus lockback folders, crown stag, filework, lanyard rings, **$1,200** to **$2,500.** (Weyer photo)

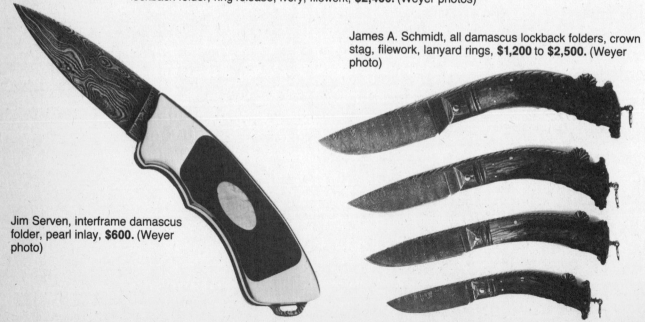

Jim Serven, interframe damascus folder, pearl inlay, **$600.** (Weyer photo)

4. DAMASCUS FOLDERS

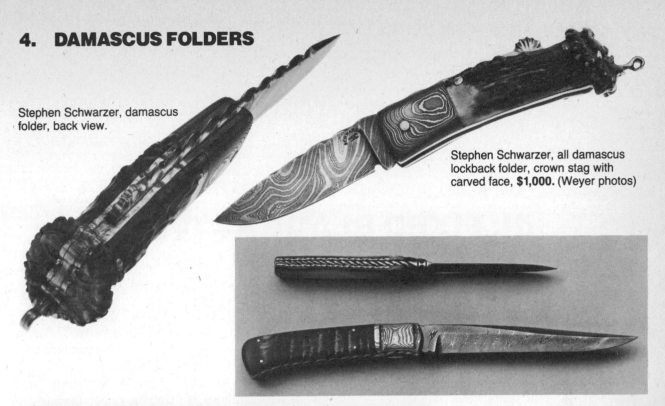

Stephen Schwarzer, damascus folder, back view.

Stephen Schwarzer, all damascus lockback folder, crown stag with carved face, **$1,000.** (Weyer photos)

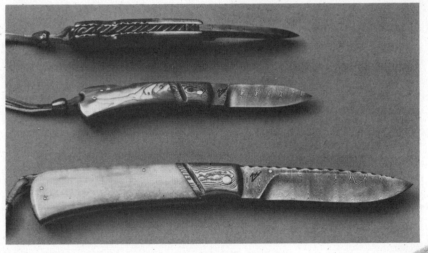

Above: Wayne Valachovic, damascus folding fighter and boot knife, **$600 each.** (Weyer photo)

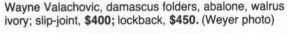

Wayne Valachovic, damascus folders, abalone, walrus ivory; slip-joint, **$400;** lockback, **$450.** (Weyer photo)

Wayne Valachovic, damascus front-lock folder, abalone, **$725.** (Crabtree photo)

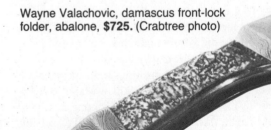

Drawing by Joanna Spivey.

III: FIXED BLADE KNIVES

THE FIXED BLADE KNIVES section begins with the history of the most celebrated of all American knives, the bowie knife. The Bowie Knives chapter explains the origin, development, and variety of this classic weapon in the period of its common use, circa 1827–1872.

The next chapter is closely related. It is the story of American Indian Trade Knives.

The third chapter follows the thread of the first two chapters up into modern times. It charts the evolution of American Hunting Knives, belt knives designed primarily for sport.

American Hunting Knives treats factory knives. The next chapters treat hand-made knives. First are chapters on four of the Pioneers of Modern Hand-Made Knives, men whose influence can be seen in almost every fixed blade knife sold in the United States today. These are followed by a lengthy chapter on Contemporary Custom and Hand-Made Fixed Blade Knives.

Then comes a history of United States Military Fixed Blade Knives, illustrated with the superb drawings of M.H. Cole. This is followed by a brief section on Foreign Military Fixed Blade Knives.

The next chapter is a detailed look at ancient and modern fixed blade knives from around the world. Much of this chapter was written by Eiler R. Cook.

Finally are chapters about knives that most of us too often take for granted: Kitchen and Butcher Knives, Industrial Knives, Table Knives, and Carving Sets.

NOTE: Throughout the Fixed Blade Knives section, each knife or type of knife is priced individually.

Bowie Knives

The Vidalia Sandbar Fight

ON September 19, 1827, on a Mississippi River sandbar just above Natchez, there was held what the participants called an ''interview'' to settle an ''affair of honor.'' Duels for the satisfaction of honor were a common enough occurence in the Old South. This particular ''interview,'' however, though it proved harmless to the two principals involved, degenerated into a ''rough fight'' among the dozen men present, leaving two of them dead and two others wounded.

One of the men wounded in the melee was James Bowie, a young land speculator then residing in Avoyelles Parish, Louisiana. Bowie was a friend of Samuel Wells, one of the principals in the duel.

In the fight, Bowie had been shot in the thigh and knocked down. He was then, according to the published account of Samuel Wells, set upon by a member of the opposing party, Major Norris Wright, who attempted to stab Bowie with a sword cane.

Bowie by then had already emptied both of his pistols, so to defend himself he drew from under his coat a large knife that his brother, Rezin Bowie, had loaned him for his protection. He struggled up to a sitting position, and with one blow of his brother's knife, James Bowie killed Major Wright. Wright's friends told a story much less flattering to Bowie (that he shot Wright, *then* stabbed him), but Wells's version was the one most widely circulated at the time.

This incident, which came to be called the ''Vidalia Sandbar Fight,'' attracted intense popular interest. The image of a wounded man, lying on the ground and struggling just to sit up, his guns empty and useless, who yet managed with one stab of a knife to kill an opponent attacking him with a sword, caught the fancy of the nation.

In the popular mind, Bowie's feat was attributed, not so much to the pluck and desperation of the man, as to some special undefined virtue of his knife. "Bowie knives" quickly became a fad, then a fashion, then a fundamental fixture of the American scene. Young men of Bowie's planter class in the South came to be called the "bowie knife and pistol gentry." And then, in 1836, James Bowie's dramatic martyrdom at the Alamo in Texas guaranteed that his name would ever after be linked to the American fighting knife.

Personal Defense

Civilian wear of the small sword, so common in the 18th century, had been fading from the scene ever since the introduction in 1807 of compact, readily concealed, single shot "cap and ball" percussion pistols. However, hardly anyone carried more than two pistols, which meant one only had two shots to deal with one's opponents, assuming the pistols happened to work. After that, one's pistols were only useful as clubs. Although daggers of various sizes had always been available, the bowie knife came along at just the right time to fill what men perceived to be a dangerous gap in their personal defenses.

For nearly half a century, the "bowie knife," was America's most popular sidearm, although in the late 1840s it was joined in the spotlight by the "Colt's" cap and ball revolvers. A pair of Colts might hold ten or 12 rounds, but the percussion system was never reliable enough for a prudent man to stake his life solely on his revolvers. Come rain or snow or sleet or gloom of night, a bowie knife was always loaded and never failed to fire.

The Bowie Knife

What exactly *is* a bowie knife? To start with, in 1827, it was "a knife like Bowie's." Bowie's knife looked much like the ordinary Mediterranean daggers prevalent in the South in his day. The gauchos (cowboys) of South America still use similar knives. To us today, his original style of bowie knife looks more than anything like a French chef's knife, which was also based on the same model [see *Foreign Exotic, Prim-*

itive, and Historical Fixed Blade Knives: A.4, C.17; also see *Kitchen and Butcher Knives*].

Today we know that this is what Bowie's knife looked like. At the time, however, only a handful of people in Louisiana and Mississippi had actually seen it. The famous sandbar fight took place before the invention of photography, and even before the common use of engravings in newspapers and magazines. The fame of the bowie knife spread at the time through written descriptions and accounts of the fight, not through pictures.

Still, it wasn't long before men all over the country wanted to have a "Bowie's knife." They did not know what one looked like, but they did the best they could to match the descriptions.

Bowie knives were made long and short, light and heavy, single-edged and double-edged, straight-backed and curved-backed, clip point and spear point, plain and decorated, fixed blade and folding [see *Folding Bowies and Folding Dirks*], with a cross guard (or two) and without. Hardly any of them looked much like *Bowie's* own knife, but no one really cared. To their makers and their owners, all of them were bowie knives.

Though shape, size, and decoration varied widely in the first two decades of the bowie knife era, all bowie knives had this in common: they were designed primarily as weapons. The coffin-shaped hilt on many early bowie knives might well have been symbolic. A sense of propriety prompted some people (including Rezin Bowie) to call bowies "hunting knives," but first and foremost they were weapons.

In addition, most bowie knives were sold with sheaths fitted up to be worn on or thrust through a belt, much like a sword scabbard. That way one's bowie knife would be handy for attack or defense. Real working hunting knives (actually small butcher knives) were then carried in the hunting bag, out of the way and safe from loss and rain.

Bowie Knife Makers

Who made these bowie knives to meet the burgeoning demand? In particular, who made the very first, the *original* bowie knife? Here legend has led many writers astray. The popular story of a "James Black" in Arkansas was made up from the whole cloth in the 1890s, and has been endlessly

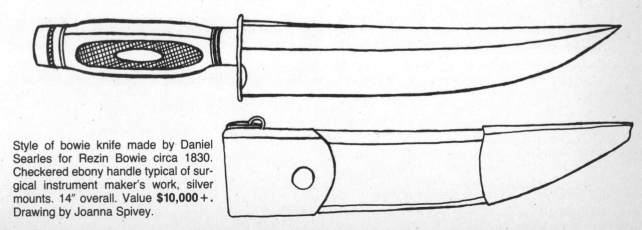

Style of bowie knife made by Daniel Searles for Rezin Bowie circa 1830. Checkered ebony handle typical of surgical instrument maker's work, silver mounts. 14″ overall. Value **$10,000+**. Drawing by Joanna Spivey.

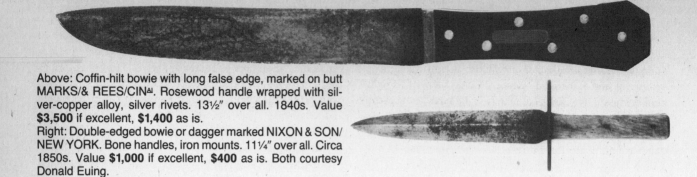

Above: Coffin-hilt bowie with long false edge, marked on butt MARKS/& REES/CINAl. Rosewood handle wrapped with silver-copper alloy, silver rivets. 13½" over all. 1840s. Value **$3,500** if excellent, **$1,400** as is.
Right: Double-edged bowie or dagger marked NIXON & SON/ NEW YORK. Bone handles, iron mounts. 11¼" over all. Circa 1850s. Value **$1,000** if excellent, **$400** as is. Both courtesy Donald Euing.

embroidered with meteors and brass backs and magical mysteries ever since then.

Rezin Bowie wrote that he himself had made the knife which he had given to his brother before the sandbar fight. Scholarship suggests that the knife might actually have been made for Rezin to his design by a blacksmith in his employ named Jesse Cliffe. In any case, it was made at or near the Bowie's home in Avoyelles Parish, southeast of Alexandria, Louisiana.

Subsequent knives made for the Bowie brothers were made, not surprisingly, by the "custom knifemakers" of their day, men called cutlers and surgical instrument makers. One or more of these merchant craftsmen could be found in nearly every American city at that time. Most of them regularly advertised "Cutlery of all descriptions on hand and made to order." Two such cutlers known to have made bowie knives for Rezin Bowie around 1830 were Henry Schively, Junior, of Philadelphia, and Daniel Searles of Baton Rouge.

Cutlers and surgical instrument makers throughout the United States (see list) were the first beneficiaries of the bowie knife fad. Though often very plain, American cutler-made bowie knives are the most prized by collectors. The rarest, of course, are the earliest, but none of them are common.

Any large or fancy bowie knife made by one of the American cutlers active while James Bowie was still alive is worth a least **$2,500** in excellent condition. Later or plainer cutler-made bowies are worth at least **$1,000.** Exceptional design, workmanship, or historical association can add significantly to these values.

European cutlers also joined in the bowie movement, some by sending knives, others by emigrating. Fancy handmade Paris bowies found favor in the Old South (value at least **$750**). Some London hunting knives might also have been sold here [see *Foreign Exotic, Primitive, and Histori-*

cal Fixed Blade Knives, C.9], but almost all of the foreign bowie knives brought to the United States came from Sheffield.

Early Sheffield Bowie Knives

News of the sandbar fight and the American demand for "bowie knives" would have reached Sheffield before the end of 1827. Sheffield cutlers had long sold knives in the United States, but it was only after of the War of 1812, which had hurt their business badly, that they had started to cater to American tastes.

By an odd coincidence, the first cutlery *factory* in Sheffield had just been completed in 1826. It had taken 4 years to build, but had opened just in time for the bowie knife craze. This first factory was followed in short order by many more.

Sheffield's first factory was built for William Greaves & Son. Besides Greaves, some of the other important Sheffield firms involved very early in the bowie knife trade were William & Samuel Butcher, Samuel C. Wragg, James Rodgers, Enoch Drabble, Charles Congreve, and George Wostenholm's Rockingham Works.

Wostenholm made his first cutlery sales trip to the United States in 1830, and thereafter devoted all of his considerable

Clip point bowie knife marked JAMES RODGERS/ROYAL CUTLERY/SHEFFIELD and CAST STEEL BOWIE KNIFE. Rosewood handle with nickel silver pins and mounts. 15½" over all. Circa 1840. Value **$1,400.** Courtesy M. H. Cole.

Straight-backed bowie with long false edge, marked SIRHENRY/A PARIS. Ivory handles, two nickel silver guards, sheath. 14¾" overall. 1830s–1840s. Value **$1,800.** Courtesy Smithsonian Institution. Note: Original sheath adds **10-20%** to the value of a bowie knife.

energies to American sales. In 1848 he built Sheffield's largest factory yet, the Washington Works. Until the 1890s his I*XL cutlery dominated the American market.

The earliest Sheffield bowies were characterized by an astounding variety of blade shapes, handle shapes, and decoration. The big, fancy, odd-shaped Sheffield bowies of this early period (circa 1827–1845) are very nearly as rare and valuable as their plainer American counterparts, with values ranging from **$2,000** up. Plainer early ones are worth at least **$1,000.**

By the late 1840s, scores of Sheffield firms were making bowie knives (and other cutlery) for America. Most of the Sheffield firms listed in the *Pocketknife Brand List* as active in the mid-19th century made, or at least sold, bowie knives. Other firms, such as Woodhead & Hartley, Broomhead & Thomas, James Westa, and John Coe, seem to have specialized in bowies.

Even in the factories, Sheffield cutlery was almost entirely hand-made [see the introduction to the *Sheffield Brand List* for more information]. However, one element of "mass-production" then prevalent in Sheffield contributed significantly to the great popularity and relatively low cost of Sheffield bowies in the United States. This was the production of fancy but inexpensive nickel silver furniture (mountings), and later entire handles, for these knives.

Nickel silver (or white "brass"), an alloy of copper and nickel, had been invented around 1810. By 1815 it was being rolled like silver into thin sheets which were then punched into three-dimensional decorative shapes with steel dies. These hollow shapes were then filled either with cutler's cement (made of rosin, beeswax, and brick dust) or with lead.

Myriad designs of furniture and handles were stamped out of nickel silver by specialist firms in Sheffield. They sold their wares to all the cutlery makers there. Many designs were made for the American market [see *Folding Bowies and Folding Dirks* for more examples]. Collectors should be aware that some of the original stamping dies have survived, and are now used to make both reproduction and counterfeit knives.

Another form of bowie decoration popular in Sheffield had the aspect of mass-production. This was decorative blade etching. The resist for these complex designs was applied with reusable brass stencils.

Clip point bowies by George Woodhead, 36 Howard Street, Sheffield.
Above: Woodhead & Hartley; ivory, half-horse/half-alligator pommel, Gold Rush etch. Value **$2,500.** Courtesy Hugh Hayes.
Right: G. Woodhead; stag, lion pommel. Value **$1,400.** Courtesy Bob Macon.

Left: Clip point bowie marked LAMSON GOODNOW & CO./S. FALLS WORKS; ivory, nickel silver guard. Circa 1850. Value **$1,000** if excellent, **$350** as is. Courtesy B. and J. Spivey.

Later Bowie Knives

Aside from their decoration, Sheffield bowie knives were hand made: forged, ground, hafted, and finished. So, too, were the American bowies made by cutlers and surgical instruments makers.

Beginning in the 1830s, America began to develop a real factory-based cutlery *industry*. Mass-production methods were applied to table knives, butcher knives, and even pocketknives.

However, it was not until the Mexican War (1846–1848) and the California Gold Rush (1849–1852) spurred new demand for bowie knives far exceeding any in the past, that these young American firms first made any factory bowie knives, at least any that we know of now.

Best known are the 1,000 Ames rifleman's knives made for the Army in 1849 [see *U.S. Military Fixed Blade Knives*].

A requisite of factory mass-production is uniformity. By the late 1840s, the wild variety of the early bowie era was becoming a thing of the past. Shapes were more standardized, options more limited. Some new bowies were still fancy, a few even elegant, but bowie knives more and more were merely a product.

In California, however, demand for bowies was so great that a local cutlery industry sprang up in San Francisco to fill it, a tiny workshop industry that created its own rich and distinctive styles (see my book, *Knifemakers of Old San Francisco*, 1978; also Warner's *Knives '82*). San Francisco bowies are now among the most sought after by collectors, commanding prices from **$1,500** to **$10,000** in excellent condition.

By contrast, the least appreciated bowie knives among collectors now are the smaller American factory-made bowies, products of New England table and kitchen knife firms in the 1840s and 1850s. A collector who learns what to look for can still find bargains in this area. Values are **$400** to **$1,200.** See *Indian Trade Knives* for explanations of the most important markings. See *American Hunting Knives* for pictures of similar but later knives that do not qualify as true bowies.

Sheffield cutlery firms responded to the California Gold Rush by unleashing a flood of cheap and flimsy bowie knives etched with gaudy motifs that proclaimed one a CALIFORNIA KNIFE, another GOOD AS GOLD, a third the GOLD SEEKER'S DEFENDER, and so on.

Despite their poor quality, these knives do have a historical value of **$250–500** in excellent condition with the etching clear and sharp (beware of fakes). Some large fine quality English and American bowies also have Gold Rush etching or stamping.

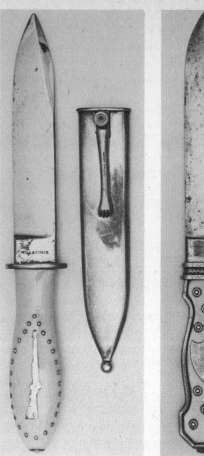
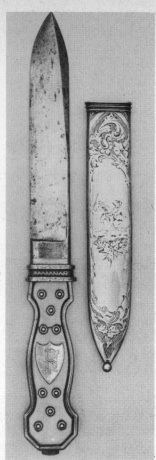

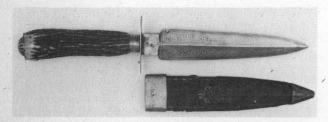

Bowie (dagger) by John Walters, Sheffield. Etched CALIFORNIA TOOTHPICK and GOLD SEEKER'S PROTECTOR. Value **$350** (**$250** as is). Courtesy Bob Macon.

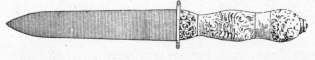

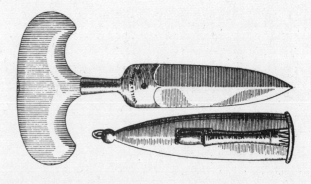

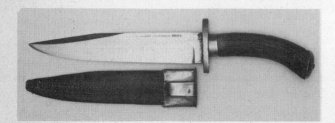

Clip point bowie marked CHEVALIER'S CALIFORNIA KNIFE, by John D. Chevalier of New York. Stag handle. Value **$1,200.** Courtesy Hugh Hayes.

San Francisco bowie knives. Top left: Will & Finck; walrus ivory handle, silver studs, gold rifle, nickel silver sheath. Circa 1871. Value **$3,500.** Top right: Michael Price; cast coin silver handle, ivory panels, gold rivets and shields, engraved silver sheath. Value **$6,500** if excellent, **$4,500** as is. Both courtesy Hugh Hayes. Center: Will & Finck; nickel silver handle inlaid with abalone shell. Value **$3,500** with sheath. Bottom: Will & Finck dirk knife or push dagger; walrus ivory handle, nickel silver sheath. Value **$4,000.** Both circa 1896. Courtesy Calif. Historical Society.

The Civil War

A decade after the Gold Rush, with the start of the Civil War, demand surged again for bowie knives. They had long been popular in the South, and this inspired some southern politicians, particularly Governor Joseph E. Brown of Georgia, to order large quantities of massive locally made bowie knives, often with "D-guards," for issue to Confederate troops and home guards. In the field, the troops found those big weapons not merely useless, but an actual encumbrance, and threw them away.

Officers and men on both sides of the conflict often carried conventional sized bowie knives and dirks (small daggers). Most of these were cheap and gaudy Sheffield knives, because only senior officers could afford the $10 to $300 for a made-to-order bowie from an American cutler or surgical instrument maker.

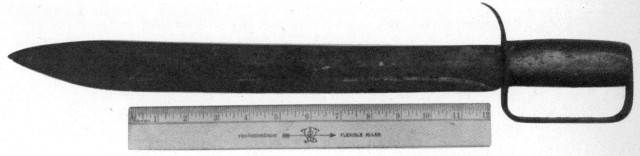

Unmarked Georgia-type D-guard bowie, 20¾" over all; wood handle, steel guard. Value **$250**. Courtesy Bill Adams.

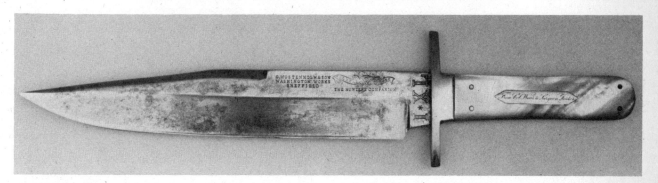

Large clip point Wostenholm bowie presented by a Civil War colonel to an Army surgeon. Pearl handles. Value **$1,200**. Courtesy Bob Macon.

Decline and Revivals

After the Civil War, the bowie knife and the percussion pistols it accompanied were rendered obsolete as everyday sidearms by the centerfire metallic pistol cartridge. This reliable, quick-loading, waterproof ammunition had first appeared around 1866, but the Colt Single Action Army revolver, introduced for it in 1872, made it really popular.

Since it was no longer required to back up cap and ball pistols, the bowie knife quietly faded away. Its soul, nonetheless, lived on.

It was transmigrated first into the factory-made bowie-style "hunting knife" which, though of doubtful utility, was virtually unchallenged in popularity until the turn of the century [see *American Hunting Knives*]. Then, in the 1940s, the bowie evolved into the Government Issue utility knife [see *U.S. Military Fixed Blade Knives*]. Most recently, the bowie knife, in new versions of its most classic forms, has been reincarnated as an art form.

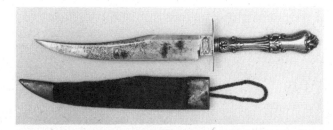

Clip point bowie marked TILLOTSON/COLUMBIA PLACE/ SHEFFIELD. Etched eagle. Nickel silver "cutlery" handle filled with cement. Value **$300** (as is **$200**). Courtesy Bob Macon.

Typical small Sheffield dirk. Value **$75** (plain) to **$250** (decorated and etched), with sheath.

AMERICAN BOWIE KNIFE MAKERS AND DEALERS

Notes: Firms or individuals marked "?" may have made or sold bowie knives, but I have never seen examples.

S.I.M. = Surgical Instrument Maker. A cutler or S.I.M. made knives to order. A cutlery manufacturer made knives for wholesale distribution.

MIDDLE ATLANTIC

EASTERN PENNSYLVANIA
Schively, Philadelphia, 17??–c1875; Cutlers & S.I.M.s (see separate chart)
J. English & Huber, Philadelphia, c1840s; Dealers?
? John Ashmore, Philadelphia, c1844; Cutler (Dealer?)
Clarenbach & Herder (L. Herder & Son), Philadelphia, 1847–present; Scissors & Table Cutlery Mfr.

MARYLAND and DISTRICT OF COLUMBIA
? Samuel Ball, Baltimore, c1796–c1830; Cutler
Samuel Jackson, Baltimore, c1833–c1870; Cutler & S.I.M.
? Benjamin Daffin, Baltimore, c1835–?; Cutler (Dealer?)
Charles C. Reinhardt, Baltimore, c1837–1869; Cutler & S.I.M.
Thomas Lamb, Washington City, c1840; Cutler & S.I.M.

NEW YORK
Peter Rose, New York, c1820s–1845; Cutler & S.I.M.
? George Tiemann, New York, 1826–1868; S.I.M. (He was American born, lived 1795–1868. Firm still exists.)
William R. Goulding, New York, c1830–1845; Cutler & S.I.M.
Gravely & Wreaks, New York, c1830–1837; Cutlery Importer (Dealer)
Alfred Hunter, New York, c1830–1835 (then to Newark, New Jersey); Cutler
? R.P. Lathrop, succeeded by James Martin, Albany; 1832–c1880, S.I.M.s
John D. Chevalier, New York, c1835–1872; Cutler & S.I.M.
John C. Nixon & Son, New York, c1830s–1864; Cutlers
? George W. Nixon, New York, 1864–c1870s; Cutler
Otto & Koehler, New York, c1857; Cutlers & S.I.M.s

NEW JERSEY
Rochus Heinisch, Newark, 1825–1914; Scissors Mfr. (bowies 1860s)
Alfred Hunter, Newark, c1835–1865 (ex-N.Y.C.); Cutler
? John Garside, Newark, c1850; Table Cutlery Mfr.

Schively, Philadelphia
The oldest Philadelphia directory I have seen is from 1785. It lists:
  John Schively, Cutler and Instrument Maker, Third between Chesnut and Walnut
  Henry Schively, Cutler, Chesnut between Third and Fourth.

The next directory I have seen is 1791:
  Elizabeth Schively, widow, 14 No. Sixth Street.
  Henry Schively, Cutler, 58 S. Third Street.
1793: Henry Schively, Cutler & Surgeon's Instrument Maker, 49 & 60 S. Third Street.
1794: Henry Schively, Cutler & Surgeon's Instrument Maker, 49 S. Third Street.
No change until 1810:
  Henry Schively, Cutler & Surgeon's Instrument Maker, 49 S. Third Street.
  Henry Schively, junior, Cutler, 45 Chesnut Street.
No change until 1813:
  Henry Schively, Cutler & Surgeon's Instrument Maker, 45 Chesnut Street.
1814: Henry Schively, Cutler & Surgeon's Instrument Maker, 25 Carter's Alley & 45 Chesnut Street.
1816: Henry Schively, Cutler & Surgeon's Instrument Maker, 75 Chesnut Street.
No change until c1840:
  H. Schively, Surgical Instrument Maker, 64 S. 8th.
No change until 1847:
  H. Schively, Surgical Instrument Maker, 64 S. 8th.
  George Schively, "   "   "   ".
  Charles Schively, "   "   "   ".
  In 1849, Henry Schively, Jr., retired, leaving the business in the hands of his sons, George and Charles. They carried it on until at least the 1870s.

NEW ENGLAND

MASSACHUSETTS
Henry Harrington, Southbridge, 1818–1876; Cutler
Ames Mfr. Co., Chicopee and Cabotville, c1829–1900; Sword & Cutlery Mfr. (*see U.S. Military Fixed Blade Knives*)
John Russell & Co., Greenfield, 1834–1870; Turners Falls, 1870–1933; Table and Kitchen Cutlery Mfr. (Now merged with Harrington in Southbridge.)
Lamson & Goodnow, Shelburne Falls, 1844–present; Table and Kitchen Cutlery Mfr.
? South River Cutlery Co., Conway, c1851–1856; Table Cutlery Mfr.
Hassam (Brothers), Boston, c1853–1872; Dealers
Buck Brothers, Worcester, 1853–1864; Millbury, 1864–19??; Edge Tool Mfrs.
W. M. Cotton, Leominster, c1860s; Cutler (?)
C. Roby, Chelmsford, c1860s; Sword Mfr.

CONNECTICUT

Collins & Co., Hartford (Collinsville), 1826– 1966; Axe and Machete Mfr.

? Pratt Ropes (Webb) & Co., Meriden, 1845–1855; Table Cutlery Mfr. (became Meriden Cutlery Co., 1855)

H. Wilkinson, Hartford, c1860s; Cutler (Dealer?)

? Lathrop & Barton, West Winsted, ?–1880; Table Cutlery Mfr.

RHODE ISLAND

John M. Schmid, Providence, 1857–1871; Cutler & S.I.M.

? J. M. Schmid & Son (Albert), Providence, 1871–1964; Dealers

SOUTH (information from Cecil Anderson and Bill Adams)

TENNESSEE

Samuel Bell, Knoxville, 1819–1852 (then to Texas); Silversmith, Cutler, first Mayor.

R. Alldeon, Memphis, c1860; Cutler

Leech & Rigdon, Memphis (later Columbus, Miss.), 1860s

LOUISIANA

Daniel Searles, Baton Rouge, c1830s; Gunsmith, Cutler also in Ball's Bluff, Alabama

? Thomas A. Potts, New Orleans, c1838; Cutler?

Alfred H. Dufilho, Sr., New Orleans, 1853–c1878; Cutler & S.I.M. (Born Paris, France, 1833; died 1907)

Cook & Bros., New Orleans, c1860

ALABAMA

James Conning, Mobile, 1840–1871; Importer (Dealer) and Sword Mfr.

T. L. Pruett, Prattville, c1861

Alexander McKinstry, Mobile, c1861; Dealer

SOUTH CAROLINA

Charles Heinz, Columbia, 1841–c1855 (then to Atlanta); Gunsmith

Courtney, Tennent & Co., Charleston, c1856–1864; Importer (Dealer)

GEORGIA

William J. McElroy, Macon, c1846–1888; Tinsmith

Daniel C. Hodgkins & Son(s), Macon, c1860; Cutlers

Etowah Iron Works (Mark A. Cooper), Etowah, c1860s; Ironworks

Bell & Davis, Atlanta, c1861

VIRGINIA

? Hiram Peabody, Richmond, c1850s–60s; Dealer

Burger & Bros., Richmond, c1860s; Sawmakers, Cutlers

Lan & Sherman, Richmond, c1861; Cutlers

? Clarkson & Co., Richmond, c1861; Dealers?

MISSISSIPPI

Rees Fitzpatrick, Natchez, c1861; Gunsmith

G.W. Stalans, Jonesboro, c1861

MISSOURI

? August Kern, Saint Louis, c1850s, Cutler (Dealer?)

WEST

WESTERN PENNSYLVANIA

Bown & Tetley, Pittsburgh, c1848–1871; Cutlers

OHIO

Marks & Rees, Cincinnati, c1840s; Cutlers

Andrew G. Hicks, Cleveland, c1846; Cutler (see *U.S. Military Fixed Blade Knives*)

UTAH TERRITORY

? William Walker, Salt Lake City, c1851; Cutler

CALIFORNIA

San Francisco makers and dealers:

  ? Justinian Caire, 1851–1897; Importer (Dealer)

  Hugh McConnell, 1852–1863; Cutler & S.I.M.

  ? Henry Bayley, 1852–1858; S.I.M.

  John W. Tucker, c1854; Jeweler (dealer)

  Frederick Kesmodel, c1856–1867; Cutler & S.I.M.

  Michael Price, c1856–1889; Cutler & S.I.M.

  Jacob H. Schintz, c1860–1906; Cutler & S.I.M.

  Will & Finck, 1863–1905 (-1932); Cutlers & S.I.M.s

  Rau & Kohnke, 1871–1875; Cutlers

  Rau & Todt, 1875–1880; Cutlers

  John Todt, 1880–1915; Cutler

  Nathan Joseph & Co., 1875–1894; Importer (Dealer)

  Michael J. Hayes (& Son), 1887–1901; Cutlers

? "Uncle Billy" Allison, Yolo County, c1850s; Cutler

? Frank Schilling (& Son), San Jose, 1862–present; Gunsmith, Cutler & S.I.M.

Fred Watson, Colusa, c1890; Cutler

Above: 19th century artist's view of
17th century Indian trade, from *Chatterbox*, a children's magazine.

Right: One consequence of the trade,
from a 19th century school history.

American Indian Trade Knives

CONTEMPORARY collectors seem to have a passion for everything to do with early-day American Indians. This collector interest includes both Indian-made objects of every type, and also industrially-manufactured objects that were traded to the Indians.

Indian-made knives were for the most part of stone, such as flint or obsidian. Stone knives are a large and specialized field unto themselves. Both lack of space and my own lack of knowledge prevent my dealing with them here. This chapter is limited to manufactured steel-bladed trade knives.

At this time there seems to be more collector interest in Indian trade knives than in Indian-made knives. At least, the trade knives command higher prices from collectors, just as they once did from the Indians. However the Indians paid a premium for trade knives because they worked best, while collectors pay more for them because they are rare.

The trade knives that collectors seek do not have to have provable Indian association. They only have to be the *types* of knives known to have been traded. This is because the documentation of purported Indian trade objects sold in the collecting marketplace is both difficult to verify and easy to fake.

The only documentation that can generally be trusted is that accompanying museum objects collected by anthropologists or dug up by archaeologists. These objects are rarely sold. Knowledgeable collectors rightly tend to discount any other documentation, in favor of a close study of the objects themselves.

Collectors, then, are seeking (and paying high prices for) European and American knives that were either used by Indians, actually traded to Indians, or of the types that are believed to have been traded to Indians. Controversy arises because history tells us that just about every type of knife there is, or at least every type of fixed blade knife, falls into one or more of these categories.

Knives Used by Indians

From the time of their first contact with European explorers, traders, and settlers, American Indians were eager to trade for, buy, or steal knives with steel blades. Indeed, Indians were perfectly happy to acquire *any* type of knife with a steel blade.

It is well known that certain patterns of knife were made especially (though never exclusively) for the Indian trade. It is also well known that, given a choice, particular groups of Indians preferred particular types of knives.

However, the fact remains, both in historical records and in the results of countless archaeological digs, that the Indians of any particular place or period used just about every type of knife (not to mention reworked swords and steel tools) that they could get their hands on, regardless of shape, age, condition, or original purpose.

The only knives Indians seem to have avoided was folding knives. They were hard on their knives, and a folding knife carelessly used is likely to maim the user. Folders were dangerous and impractical for them. If they acquired one and did not break it right away, their inclination was either to fix it so the blade could not close, or to use the blade or blades in some other tool.

Dinner Knives

One of the commonest sorts of knives in excavated post-contact Indian sites is the humble dinner knife. The plainest ones were cheap and serviceable, and shipped in large quantities to frontier settlements.

Dinner knives were plentiful: a white household would have perhaps a dozen for every larger knife it owned. White

LAMSON & GOODNOW MFG. CO./PATENTED MARCH 6, 1860 table cutlery with pinned iron bolsters. Similarly marked knives were recovered from the steam boat *Bertrand* which sank in the Missouri River on its way to Fort Benton, Montana Territory, in 1865. Value **$35 each.**

A 19th century ink eraser. Value **$5–10.**

people generally discarded dinner knives long before they were worn out, either to get new ones that were not misshapen from frequent polishing, or to upgrade their table settings in style or quality.

To an Indian, however, a worn or unfashionable dinner knife was still a perfectly serviceable tool. In fact, many are of higher quality than standard "Indian trade" knives.

Peaceable Indians traded for new low quality dinner knives (and good used ones) because they were cheap. Their more warlike brethren stole dinner knives from settlements or emigrant wagons that they raided, simply because they were useful and there for the taking. They took every other type of knife and steel tool as well, even ink eraser knives, the blades of which made superb arrow heads. Dinner knives, however, were by far the most common.

Does this mean that Indian knife collectors have lots of dinner knives in their collections? No, it does not. It is nearly impossible to prove that a particular dinner knife was used by Indians, and it is safe to assume that most were not. Even heavily-worn ones should not be assumed to be Indian, because poor people of every color used (and use) a worn knife in preference to none at all.

More to the point—to the collectors who are spending the money—a dinner knife, even one with proven Indian association, does not have much romantic allure. All of the collectors I have known will pay far more for a trade-*type* dag or butcher knife that was never near an Indian than for an undistinguished worn down dinner knife that was used for years by one. As far as I am concerned, it is their money and their hobby and their privilege to buy what they like.

Fakes

All areas of knife collecting are subject to fakery, but none more so than Indian knives. As many fake Remington, Winchester, and Case pocketknives as there are, those fakes are still only a small percentage of the genuine ones. In my experience, by contrast, the large majority of purported Indian knives are fakes of one sort or another.

Indian knife fanciers, like all other collectors, are subject to the usual perils of over-zealous "restoration," counterfeiting, and out-and-out fantasy. The most common form of Indian knife fakery, however, and usually the most difficult to detect, particularly for the over-eager collector, is false attribution.

Most "fake" Indian knives are in fact genuine old knives. What makes them fakes is that the decoration, or the sheath, or the context they are placed in, or alleged to have been found in—that is, the factors that would make them Indian—are fake.

A beaded or tack-work sheath from the plains might be genuine (though I understand that large numbers of these sheaths were made on the reservations in this century for sale to collectors), but the odds are high that the knife in it is not the knife it was made for. An unadorned old knife worn down to shapelessness might be Indian or "primitive" frontier, but it is far more likely that it is not.

There is no sure way for the collector of Indian knives to protect himself from the artful faker. However, the more he knows about the history of knife design and knife manufacturing technology, the less likely he is to be burned.

He must learn to distinguish the uneven tapered tang of a forged butcher knife blade from the parallel sided tang of a blade ground from sheet steel, a technique first used on cheap knives about 1870, and nearly universal by about 1940. He must learn to distinguish etched maker's marks (first used in the 1880s) from stamped ones. He must learn to distinguish the color and surface texture of old cast steel and shear steel from those of more modern steels. He must learn to recognize and interpret dozens of such seemingly minor details.

Most of all, the collector must accept that it is inevitable that he will make mistakes. Through eagerness or misplaced trust he will buy some pieces that are wrong. Through excessive caution he may pass up other pieces that prove to be genuine. Neither event is catastrophic. What *is* catastrophic for a collection, and sadly common as well, is for a collector to refuse to recognize his mistakes, but instead to go out and repeat them over and over again.

Trade-Type Knives

As I mentioned above, there are a number of styles of knives that were made primarily for trade to the Indians. These knives are valuable to collectors whether or not they have any Indian association. Mint examples command a hefty premium, just as mint knives do in other areas of collecting.

Contemporary illustrations of Indian trade knives are scarce (and at least as valuable as the knives themselves). Information about trade knives can be gleaned from old paintings and photographs, from the account books of traders, from actual knives collected in the 19th century, and from archaeological sites.

In the rest of this chapter, I illustrate and price the better known styles of knives that were made primarily for trade to the Indians, as well as a few ordinary styles that were often used as trade goods. Besides these trade knives, Indians used lots of bowie knives, butcher knives, and dinner knives. If you are interested in Indian knives, you should consult those sections of this book, as well.

Both Indians and frontiersmen often re-worked broken swords for use as knives or daggers. Therefore, a good sword reference book such as Harold Peterson's *American Swords* can be useful to the collector of Indian knives.

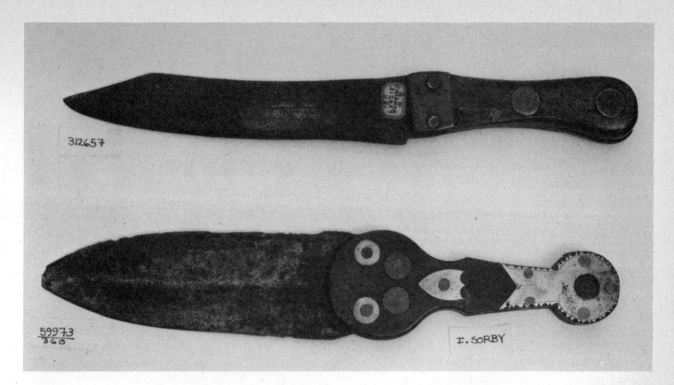

312657

59973
360

I. SORBY

1. (Above, upper) Sheffield Trade Butcher Knife.
About 13 inches over all. Very heavy clip point steel blade. Handle scales of wood or horn. Brass or iron rivets and pinned-on bolsters. Example shown marked JUKES COULSON STOKES & CO./SHEFFIELD (not a manufacturer, but a firm of factors who specialized in trade goods). Early 19th century. Value **$750.** Courtesy Smithsonian Institution.

2. (Above, lower) Sheffield Trade Dag with factory handle.
About 13 inches over all. Wide light-weight double-edged steel blade. Flat horn handle scales with inlaid brass decorations. Example shown marked I. SORBY (John Sorby, who was Master of the Sheffield Cutlers' Guild in 1806. Mark in use circa 1790–1827). Value **$1,500.** Courtesy Smithsonian Institution.

The Museum of the Fur Trade in Chadron, Nebraska, has an example by I. & H. SORBY (John and Henry Sorby. Henry was John's son. Mark used after 1827). This dag has brass handle inlays in the form of stylized pelts. Value **$2,000.**

3. (Right) Sheffield Trade Dag, blade only (as usually shipped).
About 6-inch (not including tang) flat ground double-edged steel blade. Two notches allow it to be lashed to a handle for use as a dagger, lance, or war club blade. Also used as Confederate guard spontoons. Example shown marked JUKES COULSON/STOKES & CO. Mid-19th century. Value **$500.** Courtesy Donald Euing.

4. American Trade Dagger Blade with added handle.
About 6-inch light-weight double-edged blade with push
tang. Example shown is marked SIDNEY R. BAXTER &
CO./BOSTON. Its added cylindrical pine (?) handle has a
cross deeply carved in the butt. Circa 1860s. Value **$250.**
Courtesy Donald Euing.

5. French Trade Butcher Knife.
About 10½ inches over all. Flat forged steel blade with
semi-tang. African ebony handle. Steel rivets with brass
burrs. Example shown marked PICHON & LENFESTY/VIC-
TORIA B.C. 19th century. Value **$250.** Courtesy Theo.
Fisher.

Most French butcher knives have been made in this
shape for about two centuries. The ebony handle and the
British Columbia (Canada) markings indicate that this example is a Northwest trade knife. Ordinary French butcher
knives have beechwood handles and are worth **$5–10.** The
first bowie knives made for the Bowie brothers were also
this general shape.

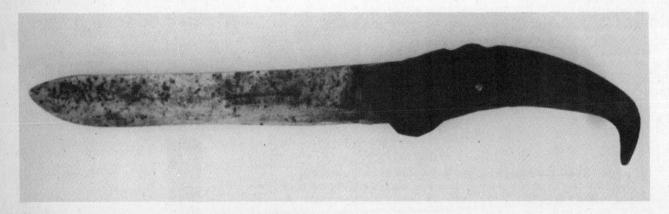

**6. American Trade Butcher Knife Blade with added
handle.**
6-inch forged steel blade with semi-tang. Example shown
marked LAMSON GOODNOW & CO./ S. [Shelburne]
FALLS WORKS, that firm's earliest mark, dating circa
1844–1855. Added horn handle secured by iron and brass
rivets. Value **$150** as shown. Courtesy Donald Euing.

7. Light Butcher-style American "Hunting Knives" of a type often traded.

Light forged blade 5–10 inches long. Acute clip point. Co-cobolo handles secured with steel or brass pins.

Examples shown (above and right) marked J. RUSSELL & CO./GREEN RIVER WORKS. Earliest (c1835–1875) Russell stamping has tiny letters, no diamond trademark. Value with that mark **$150**; with later stamped or deep etched mark **$35**; with recent surface electro-etched mark **$10**.

Stamped LAMSON GOODNOW & CO./S. FALLS WORKS (earliest mark: c1844–1855); value **$150**. Stamped LAMSON & GOODNOW MFG. CO./S. FALLS WORKS (1855–c1870) **$120**. Lamson & Goodnow with stamped anchor or USA map trademark, **$35**; with surface etched mark, **$10**.

Many variations were offered. Ebony handles: **add $10.** Checkered handles: **add $20.** Flat steel bolsters: **add $20.** Fancy cast pewter bolster(s): **add $35.** Cross-guard: **add $65.** Integral forged bolster and cap: **add $100.** Stag or ivory handles: **add $50.**

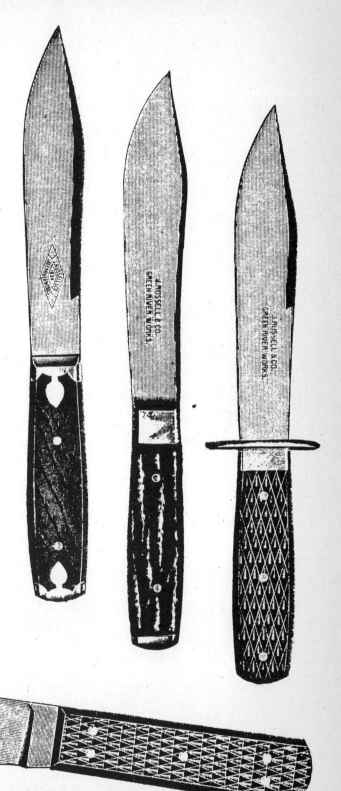

8. Heavy Butcher-style American "Hunting Knife" of a type often traded.

Heavy tapering forged blade 5–10 inches long. Checkered ebony handle scales. I have seen examples by James Ames, J. Russell & Co., and Lamson & Goodnow. Examples with early stamped marks, value **$250.** Later style marks, value **$75.** Stag handles: **add $25.**

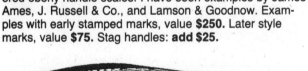

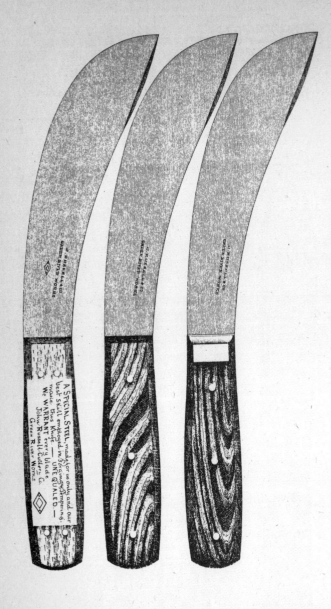

9. American Butcher-style Skinning Knives of a type sometimes traded.
5–7 inch forged steel blade. Pinned wooden handles. Sometimes have flat steel bolsters. See Number 7 for markings and values.

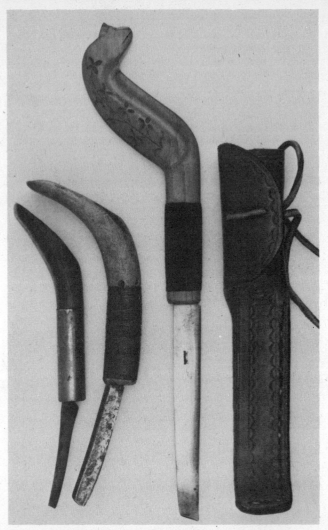

10. Northwestern U.S. and Canada. Crooked Knife.
   About 9 inches overall. Handle of wood, bone, or antler, sometimes with metal ferrule. May have leather sheath. 18th–20th centuries. First two examples locally made from "recycled" blades circa 1900–1920. Value **$75**. Third example made in England circa 1930, value **$100**.
   Northwestern Indian or Eskimo man's knife for canoe or wood carving. Held blade downward with thumb in rest. Similar "carver's hook" has no thumb rest and is usually made in Italy.

11. Arctic North America and Greenland. Ooloo.
   Up to 6-inch wide blade. Handle usually bone or walrus ivory. Older knives often lack narrow tang. 18th–20th centuries. Example shown circa 1960s. Value **$20**. Older examples much more valuable.
   Eskimo woman's seal skin scraping knife. Similar knives used throughout Eskimo regions of the Arctic. Do not confuse with similar food chopping knives used elsewhere. Courtesy Eiler R. Cook.

**Indian
Trade
Knives**

The 19th century hunter, whether
Indian, frontiersman, or dude, carried
his knife and other gear in his
hunting bag, as shown in these period
illustrations from a school history
book (top) and a children's magazine
(bottom).

**American
Hunting
Knives**

American Hunting Knives

Background

AN AMERICAN hunting knife is a stout stiff-bladed fixed blade knife normally sold with a fitted sheath. Most modern hunting knives are equipped with a small finger guard. Although the sheath knife in one form or another has been with us since the dawn of history, the American hunting knife is a recent creation that first appeared a little over a century ago.

In point of fact, the term "hunting knife" started out in the early 19th century as a synonym for "bowie knife," long before what we now call hunting knives had been invented. In addition, butcher knives small enough for convenient field use were sometimes called "hunting knives" (see *American Indian Trade Knives*). The term "hunting knife" was also applied then, as it still is now, to big folding knives.

Unlike pocket knives, butcher knives, and earlier sheath knives, the American hunting knife, as we now know it, is not intended for ordinary daily wear and use. It is a sports-man's knife intended for leisure-time pursuits. We wear our hunting knives in the field when we go hunting, fishing, or camping out.

Hunting in America

The American hunting knife is the sporting knife of the ordinary middle-class American. It reflects a social revolution in this country that is so profound yet so familiar that most of us are not aware of it.

In much of the Old World until very recently, the only people who could hunt legally were aristocrats who owned large estates. Anyone else who hunted was a poacher, a criminal. Aristocrats hunted for pleasure. Poachers hunted for food, either for themselves or to sell, often at the risk of their lives.

In America in the early days, so much of the country was wilderness and game was so abundant that anyone who wanted to could hunt. Wealthy rural landowners had brought with them from Europe the sport of hunting for pleasure. Poor people brought with them (or learned from the Indians) the skills of hunting to fill the larder. In the new free country, there were few restrictions on what and where one could hunt.

To the middle-class American of the mid-19th century, the upwardly-mobile skilled workman, clerk, merchant, or professional, hunting had two bad associations. On the one hand, hunting was a sport of self-styled aristocrats. He did not like aristocrats or anything about them, though his wife and daughters might have wished that he would become one.

On the other hand, hunting was one of the harsh necessities of survival in the rural world he recently had left. If he had grown up on a farm, as most Americans did in the 19th century, he might have enjoyed hunting on the lucky occasions when the weather was mild and game was plentiful. However, poor farm boys had to hunt often, in good weather and bad. When game was scarce, they had no choice but to spend longer hours hunting, no matter how cold and wet and miserable they were. The pressure of necessity can spoil your taste for almost anything.

Of course, after our successful American had lived in town

J. Russell butcher-style hunting knife from Russell's 1884 catalog; diamond mark, checkered ebony handle, cast pewter bolster, value $100 [see *American Indian Trade Knives*].

for a few years, or maybe a generation or two, the country life began to acquire a romantic aura. He forgot the cold and the wet, and that most of the time he had hunted barefoot in the only shirt and britches that he owned. What he remembered was the clean air, the sense of freedom, and that perfect buck he might have shot if only he had had a repeating rifle.

The Outdoor Revolution

Here is where we get our social revolution. This is the beginning of hunting as a middle-class sport, a uniquely American phenomenon.

These townsmen and city men returned to the country to hunt, not because they had to, as their parents had to, and as many of them had to as boys. They went strictly for sport, to recapture the best feelings of their youth, or of their fathers' and grandfathers' stories.

These men did not go out to hunt as New World aristocrats, with jumping horses and packs of dogs, or with an army of beaters driving birds and animals to them. They hunted like country boys, usually on foot, alone or with some friends, with a few dogs and maybe a pack horse. They went as country boys made good, with all the fine gear they ever had dreamed about: waterproof boots, a warm coat, a Winchester rifle or a Remington shotgun and, of course, a hunting knife.

The new popularity of hunting as a sport was only one facet of the outdoor revolution of the late 19th and early 20th centuries. The Boy Scouts, the Girl Scouts, and the Campfire Girls were all established around 1910 [see *Utility and Scout Knives*]. The National Park Service was established in 1916 to manage the nation's nine public recreation wilderness areas, eight of which had been created since 1890.

The American Hunting Knife

The American hunting knife was a new home-reared variety. It was a cross between the bowie knife, which was primarily a weapon, and the butcher knives used by frontiersmen, farmers, and Indians for skinning and butchering game.

What distinguishes a hunting knife from bowie knives and other combat knives is that a hunting knife is intended for peaceful camp use. It is for skinning and cutting up game, slicing bacon, and chopping kindling.

However, a hunting knife is not merely a butcher knife—old time trappers, market hunters, and Indians used small butcher knives, and sometimes butchers' skinning knives. These light-weight inexpensive knives were only rarely carried in belt sheaths, from which they might easily be lost. They were carried either in the hunting bag or under the shirt on a string worn around the neck [see *Indian Trade Knives*].

A sportsman's hunting knife is stouter than a butcher knife. It has a more solid handle, often designed for good looks as much as for practicality. The hunting knife is sold with a fitted belt sheath. It costs two to ten times as much as a butcher knife of the same size.

Bowie-Style Hunting Knives

The bowie knife as a sidearm was a great fad beginning around 1830. In the era of percussion firearms, which are imperfect at best, it was a vital backup weapon. However, with the advent of reliable cartridge ammunition in the 1870s and 1880s, the bowie knife as backup became superfluous in most situations.

Still the bowie was the knife the American townsman thought of carrying when he went out to challenge the fields and streams. In consequence, most of the commercial hunting knives sold here in the last decades of the 19th century look like clip point (or occasionally spear point) bowies, complete with a wide blade and a double cross guard. This style of "hunting knife" remained popular through the 1920s, though not among serious sportsmen. It is still made, and I doubt that it will ever disappear entirely.

Bowie-style hunting knives are not practical tools. As butcher knives they are too big and thick. As brush knives they are barely big enough. I suspect they appealed to the city boys' dime novel fantasies about fighting a ferocious grizzly bear and saving the rancher's daughter.

It is not very difficult to learn to distinguish post-circa-1880 bowie-style hunting knives from real 1830s–1870s bowies. One telling characteristic is the shape of the handle. Most of these later hunting knives have straight-sided handles that taper toward the end. I have yet to see this handle shape on an early bowie knife.

Another indication of a later hunting knife is a cross-guard with ball-shaped ends. This is not common, but when it is present, it usually signifies early to mid-20th century manufacture.

Yet another useful clue, when it is present, is the construction of the original sheath. Every hunting knife in the bowie style that I have seen was sold with an all-leather sheath. As a rule, these are flat, two-piece, stitched leather sheaths, not very different from inexpensive modern sheaths. Some are one-piece leather sheaths stitched up the back.

By contrast, the *original* sheaths of just about all real bowie knives were *not* made simply of leather. The standard Sheffield sheath was a thin morocco-like leather veneer, often colored and gold stamped, glued over a pasteboard body and reinforced with a metal throat and tip. Of course these original sheaths rapidly wore out, and were sometimes replaced by more modern leather sheaths.

American and better quality Sheffield bowies might have solid leather in place of the veneer for the body of the sheath, but the metal ends were still present. The best American sheaths, and an occasional English one, were solid metal, sometimes with a leather frog (belt hanger) or even a leather over-sheath.

Usually, the best evidence for recognizing a bowie-style hunting knife is the markings. For example, any bowie-style knife by Landers Frary & Clark (often marked L. F. & C. or UNIVERSAL) was made after about 1890. Evidently, quite a few L. F. & C. knives were sold to boys joining up for World War I, but I have yet to learn if they were allowed to take these knives overseas.

J. Russell Green River Works bowie-style knives with either an etched trademark or a diamond in the trademark were made after about 1880. Although they were advertised as "bowie knives" up into the 1910s, they were made after the bowie knife era had ended, and should be considered hunting knives.

Knives made by or for the Bridgeport Gun Implement Company date from the 1880s and after. Many of their blades were imported.

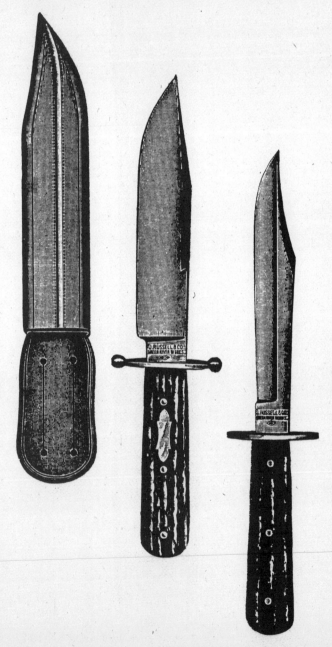

J. Russell bowie-style hunting knives circa 1900, made with 5, 6, 7, 8, 9-inch blades; standard sheath.

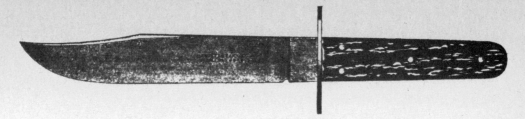

Imitation Stag Handle Hunting Knife, 6-inch Blade, Metal Guard, with Russet Leather Sheath

Stag Handle Hunting Knife. Heavy 6-inch Blade. Heavy Metal Guard, with Russet Leather Sheath

CLIP BLADE.

SPEAR POINT BLADE.
HUNTING KNIVES.
Buckhorn handles, solid bolster, solid leather sheath, heavy
blades, 6½ inch, - - - - - - - $1.25 each.

Above and below: L. F. & C. hunting knives from the 1910s.
(Below courtesy Louis Boswell and *Knife World*)

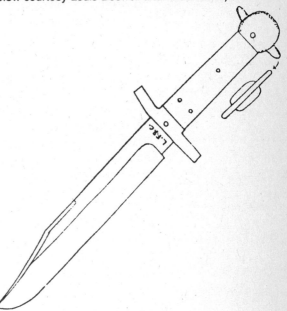

American bowie-style HUNTING KNIVES.
 Value in excellent condition, without sheath.

Russell with stag handles: **$400.**
 [also see *Indian Trade Knives*]
Landers Frary & Clark (L. F. & C.), heavy
 blade, stag handle, solid cast guard: **$150.**
[ditto] with skull-crusher pommel: **$250.**
Landers Frary & Clark (Universal), light blade,
 rough black celluloid handle, flat guard: **$75.**
Winchester: **$500+.** Keen Kutter: **$125.**
Gelston (sold by Orvis circa 1892): **$100.**

WINCHESTER (right)
 It is an odd footnote to cutlery history that the *only* style of
hunting knife ever sold by Winchester was the bowie style,
offered in the early 1920s. The only marking on these knives
is the Winchester trademark *etched* down on the bevel of the
blade. These knives are rare and worth at least **$500** in ex-
cellent condition.

HUNTING KNIVES

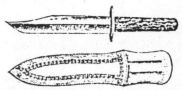

High carbon
steel saber clip
swaged blade,
highly tempered
and polished,
glazed finish.
Scale tang stag
handle. Three
nickeled pins. Nickel silver guard. Complete with
russet embossed leather sheath.

No.	Blade Length	Approx. Wgt. Per Dozen Lbs.
1981	5 in.	4¾
1982	6 in.	5

One-half Dozen in a Carton.

Brideport Gun Implement Co
Hartley & Graham 1889 Catalog of Guns Ammunition
Page 53

No. 501 Clip

Hunting Knives and Leather Sheaths

Fine imported blades rubber stag handles

No.	4"	5"	6"	7"	8"	9"	
501	$8	$10	$12	$14	$16	$18	per doz.

Fine rubber checkered grip handles

No.	4"	5"	6"	7"	8"	9"	
521	$12	$14	$16	$18	$20	$22	per doz.

Bridgeport Gun Implement Co. knives from an 1889 Hartley & Graham, New York City, sporting goods catalog. Current value **$300 each**. Courtesy M. H. Cole and *Knife World*.

Any Sheffield knife marked ENGLAND was made after 1891, so it is too recent to be a true bowie. Several Sheffield brands of bowie-style knife were made only in this later period, and these knives are still surprisingly common.

The most common later Sheffield brand is Joseph Allen & Sons (NON-XLL). This firm was in business circa 1886–1947.

Another common Sheffield brand is Alfred Williams. I do not know this firm's exact dates, but it was active from the late 1890s to at least 1918. Its knives were imported by A. Kastor & Bros. of New York, and usually bear their EBRO trademark.

Sheffield bowie-style HUNTING KNIVES (straight handle and/or ENGLAND in marking). Jigged bone handles. Blade up to 7 inches long. Value in excellent condition without sheath.

Pearl handles: **add 100–150%**
Genuine stag handles: **add 20%**
Embossed composition handles: **subtract 10%**
Plain composition handles: **subtract 30%**
Blade over 7 inches: **add 35%**
Original sheath: **add 20%**

Joseph Allen (NON-XLL): **$35.**
Alfred Williams (EBRO): **$35.**
Challenge: **$40.**
Joseph Rodgers: **$50.**
George Wostenholm (I*XL): **$60.**
Joseph Elliot: **$40.**
Slater Brothers (Venture): **$45.**

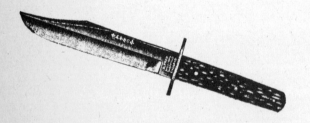

English knives marked CHALLENGE, a trademark of the New York import firm Wiebush & Hilger, are also from this latter period. However, many important English firms, including Wostenholm, Rodgers, Slater Brothers, and Joseph Elliot, made both real bowie knives and also later bowie-style hunting knives.

Any German made or marked knife in the "bowie" style is a hunting knife from after the mid-1880s. Most are from after the First World War.

German bowie-style HUNTING KNIVES (see *Pocketknife Brand List* for ratings). Original sheath: **add 20%**

High (e.g. Henckels): **$75.**
Medium (e.g. Wingen): **$35.**
Low (e.g. Richartz): **$15.**

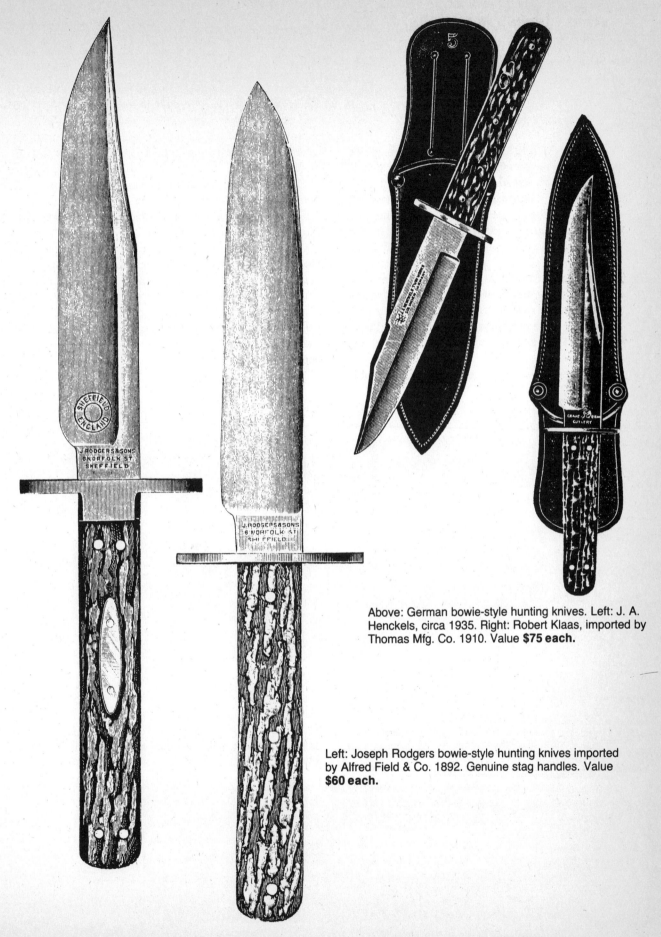

Above: German bowie-style hunting knives. Left: J. A. Henckels, circa 1935. Right: Robert Klaas, imported by Thomas Mfg. Co. 1910. Value **$75 each.**

Left: Joseph Rodgers bowie-style hunting knives imported by Alfred Field & Co. 1892. Genuine stag handles. Value **$60 each.**

The First American Hunting Knives

True American hunting knives, practical camp or skinning sheath knives designed for the prosperous sportsman and man of leisure, seem first to have been made in San Francisco in about the late 1860s or early 1870s. They were expensive hand-made knives, some of them custom-made, or as the term was then, "made to order."

In my first book, in 1978, I wrote that the Knifemakers of Old San Francisco (that's the title) "made the most exotic, the most costly, and perhaps the most beautiful knives ever produced in the United States." Their knives have more recently been equalled in these regards, and perhaps even surpassed [see *Custom and Hand-Made Fixed Blade Knives*], but their place in history as design pioneers remains secure.

San Francisco around 1870 was a logical place for the hunting knife to appear. The city was energetic and wealthy. Many of the residents had braved the hardships of the round-the-horn passage, the overland trek from Missouri, the gold mines of central California, or the silver mines of Nevada. Now free of the necessity, many San Franciscans and other California townsmen were still keen outdoorsmen by choice.

The climate and situation of northern California were ideal for hunting, fishing, and camping out. For 7 months of the year they could be sure of mild weather and no rain. From San Francisco, an hour by boat to the north or east, or an hour on horseback to the south, brought one to the edge of unbroken miles of wild forest and field. A leisurely half-day train ride would bring one to the heart of the Sierra Nevada mountains.

Those successful Californians wanted the best of everything, at home and in the field. It was for them that Michael Price, Will & Finck, John Todt, and the others made California hunting knives.

California camp and hunting knives clearly show their mixed parentage. In profile they look like butcher knives. In heft and handle material they resemble bowies. An innovative feature on most of them is the sharp false edge. It is not as sharp or as acute as the false edge on a bowie, because it is not meant for stabbing. It is designed for chopping wood and animal bones. This feature has been used on many later hunting knives.

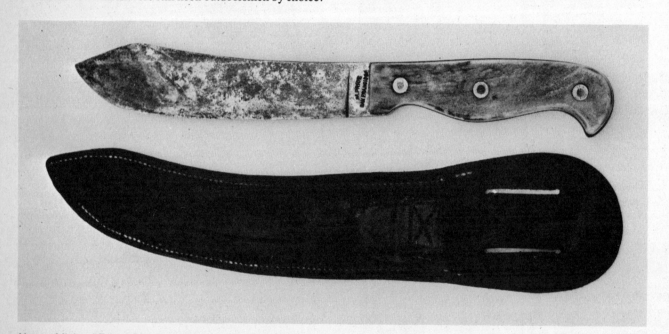

Above: Michael Price, San Francisco, classic California hunting knife with sheath. Circa 1870s–1880s. Elk antler handles. Value **$600**. Courtesy Donald Euing. Similar knife with walrus ivory handles, value **$800**.

Below: John Todt, San Francisco, hunter's skinning knife with elk handles. Value **$450**. Courtesy Doug Royal.

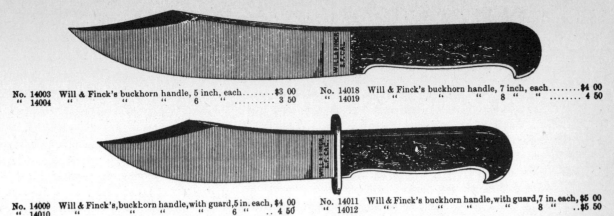

No. 14003   Will & Finck's buckhorn handle, 5 inch, each........$3 00
" 14004   "   "   "   6   " 3 50

No. 14018   Will & Finck's buckhorn handle, 7 inch, each........$4 00
" 14019   "   "   "   8   "   " 4 50

No. 14009   Will & Finck's, buckhorn handle, with guard, 5 in. each, $4 00
" 14010   "   "   "   "   6   " .. 4 50

No. 14011   Will & Finck's buckhorn handle, with guard, 7 in. each, $5 00
" 14012   "   "   "   "   8   " ..$5 50

Will & Finck, San Francisco, California hunting knives with elk handles, from their 1896 mail order catalog. Current value range: **$500** (small, without guard) to **$2,000** (large, with guard). Courtesy California Historical Society.

The Abercrombie & Fitch Special

Toward the end of the 19th century, a novel style of factory-made hunting knife appeared on the scene. In their catalogs, the famous New York City sportsman's outfitter, Abercrombie & Fitch (established 1892), took credit for its design. Authentic A. & F. Specials were manufactured by J. Russell & Company in two sizes, 4½-inch blade and 6-inch blade. The A. & F. design was never patented, so other cutlery firms made similar knives and other retailers sold them.

These knives have one-piece checkered ebony handles with integral pommels. The pommels are thistle shaped, which suggests that the design is a "modern" utilitarian interpretation of the Scottish dirk [see *Foreign Exotic, Primitive, and Historical Fixed Blade Knives*]. The fact that so many of these knives that I have seen were made in Sheffield, suggests that the design might actually have originated in Britain.

Whatever its origin, this Abercrombie & Fitch Special must stand as one of the first mass-produced American sheath knives designed exclusively for hunting as a sport. Its vogue seems to have lasted only until about the middle 1910s, by which time it had been surpassed and supplanted by the even more practical Marble's knives, and their many imitators.

ABERCROMBIE & FITCH SPECIALS Value in excellent condition; without sheath: Original drop-in sheath: **add 20%**
Russell 6-inch marked "Abercrombie & Fitch:" **$120.**
Russell 4½-inch marked "Abercrombie & Fitch:" **$100.**
Russell not marked "Abercrombie & Fitch:" **$75–85.**
Other American: maker **$75**
Rodgers or Wostenholm: **$65.**
Other English maker: **$40.**
German maker: **$30–60.**

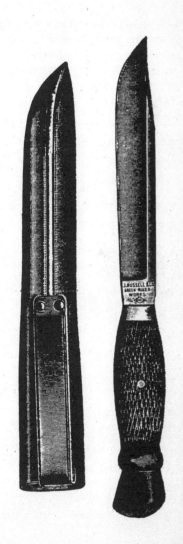

Webster L. Marble and Marble's Knives and Axes

The knifemakers of old San Francisco sold their camp and hunting knives mainly to California sportsmen. Abercrombie & Fitch, in their early years, sold mainly to New Yorkers. It took a Michigan sportsman with an inventive turn of mind to bring the sportsman's hunting knife to the rest of the United States. His name was Webster L. Marble.

Webster Marble was born into a prosperous manufacturing family in Wisconsin in 1854. The family soon moved to Vassar, Michigan, then to Traverse City on an arm of Lake Michigan. His father taught him outdoor skills, hunting, fishing, trapping. As a young man, he became a timber cruiser and surveyor.

Never satisfied with existing methods and equipment, Marble experimented with new and practical designs. In 1898 he built a small factory in Gladstone, Michigan, to manufacture the waterproof match box and the safety pocket axe that he had invented.

The following year Marble took in a partner named Frank H. Van Cleve and they began to advertise their products in national outdoors magazines. In 1901 they introduced their first hunting knife, the Ideal. In 1902 they added a folding hunter, invented by Milton H. Rowland, that combined the virtues of the Ideal with those of their folding safety axe.

More knife designs and phenomenal success followed rapidly. I have reproduced here the cutlery pages from Marble's 1908 catalog (see pages 337–342). These explain in Marble's own words the principles of his designs. Note the Special (No. 57) which is Marble's version of the M. Price hunting knife.

The pocketknives shown in this catalog, with the exception of the Safety Hunting Knife, were contract knives. By design and by pattern numbering, they appear to have been made by Case Brothers of Little Valley, New York. A few patterns were also imported from Germany. The pocketknives were offered from about 1902 to 1908.

Marble's was the first knife company to bring the stacked leather washer handle into widespread use and acceptance in the United States. I do not know the origin of this handle construction, but the oldest examples I have seen were knives and machetes made by Collins & Company, of Connecticut, possibly as early as the 1870s.

In this catalog, Marble's stated that they planned to replace the crown stag knife "handle tips" with lignum vitae. In fact they switched instead to an aluminum alloy, with crown stag still offered as a more costly option. (Continued on page 342)

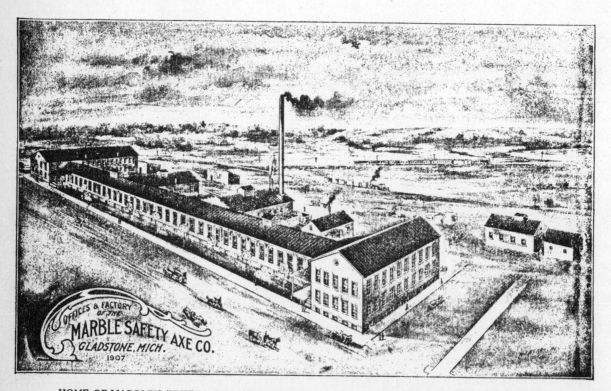

HOME OF MARBLE'S "EXTRA QUALITY" SPECIALTIES MADE BY SPORTSMEN FOR SPORTSMEN

The business was established in 1899. The amount of business has been greatly increased each year over the preceding year. The factory has been running day and night during the summer, and at the time of issuing this catalog (September 1, 1908) it is expected that it will continue to do so for an indefinite period. A large export business is done and Marble Specialties are known and used in nearly every country. Advertisements are carried all the year round in twenty to thirty magazines. In 1907 and 1908 nearly one million catalogs were distributed. Lieutenant Peary carried a full equipment of Marble Specialties on his last two trips in quest of the North Pole.

Safety Axe with Folding Pick

This tool is indispensable to every mountaineer, prospector, miner, and geologist. It means three tools in one and those just the tools one must have if an expedition is to be even a moderate success.

The pick can be securely and instantly locked either up or down. It will stand unlimited service and will be found handy when climbing. When folded the axe head can be safely used as a hammer. The Safety Axe is "the handiest tool a sportsman ever carried."

The pick is attached only to the No. 2, 20-ounce Axe. Order as follows:

No. 2-P prepaid $4.00

Safety Axe with Folding Nail Claw

"Couldn't be improved upon," has been the universal opinion of users of the Marble Safety Axe, but now Mr. Marble himself has accepted the implied challenge and "made good." The nail claw doubles the value of the axe and adds only 25c to its cost. It is strong enough to pull a ten-penny nail from a seasoned hemlock plank. One can get at and pull a nail with the axe blade and claw that could not be removed with a hammer alone.

The Claw is furnished only on the No. 2 Safety Axe. Order as follows:

No. 2½, prepaid $2.75

Leather and Canvas Axe Sheaths

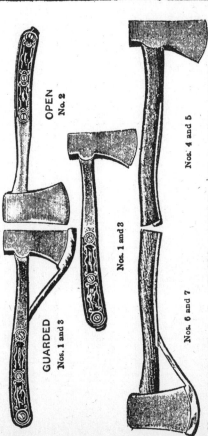

All Marble Safety Axes can be carried in hip or side pocket, or we will furnish handsome leather case, or leather bound, 10-ounce canvas case, suitable for attaching to any size belt. The long sheaths are made open at the bottom so that axe may be pushed up by the end of handle. Beautifully hand embossed and carved when ordered.

Colors: Orange or Black, as desired.

No. 19—Leather Sheath, full length, postpaid...... $1.00   Carved...... $2.25
No. 20—Leather Sheath, half length, postpaid...... .75   Carved...... 1.75
No. 21—Canvas Sheath, full length, postpaid...... .35

5

Marble's Safety Pocket Axes

Richard Harding Davis, the famous author and war corresponden., in an article entitled, "Kits and Outfits" in the April, 1903, "Scribner's Magazine," says, "The best axe I have seen is the Marble Safety Axe, made at Gladstone, Mich. You can carry it in your hip pocket and you can cut down a tree with it."

In camp it serves all the purposes of an axe, hatchet and hammer. A perfect axe for "blazing," clearing a trail, setting a tent, and as necessary in the woods as a gun or knife. Caught far from camp at nightfall the hunter can in a few moments provide himself with shelter and a bed of boughs and the fire-wood necessary to make himself comfortable for the night.

There are now over 100,000 of them in the hands of satisfied users.

Construction

The nickel-plated guard is lined with lead and is hinged on a spring in such a manner that either open or closed it is firmly held in position. The blades are of finest tool steel and are fully guaranteed. The metal handles are nickel-plated and side plates are of engraved black hard rubber. The wood handles are of selected hickory with steel lined groove and folding guard nickel plated.

OPEN
No. 2

GUARDED
Nos. 1 and 3

Nos. 1 and 3

Nos. 6 and 7

Nos. 4 and 5

No. 1—Weight, 16 oz.	Length, 10 in.	Solid Steel Blade. 2⅛ in. x 3⅞ in.	$2.50
No. 2—Weight, 20 oz.	Length, 11 in.	Solid Steel Blade. 2⅜ in. x 4 in.	2.50
No. 3—Weight, 27 oz.	Length, 12 in.	Solid Steel Blade. 2½ in. x 4⅜ in.	3.00
No. 4—Weight, 24 oz.	Length, 12 in.	Solid Steel Blade. 2¾ in. x 4¾ in.	1.75
No. 5—Weight, 16 oz.	Length, 11 in.	Solid Steel Blade. 2½ in. x 4½ in.	1.50
No. 6—Weight, 20 oz.	Length, 12 in.	Welded Steel Bit. 2⅞ in. x 4¾ in.	1.50
No. 7—Weight, 14 oz.	Length, 11 in.	Welded Steel Bit. 2⅜ in. x 4¼ in.	1.50

Wood handle complete with lining and guard, 50c.
Return old guard and lining, only, for credit, 20c.
Rubber handle plate 20c. State if left or right side.
Send drawing of part wanted if possible.

The Wellman Arctic Expedition was fully equipped with our Specialties.

Marble's Sharpening Stone

We have had this stone made to our order to meet the demand of those who desire a small stone for all-round use. It cuts tempered steel very rapidly and produces a fine smooth edge.

No. 31—Price, postpaid..............25c

Size, 3½x¾x1⅝ inches.

Don't fail to read—

Concerning Hunting Knives

Every knife described in this catalog is made from the finest cutlery steel, and the greatest possible care is taken in tempering and testing it. No matter which one of the varied assortment you may select, you are going to possess the most perfect knife that can be produced by the combination of the best material and skill that money can buy. We fully guarantee each knife.

Handle Construction

The "Leather handle" knives are made of leather washers, trimmings of brass and colored hard fibre washers and a brass bolster. The parts are all a driving fit on the tang and are held in place by a half-inch brass nut countersunk into the end of the tip. The nut engages with the threaded end of tang.

The "Stag handle" knives are of same construction as the Leather handle knives, except that the center is composed of two grooved slabs of selected German stag horn riveted together and driven on the tang.

The "Cocobolo handle" knives are constructed tho same as the Leather and Stag handle knives, except that the center is made of one piece of cocobolo mortised to closely fit the tang. This wood is harder and lighter in color than Rosewood, and makes the most handsome handle of all.

The "Rubber handle" knives are made of one piece of engraved black hard rubber with German silver bolster. The handle is mortised to closely fit the tang and is held in place by a nut as explained above. This handle is considered by some to be superior to any other.

This cut shows construction of Leather Handle Knives:

Marble's Trailmaker Knife. Will not be made before 1909. Blade, 10 inches. Handle, 5 inches. Weight, 13 ounces. Price, $5.00.

We have never made this knife, but if we get a sufficient number of orders before July 1909, to warrant us in doing so we will put it on the market then

6

Notice—Concerning Knife Handle Tips

The tips of all our Ideal and Canoe leather handle knives and Expert knives will be made of Lignumvitæ. We were forced to find some other material than stag horn on account of the growing scarcity of the kind suitable for tips. After testing many different materials with unsatisfactory results we have finally hit upon Lignumvitæ, which we guarantee to be equal if not superior to stag horn in every way. Lignumvitæ is the material of which bowling and croquet balls are made; is the hardest and toughest wood known and takes a beautiful and lasting polish.

Tube Sheath with Aluminum Sheath Protector

We are now furnishing, without additional cost, an Aluminum Sheath Protector and the regular tube sheath, shown above, with every Marble Hunting Knife. Orange sheath will be sent unless Black is asked for.

No. 33. Extra Sheath Protector, prepaid..............15c
No. 34. Extra Tube Sheath, in sizes for blades up to 8 inches, prepaid.....50c

Hilt Knife Sheath

This sheath is the style furnished free with our knives with hilt.

No. 39. Extra Hilt Knife Sheath, in sizes for blades up to 8 inches, prepaid. .50c

Marble's Canoe Knife

Some of the prominent canoeists of the country requested that we make a knife for their use. This knife was designed and has their approval. It is "short and stout." Not furnished with hilt.

Blade 4½ inches. Handle, 3¾ inches. Weight with sheath, 5 ounces.

No. 52.   No. 51 has leather handle.

No. 51—Leather handle, prepaid................$2.25
No. 52—Stag handle, prepaid....................2.75

7

For the "old-timer."

Marble's "Expert" Hunting Knives

These knives were particularly designed to meet the requirements of the professional hunter, trapper and guide who requires a thin, keen edge for dressing skins and furs. The back of the blade is designed for scraping skins while on the forms.

They will stand almost unlimited service for the purpose intended, but are not recommended for such general and heavy work as the Ideal and Special knives and should not be used for prying, opening tin cans or chopping bones.

No. 545.—5-inch blade, prepaid.....$2.25   No. 556.—6-inch blade, prepaid......$2.50

Cocobolo Handle.
READ PAGES 6 and 7.

5-in. blade

Marble's Special Hunting Knife
READ PAGES 6 and 7.

Stewart Edward White, the noted writer and authority on all matters pertaining to woodcraft, carried one of our knives, similar to this, on a six months' trip in the Northwest. Although subjected to the severest usage during the entire trip, he brought the knife home in good condition; the only sharpening it received being an occasional stropping on his boot.

The blades are bevel ground and have bone chopper at back of point. The tang is of same thickness as back of blade and two oblong recesses are forged in both sides of it. These reduce the weight of the handle and make the knife balance perfectly. Side plates are of selected slabs of German stag horn.

These knives were expressly designed to secure the greatest possible strength, together with the fewest parts obtainable in hunting knife construction. They are pronounced by many expert woodsmen to be the acme of perfection, for an all-round knife.

Made with 5-inch blade only.   No. 57—Prepaid, $2.50

9

Marble's Ideal Hunting Knife

Knives with a record

This was the first knife designed by Mr. Marble and on account of its quality, combination of several excellent features and beauty of design and finish, has won for us a world-wide reputation for exactly meeting the requirements of the users of hunting knives.

The blade is adapted to sticking and skinning. It is oval-ground at back of point for chopping bones and other hard substances.

No. 41, Leather handle Ideal. Sheath shown on page 7.

No. 45, Leather handle Ideal. ("Ideal Hilt Knife.") Sheath shown on page 7.

No. 42, Stag handle Ideal. (With Hilt, this is No. 46.)

No. 43, Rubber handle Ideal. (With Hilt, this is No. 47.)

Handle No. 41 or 45.			Handle No. 42 or 46.		
Blade 5-inch, prepaid.......$2.25			Blade 5-inch, prepaid........$2.75		
" 6- " " 2.50			" 6- " " 3.00		
" 7- " " 2.75			" 7- " " 3.25		
" 8- " " 3.00			" 8- " " 3.50		
			Handle No 43 or 47. Blade 6-inch only.............3.00		

Tube Sheath and Protector furnished with each knife

6-inch Ideal Sectional view.

Haines Model Hunting Knife

This knife was designed by Mr. Ashley A. Haines of Salmon Arm, B. C., a well known authority on firearms, ballistics and sporting equipment. Its shape, "hang," and "feel" make it desirable for all purposes. We are not marketing this knife, but if we should get a sufficient number of orders before July, 1909, to warrant us in doing so we will put it on the market then.

It would be made with an engraved rubber handle, with or without hilt, and would sell, with sheath, for $2.50. If interested, send us your name, now.

8

Marble's Safety Fish Knife

(Dotted lines show blade folded within folding handle.)

The blade is made sharp at back of point for ripping and the back is an excellent fish scaler. It is a good all-round pocket knife for sportsmen, ranchmen and stockmen.

As shown by the dotted lines the blade, when folded, is entirely protected by the unique, but simply constructed and operated handle. When open it is as safe and rigid as a one-piece knife.

No. 78—4 inch blade, German silver handle, postpaid.............$1.25

Marble's Safety Carver.

Combines novelty and utility to a remarkable degree. We may justly describe it as an "eight-inch pocket-knife," for when folded it is absolutely safe the entire length of the blade and occupies a space of only 5-16 inches thick by 8 inches long. It weighs only 4 ounces.

The blade is of razor steel. The U shaped handle sections are of German Silver, heavily reinforced at end where blade bears on them. When open the knife is as rigid as a one-piece knife. Boiling water cannot injure this handle.

The knife may be quickly and easily closed by pushing back the clasp, grasping the sides of the blade with one hand and with the other pulling the outer handle down and back; then the blade is folded and the clasp pushed over it.

Many western guides use this knife and all claim it fills to perfection a long felt want.

Open, ⅓ Size.

Folded, ⅓ Size.

No. 76—Blade, 8-inches. Weight, 4 ounces...........$1.25

Dear Sir:—The Rear Sight came all O. K. Fabious, N. Y., April 10, 1905. It is much ahead of the rear sight, even at the same price, and when used with your Improved Front Sight and Savage Rifle, it is perfection. Truly yours, NEWEL ROWLEY.

11

A knife approved by Dall DeWeese must be good.

Marble's "De Weese" Knife

READ PAGES 6 and 7.

Cross Section of Blade

This hunting knife was designed by Mr. Dall De Weese, of Canon City, Colorado, one of the most successful big game hunters in the United States. The fact that Mr. De Weese uses a knife of this pattern on his expeditions after big game, where every item of the outfit has to be figured down to the lightest and most compact form possible, is a sufficient guaranty of its utility.

It has a dull saw back on which the thumb is placed when skinning, or cutting hard substances. When sticking, the little finger should be doubled up, letting the end of handle rest against it. This takes the place of a hilt.

Length of blade, 4 inches; length of handle, 3¼ inches; weight, with full leather sheath, 4 ounces.

No. 62—German stag horn handle, prepaid. $1.75

Marble's Skinning Knife

This knife is of the same high-grade material and workmanship as our other knives. It is made on the most approved pattern and is beautifully finished. No. 66. Handle of German stag. Blade 5 inches; weight 5 ounces. With leather tube sheath, prepaid...........$1.50

Marble's Camp Carver

Many of the people who are using these knives have told us that they are so superior to any carvers they have ever been able to buy that they are using them at home in place of the ones in their high-priced carving sets.

They are very valuable around camp, where the long thin blade of superior temper is particularly desirable for slicing meats, bread, vegetables, etc.

Every camping outfit and home should contain one of these handsome knives.

No. 74—Handle of German stag. Blade 8 inches; prepaid...........$1.50

Furnished with orange leather tube sheath at 50 cents extra.

10

Marble's Pocket-Knives

Knowing that the many thousands of sportsmen we annually supply with outfits consider *quality* of supreme importance and price only an incident, we offer a line of pocket-knives that are just as perfect in every detail of material and workmanship as it is possible to produce anywhere at any price. In fact, we could not produce anything better than this line at ten times the price. The blades are hand-forged by experts of many years of experience. These men are the descendants of many generations of knife-blade forgers.

Should a knife prove defective we will cheerfully replace it free of charge.

All knives have German silver bolsters and brass linings, except when stated differently. The blades of the Pearl Handle knives are very highly polished.

No. 8250 and 5250.

No. 8250. One 2⅜ and one 1⅞ inch blade, Pearl handle..........$4.00
No. 5250. Same blades, but Genuine Stag handle..................2.00

An excellent knife for heavy work.

Nos. 5347 and 8347.

No. 5347. One 2⅝ and two 2-inch blades. Genuine Stag handle...$1.75
No. 8347. Same blades, pearl handle.....$3.00

A very popular knife with ranchmen, stockmen and sportsmen.

No. 5111.

No. 5111. One 3½-inch blade. Spring lock. Genuine Stag handle. Price....................$1.50

No. 5294.

No. 5294. One 3 inch and one 2¼ inch blade. Genuine Stag handle Price.............$1.50

13

Marble's Safety Saw

Folds Like Carver

Open, ⅔ size

This tool is folded and constructed the same as the Safety Carver, except that the blade, when folded, is held in place by an inside clasp.

On account of being so safe, light and easy to carry, this saw is invaluable to all people who go into the woods and especially so to the student of forestry and botany.

No. 77.—8 inches, 4 ounces, prepaid..........................$1.00

Marble's Safety Hunting Knife

These knives will appeal especially to that class of woodsmen and sportsmen who object to a sheath knife, and yet want a knife that is heavy, strong and rigid. However, we furnish with each knife a sheath to fit it when folded, so that it can be carried at the belt when desired.

They have a long blade with a short handle—utilizing the extension guard as a safety lock when the knife is open. The guard as well as blade is held in position by a spring, when either open or closed. The blades have bone chopper at back of point. The hilts—one on each side of the blade—and the bolsters and linings are of German silver. Side plates are of engraved black hard rubber.

All parts are hand fitted with the utmost care, so that when knife is open it is as rigid as a one-piece knife.

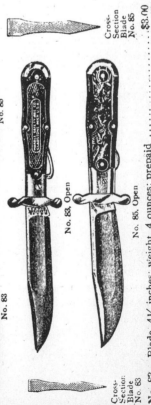

Cross-Section Blade No. 83

No. 83

No. 83, Open

No. 85, Open

No. 85

Cross-Section Blade No. 85

No. 83.—Blade, 4¼ inches; weight, 4 ounces; prepaid $3.00
No. 85.—Blade, 5 inches; weight, 6 ounces; prepaid.............4.00

Option of German stag handle plates at 50 cts. extra per knife, Pearl handles, double price. Ivory handles, 50 per cent. additional.

12

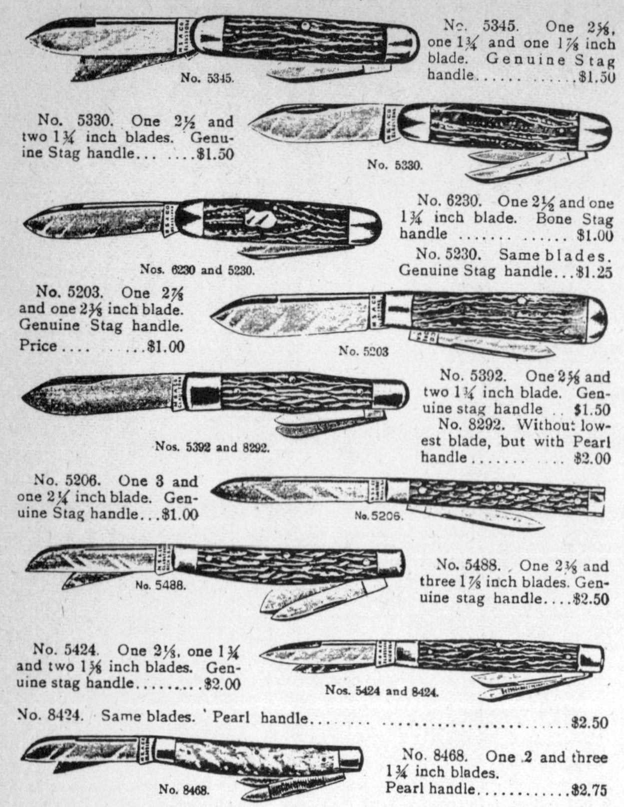

Marble's Pocket-Knives

(Continued)

No. 5345.
No. 5330.
Nos. 6230 and 5230.
No. 5203
Nos. 5392 and 8292.
No. 5206.
No. 5488.
Nos. 5424 and 8424.
No. 8468.

No. 5345. One 2⅝, one 1¾ and one 1⅞ inch blade. Genuine Stag handle............$1.50

No. 5330. One 2½ and two 1¾ inch blades. Genuine Stag handle........$1.50

No. 6230. One 2⅛ and one 1¾ inch blade. Bone Stag handle $1.00
No. 5230. Same blades. Genuine Stag handle...$1.25

No. 5203. One 2⅞ and one 2⅜ inch blade. Genuine Stag handle. Price..........$1.00

No. 5392. One 2⅝ and two 1¾ inch blade. Genuine stag handle .. $1.50
No. 8292. Without lowest blade, but with Pearl handle.......... $2.00

No. 5206. One 3 and one 2¼ inch blade. Genuine Stag handle...$1.00

No. 5488. One 2⅜ and three 1⅞ inch blades. Genuine stag handle....$2.50

No. 5424. One 2⅛, one 1¾ and two 1⅜ inch blades. Genuine stag handle.........$2.00

No. 8424. Same blades. Pearl handle..............................$2.50

No. 8468. One 2 and three 1¾ inch blades. Pearl handle............$2.75

14

Not shown in the 1908 catalog are several important Marble's knives that came later. One was the Woodcraft, whose design was patented in 1916. Another was the Sport knife, a smaller version of the Expert, introduced about 1930. Ideals with 4¼-inch blades were introduced after World War I, in place of the Canoe, which was dropped.

MARBLE'S WOODCRAFT KNIFE

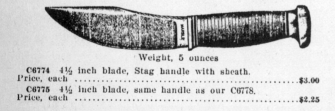

Weight, 5 ounces

C6774 4½ inch blade, Stag handle with sheath. Price, each $3.00
C6775 4½ inch blade, same handle as our C6778. Price, each $2.25

In 1930, Webster Marble died at the age of 76. The company he had founded continued to thrive, but it had faced increasingly stiff competition since the early 1920s. None of the competitors ever quite matched Marble's in quality, but most offered lower prices.

In the 1930s, some Woodcraft and Sport knives were made as Official Boy Scout and Girl Scout knives. Also in the 1930s, Marble's introduced the Outer's Knife and the Outdoor knife. Both of these were light-weight inexpensive knives with integral hilts. The Outer's had jigged bone slab handles while the Outdoor had a one-piece wooden handle.

Current values of MARBLE'S knives and axes in excellent unsharpened condition. (This price chart was compiled with the assistance of Bill Lung, a leading collector of Marble's material.)

AXES:
Examples marked M.S.A.: **add 25%**

First Type (head secured by screw): **$350–400.**

Second Type (as illustrated in the catalog pages):

1. **$250.**	2½. **$300.**	5. **$200.**
2. **$250.**	3. **$250.**	6. **$175.**
2-P. **$300.**	4. **$200.**	7. **$175.**

Third Type (squarer butt, 2 screws per handle):
2. **$150.** 3. **$150.**

M.S.A. AND MARBLE'S SHEATH KNIVES:
Knife prices are without sheath.
Original sheath: **add 25%**
Examples marked M.S.A. CO.: **add 25%**

Ideal: Blade Length:	5″-6″	7″-8″
Stag handle Ideal:	**$175.**	**$200–250.**
Leather with stag butt:	**$100.**	**$150–175.**
Leather with aluminum butt:	**$75.**	**$125–150.**
Rubber handle Ideal:	**$200.**	**X**

Notes: After 1942, all Ideals had double hilts; hilt does not affect value. Later 4¼″ Ideal valued the same as 5″.

Yacht Knife (a light drop-point Ideal): 5½″ blade.
Stag handle Yacht Knife: **$175.** (rare)
Leather with stag butt: **$125.** (rare)

Canoe: 4½″ blade.
Stag handle Canoe: **$175.** (rare)
Leather with stag butt: **$125.** (rare)

Expert: 5″ or 6″ blade.
Cocobolo handle Expert: **$100.**
Leather handle Expert: **$80.**
Stag handle Expert (post-WWII): **$65.**

Trailmaker: 10″ blade, leather handle.
Stag butt Trailmaker: **$225.**
Aluminum butt Trailmaker: **$200.**

Haines: 6″ blade.
Stag handle Haines: **$200.** (rare)
Rubber handle Haines: **$300.** (rare)

Special: 5″ blade.
Stag handle Special: **$200.**

Dall DeWeese: 4″ blade.
Stag handle DeWeese: **$350.**

Skinning: 5″ blade.
Stag handle Skinning: **$125.**

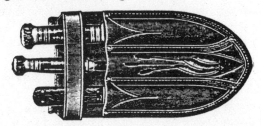

Coquina Outfit: includes 1 Ideal, 1 Skinning, 1 leather or stag handled Sharpening Steel, in a 3-pocket sheath. Named for "Coquina" (pen name of G. O. Shields, editor of *Shield's Magazine*). Value: **$1,000+**.
Sharpening Steel only: Stag: **$100**
    Leather: **$75.**

Camp Carver: 8″ blade.
Stag handle Camp Carver: **$125.**

Camp or Kitchen Knife: 6″, 7″, 8″
Wood handle, with guard: **$100.**

No. 79—2½-inch blade.

No. 80—2½-inch blade.

No. 81—3½-inch blade.

Handy Fish Knife: 2″ blade.
Wood handle, nickel silver fish: **$100.**

MARBLE'S NEW TROUT KNIFE

Trout Knife: 5⅝″.
All steel: **$50.**

Woodcraft: 4½″ blade
Stag handle Woodcraft: **$150.**
Leather with stag butt: **$75.**
Leather with aluminum butt: **$65.**
ditto, Official Boy Scout: **$175.** (rare)

Sport Knife: 4″ blade.
Leather with aluminum butt: **$65.**
ditto, Official Boy Scout: **$175.**
ditto, Official Girl Scout: **$175.** (rare)

Outers: 4″ blade.
Bone stag handle Outers: **$90.**

Outdoor: 4½″ blade.
Wood handle Outdoor: **$75.**

Marble's Safety Folding Knives

SAFETY HUNTING KNIFE:
Pre-World War I: Swell-center; thong hole in extension guard; lobed folding hilt. M.S.A.CO.

Blade length:	4¼″	5″
Rubber handles, name in ribbon:	**$700.**	**$800.**
Rubber handles, name in panel:	**$700.**	**$800.**
ditto, plain bolsters:	**$600.**	**$800.**
Stag handles:	**$700.**	**$700.**
ditto, plain bolsters:	**$600.**	**$800.**
Pearl or ivory handles:	**$900.**	**$1,000.**

Post-World War I: Regular jack; nail nick in extension guard; straight folding hilt. MARBLE'S.
Stag handles: **$500.**   **$600.**

"Safety Hunting"—
Stag Horn Handle

METAL HANDLED SAFETY KNIVES:
Safety Carver: **$200.**
Safety Fish Knife: **$125.**
Safety Saw: **$200.**

Other 20th Century American Hunting Knives

I have yet to discover the reason, but established cutlery manufacturers in the United States were very slow to enter into competition with Marble's in the manufacture of sport hunting knives. For example, of the sixteen firms listed as suppliers of "hunting knives" in the 1912 *Sporting Goods Trade Directory*, Marble's was the only one, so far as I know, that then made modern style hunting knives.* Indeed, I have seen no evidence of any firm besides Marble's making what we would now call a hunting knife before the end of World War I. One writer asserts that Case first made hunting knives in 1903, but she offers no evidence. Maybe knife companies believed that the hunting knife was a fad which would soon die out, the way American car makers viewed compact cars in the 1950s.

Although cutlery firms remained wary of the sport hunting knife market before about 1920, custom makers were not so shy. Following in the tradition of the American cutlers and surgical instrument makers of the 19th century [see *Bowie Knives*], a few early 20th century makers offered their own versions of the hunting knife to sportsmen and retail dealers. Best known of the early 20th century makers was William Scagel, who made his first hunting knife in 1903. [See *Pioneers of Modern Hand-Made Knives*.]

* The firms listed were:

Billings & Spencer, inventor of the butterfly knife [see *Foreign Exotic, . . . Folding Knives*].
H. Boker & Company (maker of folding hunters).
Colclesser Bros., Eldorado, Pa. (no information).
Alfred Field & Company (importer of bowie-style).
A. Kastor & Brothers (importer of bowie-style).
R. C. Kruschke, Duluth, Minn. (no information).
Landers Frary & Clark (maker of bowie-style).
Marble's.
William Mills & Son, New York (wholesaler?).
Northfield Knife Co. (maker of folding hunters).
Jno. Russell Cutlery Co. (maker of bowie-style).
Smith & Hemenway Co. (wholesaler).
Edw. K. Tryon Co. (wholesale and retail).
U. J. Ulery Co. (wholesaler).
Wiebusch & Hilger (importer of bowie-style).
Wilkinson Shear & Cutlery Co., Reading Pa. (no info.).

Eight of these firms were also listed under "sportsmen's knives." That category also included:
Abbey & Imbrie (fishing tackle wholesale).
Goodell Co. (kitchen cutlery manufacturer).

The Ellery Hunter

I know of only one American commercial sport hunting knife design created outside of Gladstone, Michigan, between 1900 and about 1920. This was the Ellery Hunter.

The Ellery Hunter is a modified butcher's skinning knife with a black self-guard wooden handle. It was sold with a fitted sheath.

The Ellery Hunter was designed by William Ellery, a San Francisco sporting goods retailer and expedition outfitter in business from 1909 to 1933. He secured a patent on the design in 1916 (the same year the Marble's Woodcraft design was patented), but he had already been selling the knife for several years. An article in *Outing* magazine of June, 1913, (excerpted on pages 14–16 of the May 1983 *Knife World*) extols the virtues of the design.

Ellery Hunters were made on contract. Before 1917 and after about 1920, they were made in Solingen by J. A. Henckels. In the war years they were made by Union Cutlery Company of Olean, New York (I have seen one of these made for E. C. Simmons, Keen Kutter). In the 1930s, Henckels included the Ellery Hunter as part of its regular American line.

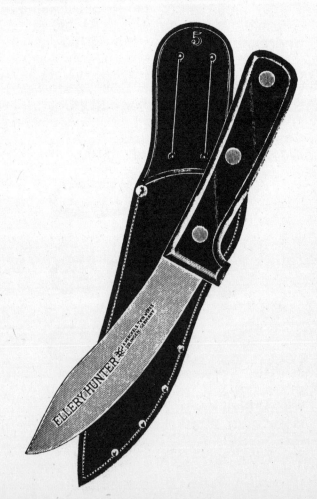

Ellery Hunter from a 1930s Henckels catalog. Values:
Henckels: **$60.**   Union: **$70.**   Keen Kutter: **$60.**
Original sheath: **add 20%.**

Wade & Butcher

There is not enough evidence to tell which cutlery firm was the first to challenge Marble's near monopoly of the American sport hunting knife market after World War I. A likely candidate for first, and certainly one of the first, was a Sheffield firm, Wade & Butcher.

Wade & Butcher's predecessor firm, William & Samuel Butcher, founded in 1819, was one of the first Sheffield firms to cash in on the bowie knife bonanza back in the 1830s and 1840s. Since that time, Wade & Butcher's main business, at least their main export to the United States, had been straight razors.

The First World War introduced a whole generation of young men to the convenience of the safety razor. The demand for straight razors plummeted, so Wade & Butcher needed a new product to sell in America. The hunting knife was it.

Two types of English-made hunting knife in the American style were put on the market here in 1918. One type was exact copies of the 5-inch, 6-inch, and 7-inch Marble's Ideals that cost 10% *more* than the originals. They had leather washer handles and stag pommels. The other type had a bowie-style blade and hilt attached to a Marble's style handle.

MARBLE PATTERN

No. 350

Marble pattern blade, forged from best quality razor steel, brass guard, laminated leather handle, stag tip, with leather sheath.

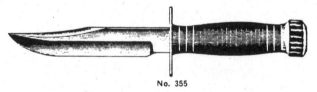

No. 355

Regular clip blade, forged from best quality razor steel, brass guard, laminated leather handle, stag tip, with leather sheath.

I am not certain that those two knives were made by Wade & Butcher, but the "Boone" and the "Teddy," first put on the market in about 1921, definitely were. The 4-inch bladed Boone, though not an exact copy of the 4½-inch bladed Marble's Woodcraft, was clearly inspired by it. Thanks in part to the tariff, the Boone cost nearly 50% more than the Woodcraft.

The Teddy is the same pattern as the Boone, but it cost about ⅓ *more*. It cost so much ($4.35 retail) because it was the first stainless steel hunting knife ever put on the market.

Stainless steel was invented in 1914 by two men working independently: Harry Brearley in England and Elwood Haynes in Kokomo, Indiana. Rather than battle each other in court, the two inventors formed a corporation to hold their patents jointly and license them to steel-makers. The first

"MANITOU"

A knife with real backbone. Made in England, from the finest razor steel, hand tempered, tested and honed to a keen edge. Oval ground at back of point for chopping bones and other hard substances. Laminated leather handle with red hard fiber and brass washers. Flush aluminum tip. With heavy leather riveted case.

C6750 5 in. blade. Wt. 7 oz.
Price, each ....$3.25 net
C6751 6 in. blade. Wt. 8 oz.
Price, each .... 3.50 net
C6751A 7 in. blade. Wt. 9 oz.
Price, each .... 3.75 net
C6751B. 8 in. blade. Wt. 10 oz.
Price, each .... 4.00 net

"TEDDY"

Made of the famous patented "Firth Sterling Stainless Steel" that resists corrosion by salt air or rain. Blade, 4¾ in. Handle of variegated segments of richly colored leather, brass and bakelite, nickel silver hilt and polished aluminum head.

C6752 Price, each ....$4.35 net

English steel-maker to secure a stainless steel license was Mark Firth.

The war intervened to forestall perfection of the process, but by 1921 the English were marketing stainless cutlery here and at home. Early stainless dinner knives are marked "Firth-Brearley Stainless." Wade & Butcher advertised that the Teddy was made from "Firth Sterling Stainless Steel," another name for the same material.

By 1925 Wade & Butcher was offering copies of the Marble's Ideal in 4½, 5, 6, 7, and 8-inch blade versions. They all had leather handles and aluminum pommels. I have seen this style advertised both as the "Pioneer" and as the "Manitou." For tenderfoot outdoorsmen, they also sold a bowie-style hunting knife with slab handles called the "Hunter."

WADE & BUTCHER HUNTING KNIVES,
Values without sheath, in excellent condition.
Original sheath: **add 20%.**

Bowie-style, slab handles:
Hunter (5–7 inch blade): **$60.**

Leather handle, stag pommel:
Marble's Ideal copy: **$60.**
Bowie-style: **$55.**

Leather handle, aluminum pommel:
Boone: **$40.** Teddy (stainless): **$60.**
Pioneer or Manitou, 4½ to 6-inch blade: **$50.**
Pioneer or Manitou, 6 to 8-inch blade: **$60.**

Ka-Bar

In the next few years, Union/Ka-Bar added dozens of other hunting knives to their product line. Values of these, with Union Cutlery markings, are **$35–100** now. Larger sizes and fancy handle materials command the higher prices.

Jaeger Brothers

One of the first American entrants into the hunting knife market after World War I was Jaeger Brothers of Marinette, Wisconsin, owners of the Aerial Manufacturing Company [see *Picture Handled Knives* in the *Pocketknife Brand History* section]. In a catalog from right around 1920, they offered three new hunting knife models:

K17B ''Trailer'': 5-inch straight blade, single guard.
K16B ''Ranger'': 5-inch straight blade, double guard.
K18B ''Trapper'': 5-inch skinning blade, single guard.

All three have stacked washer handles, not of leather, but of fiber, varied hardwoods, and brass. They were marked ''Jaeger Bros.'' The original prices, $3.50 each, included a sheath.

Current value: **$90.**

The firm also offered a small bowie-style ''Belt Hunting Knife'' with picture handles for $3. It was marked ''Aerial.''

Current value: **$75–150** depending on the picture.

Union Cutlery Company (Ka-Bar)

This upstate New York pocketknife firm offered three styles of hunter's skinning knives in its 1921 or 1922 catalog. The catalog is not dated, but it was issued before the firm adopted the Ka-Bar trademark in 1923, yet after the introduction of stainless steel in 1921. All three models, as well as 5-inch, 6-inch, and 7-inch bowie style hunting knives, were offered in a choice of stainless or carbon steel. Those first models are worth **$100–150** now.

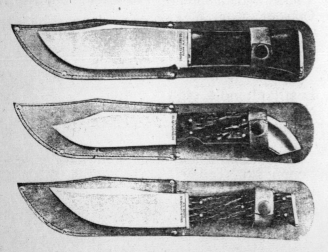

LITTLE HUNTER A

A great little knife designed for the use of the boy who wants a knife with the style and quality of a big knife. Length over all—6½". Two color unbreakable handle, genuine stag butt, nickel silver guard—grooved blade.
Little Hunter A—3½" blade with sheath $2.00

LITTLE HUNTER S

Same size as Little Hunter A except sabre blade. genuine stag handle and butt, nickel silver guard.
Little Hunter S—3½" blade with sheath $2.00

No. 3000

Threaded knob at end of handle, has reliable compass set into the under side of it. Knob opens water-proof match compartment in composition rubber handle. Thumb notch in blade is finely corrugated.
No. 3000—4½" blade with sheath $3.00

No. 2000

Same as No. 3000 except handle is aluminum.
No. 2000—4½" blade with sheath $3.00

No. 2071

Aluminum handle with match case and compass same as No. 2000—same blade as No. 571.
No. 2071—5" blade with sheath $3.25
No. 2071—6" blade with sheath 3.50

No. 3071

Same handle as No. 3000 with No. 571 blade.
No. 3071—5" $3.25

No. 386SS

A knife designed especially for nautical purposes. Heavy stainless steel blade and marlin spike. Both fit into a special sheath with separate compartments for knife and spike. Nickel silver bolsters and cocobola handle. Handle is shaped to fit in the hand.
No. 386SS knife, spike and special sheath $4.50

Remington/Pal

As recounted in the *Pocketknife Brand History* section, the Remington Arms Company entered the pocketknife business in 1919. After just a few years, with their sophisticated technology and aggressive advertising, Remington came to dominate the industry.

In 1925, Remington management decided that the American hunting knife was more than a passing fad, and entered that market as well. In typical Remington style, they introduced a very extensive hunting knife line all at once. They included many copies of their competitors' most successful patterns, plus a few novel designs of their own. Then, as they gained market experience, they dropped some numbers and added others. Kitchen and butcher knives were added to the Remington line in February of 1927. Remington hunting knives are worth **$35** to **$65** in excellent condition.

OFFICIAL GIRL SCOUT.

After losing a good chunk of money on cutlery production in 1940, Remington sold off its entire cutlery division to Pal Cutlery Company of Plattsburgh, New York. I do not believe that Pal made hunting knives before 1940, but they made plenty afterwards. Most were made with Remington dies and have Remington (RH) pattern numbers. Many were made for the government during the Second World War [see *U.S. Military Fixed Blade Knives*]. Most Pal hunting knives are worth around **$20**.

W. R. Case & Sons
Cattaraugus
Kinfolks

Though Case may have made hunting knives earlier, the first record of the firm offering them is from November, 1925. That year, Case and Cattaraugus jointly founded Kinfolks, Incorporated, in Little Valley, New York, primarily to manufacture hunting knives for these two pocketknife firms to sell. It is thus no accident that early Case and Cattaraugus hunting knives look similar. Case's first model was the No. 63-6″.

Later, the three firms went their own ways in the design and manufacture of hunting knives. Kinfolks marketed many under its own name, as well as under the name Jean Case. The most interesting Kinfolks hunting knives have imitation amber celluloid handles. They are handsome knives, but of only fair quality.

Case is still a force in the hunting knife market. However, among collectors, as with Remington, Case hunting knives are not nearly as highly regarded as Case pocketknives. The range of value is **$25** to **$75** of just about all of them in exellent condition, with sheath. Larger and more handsome examples are worth the most.

Cattaraugus and Kinfolks went out of business in the 1950s. Their hunting knives are worth about **75%** of the value of similar styles of Case knives.

No. 362

No. 516-5

No. RE 66

No. 523-5

No. 208

No. 325

No. 62-5

Knife-Axes

Case and Kinfolks, and also Western States (see below), offered an odd gadget called a ''Knife-Axe'' that has a little more collector appeal than their regular hunting knives. A Knife-Axe is a hunting knife handle with two interchangeable snap-in blades, a knife and a hatchet [see *Tool Kit Knives* for a similar mechanism]. All three pieces fit into a special sheath.

KNIFE-AXES, current values complete:

Case Tested XX, Case XX, or Case:
Stag: **$300.**   Wood: **$200.**   Celluloid: **$275.**

Case XX / Made in U.S.A.
Stag: **$200.**   Wood: **$100.**

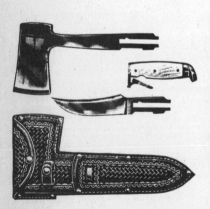

AXE-KNIFE COMBINATION

No. 23910. Axe or blade used interchangeably in nonbreakable pearl composition handle. Convenient locking device secures axe or blade to handle. Full set weighs only 1 lb. 7 ozs. in sheath. Axe and handle are 10¾''. Blade is 4¾''. Genuine sole leather embossed sheath. Packed in attractive gift boxes. Convenient for cleaning game on the spot. Net wt. each, 1 lb. 7 ozs.

Western States, celluloid: **$175.**
Kinfolks, celluloid: **$100.**

Case also made a changeable blade hunting knife with three blades. It is called the ''Sportsman's Set.'' A complete Sportsman's Set with sheath is worth about **$1,800.** A similar unbranded set marked only HOBO is worth about **$500.**

Western States

One of today's leading American producers of hunting knives is Western Cutlery Company of Colorado. Western, then called Western States, made its first hunting knife in 1928.

The first pattern that Western States made was the number 63, an inexpensive scale-tang self-guard little knife. This design was copied a few years later by Marble's as the ''Outer's.''

The second style was, of all things, a bowie-style hunter, the number 45. However, this was followed in short order by dozens upon dozens of other more modern and practical styles. Most older Western sheath knives are worth **$20** to **$35.**

About 1935 Western States patented a new type of hunting knife construction using a full width tang open along the center. The construction was used on both leather handled and celluloid handled knives. Most knives with this construction also have a streamlined pommel. Western States made knives of this type on contract for a number of distributors including Montgomery Wards (Ward's Western Pride).

No. 238 Blade 4½''. Over-all size 8⅜''. Composition pearl handles.

No. BX43 Blade 4¾''. Over-all size 8½''. Varigated colored bakelite handle. Also made in black bakelite handle with decorated red ring next to front guard **No. BX43R**.

No. 48BGH. Blade 4⅜''. Over-all size 8¼''. Assorted orange, yellow and green molded tenite handles. Finnish type Hunting Knife with deep blood groove in blade. Supplied with a fine quality attractively embossed sheath with an inside wooden lining to prevent cutting.

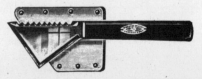

No. 990 Blade 3⅛''. Over-all size 7¾''. Highest quality stainless steel blade.

Western

"39" SERIES

Other Brands

In the 1930s, Imperial, Utica, Camillus, and Colonial, each offered at least a few patterns of hunting knives. In the 1940s, these same firms made sheath knives for the government, and were joined in this endeavor by Queen, Boker, and Robeson (and, of course, most of the previously mentioned firms that were already in the sheath knife business). Schrade-Walden first made sheath knives after the war. None of these firms' *commercial* hunting knives have yet attracted much collector interest. Their value is using value, in the range of **$8** to **$20**.

Two of the leaders in hunting knife production today are Buck and Gerber. The history of Buck is covered in a later chapter.

Gerber

Gerber Legendary Blades of Portland, Oregon, began in 1939 with the inspiration of advertising man Joseph R. Gerber, who wanted a better looking carving knife. A fellow had made him a knife that worked well enough, but it was pretty unappealing to look at. Gerber and an art director sat down and designed an improved version with a sleek cast aluminum handle.

Then Gerber arranged for knifemaker David Murphy to make two dozen according to his design. These knives were then distributed as Christmas presents.

One of those first two dozen Gerber "Legendary" blades found its way to Abercrombie & Fitch, which for more than three-quarters of a century was a patron and promoter of innovative knife design. Abercrombie's offered to buy all the knives that Gerber could produce. Gerber has grown and diversified steadily since that time.

Today there is some collector interest in older Gerber knives, particularly in their combat models. However, the values of the older knives are as yet not significantly higher than the retail prices of current production Gerber knives.

New Gerber Benchmark Carolina and Hawkeye with genuine stag handles. List prices: **$125 each**, with sheath.

Scagel Knives

By Frank Gamble

Frank Gamble is a knifemaker. He collects Scagel knives and occasionally makes a knife in the Scagel style.

BILL SCAGEL was the first well-known custom knife-maker of the 20th century. He directly inspired W. D. Randall to become a knifemaker [see the next chapter], and has indirectly influenced hundreds of other makers. All knife-makers and collectors owe him a debt of gratitude.

William Wales Scagel was born February 12, 1873, in Alpena County, Michigan, the oldest of five sons. Their father was in the ship-building trade at Sarnia, Ontario, and all five boys followed him in that line of work. Because he was born in the United States to Canadian parents, Bill Scagel held dual Canadian and American citizenship.

In 1905 or 1906, Bill Scagel left home to join the British merchant marine, and made several trips around the world. According to his own account, Scagel first had made knives for sale in 1903 (see the letter below). It is not clear if he continued this endeavor while he was at sea.

After a few years at sea, Scagel returned to the United States and a whole series of occupations and adventures. One old-timer in the Fruitport, Michigan, area recalled working with Scagel in a lumber camp in northern Wisconsin in those early days. He says that Bill would work days as a blacksmith and mechanic. At night he would make knives in a tent he had set up away from the camp.

In 1916 or 1917 Scagel returned to Michigan. He settled in Durand, which is just west of Flint, got married, and went to work for the Grand Trunk Railroad as a mechanic and trouble-shooter. Before long his marriage failed, in part because his job kept him away from home so much of the time. He never remarried.

About 1919, while he was still at Durand, Scagel resumed making knives in his spare time. In 1920, he moved across the Michigan Peninsula to Muskegon, on the shore of Lake Michigan. There he was employed in the metal-working trade, and finally set up a blacksmith shop of his own on Jackson Street in Muskegon.

In 1935 Scagel's blacksmith shop burned to the ground, destroying everything that he owned. Undaunted, he put up a corrugated iron shed to shelter a forge, pitched a tent to live in, and was back at work within a matter of days.

By 1936, Scagel had made enough money to purchase a one-acre triangular piece of property on the Fruitport-Muskegon Road. He called this place "Dogwood Nub." Alone he built himself a new workshop there, and was ready to move in by 1937. He was then 64 years old. Many men think about retiring at that age. For Scagel, it was merely time for a fresh start.

Some of Scagel's neighbors considered him an eccentric and a recluse. It would be more accurate to say that he would not waste his time on people whom he did not find interest-

Scagel's letterhead. (Courtesy W. D. Randall)

SCAGEL
HANDMADE
THEY ARE THE BEST

W. Scagel

HAND FORGED AND FINISHED
HUNTING KNIVES AND AXES

MUSKEGON, MICHIGAN,

Three Scagel hunting knives, courtesy Frank Gamble. Large hunting knives are worth **$400** to **$700**, small hunting knives **$150** to **$400**, folding knives and fancy bowies **$750** and up, paring knives about **$50**, carving sets about **$250**, axes **$300** and up. Values are for items in excellent unsharpened condition.

ing, or who merely wanted to pass the time and interrupt his work.

Scagel believed in self-sufficiency and he had no use for the local power company. To produce electricity, he built a windmill generator equipped with World War I surplus submarine storage batteries. This was backed up by another generator powered by the motor out of a yellow 1925 Cadillac.

Scagel raised much of his own food, and was a strict vegetarian. However, he was famous as a crack shot, and hunted deer (with a revolver) to feed his dogs.

For the next quarter-century Scagel lived and worked at Dogwood Nub. He constantly improved the place, building a second story on the shop, and then a separate bungalow to live in. He decorated the buildings and grounds with whimsical wrought iron ornaments of his own design. During this time, he made between one and 30 knives per week.

Finally, in the winter of 1961, Scagel's arthritis got so severe that he could no longer work. He was then 88. Bill Scagel died March 26, 1963.

V. L. & A. HAND MADE HUNTING AND SKINNING KNIVES

The blades are finely tempered and drawn by hand from one inch square blocks of Jessup Silver Steel, and fully polished. Plenty of metal is left on back of blade for breaking bones, etc. Handle is made of leather and fiber, with brass bolsters and stag horn cap. The best hunting knife ever produced. A fine sheath made of extra heavy black or tan bridle leather, hand laced with white rawhide and riveted. Inasmuch as these knives are strictly hand made there will be no two exactly alike.

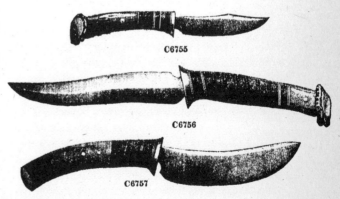

C6755

C6756

C6757

C6755 Trout Knives. Price, each..........................$5.00 net
C6756 Hunting Knives—4, 4½, 5, and 6 in. blades. Price, each ....$15.00 net
C6756 Skinning Knives—4, 4½, and 5 in. blades. Price, each ....$15.00 net

Scagel knives shown in the 1925 Von Lengerke and Antoine (Chicago) sporting goods catalog. Current values are about 40 times the original prices. Courtesy Frank Gamble.

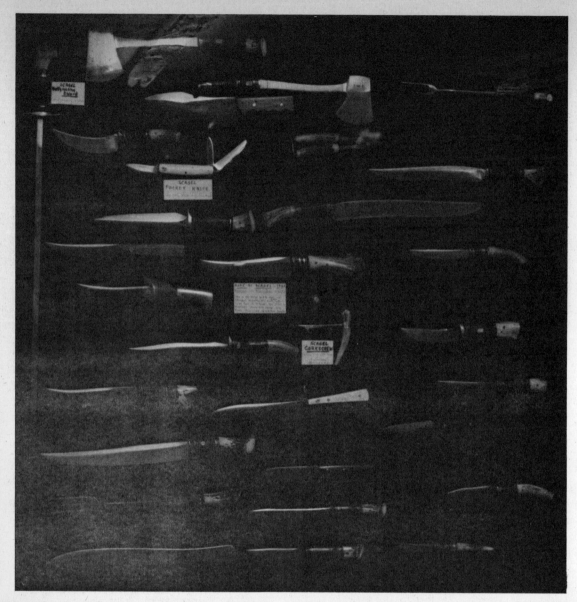

W. D. Randall's collection of 30 Scagel items on display in his private knife museum. They include hunting knives, fighting knives, brush knives, carving sets, paring knives, a poultry shears, a corkscrew, two hatchets, a throwing knife, a three-bladed folding knife, and a bull fighting sword. In the center, just above the largest white card, is the famous "boat-scraping" Scagel knife that started Randall in the knife business in 1937. The knife was made in 1931.

At present, the values of Scagel knives vary widely. Several old collections have sold for less than the asking price on certain single items. Bill Scagel made knives for nearly 60 years, and many hundreds of them survive. These range from simple paring knives to fancy decorated bowies.

In my opinion, one of the most important considerations in the value of a Scagel is its condition. Most saw heavy use, and many have recently been refinished. The value of a used or refinished Scagel is half or less of the indicated amounts. Also, a few fake Scagels have appeared on the market, so the buyer must beware.

For more about Scagel, see the new booklet called *Scagel, The Man and His Knives* by Harry McEvoy, published by *Knife World*, Box 3395, Knoxville TN 37927.

The two letters which follow are from the files of W. D. Randall and are reproduced with his permission:

Muskegon, Michigan, 9/9-37

Mr. W. D. Randall, Jr.
Orlando.

Dear Sir,

You will just have to let me off this time for not answering your letter, but it could not be helped. I crushed the bone in the forefinger of my right hand and had to wait until it got better. It was too late to write then, so I just made the knife and sent it by express yesterday, and if it is not just what you want please send it back at my expense, for some of the lines on your sketch I could not follow.

I note the article you sent on the only custom knife-maker*, but I do not make freaks or daggers. I make an effort to give a man something serviceable & practical, this fellow thinks he is practical and the only one. I note in the piece he has been working at it for 6 years, and designing different knives (115 in all).

I have been making knives for A. & F. Co., N. Y. [Abercrombie & Fitch], V. L. & A., Chicago [Von Lengerke & Antoine], P. A. Co., San Francisco [Pacific Arms Corporation], Alcock Late & Westwood, Toronto, also their house in London, England, for this past 34 years, and in all the hundreds of knives I have made there have been no two alike. I have several private customers all over the world. Some of these have goods made that are ivory and silver or gold or platinum trimmed. I just finished one in ivory & silver along with yours. That went to Toledo, Ohio.

Thank you kindly for your valued order and trust it will be satisfactory. If not just send it back.

With kindest regards I beg to remain

Very Truly Yours,
W Scagel
1075 Marquette Ave.
Muskegon

---

* Amy Lyon of the San Francisco Mechanics Institute Library identified this article for me. It is "Novel Workshop Produces Custom-Built Knives" by Robert E. Martin, in the September, 1937, *Popular Science Monthly*. The knife-maker written up was Giles P. Wetherill of Philadelphia. Here is what he meant by "Custom-Built:"

"In making special designs for customers, Wetherill, whenever possible, 'tailors' the knives to the physical 'build' of the men who will use them. He takes seven measurements, including the length of the arm and the forearm, before he begins work on the design of the knife. Usually, he submits three or four patterns, out of which the purchaser chooses one. When an exclusive pattern is desired—that is, one which is not to be sold to anyone else—an additional 'design charge' of twenty-five dollars is added."

Evidently one of the seven measurements Wetherill took

The Clock Shop
Muskegon Heights, Michigan
November 23, 1953

Mr. Wyatt Blassingame
% Fawcett Publications Inc.

Sir:-

After reading your article "How do you make a perfect knife?" in the December [1953] issue of TRUE I thought that perhaps you would be interested in some of the facts concerning Wm. Scagel.

I have known this man for the past thirty years and have had occasion to visit him once or twice a week during this period. He is surely a genius in the processing of any kind of metal. He was seventy-eight years old** on February 12, 1953, and lives alone with his two dogs, Zip and Stubby. He is in remarkable physical condition in spite of his age. He forges all of his knives by hand, swinging an eight pound sledge for days at a time. He also has made all sorts of tools for this processing. He even makes his own grinding and polishing wheels.

His work is never done, on account of receiving orders for special knives from all over the world. These orders come mostly for G.I.'s and he has shipped knives in large quantities to Japan and Alaska. And persons from all over the United States beat a path to his door requesting the processing of knives, carving sets, hunting axes, etc. He has also made such equipment as brush knives etc. for expeditions to the jungles of Africa. He also designs handles in ivory, horns, silver, and imported woods.

The above are only part of his accomplishments. He also makes copper frying pans and cooking utensils, inlaid furniture and metal boats. He also has built his own shop buildings and equipment. Also his living cottages with fireplaces and paneled walls with oil paintings by himself of scenes he remembers while serving in the English merchant marine.

Trusting that this meager information may be of interest to you, I am,

Yours very truly,
Roy W. Ferris

**According to most sources, that was actually Scagel's eightieth birthday.

---

was the depth of the customer's purse. He reportedly charged as much as $1,200 for some of his fancier knives. This, and Martin's assertion that Wetherill's shop was "the only one of its kind in America to produce custom-built knives for sportsmen" were probably what angered Scagel about the article.

Randall Made, Orlando, Florida

New Knives Made the Old Way

IN THE WINTER of 1985, my dad and I went to Orlando to meet W. D. "Bo" Randall and his son Gary, visit their knife museum, and see how their celebrated knives are made. If a knifemaker from 1885 had accompanied us on our visit to their workshop, none of the methods and little of the equipment he saw there would have surprised him.

Of course Norton sharpening stone cradles, rubber wheel belt sanders, epoxy cement, and motors driven by electricity would have been new to our time traveler. However, everything else in the Randall shop—the forges, the trip hammers, the grinding and polishing wheels—all would have looked familiar.

What would have most surprised our time-traveling knifemaker would be the Randall knives themselves. All of them, traditional as their designs have come to seem, are creations entirely of the 20th century.

A few Randall patterns were inspired by earlier 20th century makers such as Scagel and Marble. A few others were designed by customers. Most of them, however, were designed by the Randalls themselves. Many of their designs have been flattered by imitation, but with Randall knives, as with most fine objects, there is nothing like the real McCoy.

The Beginning

The story of how W. D. Randall, the orange grower, became W. D. Randall, the knife man, has been told so many times that it has acquired something of the flavor of legend. In the late 1930s, Randall was vacationing in western Michigan, the stomping ground of the renowned knifemaker, William Scagel. One day, Randall saw a man industriously scraping paint from his boat with a remarkable looking knife—a knife that proved to be a Scagel.

The fellow would not desist from abusing his knife, nor could he be persuaded to part with it. Randall therefore determined to try his hand making one like it.

Almost half a century and 200,000 Randall knives later, W. D. Randall is one of the best known knifemakers of our time. Soldiers, sportsmen, and collectors have carried his knives to every corner of the world, and even into space.

The hands of the master: W.D. Randall in his office.
Address: Randall Knives, Box 1988, Orlando FL 32802.

Opposite page: This famous photo shows most of the Randall line. Prices are projected 1986 list prices with sheath direct from Randall. See the Randall catalog for more information. Prices for immediate delivery from stocking dealers are somewhat higher. Used Randalls in excellent condition are worth about **75%**. Some models were also sold with Solingen factory blades: **subtract 40%**. World War II "Springfield" Randalls are worth about the same as Orlando knives.

From bottom left, clockwise (stag handles, **add $20**): Model 8 Trout and Bird **$130**. Model 19 Bushmaster **$135**. Model 3 Hunter **$135**. Model 11 Alaskan Skinner **$130**. Model 18 Attack-Survival **$200**. Model 12 6'' Sportsman's Bowie **$160**. Model 12 6'' Bear Bowie **$150**. Model 4 Big Game **$135**. Model 3 Hunter **$140**. Model 14 Attack **$165**. Model 1 All Purpose Fighting **$145**. Model 12 Bear Bowie **$240**. Model 13 Arkansas Toothpick **$350**.

Model 2 Fighting Stiletto **$150**. Model 18 large Attack Survival **$210**. Model 10 Salt Fisherman **$70**. Model 5 Camp and Trail **$135**. Model 16 Diver's **$170**. Model 1 All Purpose Fighting **$145**. Model 13 small Arkansas Toothpick **$150**. Model 15 Airman **$155**. Model 7 Fisherman-Hunter **$130**. Model 17 Astro **$240**. Model 20 Yukon Skinner **$135**. Model 21 Little Game **$120**.

Center, top to bottom: Model 2 Boot Knife **$135**. Model 22 Outdoorsman **$200**. Fork **$35**. Model 6 Carving Knife and Sharpener **$160**. Model 12 Confederate and Raymond Thorp Bowies **$340**. Model 9 Pro-Thrower **$60**.

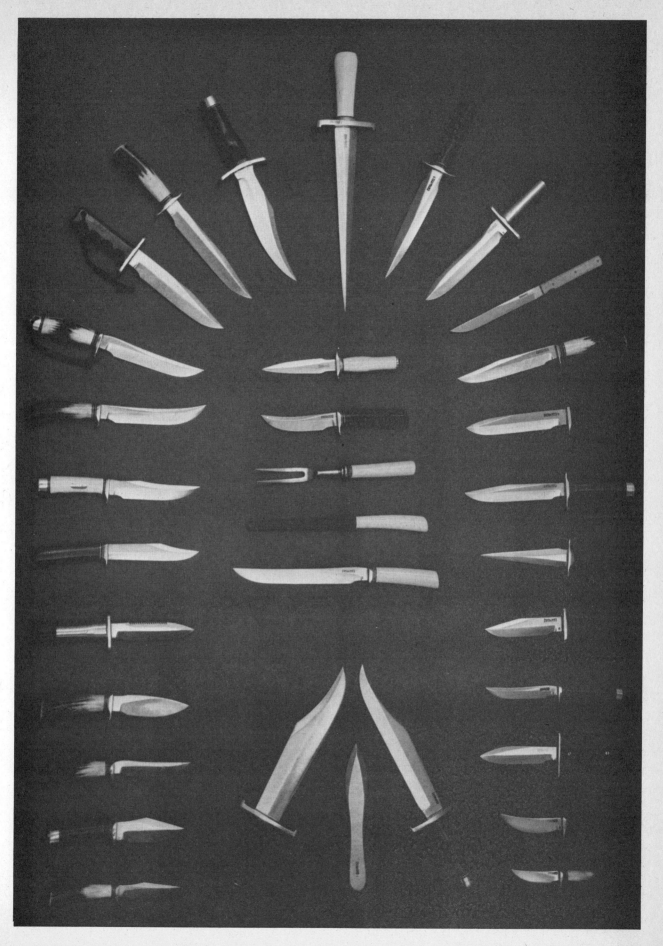

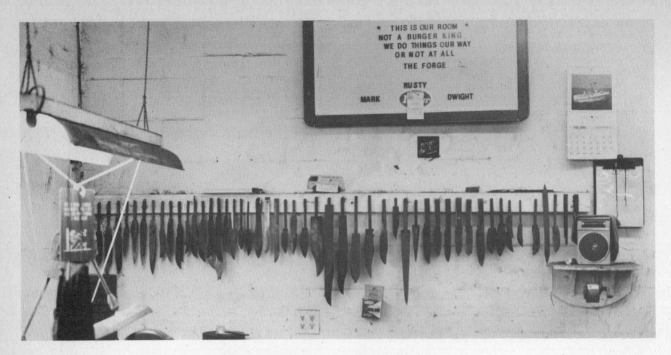

Blade patterns in the Randall forging shop.

Hand Forging.

Power forging.

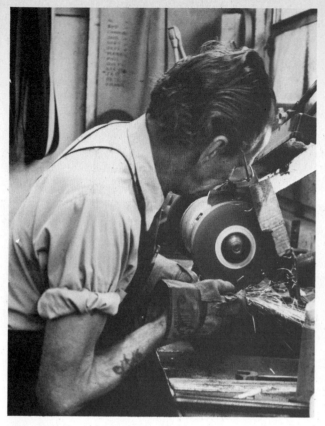

Grinding

Honing.

Polishing.

Honing.

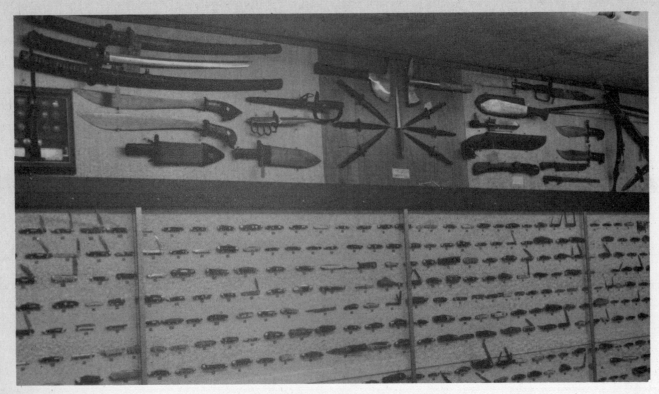

Part of one wall in the Randall's knife museum.

Not long after seeing that first Scagel knife, Randall sought out its maker, and the two men became friends. Randall began to collect Scagel knives, and now has about 30 which are on display in his private knife museum. The centerpiece of the collection is that first paint-scraping Scagel, a gift many years later from its original owner [see the previous chapter].

The Knife Museum

The Randall's knife museum is a seven days wonder in itself. Back in the 1960s, W. D. Randall heard about a collection of knives that a physician had been assembling since 1900. That man had died in 1960, and the subsequent owner was looking for a purchaser for the entire collection. Randall purchased the collection of many thousand unused knives, and this became the core of his museum.

Besides his Scagels, Randall has added many other knives to this outstanding collection. He also displays all sorts of interesting Randall memorabilia, including many testimonials from famous customers.

Perhaps the most interesting display in the museum is a group of showcases containing one of every Randall knife ever made. All the regular models are included, of course, in all their variations. In addition, there is one of every custom or special order knife made in the Randall workshop.

You see, when the Randalls get a special order for one knife, the shop makes two knives. The customer gets the better of the two, and the museum gets the other. If the order is for five knives, the shop makes six.

Special Designs

Bo Randall showed me some of the original sketches submitted for special order knives. This sketch for a diver's knife was sent in January, 1958, by novelist James Jones, who was long a devotee of Randall knives. He wanted five made just like it. His design was adopted as Model 16 of the regular Randall line in April of that year.

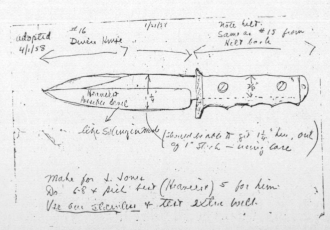

This knife was made in 1958 for Air Force Lieutenant James A. Ary, an instructor in individual combat at Pine Castle Air Force Base. The extra-long handle is leather. The blade is 9 inches long and sharpened on both sides. It has no point, as it was intended entirely for slashing. Ary taught his students to slash at the tendons behind the knees of their opponents, an unexpected and effective method of attack. The cost in 1958 was $24 without sheath.

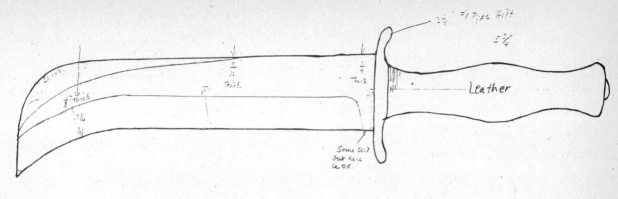

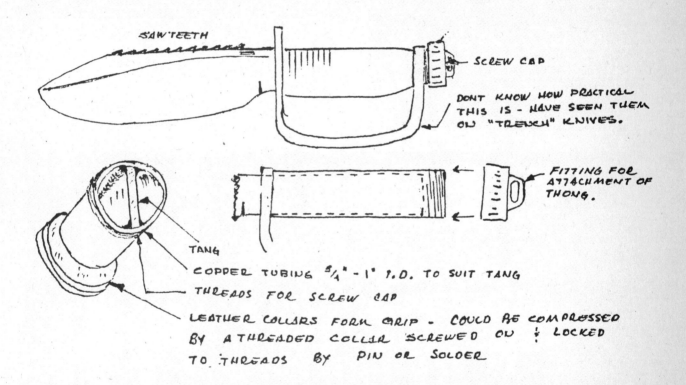

This sketch was sent from Viet Nam in January, 1963, by Captain George W. Ingraham, 94th Medical Detachment, U.S. Army. It was his design for a rescue and survival knife for helicopter pilots and crew members, based on the Randall Model 14 "Attack."

The saw teeth were for cutting through aluminum and plexiglas on wrecked aircraft. The hollow handle would hold matches, water purification tablets, Dexedrine (stimulant), and Demerol (pain killer).

The hollow handle itself was not a new idea. In his book *Survival Knives and Survival*, J.E. Smith, Jr., shows several hollow handle commercial hunting knives from circa 1940. Ingraham's reason for having minimal survival needs in the knife one wears was very simple. In his words, "no one is foolish enough to waste time hunting through wreckage for his survival gear when the gas tank many explode at any minute."

The Randalls experimented with the design, and made several changes to keep costs reasonable. They eliminated the knuckle bow and shortened the tang. They replaced the threaded end with a rubber crutch tip. They used stainless steel for the handle, instead of copper, and they left the metal bare. This way the user could wrap it with fish-line, tape, cord, boot laces, or whatever he might find useful. This knife then became the Model 18 in the Randall line. Later, a threaded butt cap was offered as an option. The original cost was $28.50 with sheath.

Original Morseth marking, 1949–1973.

Original 1934 Morseth knife.

Harry Morseth in the 1950s.

Four 1949 laminated Morseth knives.

Morseth Knives
By Steve Morseth and Bernard Levine

Steve Morseth is Harry Morseth's grandson. He now makes S. MORSETH knives.

Harry Morseth

BACK IN 1906, a 17-year-old Norwegian youth named Harry Morseth left his parents' homeland to settle in the United States. He traveled across the country, to the vicinity of Everett, Washington. On the map, that part of Washington looks as if it had been transplanted from the coast of Norway. There, in 1910, young Harry Morseth found work in the Walton lumber mill. Forty years later he retired from Walton Lumber Company as foreman of the mill, but along the way he decided to embark in the knife business.

In the 1950s, Harry Morseth wrote:

> Frankly, I'm a crank about knives. I've been going hunting since I was a boy in Norway, . . . and from first hand experience I've learned what hunters want and need from an all-purpose hunting and skinning knife. The precise details of knife design and construction have been of life-long interest to me, including blade steel, temper, shape, width, length, thickness, taper, bevel, tang, hilt, handle, and sheath. For my own pleasure, and as a hobby, I have made an endless number of knives and sheaths to develop the most nearly perfect combination of features.

In 1934 Harry Morseth made his first knife for commercial sale. It was a hunting knife similar in design to the Marble's knives then in vogue. Like many of the Marble's knives, Morseth's first knife had a stag handle and a crown stag butt. Unlike the Marble's, which have pinned two-piece stag handle scales, his knife had a one-piece handle.

For the blade of his first commercial knives, Harry Morseth used a material familiar to him from the saw mill: planer blade steel. This steel worked well, but not as well as the laminated steel he had seen in knives from his old home in Norway.

Laminated Steel

One of the strengths of the samurai swords of old Japan is that their blades are laminated. A thin cutting edge of extremely hard steel is laminated between layers of tough resilient iron or mild steel. The hard steel edge provides keen cutting ability, while the mild sides support the edge and keep it from breaking.

Independently of the Japanese, the Norwegians discovered the virtues of laminated steel for blades. Unlike Japanese laminated blades, which are forged painstakingly by hand, Norwegian laminated blades are mass produced in a rolling mill. The outer layer of mild Norway iron is wrapped around and welded to the core of high carbon steel in one continuous operation. Many an inexpensive Norwegian *Tollekniv* [see *Foreign Exotic, Primitive, and Historical Fixed Blade Knives*] has a composite blade made this way.

In 1939, Harry Morseth went to Norway and visited the factory where strips of laminated blade steel were rolled. He ordered a batch of the steel and returned home. However, before his order could be shipped, World War II began, Norway was conquered, and all of its steel output was given over to German war production.

In the 1940s, Harry Morseth continued to make knives out of planer blade and other tool steels. Finally, in 1949, he received his first shipment of laminated steel.

Actually, what he received was not steel bars. Instead he received blade blanks that had been stamped out to his own design in the factory. Because they were blade blanks and not simply raw steel stock, U. S. Customs required that they be marked to show their origin. In consequence these first laminated Morseth blades are stamped: BRUSLETTO/GEILO/MADE IN NORWAY.

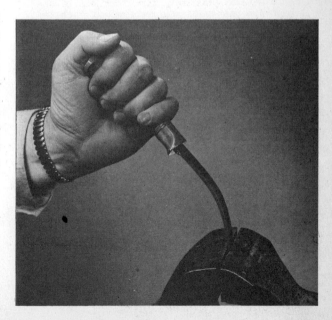

Morseth Laminated Knives

By this time, in 1949, Morseth had considerably refined his techniques and his blade design. At this time, all Morseth hunting knives had the same 5-inch blade style, the one he had settled upon as ideal. He hardened his blades to RC-63, significantly harder than the RC-57 Brusletto used on its own knives.

Morseth offered four handle options with his basic blade. Model 1 had a one-piece stag handle. Model 2 had his distinctive three-piece stag handle. Model 2A had his original two-piece stag handle. Model 3 had a leather washer handle with a stag butt. Until 1951, all Morseth knives had brass hilts; afterwards they all had nickel silver.

Morseth knives were expensive for their day. Model 1 cost $18, 2 and 2A cost $16, and 3 cost $14. The price of each knife included an ingenious Morseth Safe-Lok sheath (U. S. Pat. 2,650,008, granted 1953).

2,650,008
SCABBARD
Harry Morseth, Everett, Wash.
Application June 18, 1951, Serial No. 232,177
1 Claim.   (Cl. 224—2)

A scabbard for a hunting knife or the like comprising a relatively flexible outer case providing an elongated pocket open at its upper end, a liner for the pocket secured to the outer casing and comprising a flattened, relatively rigid, fiber tube that is substantially coextensive with said pocket and is closed at its lower end, the front and back walls of the liner tube at the upper end portion of the same being flared outwardly to receive therebetween the hilt end portion of a knife, and said liner tube being provided in the upper end portion thereof with recesses extending longitudinally along the side edge portions thereof inwardly from the upper end of the same between said outwardly flared portions of the front and back walls, said recesses being adapted to receive the ends of the hilt of a knife positioned in the liner tube, and said recesses being similarly formed and each having an enlarged lower part and a restricted upper portion leading outwardly therefrom and having outwardly converging walls adapted to yieldingly embrace the hilt of a knife positioned in the liner tube and to retain the same therein against accidental displacement.

This leather sheath is lined with vulcanized fiber (the same material used for handle spacers). The fiber protects the leather (and the wearer) from the point and cutting edge of the knife, and its springiness helps retain the hilt of the knife in place. The leather hold-down collar slips over the handle for further protection.

New Models

The prices of Morseth knives put them out of reach of most sportsmen. In 1953, demand for high priced hand-made knives was the slackest it had been since before World War II. In consequence, Harry Morseth began to offer a relatively inexpensive plain utility knife.

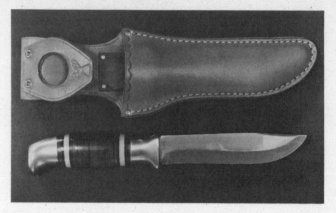

1953 Morseth $8.95 utility knife.

The utility knife had a 5-inch blade and a leather washer handle with aluminum alloy mounts. The first ones had white fiber spacers as shown, but most did not. With a plain Safe-Lok sheath, the utility knife cost $8.95. It was produced until about 1960.

In 1954, responding to revived customer demand, Harry Morseth added another new model to his practical, but limited line. The new knife was called the Morseth Bowie. It differed from the older models in that it had a 6-inch blade with a sharp false edge.

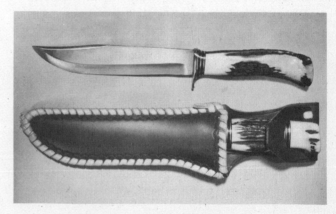

1954 Morseth 6-inch modified bowies.

The new knife was offered in a choice of one-piece stag, three-piece stag, or leather washer and stag handles. In addition, the bowie and the original hunting knife were now offered with a one-piece Scandinavian style wooden handle. Woods available were ebony, teak, and purple heart. The Safe-Lok sheath could now be had in a plain stitched version, as well as the original fancy laced style.

Later Years

In 1956, Harry Morseth moved across the strait from Everett to the village of Clinton, Washington, on Whidbey Island. A few minor design changes can help to distinguish later Morseth hunting knives from earlier ones. In 1958, the nickel silver handle spacers were replaced by white fiber. In 1961, the hilt or guard was made slightly curved, instead of straight, as it had been.

In 1961, Harry Morseth's grandson, Steve, began to make knives. As Steve describes it,

> By early 1965 it was pretty much decided I had the necessary ability (or stupidity), and a corporation would be formed and I would take over the manufacture of the 'Morseth' knife. . . . In January, 1966, Harry Morseth retired from knifemaking and the corporation was formed. Immediately I ordered laminated bar stock and blade blanks in 5mm stock (3/16-inch) for my five new models. . . . Harry Morseth passed away on October 9, 1967.

Steve Morseth began his manufacturing with a total of seven models. These were:
1. Original Morseth 5-inch blade hunting knife.
2. 6-inch blade modified bowie, introduced 1954.
3. 5-inch blade modified bowie.
4. Morseth Michigan with 3¾-inch blade.
5. Morseth Cascade Skinner with 4¼-inch blade.
6. Military Survival with 6-inch blade.
7. Military Survival with 7-inch blade.

Models 6 and 7 came with a special quick-draw military sheath with a stone pocket, and as an option could be fitted with a lugged double brass hilt. All models were offered with a choice of wood, leather, one-piece stag, or three-piece stag handle. Besides making these standard Morseth models, Steve also made many custom knives in this period.

Division

On December 14, 1971, Gordon Morseth of Michigan, Harry's son and Steve's father, who owned a controlling interest in the corporation, Morseth Sports Equipment Co., Inc., sold the corporation to A. G. Russell of Arkansas. From what I can gather, no one at the time was entirely happy with the results of this transaction.

In any case, the upshot has been that A. G. Russell now manufactures MORSETH knives in Springdale, Arkansas, while Steve Morseth makes S. MORSETH knives in Washington (Box 508, Selah WA 98942).

A. G. Russell still uses imported laminated steel for his MORSETH knives, while Steve Morseth has recently switched to 154CM, a modern stainless alloy. Steve still makes the Safe-Lok sheaths, while A. G. makes plain leather sheaths. Both men have recently introduced several new models.

Steve and Harry Morseth on Whidbey Island in 1967.

PRICE GUIDE TO OLDER MORSETH KNIVES*

Original Morseth from planer blade: **$400;** with copper lined sheath used prior to fiber lining: **$2,500.**

Morseths marked BRUSLETTO/GEILO/ MADE IN NORWAY. with Safe-Lok sheath. No sheath, **subtract 40%.**
5-inch blade original design.
   Stag: **$300.** Leather: **$200.** Wood: **$200.**
5-inch blade utility, leather and aluminum: **$110.**
6-inch blade modified bowie.
   Stag: **$300.** Leather: **$200.** Wood: **$200.**

Post-1966 Models
5-inch blade modified bowie.
   Stag: **$250** Leather: **$175** Wood: **$175.**
Morseth Michigan with 3¾-inch blade.
   Stag: **$200.** Leather: **$150.** Wood: **$150.**
Morseth Cascade Skinner with 4¼-inch blade.
   Stag: **$225.** Leather: **$200.** Wood: **$200.**
Military Survival with 6-inch blade.
   Stag: **$200.** Leather: **$150.** Wood: **$150.**
Military Survival with 7-inch blade.
   Stag: **$225.** Leather: **$175.** Wood: **$175.**
Lugged hilt on military survival: **add $40.**

*Prices shown are averages of those supplied by Steve Morseth and those supplied by several dealers.

Hoyt Heath Buck holding a Lucite handled Buck 105 in 1946.

Al Buck in front of the Buck
Knives factory in 1979.

A WORD FROM THE PRESIDENT OF BUCK KNIVES

If this is your first Buck Knife, "welcome aboard". You are now part of a very large family. Although we're talking about a few million people, we still like to think of each one of our users as a member of the Buck Knives Family and take a personal interest in the knife that was bought. With normal use, you should never have to buy another.

Now that you are family, you might like to know a little more about our organization. The fantastic growth of Buck Knives, Inc. was no accident. From the beginning, a Christian Management determined to make God the Senior Partner. In a crisis, the problem was turned over to Him, and He hasn't failed to help us with the answer. Each knife must reflect the integrity of management, including our Senior Partner. If sometimes we fail on our end, because we are human, we find it imperative to do our utmost to make it right. Of course, to us, besides being Senior Partner, He is our Heavenly Father also, and it's a great blessing to us to have this security in these troubled times. If any of you are troubled or perplexed and looking for answers, may we invite you to look to Him, for God loves you.

Al Buck

This message is en-
closed with every new
Buck knife.

Buck Fixed Blade Knives

By Vern Taylor

Vern Taylor has been a sales representative for Buck since 1967, and he has an extensive collection of early Buck knives.

Buck Principles

Millions of knives have been made bearing the name Buck. This name is now recognized and respected around the world. One reason for the company's good reputation is that it has never sold seconds. Al Buck, the founder of the modern company, established as his policy, "If it's not the best we can do, it's not good enough to put our name on."

For many years Buck made a practice of destroying any knives that were not up to the standards Al Buck had set. Today, knives rejected for cosmetic flaws (not structural flaws) are shipped to Christian missionaries in Third-World countries. They barter them to local people for goods and services. Since the missionaries are usually short of cash, this arrangement benefits both them and the people they are trying to reach with God's word.

YOU CAN FIND new Buck knives today in most good sporting goods, hardware, and cutlery stores. For the dedicated collector, however, there is a treasure trove of old Buck knives out there, also, just waiting to be discovered. Finding those knives is, of course, a lot more of a challenge.

Many of the older Buck knives are distinctively different from the ones made now. Others look similar to new knives, but they can be distinguished from new ones by differences in markings and in construction details.

In this chapter, you will find descriptions of the basic types of Buck fixed blade knives made over the years. You will see how to identify and date the major variations in each type. You will also find my estimate of each variation's current value in excellent unsharpened condition.

The detailed history of the Buck family and complete descriptions of the full range of Buck knives and all their variations will take a whole book in itself. This book, *The Buck Knife Story*, is scheduled for publication in 1986. It will have over 100 illustrations, many in full color.

The basic categories of Buck knives are easy to distinguish. Any of these categories might make an interesting collecting specialty. In most of these categories it should be relatively easy to assemble a complete collection. Even the earliest Buck knives were sold by mail all over the country, so no matter where you live, you have a good chance of adding such knives to your collection. One of a kind custom knives are still available from the Buck custom shop, if your interest is in this area.

The History of Buck

It was near the turn of the century that Hoyt Heath Buck, the father of Al Buck, made his first knife. He was a blacksmith's apprentice and had discovered a new and effective method of tempering. He used his method in rebuilding worn out grub hoes which he fitted with new cutting edges by forge-welding worn-out horseshoer's files to them. H. H. Buck's rebuilt grub hoes lasted many times longer than brand new ones.

One day, one of Hoyt Buck's satisfied customers asked the young blacksmith to make a knife for him. The knife was more than satisfactory, and before long, Buck was making knives regularly. He used the same type of files and the same tempering method that he used in rebuilding hoes.

H. H. Buck and his wife, the former Daisy Green, lived in the Tacoma, Washington, area from about 1908 to 1930. Buck worked in the state's logging industry but he also made knives in his spare time.

Hoyt and Daisy Buck's first child, Al Buck, was born in 1910. They named him Alfred Charles after the traveling evangelist who had inspired Hoyt to become a born-again Christian. This event was to play a major part in the future of the family and the destiny of the company called Buck Knives.

In 1932, Al Buck left home to join the Coast Guard. He served for 8 years, until 1940. Upon his discharge he settled in San Diego, California.

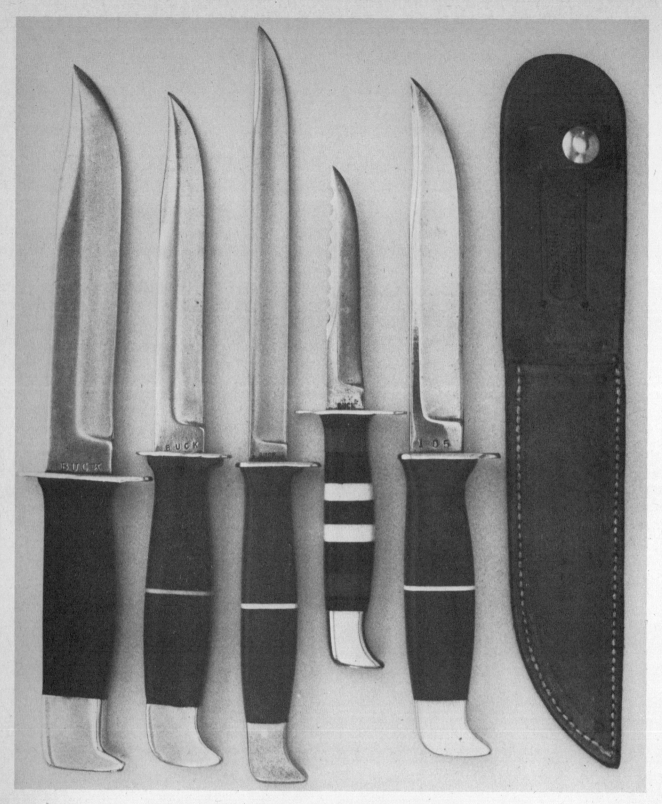

Early hand-made Buck knives, circa 1945–1955 (left to right).
Note: all of the model numbers were changed in 1960.
A. Model 104 with 5½-inch blade, green Lucite slab handles: **$50–150.**
B. Model 102 with 5-inch blade, blue stacked Lucite handle: **$50–90.**
C. Model 120 6-inch blade filet knife, red Lucite handle: **$50–100.**
D. Model 107 3½-inch pan fish knife, multi-color Lucite: **$65–125.**
E. Model 105 with red stacked Lucite handle: **$50–90.**
F. Sheath of the type included with all of these knives. Note the
   address stamp: BUCK KNIFE CO./1272 MORENA/SAN DIEGO, CAL.

Early Buck Knives

By the beginning of World War II, Hoyt Buck had been ordained as a minister and was pastor of a small church in Mountain Home, Idaho. His small forge was set up in the basement of the church. He made knives there for the local people. He also worked as millwright supervisor at the Anderson Ranch Dam.

When hometown boys left for military duty in the war, many of them wanted good knives. Hoyt responded to the need by making more knives than he ever had made before.

The war brought those kids from rural Idaho together with young men from all over the country. In barracks and fox holes thousands of miles from home, they spread the fame and reputation of Buck knives.

In 1945, Hoyt and Daisy Buck moved to San Diego to join their son, Al. The brutal Idaho winters had proven damaging to Daisy's health.

The full story of the move to San Diego and what followed is told in *The Buck Knife Story*. Suffice it to say that Hoyt persuaded Al to join him in making knives to be sold by mail through the outdoor magazines.

blades. The usual handle material was Lucite plastic in a variety of bright colors. Later, the favored handle material was lignum vitae from South America. Some knives at this time were handled in elk horn and others in ironwood cut in the deserts east of San Diego.

In 1949 Hoyt H. Buck went to face the Judgement Day foretold in the Bible he knew so well. He had expressed many times that it was a day he did not fear, knowing he had lived in God's will since accepting Jesus as his personal savior in 1908.

For the next 10 years, Al Buck continued to make knives alone in his shop at 1272 Morena Avenue, San Diego. The war in Korea brought a severe downturn in his business. Unlike the situation at the start of World War II, the military now had a large inventory of issue knives, so they discouraged men from buying their own. After the truce was signed in July, 1953, the fortunes of Buck Knives turned upwards even more markedly than they had after World War II.

In 1959, Al's son, Charles T. Buck completed his tour of duty in the U. S. Navy and joined his father in business. Most of their daily living money at that time was earned by sharpening the old reel type lawn mowers.

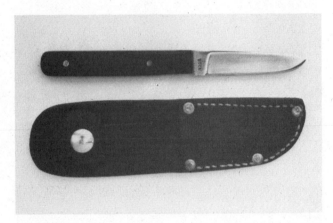

Budget utility knife. Hundreds were made c1947–1955 in times when business was slow. Never listed in catalog. Knife with black plastic or micarta handles, marked BUCK on ricasso. Sheath marked BUCK. **$30–60.**

One of very few bowies made by Al Buck, mid to late 1950s. Leather washer handle with exposed nut on pommel. **$300–500.** Lightly engraved on blade: CUSTOM MADE BY BUCK FOR "CURLY" SHOPPE.

Hoyt guessed that many of the readers of *Field and Stream, Outdoor Life,* and *Sports Afield* were the same young men who had already heard about the Buck knife from an army buddy or navy shipmate. If they could find just a few hundred customers from among those readers, this would be enough to launch them in the knifemaking business.

From 1945 to 1949 Hoyt and Al Buck made knives for sale by mail. All the Buck knives thus far and for the next decade and a half were fixed blades. In this period, Al Buck worked as a bus driver. When he drove nights, he made knives in the daytime, and when he drove days, he made knives at night.

Most of the Buck knives of the late 1940s and early 1950s were made from either old files or from power hack saw

Four knives with lignum vitae handles and small butt caps made by Al Buck circa 1952. **$40–90 each.**
(Courtesy Buck Knives)

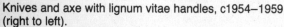

Knives and axe with lignum vitae handles, c1954–1959 (right to left).
A. Early Model 119: **$40–90.**
B. BUCK LIFETIME axe with original welded and brazed joints: **$75–150.**
C. Model 105: **$40–90.**
D. Model 120: **$50–100.**

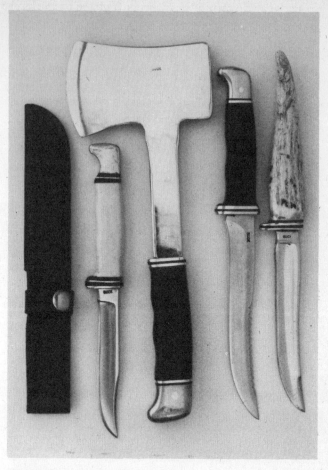

Very early production knives and axe, c1961–1962 (left to right).
A & B. White handled 102 with second version production sheath: **$50–75.**
C. Model 106 axe: **$30–50.**
D. Model 121 with earliest stamp: **$50–75.**
E. Model 105 with special order handle: **$75–100.**

Production Knives

In *The Buck Knife Story*, you will find all the details of the transition of this two-man shop to a full scale production facility. Briefly, Buck Knives was incorporated in 1961 and stock was sold. The workshop was moved from Morena Avenue to a corrugated metal building at 3220 Congress Street near Old Town in San Diego. Production began there with three employees.

Until this time, the Bucks had cut out individual hunting knife blades on a band saw or fashioned them from files. Now this time-consuming job gave way to having them forged by a commercial forging company in Los Angeles.

Al Buck took to the road in his Volkswagen bus. He set out to persuade sporting goods dealers that his $13 to $20 knives were a bargain, even though competitive hunting knives then sold for $8. Often, when he returned from a sales trip, Al would help make knives to fill the orders he had sent back.

Buck knives had long been tested and demonstrated by being driven straight and true through a bolt or a heavy nail. A picture of this was now adopted by Buck Knives as a trademark. I have talked to several of Buck's first dealers who still remember Al demonstrating his knives on 10-penny nails.

Identifying Early Production Buck Knives

At this time, the Buck Knives line consisted of seven fixed blade hunting knives and one filet knife. These designs were very similar to the ones cut from steel blanks and old files a few years earlier.

These were the models:

120 General	119 Special
105 Pathfinder	118 Personal
103 Skinner	102 Woodsman
116 Caper (added 1962)	121 Fisherman

All of these knives were stamped on the blade with just the one word BUCK. On the 121, the location of the stamp was changed quite early. Its fish scaling teeth were dropped about 1965. Model 116s were made with and without guards.

The earliest production Buck knives were assembled in the same manner as the hand-made knives of the '40s and '50s. Their tangs were threaded; a barrel nut was tightened on with the butt in place; then a plug of aluminum to match

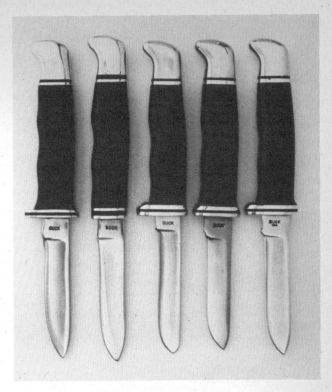

Model 116s made 1961–1968 (left to right).
Note variations in guards made by different workmen.
A & B. Early "barrel nut" models: **$35–50.**
C & D. "Flat tang" models marked BUCK: **$25–35.**
E. "Flat tang" model marked BUCK/U.S.A.: **$20–30.**

the butt was inserted into the hole to hide the nut. These knives, with the plug in the end of the butt, are the "barrel nut models."

In 1962 Buck switched over to a flat tang. The butts were pressed on and pinned in place through a hole drilled from the side through butt and tang. These are called "flat tang models."

The standard production Buck knives of the early 1960s had handles of black phenolic resin similar to the ones made today. At that time, however, white handles were also available on special order. The white handles were discontinued when it was learned that the white melamine material cracked in cold climates. In addition, custom handles, mainly of desert ironwood, were also available.

The original standard sheath was black leather with a strap at the butt end. After about 5 months in production, the strap was moved to just above the guard. This eliminated the possibility of the knife slipping out of the sheath. The familar flap style sheath came into use about 1964.

In 1968, Buck began to market knives in Canada. In consequence, the blade stamping was changed to BUCK/U.S.A.

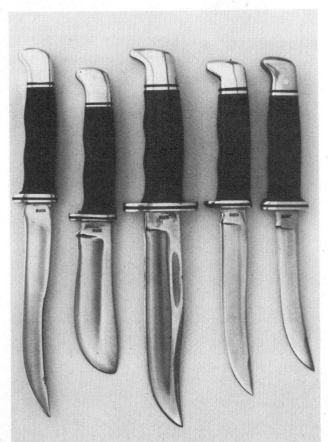

Early production knives, c1961–1963 (left to right).
A. 121 (with second type stamp): **$30–50.**
B. 103: **$30–40.**
C. 119: **$35–50.**
D. 105: **$30–40.**
E. 118: **$30–40.**

Blade Designs of the Buck Knife are the result of a vast compilation of sketches and descriptions suggested by professional sportsmen. Each knife is designed to fulfill a specific purpose . . . years of research and field testing went into each design.

GENERAL — Model #120 — Heavy Bowie-styled knife similar in shape to the #119 but with 7½" blade. This knife is used by many as a survival knife. Good for all-around camp use, chopping, game and as a fighting knife. **$22.00**

SPECIAL — Model #119 — A practical Bowie-styled knife with a 6" blade and blood groove. Beautifully balanced and shaped. Designed for heavy all-around knife work. **$20.00**

CAPER — Model #116 — A short 3¼" blade designed for saving the trophy. Best suited for working around the horns and ears. It is also a splendid knife for pan fish, small game and birds. **$14.00**

SKINNER — Model #103 — Wide 4" blade, heavy, fine edge. Weight, size and design of this knife makes the toughest skinning jobs simple. **$18.00**

PATHFINDER — Model #105 — This heavy duty, 5" blade is a wonderful all-purpose knife for general outdoor use. Much heavier blade than Model #118. For those who need a rugged knife. **$16.00**

WOODSMAN — Model #102 — A 4" straight blade with a fine point for fish and small game. **$13.00**

PERSONAL — Model #118 — This famous Buck knife combines the skinning sweep of the wide skinner with a 4½" slender blade of a small game knife. **$14.00**

FOLDING — Model #110 — 4" blade pivots on ¼" bearing and has positive lock in open position. Handle of golden-grain Macassar ebony wood with solid brass bolsters and liner cast in one piece. May be carried in pocket or sheath. An ideal heavy duty outdoor knife for those preferring a folding blade. Over-all length 5". **$16.00**

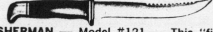

FISHERMAN — Model #121 — This "fisherman's dream" is 10 inches over-all with a gentle curving flexible blade for perfect filleting, it also has a scaler added for extra convenience. This is the perfect knife for all kinds of fishing from ultra light to deep sea sport fishing. **$14.00**

#104 TWINSET
#104 Twinset (shown) combines the #102 Woodsman and the #103 Skinner in a combination sheath. **$28.50**

#115 SPORTSMAN'S SET
Combines #118 Personal with the #103 Skinner in a combination sheath. **$29.50**

#117 TROPHY SET
Combines #116 Caper with the #103 Skinner in a combination sheath. **$29.50**

HUNTER'S AXE — Model #106 — 4" head 2½" cutting edge, 10½" over-all. Triple plated high impact tool steel. Ideal for dressing big game and for all-around camp and trail use. **$20.00**

Circa 1964 Buck catalog showing original production models and 1964 prices.

In the years since 1968, Buck has added many new models, both fixed blade and folding. However, all of the original hunting knife numbers are still in production. For more information on Buck, see the chapters *Buck Folding Knives* and *Buck Custom and Limited Edition Knives*.

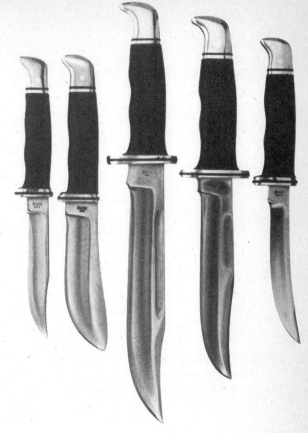

Post-1968 knives marked BUCK/U.S.A.
Values: **$35** (smallest) to **$60** (largest).

(Top to bottom).
A. Current Model 124 Frontiersman: list price.
B. Early 1970s Model 124 (this knife with serrations is
   Model 122 Nemo): **$75–100.**
C. Last Model 122 Nemo (discontinued): **$75–90.**

Custom and Hand-Made Fixed Blade Knives

Introduction

WITH THE HELP of two dedicated collectors, Bill and Joanna Spivey, and also with the help of the makers' own descriptions, I have divided custom and hand-made fixed blade knives into nine categories. Because custom knives show so much variety, the boundaries between these categories are at times a little fuzzy. Most knives fit readily into one of the categories, but there are few about which the three of us had three (or more) different opinions.

Ultimately, shape was the deciding feature. Therefore, for example, a hunting knife, no matter how exquisitely wrought or decorated, we still classed as a hunting knife.

A list of the nine categories follows. Within each category, the knives are arranged alphabetically by maker. Participation in this book by makers was largely voluntary. I have included a few pictures of knives from my own files, but about 90 percent were sent by the makers themselves.

The listed prices are current market value, usually as indicated by the maker. Prices of similar knives from knife dealers will often be higher. See the chapters on buying and selling knives and on custom folding knives for more information on prices. See Ken Warner's latest *Knives* annual for addresses of makers.

Categories

1. **Hunting, Fishing, and Utility Knives.** These are practical shaped working knives, though some of them are quite fancy and expensive.
2. **Combat and Survival Knives.** You could call these modern or high-tech bowies.
3. **Traditional Bowies.**
4. **Daggers and Boot Knives.** Like the knives in Class 1, these weapons are, or at least seem, practical.
5. **Art Daggers.** No doubt these would all "work," but they were made to be looked at—and admired.
6. **Exotic, Fantasy, and Mid-East Style Knives.** Like Class 5 in intention, but different shapes.
7. **Japanese Inspired Knives and Swords.**
8. **European and Fantasy Style Axes and Swords.**
9. **Miniatures.**

1. HUNTING, FISHING AND UTILITY KNIVES

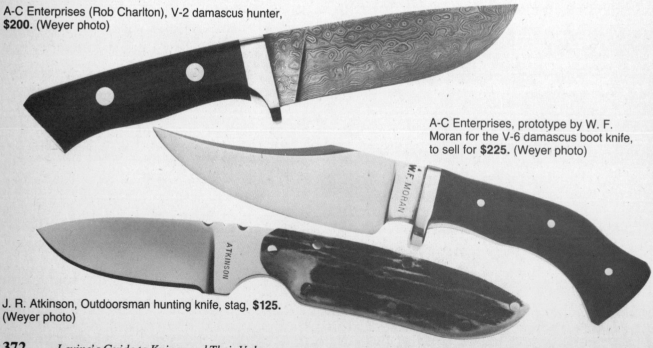

A-C Enterprises (Rob Charlton), V-2 damascus hunter, **$200.** (Weyer photo)

A-C Enterprises, prototype by W. F. Moran for the V-6 damascus boot knife, to sell for **$225.** (Weyer photo)

J. R. Atkinson, Outdoorsman hunting knife, stag, **$125.** (Weyer photo)

1. HUNTING, FISHING AND UTILITY KNIVES

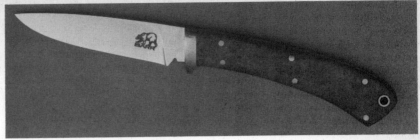

BARR (Barr Quarton), ultra light hunting knife, cherry burl, **$180** with sheath.

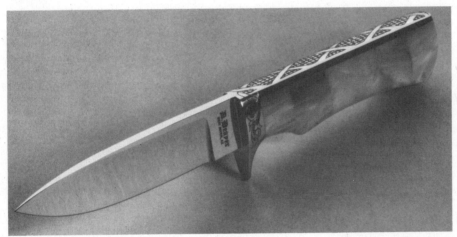

James J. Barry, fish filet knife, wood micarta and brass, **$125**.

Gene Baskett, fancy drop point hunter, **$225** with sheath.

Devon Beaver, amber backstrap hunter, 154CM blade, 416SS guard and backstrap, **$500**. (Lenz photo)

Leroy Besic, semi-skinner, ebony and stainless, **$160** with sheath.

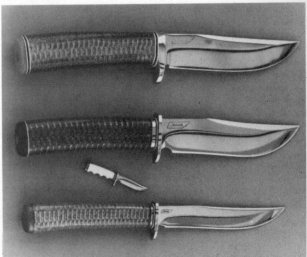

William Bennett, 3 corn cob handled hunting knives, **$65-75** each, miniature **$35**.

1. HUNTING, FISHING AND UTILITY KNIVES

Wayne Clay, Howard white tail hunter, 154CM blade, buffalo horn, **$150.** (Color Grafix photo)

Wayne Clay, kitchen set of chef, boning, and slicing knives, 154CM blades, black micarta, **$225/set.**

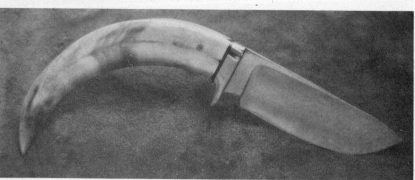

Right: Keith Coleman, hunting knife, tusk handle, **$120.**

Eldon Courtney, upswept skinner, L6 blade, stag phenolic and bronze, **$160** with sheath.

Pat Crawford, hunting knives, stag with guard **$160**; micarta **$150.**

Below: Sam Cox, duck knife and duck call: stainless, **$405/set**; damascus, **$550/set.**

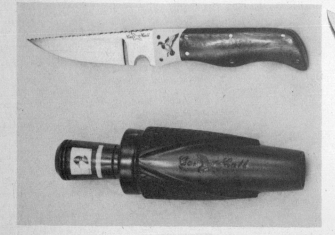

1. HUNTING, FISHING AND UTILITY KNIVES

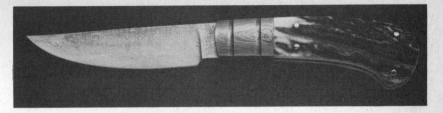

Right: James Crowell, 4½″ blade damascus hunter, stag, **$600.** (Weyer photo)

Left: James Crowell, 4″ blade damascus letter opener, **$200.** (Weyer photo)

Patrick Donovan, hunting knife with engraved fittings, **$350.**

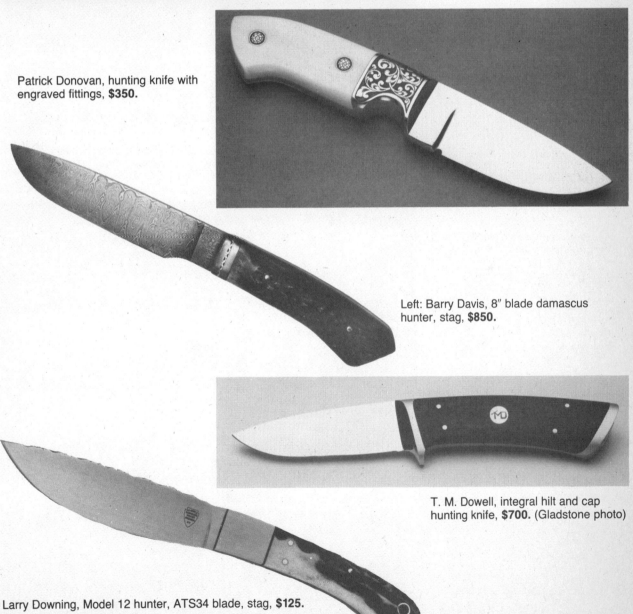

Left: Barry Davis, 8″ blade damascus hunter, stag, **$850.**

T. M. Dowell, integral hilt and cap hunting knife, **$700.** (Gladstone photo)

Larry Downing, Model 12 hunter, ATS34 blade, stag, **$125.**

1. HUNTING, FISHING AND UTILITY KNIVES

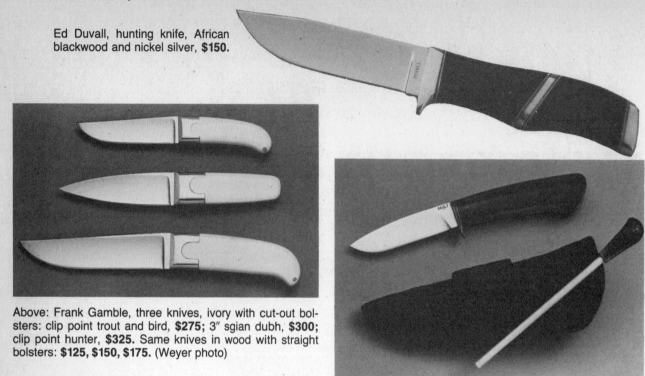

Ed Duvall, hunting knife, African blackwood and nickel silver, **$150.**

Above: Frank Gamble, three knives, ivory with cut-out bolsters: clip point trout and bird, **$275;** 3″ sgian dubh, **$300;** clip point hunter, **$325.** Same knives in wood with straight bolsters: **$125, $150, $175.** (Weyer photo)

Above: Clay R. Gault, hunting knife, oosic handles, elephant hide sheath, engraving, sharpener, **$340.** (Weyer photo)

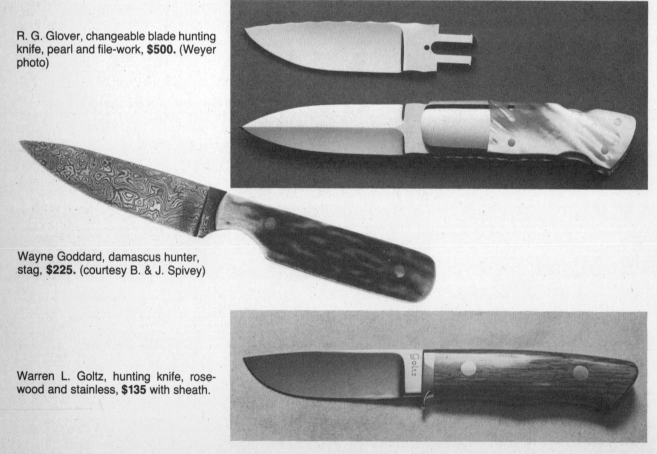

R. G. Glover, changeable blade hunting knife, pearl and file-work, **$500.** (Weyer photo)

Wayne Goddard, damascus hunter, stag, **$225.** (courtesy B. & J. Spivey)

Warren L. Goltz, hunting knife, rosewood and stainless, **$135** with sheath.

1. HUNTING, FISHING AND UTILITY KNIVES

William Harsey, trout knife, 154CM blade, ivory micarta, etched rainbow trout, **$300.** Without etching, **$150.**

William Harsey, hunting knives, 154CM blades, bubinga wood, **$250 each.**

Bob Hayes, hunting knife, **$750.** (Courtesy Steven Weiss)

Larry Hendricks, kangaroo hunting knife and caper, **$1,200.**

Bill Herndon, small hunting knife, American buffalo horn, engraving, **$180.**

Bill Herndon, hunting knives: smaller, tulip wood, **$130;** larger, cocobolo and white fiber, **$165.**

1. HUNTING, FISHING AND UTILITY KNIVES

Ron Holstrom, hunting knife, cocobolo and stainless, Byron Burgess engraving, **$195.**

Arthur J. Hubbard, working knife, maple, **$105.**

Arthur J. Hubbard, small working knife, rosewood, **$85.**

Dennis Husman, three knives: hunter, stag, **$125;** gentleman's knife (Scooter's), 154CM blade, ironwood and nickel silver, **$125;** large utility knife, 0-1 blade, black micarta, **$85.** All with sheaths.

Above: Ronald B. Johnson, hunting knives, smaller, horn, **$175;** larger, stag, engraving, **$190.** (Weyer photo).

Right: S. R. Johnson, hunting knives, nickel silver guards; larger: Bill's drop, bighorn, **$425;** smaller, mini Bill's drop, stag, **$275.** (Ruby photo)

1. HUNTING, FISHING AND UTILITY KNIVES

Above: Tommy Lee, classic hunters, ebony and ivory, **$225 each.**

Below: Lee Bench Made, utility knife, white micarta, scrimshaw by Bob Burdette, **$125** with sheath. (Weyer photo)

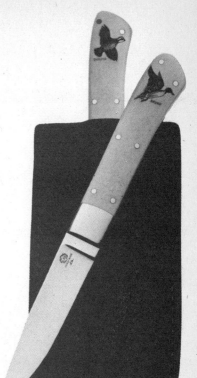

Above: Norman Levine, extra heavy duty hunters, ivory and stainless, **$275 each** without scrimshaw. Scrimshaw of Quana Parker by Adam Funmaker; of John Wayne by Bob Engnath.

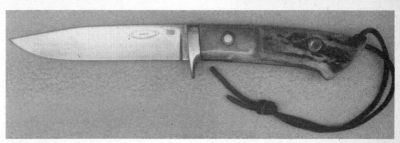

Robert W. Loveless (Lawndale mark), clip point hunting knife, stag, **$1,000–1,250** with sheath.

R. W. Loveless (Riverside & nude mark), hunting knife, stag, engraving, **$1,200** with sheath. Without engraving, **$700–1,000.**

R. W. Loveless (Riverside mark), drop point hunting knife, micarta, **$600–1,000** with sheath. (Loveless knives courtesy S. F. Gun Exchange)

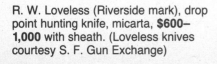

1. HUNTING, FISHING AND UTILITY KNIVES

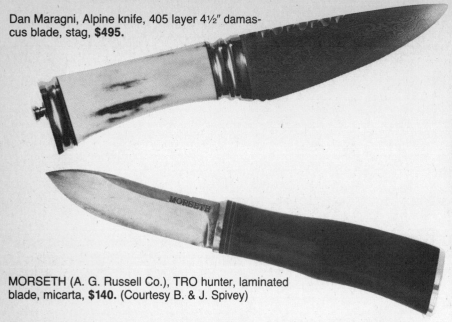

Dan Maragni, Alpine knife, 405 layer 4½″ damascus blade, stag, **$495.**

MORSETH (A. G. Russell Co.), TRO hunter, laminated blade, micarta, **$140.** (Courtesy B. & J. Spivey)

James McLeod, American collection caper, briar, **$85.**

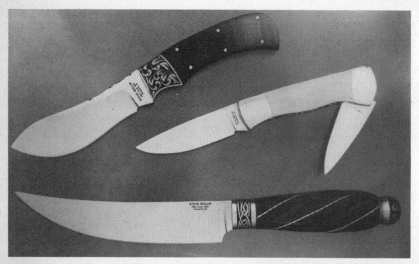

Above: Steve Mullin: three knives: skinner, bighorn, engraving, **$310;** German hunter with folding auxiliary blade, ivory micarta, **$250;** twist handle camp knife, cocobolo, silver wire, nickel silver and brass, engraving, **$375.**

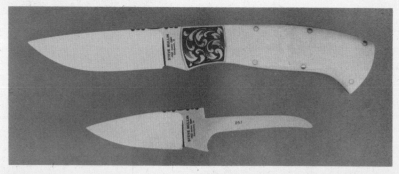

Steve Mullin, changeable blade hunting knife, ivory, engraving, **$410.**

Dave Murphy, utility knife, F-8 blade, tulip wood, brass, green micarta, **$225.**

1. HUNTING, FISHING AND UTILITY KNIVES

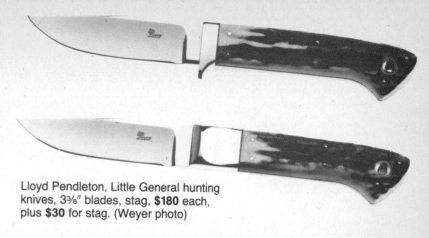

Lloyd Pendleton, Little General hunting knives, 3⅜″ blades, stag, **$180** each, plus **$30** for stag. (Weyer photo)

Paul Myers, hunter, micarta, wrap-around color scrimshaw by Mary Austin Talley, engraving by Gary Blanchard, **$1,000.** (L. Talley photo)

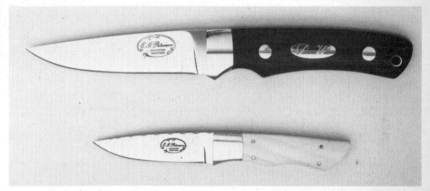

E. G. Peterson, hunting knives: large, **$100** with sheath, inlay extra; small, **$70** with sheath, ivory extra.

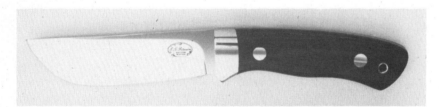

E. G. Peterson, skinning knife, ATS34 blade, wood micarta, **$125** with sheath.

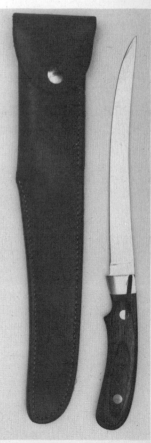

Right: E. G. Peterson, fish filet knife, wood micarta, **$100** with sheath.

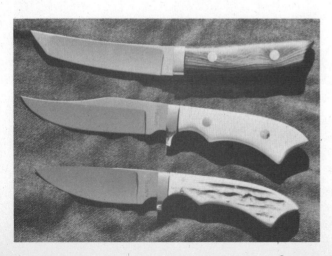

Left: Steve Price, 3 hunting knives: tanto style **$145,** trailing point **$190,** drop point, stag, **$145.**

1. HUNTING, FISHING AND UTILITY KNIVES

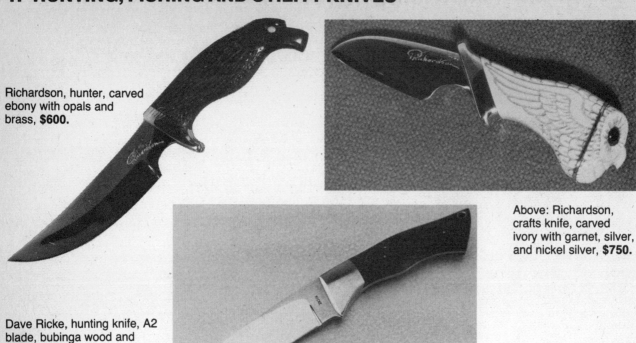

Richardson, hunter, carved ebony with opals and brass, **$600.**

Above: Richardson, crafts knife, carved ivory with garnet, silver, and nickel silver, **$750.**

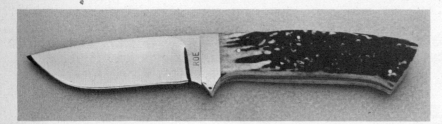

Dave Ricke, hunting knife, A2 blade, bubinga wood and brass, **$125.**

Fred Roe, Model R-15 drop point hunter, stag, **$100;** as shown: 154CM blade, tapered tang, **$125.** (Scadlock photo)

Fred Roe, Small Game Specials, engraving: ivory, **$200;** pearl, **$225.** (Scadlock photo)

Mark Roper, hunting knives, hardwood handles, without guard **$105;** with guard, **$115 each.** (Weyer photo).

1. HUNTING, FISHING AND UTILITY KNIVES

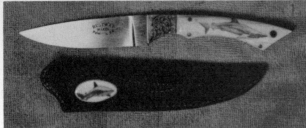

Left: RUSTWAY (Charles Rust), hunting knife, 154CM blade, walrus ivory, engraving by George Sherwood, scrimshaw by Bob Engnath, **$500** with sheath.

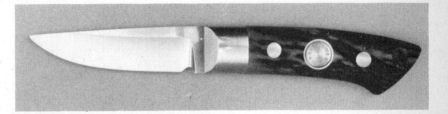

RUSTWAY (Charles Rust), hunting knife, 154CM blade, laminated ivory and buffalo horn, nickel silver, **$450.**

Herman J. Schneider, hunting knife, stag, bolsters, **$850.**

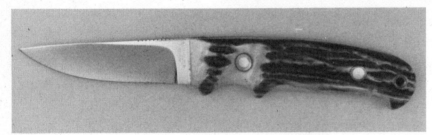

Herman J. Schneider, hunting knife, stag, **$750.** (Courtesy S. F. Gun Exchange)

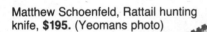

Matthew Schoenfeld, Rattail hunting knife, **$195.** (Yeomans photo)

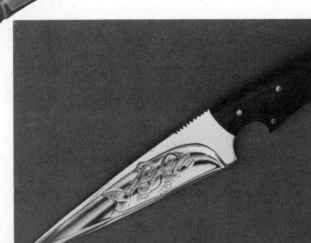

Matthew Schoenfeld, fish knife, etched by Shirley McLean, **$350.** (Yeomans photo)

1. HUNTING, FISHING AND UTILITY KNIVES

Stephen Schwarzer, damascus hunter, ivory, **$700.** (Weyer photo)

Stephen Schwarzer, damascus hunter, carved stag, **$365.** (Weyer photo).

Above: Corbet R. Sigman, Model #4-4″ hunter, quilted maple, **$270.**

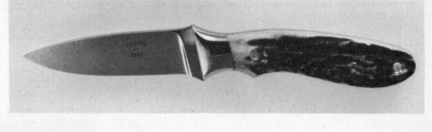

Right: Corbet R. Sigman, Model #2-3½″ hunter, India stag, **$310.**

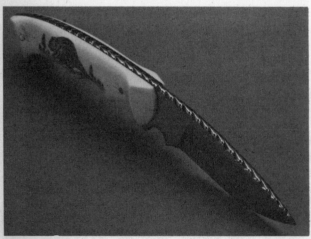

Harry Stalter, hunting knife, ivory, file-work, scrimshaw, **$250.** (Tallyn photo)

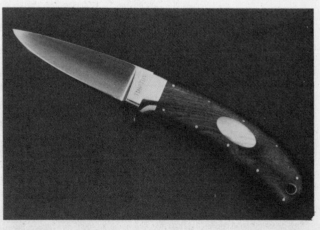

TIMOTHY (Tim Wright), bird knife, ironwood stainless and pearl, **$240.**

1. HUNTING, FISHING AND UTILITY KNIVES

R. A. Turnbull, drop point hunter, 154CM blade, cocobolo and bronze, engraving by Dennis Brooker, **$350.** Without engraving, **$250.** (Weyer photo)

W. W. Wood, fancy skinner, **$400.** (Weyer photo)

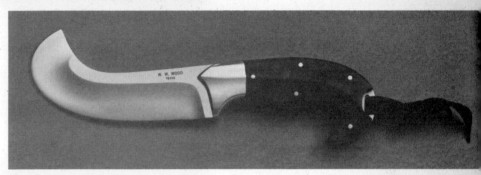

Webster Wood, large elaborate drop point hunter, **$450.**

Cliff Young, Model 15 Lac Dumoine filet knife, **$120.** (Young photo)

Below: Michael Zscherny, three knives: smallest, ivory micarta, **$110;** longest, double edged, hardwood, **$155.** medium hunting knife, stag, **$125.**

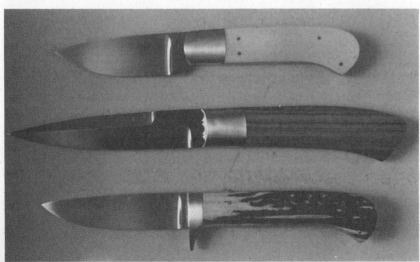

2. COMBAT AND SURVIVAL KNIVES

Leroy Besic, Mini-bowie, rosewood, **$325.** (Fitzgerald photo)

Fred Carter, Hell Razor fighter, ivory, stainless, engraving, **$1,000.** (Weyer photo)

Right: Frank and Mark Centofante, Model 6 6″ fighter, **$300.** (Weyer photo)

Below: Keith E. Coleman, survival knives: flat sawtooth, **$90;** hollow handle sawtooth, **$200;** double edge, **$175.**

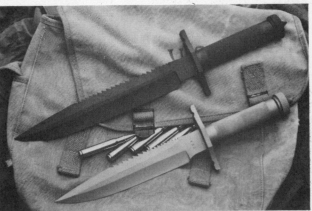

Above: Colin Cox, Fierce Blood survival knives, **$475 each.**

Left: Pat Crawford, combat knives: standard, stag, **$250;** sub-hilt, wood, **$290.** (Weyer photo)

2. COMBAT AND SURVIVAL KNIVES

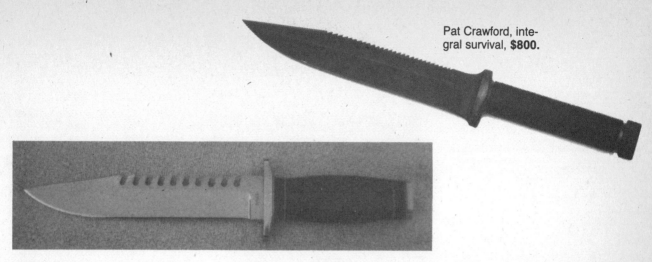

Pat Crawford, integral survival, **$800.**

Above: Ed Duvall, survival, cocobolo, buffalo horn, nickel silver, **$325.**

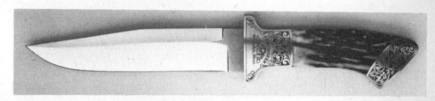

Above: Pete Forthofer, fighter, stag, stainless, engraving by Tony Tuscano, **$395.**

Frank Gamble, 25th Century Fighting Knife, amber, 10″ blade, **$700.** (Weyer photo)

Frank Gamble, Scagel camp knife replica, stag, **$350.** (Weyer photo)

Warren L. Goltz, fighter, desert iron-wood, stainless, **$295** with presentation box.

3. COMBAT AND SURVIVAL KNIVES

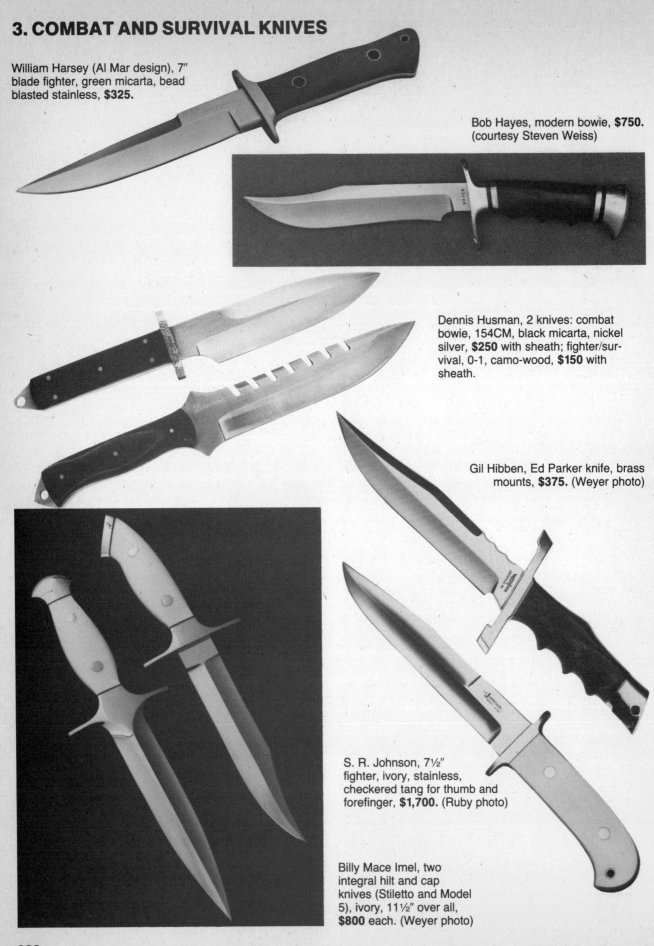

William Harsey (Al Mar design), 7″ blade fighter, green micarta, bead blasted stainless, **$325.**

Bob Hayes, modern bowie, **$750.** (courtesy Steven Weiss)

Dennis Husman, 2 knives: combat bowie, 154CM, black micarta, nickel silver, **$250** with sheath; fighter/survival, 0-1, camo-wood, **$150** with sheath.

Gil Hibben, Ed Parker knife, brass mounts, **$375.** (Weyer photo)

S. R. Johnson, 7½″ fighter, ivory, stainless, checkered tang for thumb and forefinger, **$1,700.** (Ruby photo)

Billy Mace Imel, two integral hilt and cap knives (Stiletto and Model 5), ivory, 11½″ over all, **$800** each. (Weyer photo)

2. COMBAT AND SURVIVAL KNIVES

Lee Benchmade, damascus fighter, curly maple, **$385;** two damascus boot knives: curly maple, stag, **$160** each. (Scadlock photo)

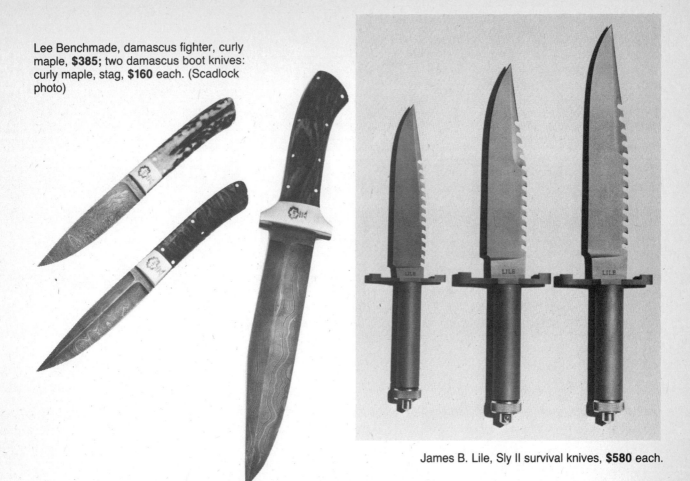

James B. Lile, Sly II survival knives, **$580** each.

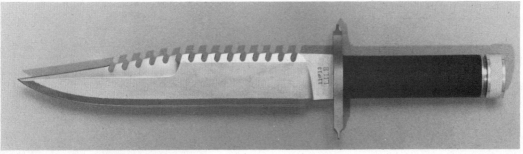

James B. Lile, First Blood survival knife, 1 of 13, **$4,000–$11,000** (when available).

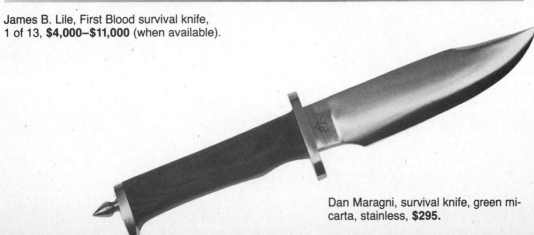

Dan Maragni, survival knife, green micarta, stainless, **$295.**

2. COMBAT AND SURVIVAL KNIVES

Tom Maringer, Vorpal 2 combat knife, 154CM, 10″ overall, **$250** with leather sheath, **$200** with Kydex sheath. (Verhoeven photo)

Lloyd Pendleton, 5½″ blade fighter, **$600.** (Weyer photo)

Lloyd Pendleton, 8″ blade sub-hilt fighter, **$1,300.** (Weyer photo)

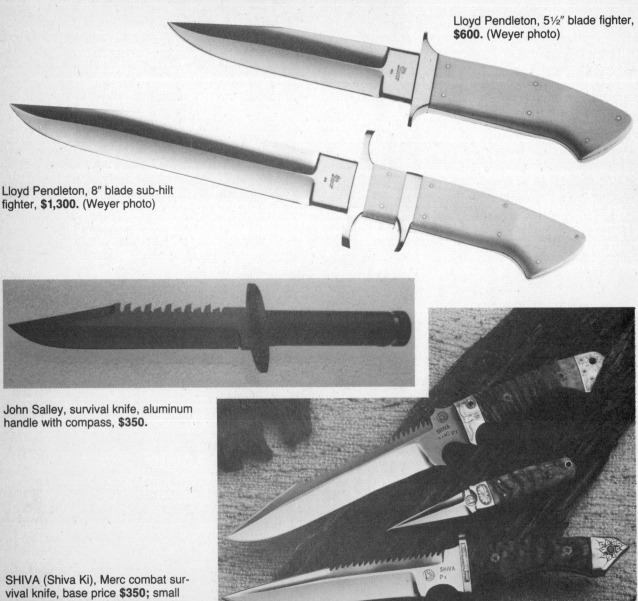

John Salley, survival knife, aluminum handle with compass, **$350.**

SHIVA (Shiva Ki), Merc combat survival knife, base price **$350;** small dagger, base price **$165;** sheep-horn and engraving extra. (Weyer photo)

2. COMBAT AND SURVIVAL KNIVES

SHIVA (Shiva Ki), damascus fighting knives, **$1,000–1,500;** small knife **$300.**

Below: R. A. Turnbull, knife, rosewood, nickel silver, **$250.**

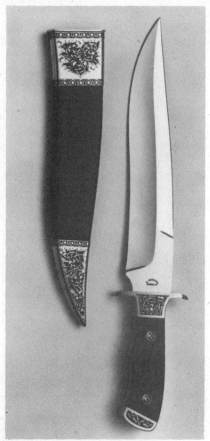

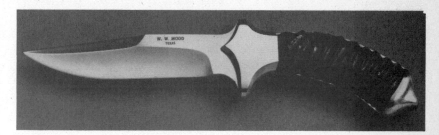

W. W. Wood, combat knife, fancy horn handle, **$450.** (Weyer photo)

Buster Warenski, 11″ blade fighting knife, rosewood burl, stainless, engraving by Steve Lindsay, **$5,200** with leather and nickel silver sheath. (Weyer photo)

Cliff Young, fighter, stag, **$295.** (Young photo)

Tim Zowada, two damascus fighters, **$450 each.** (Weyer photo)

Jack W. Crain, Siege Bowies, 13-knife set illustrating
the siege of the Alamo, silver mounts. Unique set.

3. TRADITIONAL BOWIES

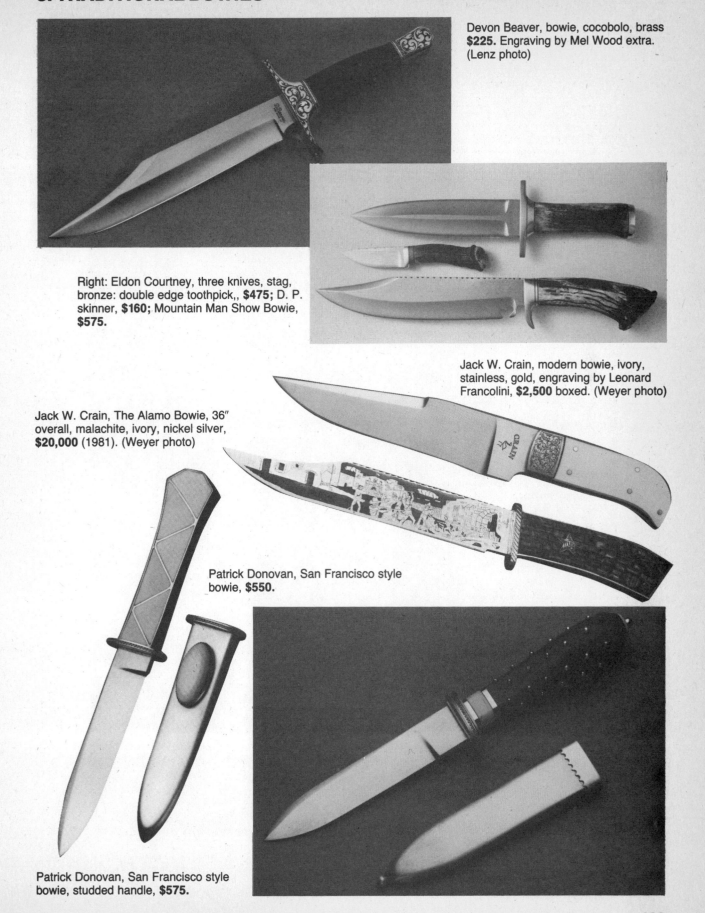

Devon Beaver, bowie, cocobolo, brass **$225.** Engraving by Mel Wood extra. (Lenz photo)

Right: Eldon Courtney, three knives, stag, bronze: double edge toothpick,, **$475;** D. P. skinner, **$160;** Mountain Man Show Bowie, **$575.**

Jack W. Crain, modern bowie, ivory, stainless, gold, engraving by Leonard Francolini, **$2,500** boxed. (Weyer photo)

Jack W. Crain, The Alamo Bowie, 36″ overall, malachite, ivory, nickel silver, **$20,000** (1981). (Weyer photo)

Patrick Donovan, San Francisco style bowie, **$550.**

Patrick Donovan, San Francisco style bowie, studded handle, **$575.**

3. TRADITIONAL BOWIES

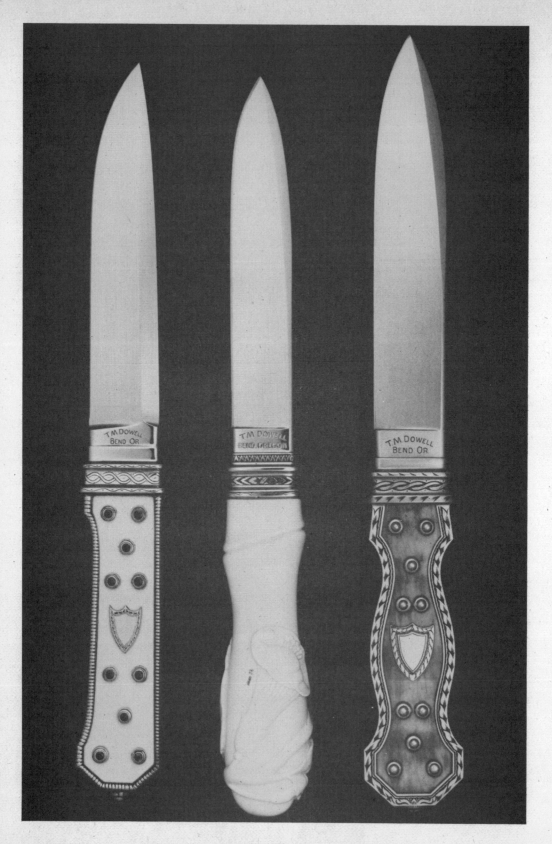

T. M. Dowell, three integral construction replica Michael Price bowies. Left: ivory grips set with rubies, engraving by Buster Warenski, **$5,000.** Center: ivory, carved poppy and engraving by Ron Skaggs, **$4,000.** Right: Bradford knife, engraving by Ron Skaggs, **$5,000.** (Gladstone photo)

3. TRADITIONAL BOWIES

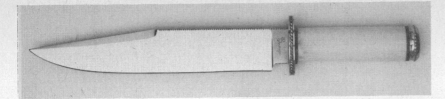

Pete Forthofer, bowie, ivory, nickel silver, **$450.**

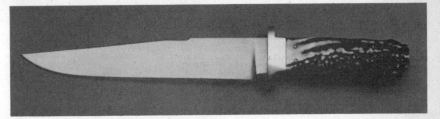

Frank Gamble, classic English bowie, stag, **$500.** (Weyer photo)

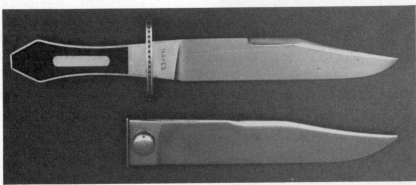

Bob Hayes, coffin hilt bowie, **$2,000.** (courtesy Steven Weiss)

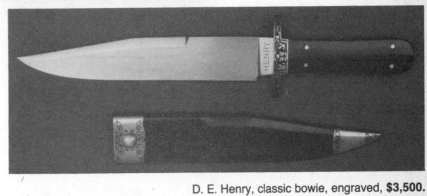

D. E. Henry, classic bowie, engraved, **$3,500.**

Jess Horn, bowie, engraved, **$1,500.**

D. E. Henry, Big Bear bowie, stag, **$2,000.**

3. TRADITIONAL BOWIES

KLH (Kevin L. Hoffman), bowie, stag, **$500**; heart boot knife, stag **$265** with sheath; hunter, horn, silver, **$500**.

James B. Lile, English style bowie, 11″ blade, ivory, nickel silver, engraving, **$3,000** with sheath.

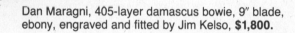

Dan Maragni, 405-layer damascus bowie, 9″ blade, ebony, engraved and fitted by Jim Kelso, **$1,800**.

W. D. Pease, bowie, stag, file-worked guard, **$800**. (Weyer photo)

Steve Price, bowie, stag, brass, **$225** with beaded sheath. (Fedorak photo)

RUSTWAY (Charles Rust), classic bowie, mastodon ivory, scrimshaw, **$1,200** with boa and lizard skin sheath.

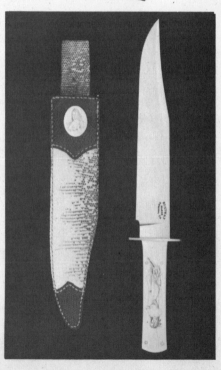

3. TRADITIONAL BOWIES

Salamander Armoury, bowie, **$175.**

Stephen Schwarzer, massive damascus bowie, **$1,850.** (Weyer photo)

Ken Ward, bowie, stag, **$250.**

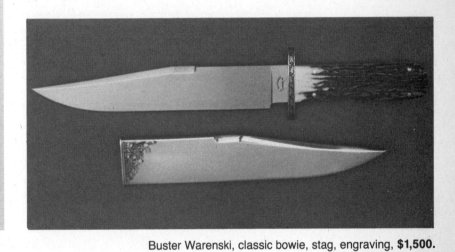

Glen A. Soares, San Francisco style bowie, abalone, nickel silver, **$800.** (Courtesy Paul Friedrich)

Buster Warenski, classic bowie, stag, engraving, **$1,500.**

Michael Zscherny, bowie, stag, engraving, **$600.**

4. DAGGERS AND BOOT KNIVES

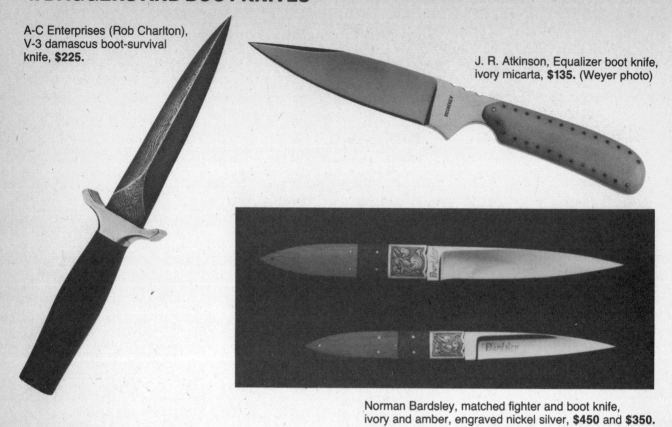

A-C Enterprises (Rob Charlton), V-3 damascus boot-survival knife, **$225.**

J. R. Atkinson, Equalizer boot knife, ivory micarta, **$135.** (Weyer photo)

Norman Bardsley, matched fighter and boot knife, ivory and amber, engraved nickel silver, **$450** and **$350.**

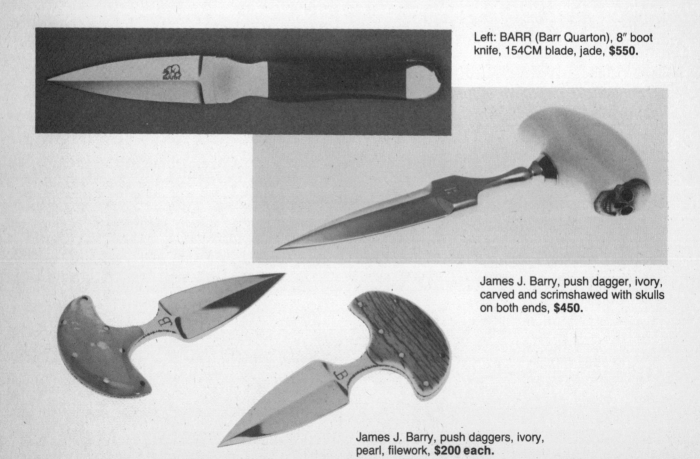

Left: BARR (Barr Quarton), 8″ boot knife, 154CM blade, jade, **$550.**

James J. Barry, push dagger, ivory, carved and scrimshawed with skulls on both ends, **$450.**

James J. Barry, push daggers, ivory, pearl, filework, **$200 each.**

4. DAGGERS AND BOOT KNIVES

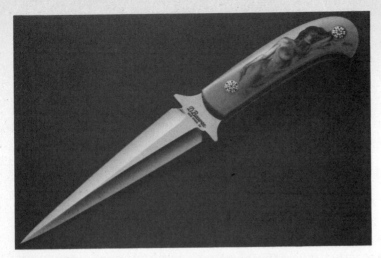

Devon Beaver, boot knife, 154CM blade, ivory micarta, **$185.** Scrimshaw by Bob Engnath extra. (Lenz photo)

Above: Keith Coleman, dagger, imitation pearl, **$250** with sheath.

Left: Pat Crawford, key-ring knife, **$35** with sheath. (Ruby photo)

Left: Pat Crawford, sleeve dagger, **$65** with sheath. (Ruby photo)

Dennis Bradley, three knives: double heart boot knife, **$300;** classic dagger, **$500;** Model 15 hunter, **$125.** (Weyer photo)

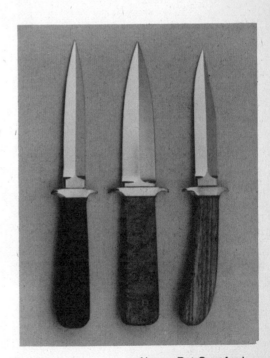

Above: Pat Crawford, three boot knives, hard-woods, **$120 each.** (Weyer photo)

4. DAGGERS AND BOOT KNIVES

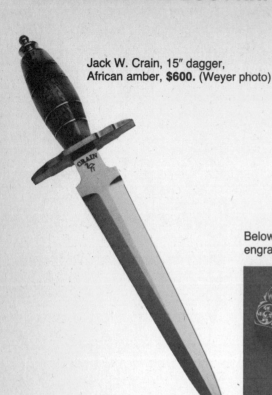

Jack W. Crain, 15″ dagger, African amber, **$600.** (Weyer photo)

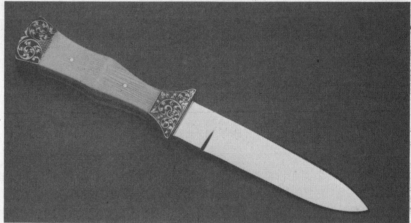

Barry Davis, damascus boot knife, ebony, ivory, **$750** with sheath.

Below: Patrick Donovan, dagger, ivory, engraving, **$475.**

Below: Frank Gamble, 4″ blade boot knife, pearl, engraving, **$750** with sheath. Base price with wood handle, **$300** with sheath. (Weyer photo)

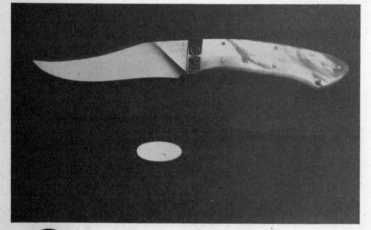

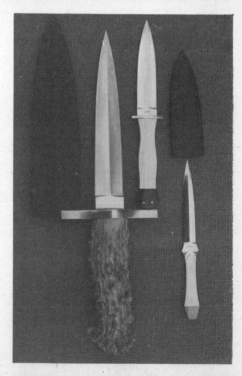

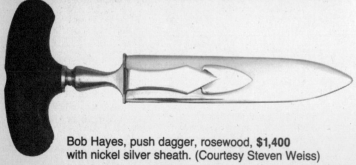

Bob Hayes, push dagger, rosewood, **$1,400** with nickel silver sheath. (Courtesy Steven Weiss)

Vernon Hicks, daggers with sheaths: small **$100 each;** large **$150.**

4. DAGGERS AND BOOT KNIVES

S. R. Johnson, 4¼″ blade dirk, stag, nickel silver, **$525.** Engraving by Lynton McKenzie **$600** extra. (Weyer photo)

Below: KLH (Kevin L. Hoffman), push dagger, **$500.**

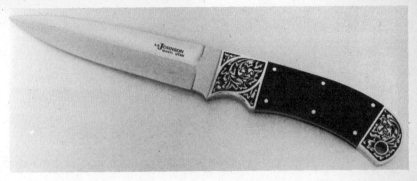

S. R. Johnson, 5″ blade special order dirk, African blackwood, nickel silver, **$1,100.** Engraving by Steve Lindsay **$1,500** extra. (Lindsay photo)

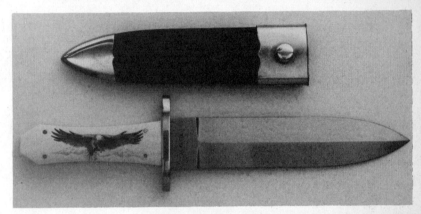

Above: Jeff Klein, dagger, **$350** with sheath. Scrimshaw by Gigi **$75** extra. (Courtesy Paul Friedrich)

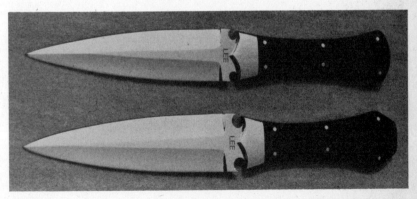

Tommy Lee, boot kives, ebony, **$250 each.**

Scott Lankton, three damascus knives with handles by P. J. Diem: boot knife, curly maple, **$500;** small boot knife, blackwood and paduc, **$450;** hunter, rosewood and ivory, **$400.** (Weyer photo)

4. DAGGERS AND BOOT KNIVES

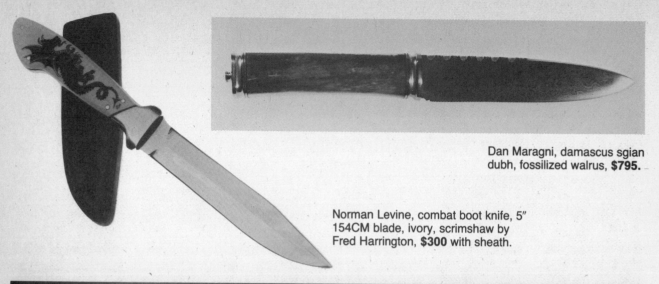

Dan Maragni, damascus sgian dubh, fossilized walrus, **$795.**

Norman Levine, combat boot knife, 5″ 154CM blade, ivory, scrimshaw by Fred Harrington, **$300** with sheath.

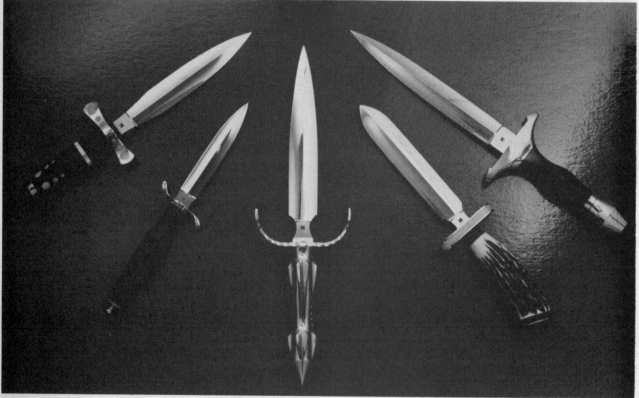

Chris Miller, Jr., five daggers: left to right: **$575, $450, $750, $375, $500.**

Morris C. Pulliam, hand-forged boot knife, hardwood, **$180.** (Scadlock photo)

4. DAGGERS AND BOOT KNIVES

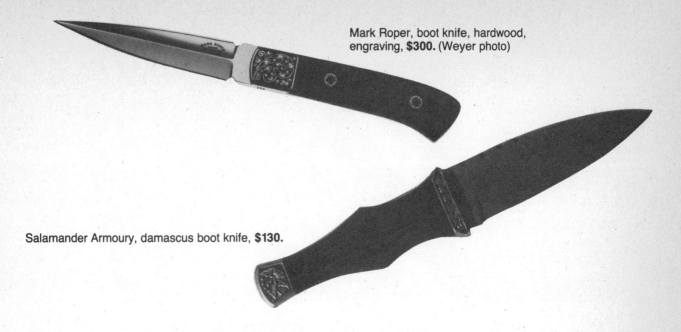

Mark Roper, boot knife, hardwood, engraving, **$300.** (Weyer photo)

Salamander Armoury, damascus boot knife, **$130.**

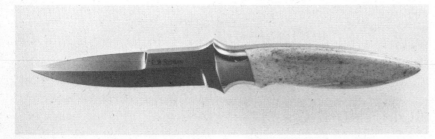

Corbet R. Sigman, boot knife, oosic handle, **$550.**

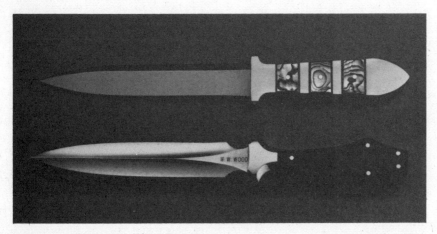

W. W. Wood, daggers: abalone, hardwood, **$300 each.** (Weyer photo)

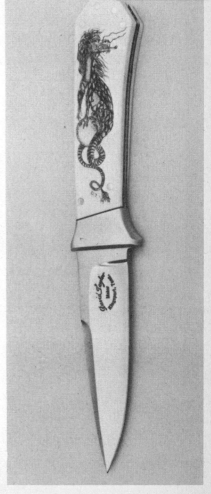

David Taylor, boot knife, scrimshaw and filework, **$150.** (Scadlock photo)

5. ART DAGGERS

Scrimshawed Canadian lynx on a Paul Myers dagger, by Mary Austin Talley. (Gladstone photo)

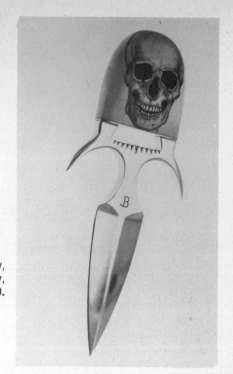

Right: James J. Barry, push dagger, walrus ivory, scrimshaw, **$650.**

Above: Fred Carter, Morning Glory Dagger, ivory, blued steel, gold wire, silver flowers, **$4,000.** (Weyer photo)

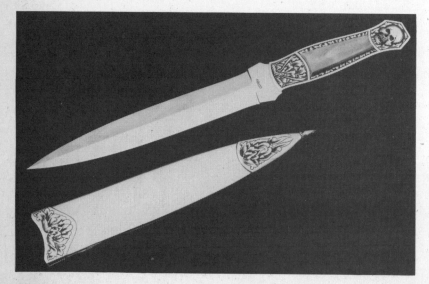

Harold Corby, Golden Dagger, engraving, **$6,700** with sheath.

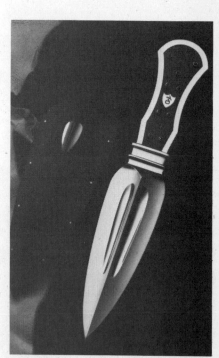

T. M. Dowell, integral Price style dagger, ebony and onyx, **$5,900** with sheath. (Weyer photo)

Harold Corby, The Rose, engraving and color scrimshaw, **$4,500.**

5. ART DAGGERS

Bill Herndon, dagger, turquoise, silver, star sapphires, **$600** with sheath.

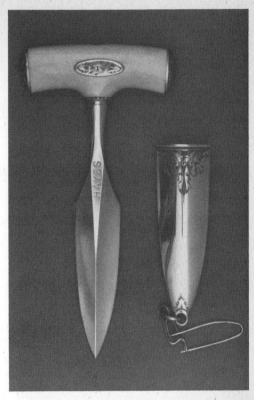

Curt Erickson, damascus dagger, ivory, **$900.** (Rasmussen photo)

Bob Hayes, push dagger, ivory, engraving, **$1,500.** (Courtesy Steven Weiss)

Left: Gil Hibben, Hornet, amber, cape buffalo horn, stainless, smoky quartz, yellow sapphires, **$2,800.** (Weyer photo)

Right: Gil Hibben (design consultant: Paul Ehlers), Dragonfly, ivory, stainless, jewels **$2,500.** (Weyer photo)

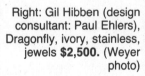

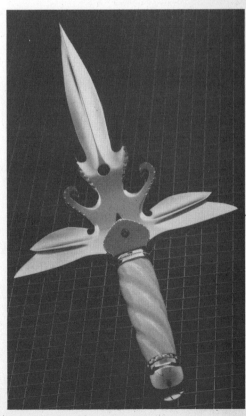

5. ART DAGGERS

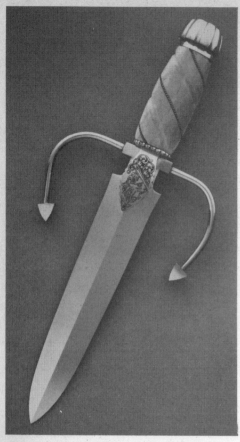

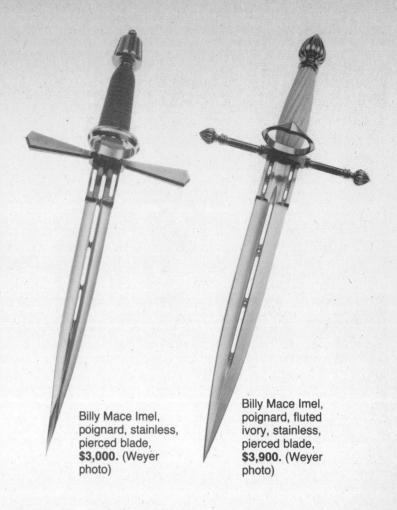

Billy Mace Imel, poignard, stainless, pierced blade, **$3,000.** (Weyer photo)

Billy Mace Imel, poignard, fluted ivory, stainless, pierced blade, **$3,900.** (Weyer photo)

Ron Holstrom, dagger, fossilized walrus ivory, stainless, engraving by Fred Harrington, **$925.** (Middle Valley photo)

KEMAL (Don Fogg and Murad Sayen), Viking Dagger, damascus, **$4,000** with sheath. (Sayen photo)

KEMAL (Don Fogg and Murad Sayen), Quillon Dagger, damascus, ivory, **$4,000.** (Sayen photo)

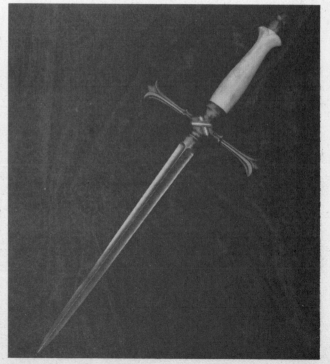

5. ART DAGGERS

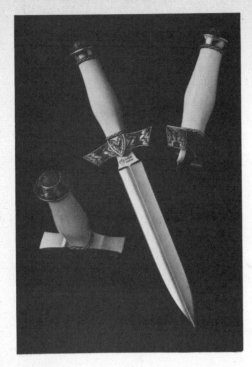

KHALSA KIRPAN (Jot Singh Khalsa), dagger, ivory, engraving, **$1,750.** (Weyer photo)

KHALSA KIRPAN (Jot Singh Khalsa), damascus dagger, **$2,000.** (Weyer photo)

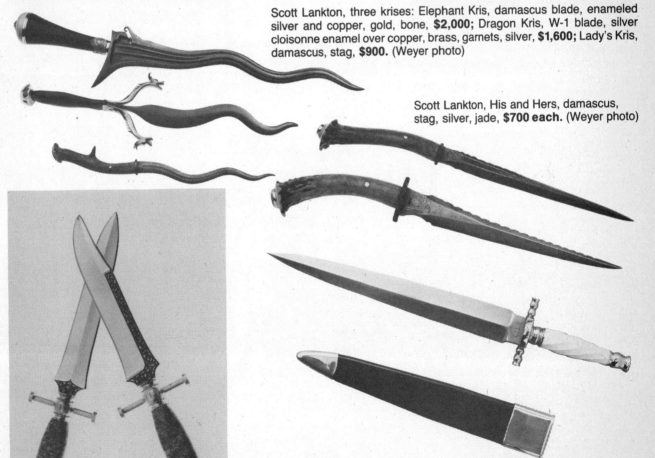

Scott Lankton, three krises: Elephant Kris, damascus blade, enameled silver and copper, gold, bone, **$2,000;** Dragon Kris, W-1 blade, silver cloisonne enamel over copper, brass, garnets, silver, **$1,600;** Lady's Kris, damascus, stag, **$900.** (Weyer photo)

Scott Lankton, His and Hers, damascus, stag, silver, jade, **$700 each.** (Weyer photo)

Norman Levine, 18-inch bowie and toothpick, solid turquoise, stainless, engraving, scrimshaw by Fred Harrington, **$7,500/pair.**

James B. Lile, 12″ Arkansas Toothpick, fluted ivory, stainless, **$2,250** with sheath.

5. ART DAGGERS

Dave Longworth, dagger, D-2 blade, cocobolo, nickel silver, **$275** with sheath.

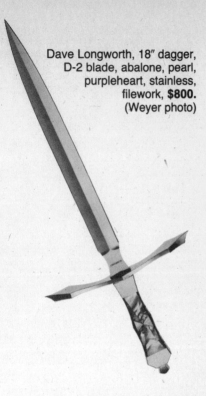

Dave Longworth, 18″ dagger, D-2 blade, abalone, pearl, purpleheart, stainless, filework, **$800.** (Weyer photo)

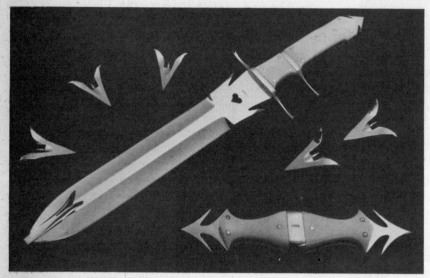

Anthony Louis, Collector's Set, ivory, **$1,500** complete.

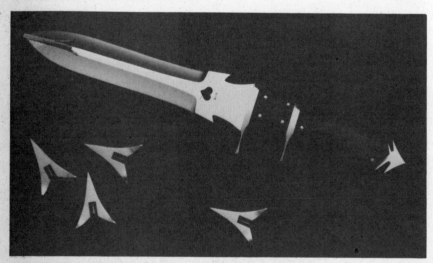

Anthony Louis, Master of Disaster, **$1,200.** (Weyer photo)

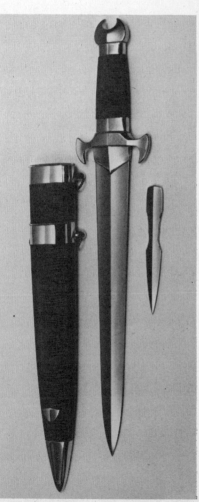

Tom Maringer, Adventurer's Dagger, 15½″ D-2 blade, stainless, maple, nickel silver, **$2,250** with sheath and throwing knife. (Verhoeven photo)

5. ART DAGGERS

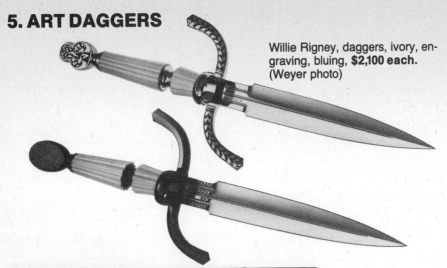

Willie Rigney, daggers, ivory, engraving, bluing, **$2,100 each.** (Weyer photo)

Herman J. Schneider, dagger, fluted ivory, engraving, **$6,000.** (Weyer photo)

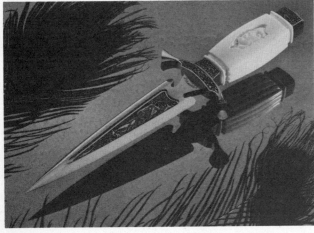

Herman J. Schneider, dagger, carved ivory, engraving, **$5,000.** (Weyer photo)

Herman J. Schneider, two damascus knives, ivory, engraving: dagger, **$4,800** with sheath; California bowie, **$4,500** with sheath. (Weyer photo)

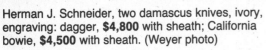

Stephen Schwarzer, damascus push dagger, carved ivory, **$1,800** with sheath. (Weyer photo)

5. ART DAGGERS

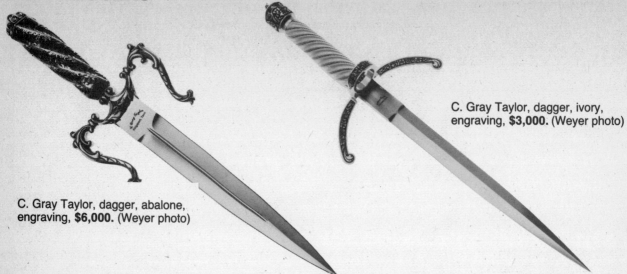

C. Gray Taylor, dagger, ivory, engraving, **$3,000.** (Weyer photo)

C. Gray Taylor, dagger, abalone, engraving, **$6,000.** (Weyer photo)

Dwight L. Towell, dagger, 10″ blade, walrus ivory, silver wire, engraving by Ron Skaggs, **$4,200.** (S. Towell photo)

Dwight L. Towell, dagger, pearl, stainless, gold, engraving by Steve Lindsay, **$2,750.** (S. Towell photo)

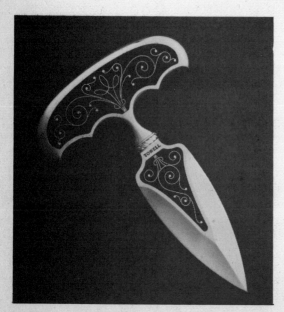

Dwight L. Towell, interframe push dagger, African blackwood, gold wire, **$4,200.** (S. Towell photo)

5. ART DAGGERS

TRO (T. R. Overeynder), dagger, fossil walrus ivory and oosic, titanium, gold plate, silver wire, **$1,000.** (Weyer photo)

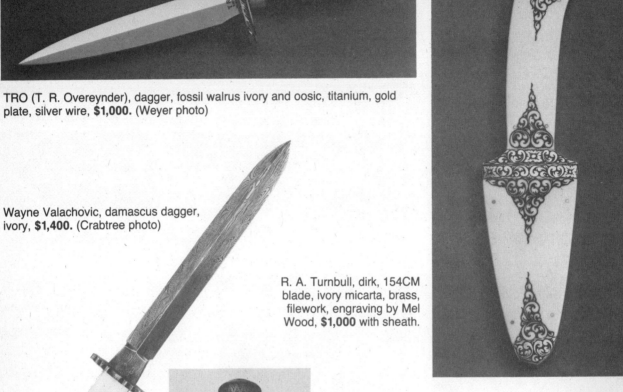

Wayne Valachovic, damascus dagger, ivory, **$1,400.** (Crabtree photo)

R. A. Turnbull, dirk, 154CM blade, ivory micarta, brass, filework, engraving by Mel Wood, **$1,000** with sheath.

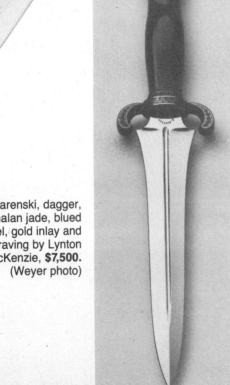

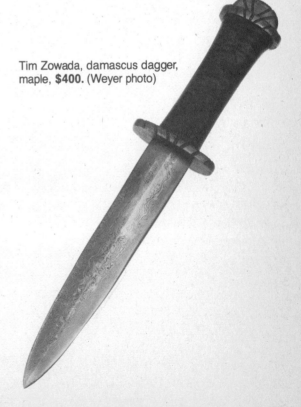

Tim Zowada, damascus dagger, maple, **$400.** (Weyer photo)

Buster Warenski, dagger, black Guatemalan jade, blued steel, gold inlay and engraving by Lynton McKenzie, **$7,500.** (Weyer photo)

6. EXOTIC, FANTASY AND MID-EAST STYLE KNIVES

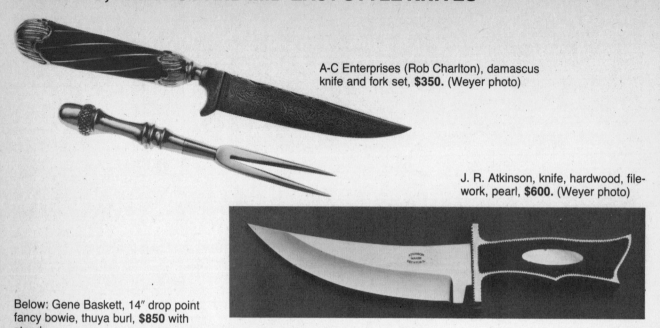

A-C Enterprises (Rob Charlton), damascus knife and fork set, **$350.** (Weyer photo)

J. R. Atkinson, knife, hardwood, file-work, pearl, **$600.** (Weyer photo)

Below: Gene Baskett, 14″ drop point fancy bowie, thuya burl, **$850** with stand.

Francis Boyd and Ken Fireman, California style damascus knife, antique walrus ivory handle, **$450.** (Tikker photo)

James Crowell, 10″ blade knife, damascus, fossilized walrus ivory, **$1,200.** (Weyer photo)

James Crowell, 9″ blade knife, damascus, ivory, **$900.** (Weyer photo)

6. EXOTIC, FANTASY AND MID-EAST STYLE KNIVES

Frank Gamble, Free Form Fighter, co-cobolo, **$150.** Filework extra. (Weyer photo)

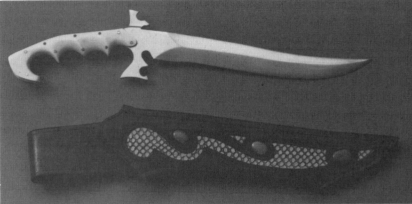

Above: Frank Gamble, 25th Century Persian, ivory, **$750** with sheath inlaid with whip snake tail and turquoise. (Weyer photo)

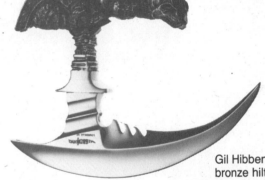

Gil Hibben, Thor's Sickle, 6″ blade, bronze hilt, **$1,000.** (Weyer photo).

Bill Herndon, small decorative knife, carved ivory micarta, **$400** with sheath.

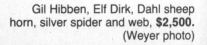

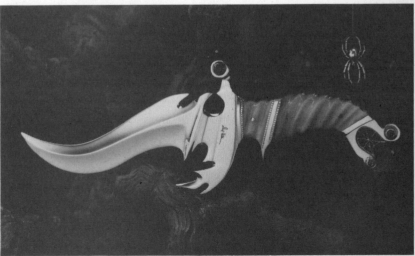

Gil Hibben, Elf Dirk, Dahl sheep horn, silver spider and web, **$2,500.** (Weyer photo)

6. EXOTIC, FANTASY AND MID-EAST STYLE KNIVES

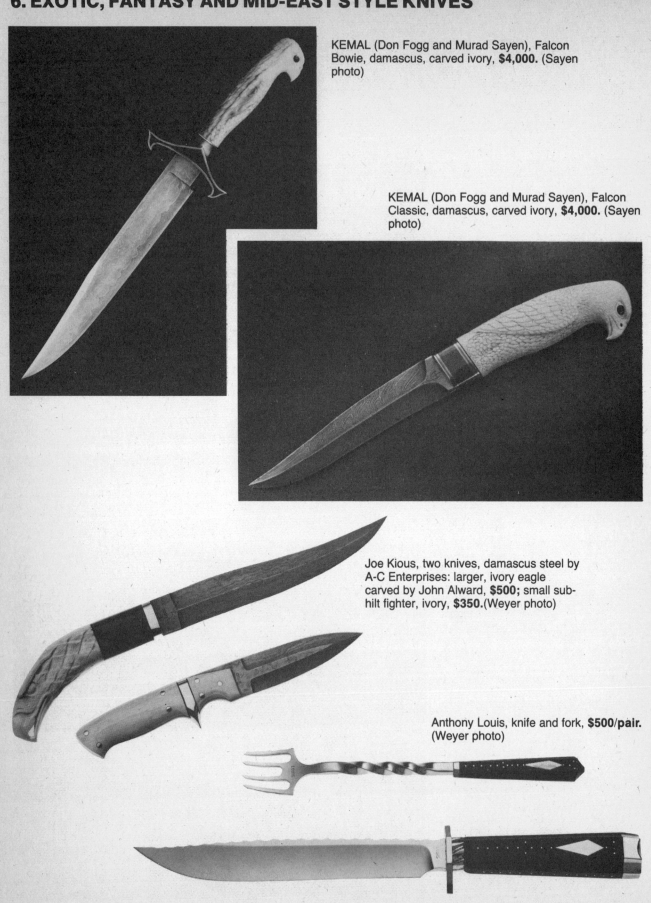

KEMAL (Don Fogg and Murad Sayen), Falcon Bowie, damascus, carved ivory, **$4,000.** (Sayen photo)

KEMAL (Don Fogg and Murad Sayen), Falcon Classic, damascus, carved ivory, **$4,000.** (Sayen photo)

Joe Kious, two knives, damascus steel by A-C Enterprises: larger, ivory eagle carved by John Alward, **$500;** small sub-hilt fighter, ivory, **$350.**(Weyer photo)

Anthony Louis, knife and fork, **$500/pair.** (Weyer photo)

6. EXOTIC, FANTASY AND MID-EAST STYLE KNIVES

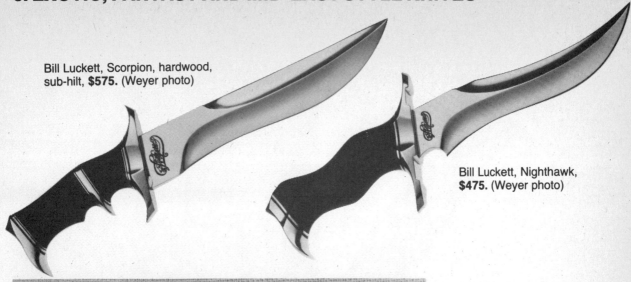

Bill Luckett, Scorpion, hardwood, sub-hilt, **$575.** (Weyer photo)

Bill Luckett, Nighthawk, **$475.** (Weyer photo)

W. F. Moran, ST-23 Combat Knife, hand forged, filework, curly maple, silver wire inlay, **$2,500** with sheath. (Holter photo)

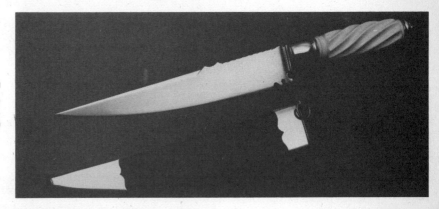

James A. Schmidt, Mediterranean Dirk, fluted ivory, nickel silver, **$2,400** with sheath. (Weyer photo)

James A. Schmidt, Gentleman's Hunter, damascus, ivory, **$1,600** with silver and frog skin sheath. (Weyer photo)

6. EXOTIC, FANTASY AND MID-EAST STYLE KNIVES

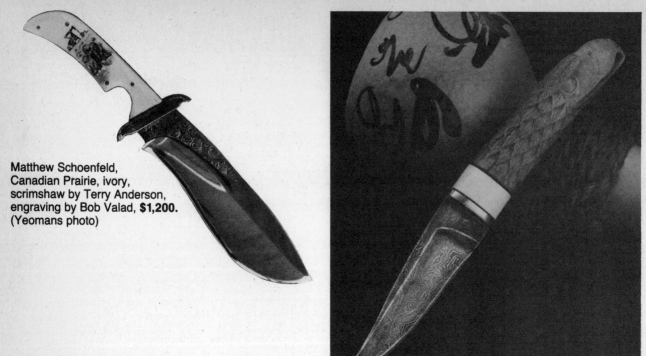

Matthew Schoenfeld,
Canadian Prairie, ivory,
scrimshaw by Terry Anderson,
engraving by Bob Valad, **$1,200.**
(Yeomans photo)

Right: SHIVA (Shiva Ki), damascus hunter, base price **$300.**
Ivory and carving by John Alward extra. (Weyer photo)

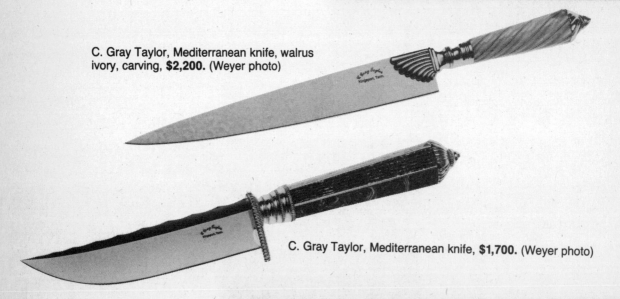

C. Gray Taylor, Mediterranean knife, walrus
ivory, carving, **$2,200.** (Weyer photo)

C. Gray Taylor, Mediterranean knife, **$1,700.** (Weyer photo)

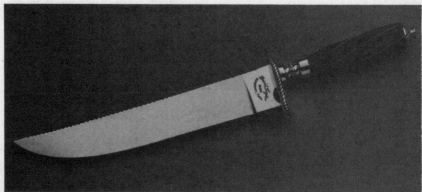

David Taylor, Mediterranean
knife, **$500.** (Weyer photo)

6. EXOTIC, FANTASY AND MID-EAST STYLE KNIVES

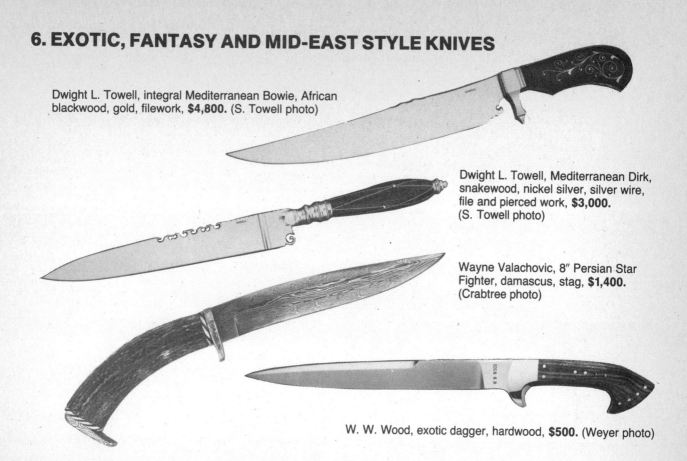

Dwight L. Towell, integral Mediterranean Bowie, African blackwood, gold, filework, **$4,800.** (S. Towell photo)

Dwight L. Towell, Mediterranean Dirk, snakewood, nickel silver, silver wire, file and pierced work, **$3,000.** (S. Towell photo)

Wayne Valachovic, 8″ Persian Star Fighter, damascus, stag, **$1,400.** (Crabtree photo)

W. W. Wood, exotic dagger, hardwood, **$500.** (Weyer photo)

Gary Barnes, damascus long knives, selective etching, left to right: **$1,750; $750; $2,500; $1,200; $2,500.** (Porterfield photo)

Gary Barnes, "Wrath of Tubal Cain," damascus. **$8,000.**

7. JAPANESE INSPIRED KNIVES AND SWORDS

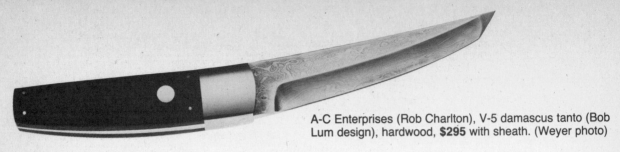

A-C Enterprises (Rob Charlton), V-5 damascus tanto (Bob Lum design), hardwood, **$295** with sheath. (Weyer photo)

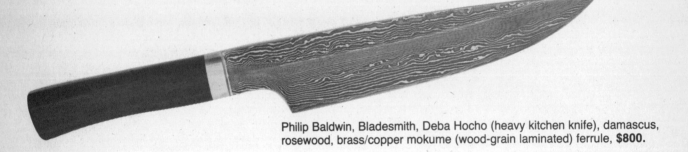

Philip Baldwin, Bladesmith, Deba Hocho (heavy kitchen knife), damascus, rosewood, brass/copper mokume (wood-grain laminated) ferrule, **$800.**

Norman Bardsley, 3¾″ blade tanto, amber, stainless, **$350** with sharkskin case.

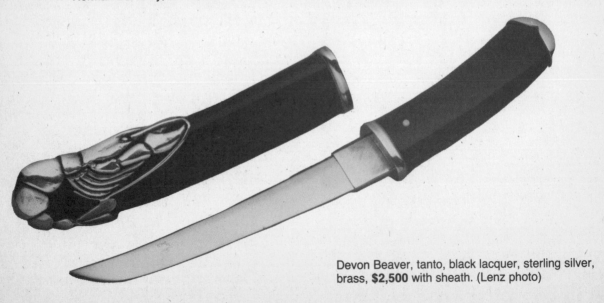

Devon Beaver, tanto, black lacquer, sterling silver, brass, **$2,500** with sheath. (Lenz photo)

7. JAPANESE INSPIRED KNIVES AND SWORDS

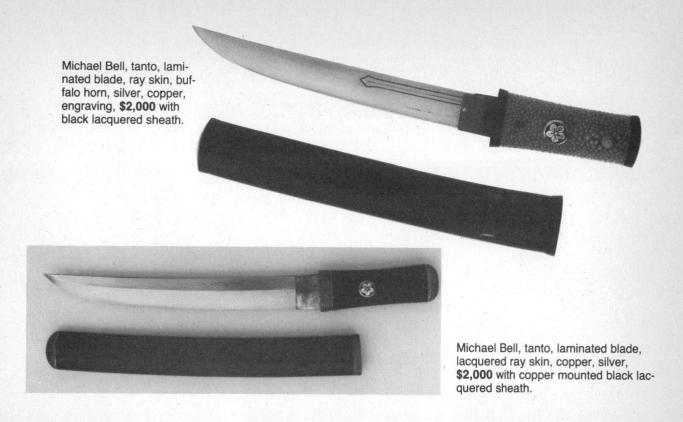

Michael Bell, tanto, laminated blade, ray skin, buffalo horn, silver, copper, engraving, **$2,000** with black lacquered sheath.

Michael Bell, tanto, laminated blade, lacquered ray skin, copper, silver, **$2,000** with copper mounted black lacquered sheath.

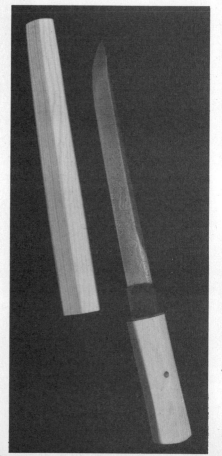

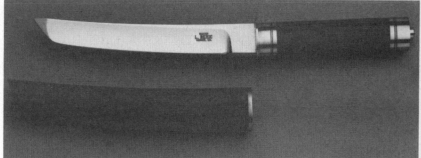

Leroy Besic, tanto, rosewood, stainless, **$550** with sheath. (Weyer photo)

Colin Cox, tanto, hardwood, engraving, **$350.** (Weyer photo)

James Crowell, 10″ aikuchi, damascus, **$1,600** in finished mounts (shown in rest mounts). (Weyer photo)

7. JAPANESE INSPIRED KNIVES AND SWORDS

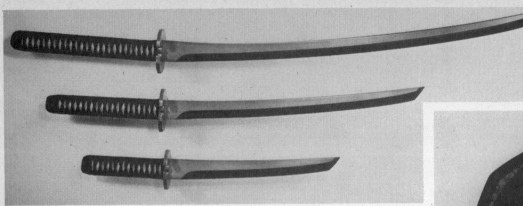

Phill Hartsfield, three swords, wrapped handles:
katana, **$2,420;** wakizashi, **$1,980;** tanto, **$1,452.**

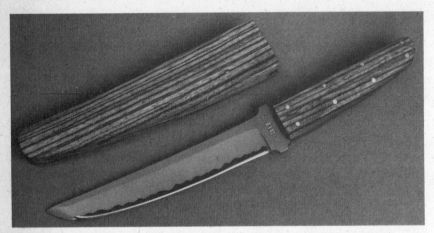

KLH (Kevin L. Hoffman), Japanese style knife, stainless, hardwood, **$200.**

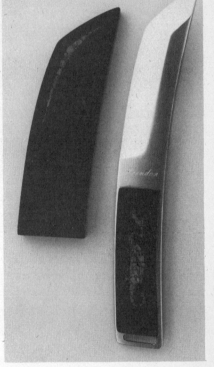

Bill Herndon, small Japanese style knife, purpleheart, turquoise, **$300.**

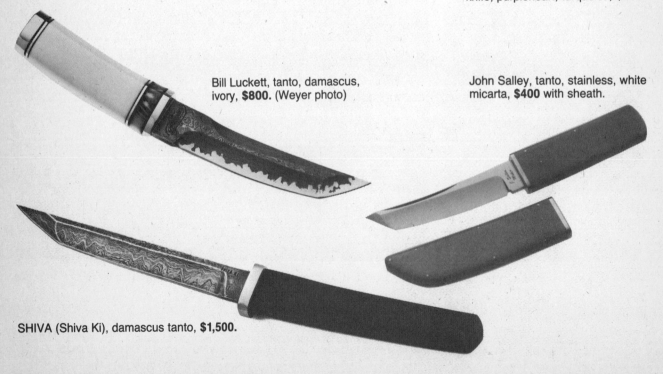

Bill Luckett, tanto, damascus, ivory, **$800.** (Weyer photo)

John Salley, tanto, stainless, white micarta, **$400** with sheath.

SHIVA (Shiva Ki), damascus tanto, **$1,500.**

8. EUROPEAN AND FANTASY STYLE AXES AND SWORDS

Phillip Baldwin, Bladesmith, Two Tears Hatchet, 8″ caustic blued damascus blade, gold and silver inlay, purpleheart and rosewood handle, silver and damascus butt cap (not shown), **$1,200.**

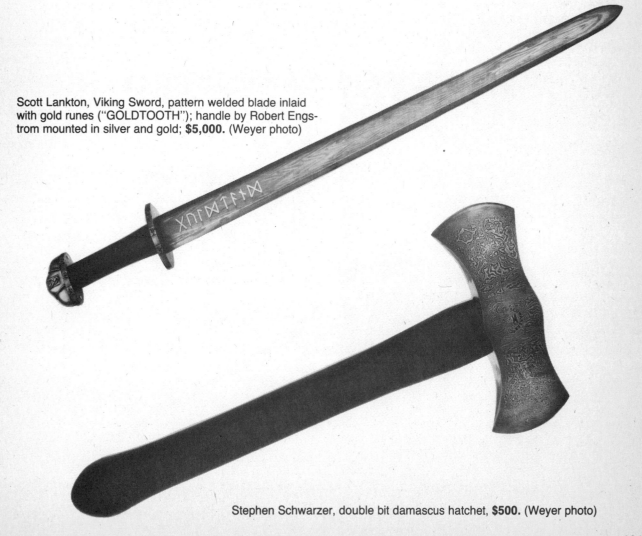

Scott Lankton, Viking Sword, pattern welded blade inlaid with gold runes ("GOLDTOOTH"); handle by Robert Engstrom mounted in silver and gold; **$5,000.** (Weyer photo)

Stephen Schwarzer, double bit damascus hatchet, **$500.** (Weyer photo)

8. EUROPEAN AND FANTASY STYLE AXES AND SWORDS

James J. Barry, 26¾″ short sword, ivory, brass, scrimshaw, **$2,500.** Miniature, ivory, **$100**.

Eldon Courtney, 33″ sword, L-6 blade, stag, stainless guard, **$1,550** with leather sheath.

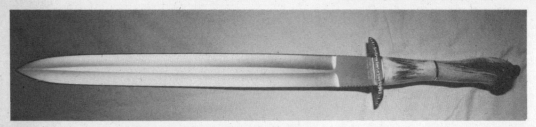

Left: John Salley, 24″ long sword, curly maple, **$2,500** with fitted chest. (Weyer photo)

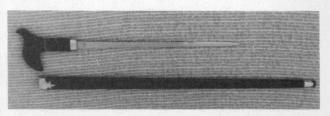

Ed Duvall, 34″ sword cane, cocobolo, nickel silver, **$1,750**.

Salamander Armoury, broadsword, **$425.**

8. EUROPEAN AND FANTASY STYLE AXES AND SWORDS

Gil Hibben, 36″ Barbarian Sword, aluminum guard and pommel, **$3,000;** Weyer dagger, **$550.** (Weyer photo)

Tom Maringer, 33″ Skysword, stainless, hickory, nickel silver, jewel, **$4,000** with sheath. (Verhoeven photo)

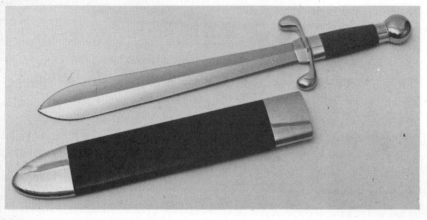

Tom Maringer, 18″ Roman Gladius, copper, stainless, ash, nickel silver, **$1,600** with goat skin covered sheath. (Verhoeven photo)

Devon Beaver, 36″ Dragon Sword, carved bronze, diamonds, African blackwood, **$4,000.** (Lenz photo)

9. MINIATURES

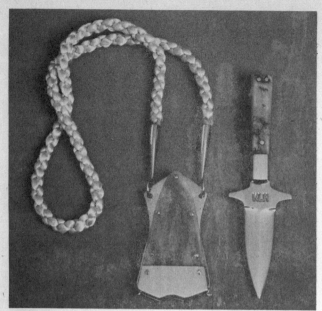

KLH (Kevin L. Hoffman), necklace dagger, **$500**.

Earl B., Witsaman, five miniatures: three swords, tempered 440-C; bowie knife and squaw axe, damascus; **$45 each,** damascus extra. (Weyer photo)

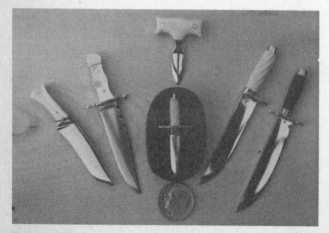

Earl B. Witsaman, six miniature bowie knives and daggers, **$30** to **$45 each.**

Glenn A. Soares, San Francisco style miniature push dagger, ivory, abalone inlay, **$200** with nickel silver sheath for use as a napkin hook.

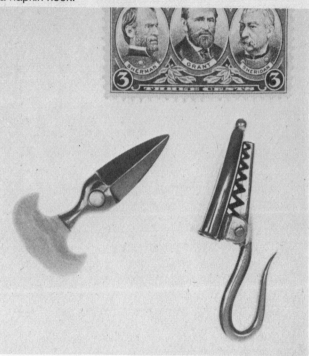

Earl B. Witsaman, eight miniature bowie and survival knives, **$30** to **$45** each. (Weyer photo)

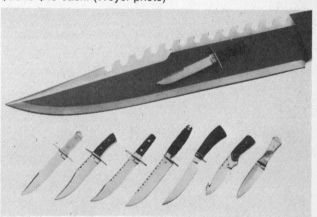

Earl B. Witsaman, miniature Randall Bear Bowie, **$45**.

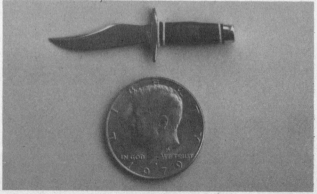

9. MINIATURES

Miniature custom knives from the collection of Marilyn Slick. Note: All of these were made to order at prices from $50 to $350 each.

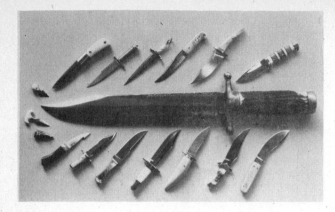

1.(Left) Miniatures surrounding a Ruana bowie. Makers, left to right:
Top row: Alex Collins, Les Berryman, Al Eaton, Sid Birt, Jim Sornberger, Frank Gamble, D'Alton Holder.
Bottom row: Glenn Soares, Dale Hunnicutt, Ruana, Ken Largin, Devon Beaver, Wayne Goddard, Bill Duff, Donald Weiler.

2. (Right) Miniatures. Top: Lloyd Pendleton upswept hunter, Don Kreibich Price-style bowie. Left: Al Eaton dagger, Sid Birt dagger pendant. Right: Jim Sornberger damascus Persian dagger with wire-inlaid handle, Paul Meyers abalone, Jim Sornberger with tiger-eye. Below silver dollar (1½" diameter): Garry Kelley damascus, Wendell Liggett damascus with abalone, Alex Rose bowie. Bottom right: Jim Sornberger damascus with tiger-eye.

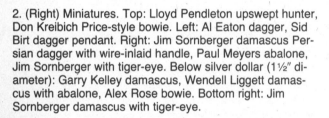

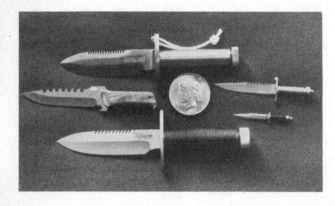

3. (Left) Miniature survival knives. Clockwise from top: Randall, Al Eaton, J. C. Strain, Devon Beaver, Dennis Casey.

4. (Right) Miniatures. Clockwise from top: Frank Lampson with engraving, Lee Berg with scrimshaw, Judy Beaver with carved ivory, Dennis Casey.

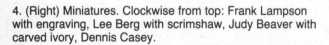

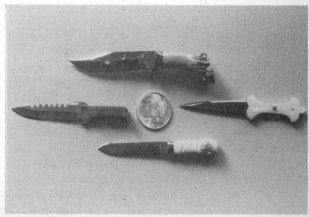

United States Military Fixed Blade Knives

Introduction

FROM THE EARLIEST days of the Republic, the armed forces of the United States have furnished enlisted soldiers and sailors with their individual weapons. Depending on period and branch of service, these weapons have included muskets or rifles (with bayonets), pistols, and swords. Commissioned officers purchased their own swords, but enlisted men in branches that used swords were issued them.

However, with the exception of a few riflemen's knives in the 1840s, none of our branches of service issued sheath knives to their men until after 1880. The first standard issue U.S. military sheath knife was the Army Model 1880 Hunting Knife. The Navy did not get around to issuing sheath knives until World War II, though American sailors have been issued folding knives since well before the Civil War.

Of course, this does not mean that soldiers before 1880 did not use sheath knives. At least on active service, many of them did. It simply means that there was no standard pattern of sheath knife that was made or purchased by the government for issue to the troops.

Rifle Knives

In the decade before the Civil War, companies of trained riflemen were the elite combat troops of both the U.S. Army and the state militias. Soldiers in regular line outfits used smooth-bore muskets.

Unlike the regular troops who furnished their own knives, riflemen were sometimes issued belt knives for use as tools and weapons. Two of these knives from the 1840s have been identified:

Hicks Knife

The earliest is the Hicks knife made by Andrew Hicks of Cleveland, Ohio, circa 1840. It has a 10-inch blade, a brass guard, and a brass-bound wooden handle. Some have a brass half-knuckle-bow; others have an iron butt cap. The sheath

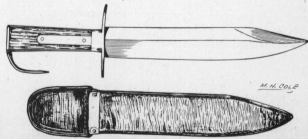

NOTE: The line drawings in this section are reproduced from U.S. Military Knives Bayonets and Machetes, Book III, *copyright 1979, by permission of the author and publisher, M. H. Cole. Mr. Cole's book shows and describes almost every variation of issue and privately purchased United States military sheath and pocket knives. It is available for $23 postpaid direct from: M. H. Cole, 501 Ridge Road, Birmingham, Alabama 35206.*

Price estimates in this section were prepared with the assistance of several collectors and dealers who specialize in U.S. military knives. Most important was the work of Larry Thomas, probably the leading collector and dealer of this material in the world. Mr. Thomas can be reached by mail at 2705 Tennyson, Sinking Springs, Pennsylvania 19608. Also important was the help of Bill Adams, Atlanta Cutlery, Box 839, Conyers, Georgia 30207; Robert Hedden, 20820 Canyon View Drive, Saratoga, California 95070; and John Moss, San Francisco Gun Exchange, 124 Second Street, San Francisco, California 94105.

WARNING: Most fixed blade military knives are of relatively simple design and construction. Some of them are quite rare and valuable. These two facts together have provided an irresistible lure both to fakers and to the manufacturers of reproductions.

At the time of writing, I have seen fakes of the following knives: Ames 1849, Model 1917–1918 trench knife, Mark 1 trench knife, Mark 2, M3, and 1st Ranger Battalion knife. Time and rising values are sure to bring forth others.

A legitimate reproduction is one that is clearly and permanently marked as a reproduction. Some presentation grade reproductions cost as much as original knives, but you don't have to spend months or years searching for them. A leading supplier of fine presentation grade military reproductions and commemoratives is the American Historical Foundation, 1022 West Franklin Street, Richmond, Virginia 23220.

is black leather. No surviving examples have any government markings, and evidence for their having been issued is circumstantial. Documents indicate that some knives made by Hicks were purchased by an arsenal, but those knives were not described.

Ames Knife

In 1849, the Army let its first contract for a specific pattern of knife. It ordered 1,000 knives from the Ames Manufacturing Company of Cabotville, Mass., for issue to the Regiment of Mounted Riflemen.

The Ames rifleman's knife is a spear point bowie with a 12-inch blade, brass mounts, and walnut handles secured by iron rivets. It has a black leather sheath with brass throat, tip, and frog stud.

The front ricasso is lightly marked AMES MFG. CO./ CABOTVILLE/1849. The rear is marked US/WD. The guard is stamped WD and JWR. The frog stud is stamped D.

The Ames sheath is much sturdier than the Hicks sheath. Perhaps for this reason Ames knives are usually found with their original sheaths, while Hicks knives usually are not.

A well-made counterfeit of the Ames knive has been on the market for several years. Its ricasso stampings are much deeper than those on the original, and one of the inspector's initials on the guard is incorrect.

RIFLEMEN'S KNIVES, current values in excellent condition.

Hicks knife, any variant: **$2,500–4,000.**
　with original sheath: **add $1,000.**
Ames knife with sheath: **$3,000–3,500.**
　sheath missing: **subtract $500–1,000.**
Counterfeit Ames knife: **$300.**

This Ames knife shows some blade wear and pitting. The frog stud is missing from the sheath. Value **$2,500.**

Model 1880 Hunting Knife

The Model 1880 was the first general issue Army sheath knife. As such, it has been the subject of much study; the full story of its development, production, and use is told in the book *Light But Efficient*, 1973, by Albert Hardin and Robert Hedden (available for $7.95 plus $1 postage from Robert Hedden, 20820 Canyon View Drive, Saratoga, California 95070.

The Model 1880 Hunting Knife has an 8½-inch long 2-inch wide double-edged steel blade, a stout metal guard (some are iron, most are brass), and a turned hardwood handle. All were issued in a stout black leather sheath with a brass throat, though there is a variety of sheath attachments.

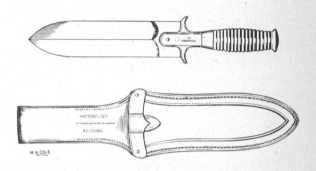

The Model 1880 was designed to serve three functions in the Indian campaigns on the plains: It was to be a butcher knife for cattle and wild game; it was to be an entrenching tool; and it was to be a last-ditch weapon.

In the field, the Model 1880's main function proved to be digging firing positions ("rifle pits"), so in 1890 its designation was changed to "Model 1890 Intrenching Knife." In fact, the Model 1880/1890 knives are similar in shape to the flat-bladed short-lived Model 1873 Intrenching Tool.

Approximately 11,000 Model 1880s and 500 Model 1890s were made, all at Springfield Armory. The scabbards were made at Watervliet Arsenal and, later, at Rock Island Arsenal. The Model 1880s are serial numbered in two series.

MODELS 1880 and 1890, current values in excellent, unsharpened condition. For mint condition, **add 150%.** For worn condition, **subtract 50%.**

Model 1880, iron guard, no sheath: **$400.**
Model 1880, brass guard, no sheath: **$180.**
Model 1890, brass guard, no sheath: **$300.**
　　(all Model 1890s are dated 1892)
　Unmodified sheath, leather belt loop:
　　$100.
　Sheath with hinged brass catch: **$50.**
　Sheath with brass hook: **$50.**
Model 1873 Intrenching Tool: **$125.**
　(like M1880 but has sheet steel blade)
　Sheath for M1873, with ring: **$125.**

Bolos and Hospital Corps Knives

MODEL 1887 BOLO

The U.S. Army's next issue knife looks like a longer slimmer version of the Model 1880. It is the Model 1887 Hospital Corps Knife. This has a 12-inch bright blade with an etched panel. Its wood handle and leather sheath look similar to those of the Model 1880.

About 1,000 of these knives were made, also at Springfield Armory. They were intended for the use of field hospital personnel in clearing brush and cutting saplings for making emergency litters and shelters. There are two variations in blade shape.

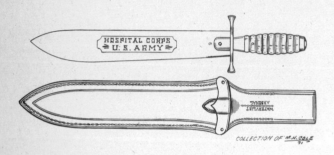

COLLECTION OF M.H.COLE 71

MODEL 1887 BOLO, current value in excellent unsharpened condition. For mint condition, **add 150%.** For worn condition, **subtract 50%.**

Knife only, straight cutting edge: **$400.**
Knife only, bellied cutting edge: **$500.**
  Sheath, unmodified leather belt loop: **$50.**
  Sheath with brass hook: **$50.**
Similar knife made by COLLINS & CO.:
  $350.

MODEL 1904 AND MODEL 1909 BOLOS

The Army's experience in the Philippine Islands during and after the Spanish American War demonstrated the value of a heavy-bladed bolo-type knife for campaigning in the jungle. In consequence, the Ordnance Department came up with a variety of bolo designs in the next two decades.

The first and handsomest (and costliest) of these is the Model 1904 Hospital Corps Knife. It has a 12-inch blade, walnut handles, and brown leather sheath. The first 7,000 or so had a leather belt loop on the sheath. The remainder of the nearly 40,000 made at Springfield Armory between 1904 and 1915 had a steel belt loop. All but a few first year Model 1904s were serial numbered.

The Army's second bolo, the Model 1909 with its 14-inch blade, is larger than the Model 1904. It is also plainer in construction. More than 17,000 were made at Springfield Armory between 1909 and 1915. Another 58,000 were made on contract in 1917 by the Philadelphia tool-maker Fayette R. Plumb.

MODEL 1904 and MODEL 1909 BOLOS, current values in excellent, unsharpened condition. For mint condition, **add 100%.** For worn condition, **subtract 50%.**

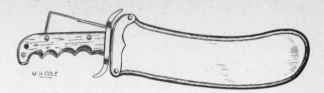

M.H.COLE

Model 1904 knife only: **$75–125.**
  Sheath with leather loop: **$50.**
  Sheath with steel loop: **$40.**

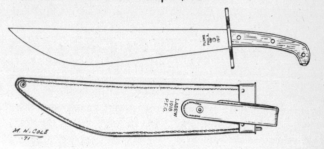

M.H.COLE .71

Model 1909 S. A. (Springfield) knife only:
  $65–115.
  Rock Island sheath for above: **$50.**
Model 1909 PLUMB knife only (dated 1917):
  $60–110.
  LADEW sheath for above: **$50.**
Similar bolo made by COLLINS & CO.:
  $400.

MODEL 1910 AND MODEL 1917 BOLOS

The Army's third bolo, the Model 1910, seemed to acknowledge that, outside of the jungle, a really big knife is more an impediment than a useful tool. This stout simple bolo with its 10⅜-inch blade was intended as a general purpose chopping and digging tool. In World War I, its principal use was in clearing fields of fire for machine gun emplacements.

The Model 1910 has wooden handle scales and a steel pommel and guard. It has a button latch to engage a hook on the sheath. Nearly 60,000 Model 1910s were made at Springfield Armory up through 1918.

The standard sheath is wood with a metal throat. It is covered with cloth and has a leather tip. It is the first Army knife sheath to have wire hooks for hanging from the cartridge belt. Experimental all-metal sheaths were made on contract by Landers Frary & Clark in 1918.

The Model 1917 Bolo is identical to the 1910, except that the button latch was eliminated. The Model 1917 C.T. is further modified in having the pommel integral with the tang. The 1917 models were made on contract by two firms: Plumb and the American Cutlery Company of Chicago. The latter was a manufacturer of low-priced kitchen knives. A.C. Co. went out of business shortly after World War I.

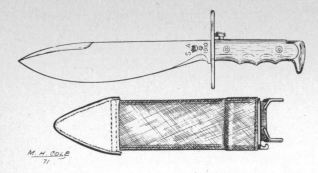

M. H. COLE 71

So many of these bolos were made, particularly of the Model 1917s, that even World War II did not exhaust the supply. Model 1917s are still very common.

MODEL 1910 and MODEL 1917 BOLOS, current values in excellent, unsharpened condition. For mint condition, add 100%. For worn condition, subtract 75%.

Model 1910 knife only: **$75–95.**
Model 1917 PLUMB knife only: **$25–35.**
Model 1917 C.T. PLUMB knife only: **$25–35.**
Model 1917 C.T. A.C.Co. knife only: **$25–35.**
  Cloth covered sheath: **$10.**
  Metal L.F.&C. sheath: **$15.**

U.S.M.C. BOLO

With World War II on the horizon, the Army found that it had all the bolos it could use left over from 1918. Since 1898, the Marine Corps had used a square-point "intrenching machete" with wood handles and a stiff sheath covered with canvas and leather. Very few were in inventory in 1941.

In 1942, for war production, this bolo design was modified to have a round sharpened end, and it was furnished with a sturdy leather sheath. These bolo-type knives were issued mainly to Navy hospital corpsmen serving with the Marines.

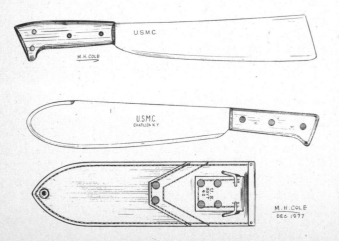

M. H. COLE DEC. 1977

U.S.M.C. BOLOS, current values in excellent, unsharpened condition. For mint condition, add 75%. For worn condition, subtract 75%.

Square point, COLLINS & CO. No. 1001, knife only: **$75–100.**
Square point, DISSTON, knife only: **$100–125.**
  Sheath for square point: **$15.**
Round point, PLUMB, knife only: **$25–30.**
Round point, CHATILLON, knife only: **$25–30.**
Round point, VILLAGE BLACKSMITH, knife only: **$40–50.**
Round point, BRIDDELL, knife only: **$25–30.**
Round point, no brand, knife only: **$40–50.**
  BOYT sheath for above: **$10.**
  Dated "42": **add 50%.**

Machetes

In addition to issuing bolos, the U.S. armed forces also issued machetes for use in jungle terrain. The first was the Collins Model 1005 Army Engineers Machete. It has a heavy curved blade about 15¼ inches long, handle scales of wood or horn, and a leather scabbard, often with brass trim. This machete was in use from the 1890s through the 1920s.

A rare World War I era machete is the Collins No. 37 Signal Corps pattern with its straight 17¾-inch blade, brass mounted leather washer handle, and leather scabbard stamped U.S./SIGNAL CORPS.

In World War II, large numbers of standard straight bladed machetes were purchased by the military. Most had 18-inch blades, but the Navy also used some with 22-inch and 26-inch blades; 18-inch machetes are still a standard issue item.

In 1934, the military adopted the Collins No. 18 bowie knife style machete as a survival knife for inclusion in the bail-out kit of pilots flying over tropical areas. These are 14 inches long over all and have either a green horn or a black composition handle. The sheath is brown leather. Black handled versions were made during World War II by Case, Western, Kinfolks, and several Australian firms. During the Pacific war, No. 18s were issued to several Marine units, particularly to Carlson's Second Marine Raiders. These knives do not have Marine Corps markings.

In 1942, the Army Air Force adopted a survival machete with a 10-inch blade for inclusion in the bail-out kit in place of the No. 18. Case, Camillus, Cattaraugus, and Imperial made plastic handled folding models, while Case made a wood handled fixed blade with a sheet steel edge cover (in *Knives '85*, D. E. Henry gives evidence that this fixed-blade Case was the *real* V-44). The folding Imperial, with its gray leather belt holster, is truly an elegant knife.

MILITARY MACHETES, current values in excellent, unsharpened condition. Mint condition **add 75%,** worn condition **subtract 50%.**

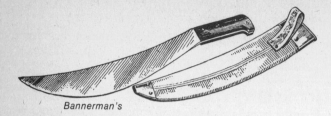

Bannerman's

Collins Engineers with military marked sheath: **$35–50.**
Collins Signal Corps with military marked sheath: **$75–100.**

18-inch military marked, U.S. made: **$10–40.**
18-inch military marked, foreign made: **$10–15.**
   Canvas sheath for 18″: **$5.**
   Leather sheath: **$20.**
Hard plastic and metal sheath for 18-inch: **$5.**
22″ Navy marked: **$20–35.**
26″ Navy marked: **$30–75.**
   Sheath for 22-inch or 26-inch: **$10.**

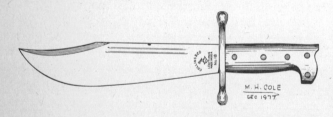

M. H. COLE
DEC 1977

Pilot's survival bowie/machetes, with sheaths:
Collins No. 18 horn: **$125–175.**
   Black: **$75–125.**
Case XX: **$125–175.**
Western: **$400–500.**
Kinfolks: **$200–250.**
Australian:
   Wood handle: **$250–350.**
   Black: **$200–300.**
   Brass D-Guard with 3-point knuckle bow: **$400–500.**
   Aluminum D-Guard: **$400–500.**
(USMC markings on a bowie/machete are probably fake)

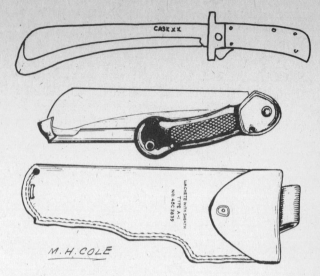

M.H. COLE

Post-1942 pilot's survival machetes:
Case fixed blade, with edge cover: **$30–50.**
Case folding: **$40–60.**
Camillus folding: **$30–50.**
Cattaraugus folding: **$30–50.**
Imperial folding: **$65.**
Holster sheath: **$25.**

Trench Knives

FIRST WORLD WAR

Almost all of the military issue knives considered so far were primarily tools. They were too heavy and unwieldy to serve as weapons, except in dire emergencies.

When the United States entered the First World War in Europe in 1917, our troops clamored for an issue fighting knife suitable for trench warfare. Both our allies and our enemies equipped their line outfits with good quality trench knives [see the chapter on *Foreign Military Fixed Blade Knives*]. The Army responded, but in a manner that was less than satisfactory.

The first effort, designed by the Philadelphia saw-making firm Henry Disston & Sons, seems to have been inspired by 19th century bayonet design spiced up with a little dime-novel fantasy. It is the Model 1917–1918 trench knife. This knife has a slim (and brittle) triangular blade, a wooden handle, and a frightening but impractical iron "brass knuckles" hand guard. There are several variations, all listed below.

This first American trench knife had several problems. It could only be used for stabbing or punching, not for cutting. The blade was delicate and easily broken. The "knucks" were poorly designed. Therefore an improved model was developed, the Mark 1.

The Mark 1 trench knife has a cast brass handle with separate finger holes and a skull-crusher spike on the butt. The blade is copied almost exactly from the very effective French issue trench knife. Indeed, the first Mark 1s were made for the U.S. Army by a French firm. Later ones were made by three of the contractors that made the Model 1917–1918.

SECOND WORLD WAR

After 1918, no more "knuckle knives" were made for the Army. However, during World War II, a couple of aluminum handled types were offered for private sale. Also, at least one outfit (the 1st Ranger Battalion) ordered a monstrous clip point knife with an awkward cast brass knuckle guard.

"KNUCKLE-DUSTER" TRENCH KNIVES, current values in excellent, unsharpened condition. For mint condition, add 100%. For worn condition, subtract 50%.

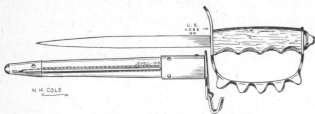

MODEL 1917–1918 TRENCH KNIFE
H.D.&S. flanged guard knife only: **$400–500.**
A.C.Co. flanged guard knife only: **$75–100.**
O.C.L. flanged guard knife only: **$200–300.**
 (Oneida Community Ltd.)
L. F. & C. 6-knobbed guard knife only: **$40–60.**
L. F. & C. 7-knobbed guard knife only: **$70–90.**
 Leather sheath: **$40.**
 Leather sheath with iron throat and tip: **$25.**

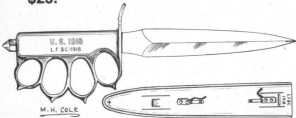

MARK 1 TRENCH KNIFE
AU LION (on blade) knife only: **$75.**
L. F. & C. knife only: **$75.**
H.D.&S. knife only: **$350.**
O.C.L. knife only: **$150.**
 Iron sheath: **$35.**

WORLD WAR II KNUCKLE KNIVES
1st Ranger Battalion.
 Knife (unmarked or US): Large: **$300–400.**
 Knife (unmarked or US); Small: **$600–700.**
 Leather sheath: **$50.**
 BEWARE OF FAKES! (Fakes are marked CASE XX on blade)
New Zealand, checkered aluminum, flimsy bow: **$75–125.**
EVERITT, well made aluminum: **$350–450.**

M3 TRENCH KNIFE

When the United States entered World War II, existing stocks of Mark 1 Trench Knives were issued and used. However, by that time the Army had realized that the Mark 1 was too much hardware for the job.

In 1943, a new and much superior trench knife was introduced. The M3 has a straight sturdy blade suitable for cutting and chopping in camp, as well as for stabbing. It has a leather washer handle and iron fittings.

In 1944, the M3 was superseded by the M4 bayonet for the M1 carbine. The M4 has the same handle and blade as the M3, but with bayonet-style fittings.

Over 2½-million M3s were made on contract in 1943 and 1944. There are many variations of blade and guard marking, and also of handle shape. Some of these are very rare. Few M3s entered the surplus market after World War II, and none of the variations can be considered common, particularly in good condition.

M3 TRENCH KNIVES, current values in excellent, unsharpened condition. Mint condition, add 100%. Worn condition or re-worked or parts replaced, subtract 50%.

M3s marked on blade: "U.S. M3" plus . . .
AERIAL/MARINETTE, WIS.: **$150.**
H.BOKER & CO./U.S.A.: **$150.**
CAMILLUS: **$100.**
CAMILLUS 1943: **$125–150.**
CASE: **$115**
CASE 1943: **$135–160.**
IMPERIAL: **$90.**
IMPERIAL 1943: **$125–150.**
KINFOLKS INC.: **$125.**
KINFOLKS INC. 1943: **$150–175.**
PAL: **$125.**   PAL 1943: **$150–175.**
R.C.CO. (Robeson): **$135.**
-UTICA: **$100.** -U.C.-1943 (Utica): **$135–160.**

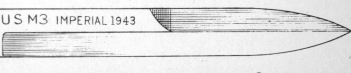

M3s marked on crossguard . . .
U.S./M3/A.C.C. (probably Aerial): **$125–150.**
US/M3/BOKER: **$100–125.**
US M3/CAMILLUS: **$100–125.**
USM3/CASE: **$125–135.**   CASE: **$135.**
USM3/IMPERIAL: **$100–125.**
US/M-3/UTICA: **$125–135.**
U.S.M3/K.I. (Kinfolks): **$100–125.**
U.S./M3/PAL: **$125–135.**

Commercially sold M3s:
Unmarked: **$50.**
"Kutmaster/MADE IN U.S.A.": **$60.**
PAL BLADE CO./MADE IN U.S.A. (on ricasso): **$150–175.**

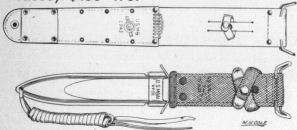

Scabbards for M3s:
M6 leather scabbard, metal reinforced: **$35.**
M8 plastic scabbard, canvas belt loop: **$10.**
M8A1 plastic scabbard, wire belt hook: **$5.**
Plain leather commercial scabbard: **$5.**

Special Combat Knives

FAIRBAIRN VARIANTS

Early in the war, the U.S. issued several types of slender daggers suitable mainly for silent assassination. These "stickers" closely resemble a well-known prototype, the British Fairbairn-Sykes commando stiletto first made in 1940. One evidently *is* a British Fairbairn. This is the unmarked O.S.S. (Office of Strategic Services, forerunner of the C.I.A.). stiletto with its distinctive "pancake flapper" metal and leather sheath. Value *with* sheath: **$400–700.**

An American-made version of the Fairbairn is the Camillus Marine Raiders' Stiletto. It has a light weight checkered metal handle and a slim double-edged blade etched with the Camillus trademark and with "U.S.M.C." in a fancy scroll. The leather sheath was usually reinforced with a square metal plate near the tip. Fewer than 15,000 were made. Value: **$700–900.** Parkerized variant: **$1,300–1,500.**

The basic Fairbairn is a fragile knife that is awkward to hold and use. In 1942 and 1943 Case came up with an improved version called the V-42 for the use of the First Special Service Force.

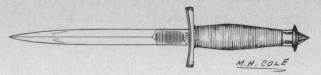

The V-42 has an oval leather handle, rather than round metal. It has a wide guard and a ricasso, both to protect the fingers. Production models are distinguished by a pointed steel "skull-crusher" pommel, grooves in the leather handle, and a "thumb-print" pressed into the ricasso. Prototypes have a round butt, smooth handle, and no "thumb-print." The sheath is leather with reinforcing staples at the throat. 3,600 V-42s were made. Value:

Issue: **$1,700–2,000.** Prototype: **$2,000–2,500.**

SMATCHET

Besides promoting his dagger design, Major Fairbairn urged the U.S. to adopt the "smatchet" as a combat knife. This is a large (16 inches overall) but light bolo-type knife with a leaf shaped blade. He only managed to convince the O.S.S., who ordered a number of smatchets, all unmarked, from W. R. Case & Sons. The handle is brown wood and the pommel is white metal. The sheath is black leather over plywood.

Value with sheath: **$500–600.**

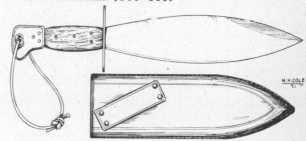

"Uncle" Henry Baer, in a letter dated January 14, 1983, reported that Ulster Knife Company made 10,000 unmarked smatchets for the O.S.S. in 1944, based on samples supplied by Case. They had black parkerized blades, wood handles, and zinc pommels. The entire lot was shipped to the Philippines, supposedly by submarine, but the rumor at the time was that the sub was lost on the way.

AUSTRALIAN-MADE COMMANDO KNIVES

These simple well-designed knives have a 5½-inch spear point blade and wooden slab handles. The blade is marked with an Australian name (Greg, East, or Barker) and on many either the blade or the guard is marked U.S. 1944. The sheath is leather. Many were issued to both American and Commonwealth troops fighting in the Pacific.

Value in excellent condition, with sheath:
With U.S. markings: **$100–150.**
Without U.S. markings: **$40–60.**

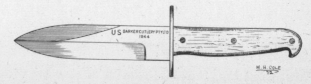

Combat Utility Knives

U.S. NAVY MARK 1

In World War II, the Navy broke with tradition and determined to issue a survival type sheath knife to its sailors. Its main function was to cut the lashings that secured the release mechanism on all Navy life rafts. The first design, the Mark 1, was a very practical 5⅛-inch blade utility knife. The Navy needed a whole lot of them right away, so they were made, in nearly three-dozen handle, fitting, and marking variants, by most of the large American cutlery firms then in business.

In addition, individual procurement officers were allowed to buy sheath knives for their men on the open market. The official issue of some of these commercial knives is well documented, and a determined interviewer could probably prove that just about every pattern of 5- to 7-inch blade commercial hunting knife available in the early 1940s found its way on to a Navy ship.

Mark 1s were made in such vast quantities that unissued lots of them *still* turn up on the surplus market, usually for between **$25** and **$40 each.** The Mark 1 is the most common U.S. military knife on the collector market, but it would be a real challenge to acquire one of each variation in excellent to mint condition.

Cole illustrates 36 Mark 1 variations. The value range of all of them is as indicated above, but if collector interest in the Mark 1 increases, the rarer variants should increase in value.

Here are the numbers of variants shown by Cole for each brand. More will no doubt be identified.

CAMILLUS: 7   BOKER: 1   COLONIAL: 3
WESTERN: 1   IMPERIAL: 3   SCHRADE-WALDEN: 1
KA-BAR: 7   PAL: 5   GENEVA FORGE: 3
ROBESON: 5

U.S. NAVY AND MARINE CORPS MARK 2

The Navy Mark 1 was a practical design for careful users. Young sailors proved not to be careful users, and often broke these lightweight knives. Also, the Mark 1 was not quite long or stout enough to serve as an effective combat knife.

In consequence, the Navy, working with Camillus Cutlery Company, developed a new knife, the Mark 2. It has a 7-inch clip point blade and is much sturdier than the Mark 1. The Mark 2 proved to be a very successful design and is still in production.

The Marine Corps promptly adopted this design, as well. Many were made with U.S.M.C. markings, but Marines were not shy about using knives with U.S.N. markings if that was what was available. Marines call their knives Ka-Bars because many of the U.S.M.C. issue knives were made by Union Cutlery Company of Olean, New York, and marked with their KA-BAR trademark. However, Camillus,

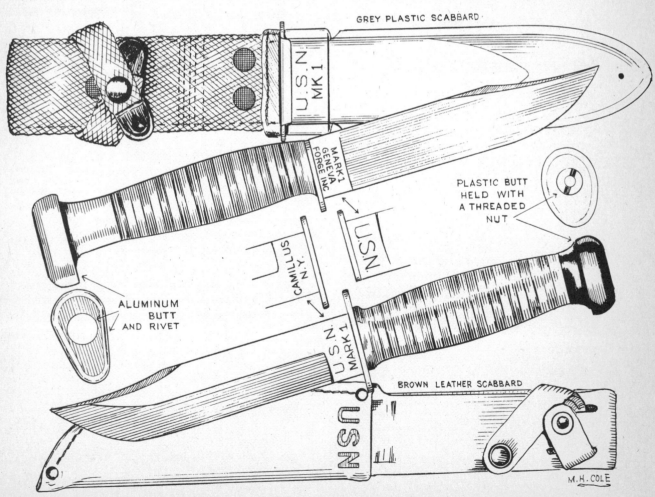

GREY PLASTIC SCABBARD

U.S.N. MK 1

MARK 1 GENEVA FORGE INC.

PLASTIC BUTT HELD WITH A THREADED NUT

CAMILLUS N.Y.

U.S.N.

ALUMINUM BUTT AND RIVET

U.S.N. MARK 1

U.S.N.

BROWN LEATHER SCABBARD

M.H. COLE

Navy and Marine
Fighting-Utility Knife

Pal, and Robeson also made Mark 2s for the Marine Corps. Union alone made about a million Mark 2s. Camillus made even more.

As with the Mark 1 and the Army M3, the Mark 2 was issued with either a leather sheath or a hard fiber and metal sheath.

MARK 2 COMBAT KNIFE, current values in excellent, unsharpened condition. Mint condition, **add 50%.** Good, used condition, **subtract 50%.**

U.S.N. marked knife, or with no branch
   marking. First version with threaded tang.
Marked on ricasso.
   CAMILLUS, N.Y.: **$40.**
   KA-BAR/OLEAN, N.Y.: **$50.**
Pinned or riveted butt. Marked on ricasso.
   CAMILLUS, N.Y.: **$40.**
   KA-BAR/OLEAN, N.Y.: **$50.**
   PAL or RH(PAL)37: **$45.**
   KA-BAR: **$50.**
   ROBESON SHUREDGE: **$45.**
Marked on guard.
   KA-BAR: **$40.**   CAMILLUS, N.Y.: **$30.**
   R.C.C.: **$40.**
Post-World War II two-line markings on
   ricasso.
   U.S./CONETTA: **$25.**
   U.S./UTICA CUT. CO.: **$30.**
   U.S./CAMILLUS N.Y.: **$20.**
U.S.N. sheaths.
   One piece leather: **$20.**
   Two piece leather: **$15.**
   Gray plastic with canvas belt loop: **$10.**
U.S.M.C. marked knife, marked on ricasso.
   CAMILLUS, N.Y.: **$65.**   KA-BAR: **$85.**
   PAL: **$100.**
   ROBESON SHUREDGE: **$150.**
Marked on guard.
   CAMILLUS: **$50.**
Leather sheath for U.S.M.C. Mark 2: **$15.**

Commercial Combat Utility Knives

The Navy and Marine Corps standard issue Mark 1 and Mark 2 were not the only U.S. combat-utility sheath knives of World War II. Many others were made for commercial sale and purchased by unit procurement officers and by individual G.I.s. Some resemble the standard patterns or the M3, while others are quite distinctive. Virtually all have leather washer handles, leather sheaths, and a military appearance.

About a dozen military-style sheath knives were produced by Western of Boulder, Colorado, during the war. These range in value from **$75** to **$150** in excellent condition. Others were made by Pal, Camillus, Kinfolks, Imperial, E.G. Waterman, Utica/Kutmaster, Robeson, Queen City, and Case. Value range is **$50** to **$250.** Most of these knives are scarce, but they excite less collector interest than the standard issue M3 and Mark 2.

Cattaraugus and Case both made similar heavy 6-inch bladed "Commando Knives" in large quantities. The Cattaraugus is still very common. Values in excellent, unsharpened condition. Mint condition **add 50%.**
   CATTARAUGUS/225Q: **$35**   CASE 337-6"Q: **$50.**

Ka-Bar made about 500,000 6-inch bladed guard-marked combat knives that look like a scaled down Mark 2. Value: **$50.**

Bench-Made Combat Utility Knives

During World War II, a handful of custom knifemakers, most notably Randall and Ek, gained national attention for making high quality sheath knives of novel design. Indeed, Randall for a time found demand for his Model 1 so great that he contracted with a cutlery firm in Springfield, Mass., to make knives to his specifications. Though they are rare, the "Springfield Randalls" I have seen for sale were valued no higher than other early Randalls. I believe this may change when the scarcity of those knives is appreciated. More on Randall can be found in the *Custom Knives* section.

Two custom makers who specialized in cast aluminum handled knives found a national market for their fighting

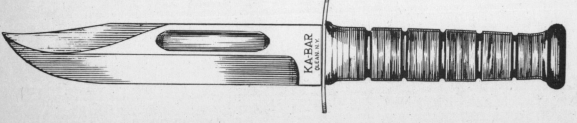

COLLECTION OF
M.H. COLE

knives during World War II. These were David Z. Murphy of Gresham, Oregon, (marked MURPHY COMBAT on the handle) and F. J. Richtig of Clarkson, Nebraska. Both, especially Richtig, also made knives with more ordinary handles. Lately I have seen sheath knives by these makers sell for **$200** to **$500**, and interest in them seems to be growing.

Besides the well-known custom makers, thousands of home craftsmen and defense plant machinists made hundreds of thousands of bench-made knives during the war, either for themselves or to be sold or given to servicemen bound overseas. Indeed, M. H. Cole, the military knife historian, made such knives himself.

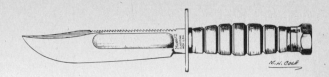

JET PILOT'S KNIFE, 6-inch blade, with sheath:

Marble's: **$200.**
Camillus with screw pommel: **$75.**
Camillus with pinned pommel: **$45.**
Jet Pilot's knife, 5-inch blade, with sheath:
Camillus: **$20.**   Ontario: **$15.**
Utica: **$100.**
Milpar, leather handle, blade marked: **$65.**
Milpar, aluminum handle and guard: **$350.**

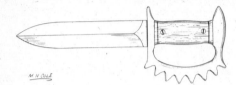

Almost all of these bench-made knives are unmarked, though a combination of detective work and luck may allow you to identify a few. Most can at least be placed in their proper period by a combination of design and materials. They look similar to commercial and issue knives of the 1940s. Many include typical materials of that time, such as purplish aircraft canopy Plexiglas fabricated into a stacked washer handle. The value of most such knives is between **$25** and **$50,** depending mainly on workmanship and condition.

A few World War II knives fall in between standard made and expedient. One such is the trench knives made early in the war from blades and parts of the Garand bayonet. These look like cut down and sharpened bayonets, *except* that they have no slots or other fittings for attachment to the rifle. Value: **$40–50.**

Another example is the ANDERSON/GLENDALE/CALIFORNIA knives with molded plastic handles, and blades made from one-third of a Patton Model 1913 cavalry saber blade. These are worth about **$75–100.**

Divers' Knives

Military divers' knives are a specialty unto themselves. Most are very rare. One you may encounter is the Navy hardhat divers' knife of World War II. It has a 6½-inch spear point blade with saw teeth on one edge, a turned wooden handle, and brass mounts. The knife screws into a massive brass scabbard, allowing it to be used as a mallet. They were used in the Navy yards, and were also stowed in the escape hatches of submarines. Most do not have Navy markings.

Value in excellent condition, with sheath:
Blade marked KA-BAR: **$300.**
All others: **$125–175.**

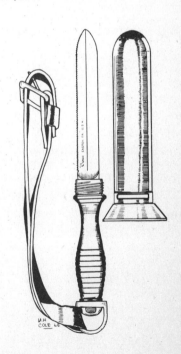

Jet Pilot's Knife

The Second World War Navy pilot's bail-out knife was a heavy 6-inch double-ended folder with a knife blade and a saw [see the *Multi-Blade Folding Knives* section]. That knife was costly to make and the saw was fragile. Many pilots carried Mark 1s instead.

In the 1950s, The Navy designed a new style of pilot's knife that combined the best features of the Mark 1, the Mark 2, and the folder. This jet pilot's knife is as stout as the Mark 2, as small and handy as the Mark 1 (actually the first model had a 6-inch blade, but after 1962 all have had a 5-inch blade), and has saw-teeth on the back. The first ones were made by Marble's.

Foreign Military Fixed Blade Knives

Plug bayonet. Western Europe, 17th–18th centuries. About 20–24″ overall. Triangular single-edged blade. Turned wooden handle with pronounced swell near guard. Brass ferrule, pommel, and cross-guard. Used jammed into the muzzle of the musket, or as a knife.

Example shown courtesy California Academy of Sciences, Rietz collections. Value **$300.**

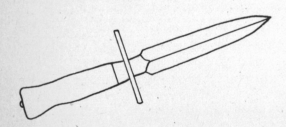

French W.W.I. trench knife. About 11″ overall. Double-edged blade with maker's mark or Thiers trademark registry number on ricasso (31-Besset; 41-Conon; 76-Bernard; etc.). Turned wooden handle. Steel mounts. Steel sheath with wire belt loops. Value **$85.**

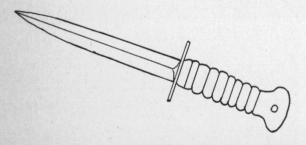

Dutch combat knife. About 13″ overall. Blued double-edged blade. Wooden handle. Oval steel guard. Leather sheath. Value **$120.**

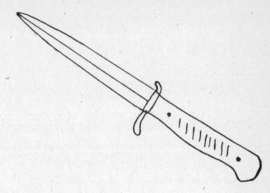

German W.W.I. trench knife. About 10½″ overall. Single-edged blade with sharp false edge, some fully double-edged. Wood or steel handle. Iron guard. Black sheet iron scabbard. Value **$45.**

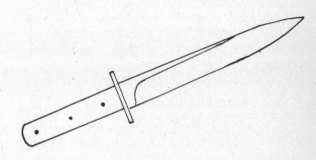

Austro-Hungarian W.W.I. trench knife. About 13″ overall. Single-edged blade with sharp false edge. Wood handles. Steel guard and scabbard. Value **$55.**

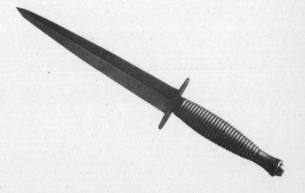

British W.W.II Fairbairn-Sykes commando knife. About 11½″ overall. Metal handle secured by nut. Leather sheath. Values with broad arrow issue mark: checkered, **$75;** beads and ribs, **$200;** ribbed, **$50.** Turned wood handle, **$150.** Example shown, current commercial, ribbed, **$20.** Courtesy Gutmann Cutlery Co.

Republic of South Africa. Recent bench-made combat knives. Photographs and values courtesy of R. C. Hogensen of American Manor House [see *Dealers List*].

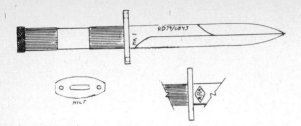

Angus Arbuckle, 1979 South African Defense Force (S.A.D.F.) combat survival knife, all steel, **$200.** Courtesy John Rullman and *Knife World*.

Angus Arbuckle, Model C, 6″ blade, micarta, **$275.**

Peter Bauchop, Alley Cat, 8½″ blade, micarta, **$275.**

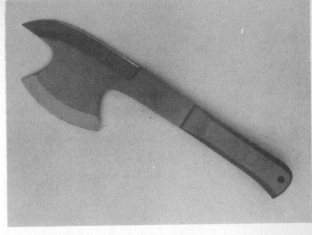

Peter Bauchop, "Knatchet," black. **$135.**

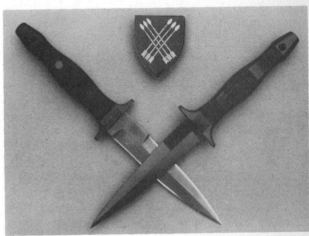

Peter Bauchop, Witch 5⅜″ blade, hot blued (left) or black (right) blade, micarta. **$185.** Shown with badge of S.A.D.F. elite unit that uses this knife.

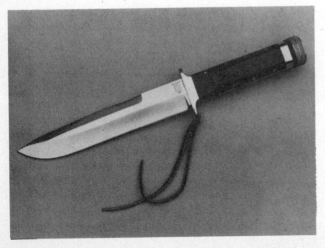

Peter Bauchop, Recce Survival 7″ blade, full-tang hollow handle. **$285.**

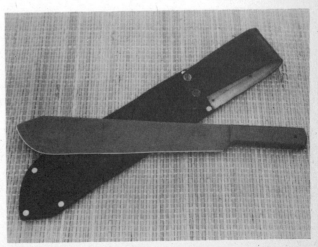

Peter Bauchop, Bushmaster, 1984 S.A.D.F. contract machete, micarta, black, no markings. **$85.**

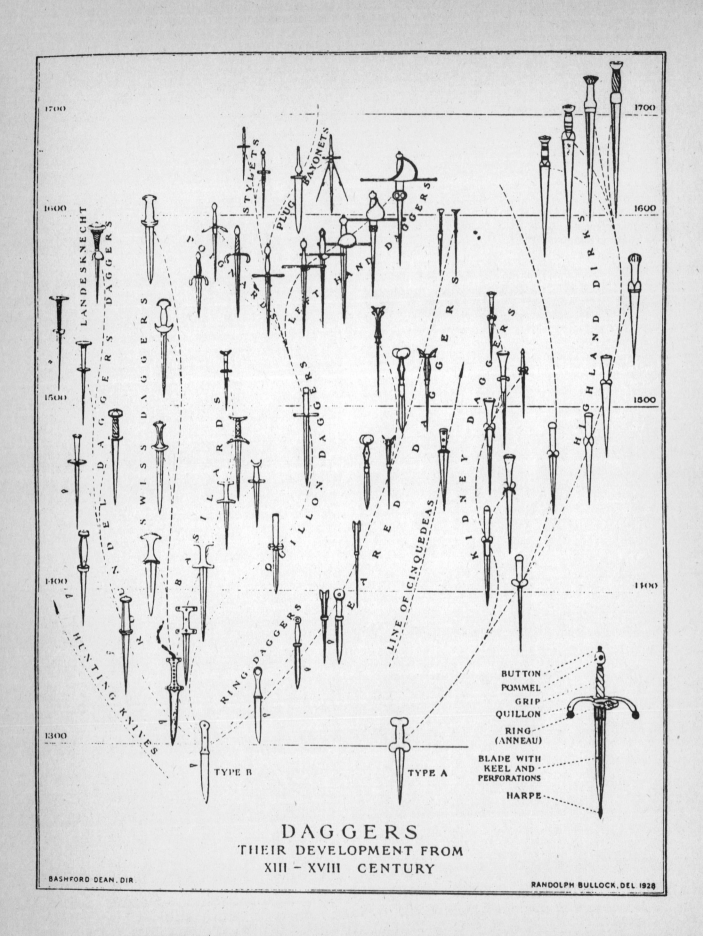

DAGGERS

THEIR DEVELOPMENT FROM

XIII – XVIII CENTURY

BASHFORD DEAN, DIR.

RANDOLPH BULLOCK, DEL. 1928

Foreign Exotic, Primitive and Historical Fixed Blade Knives

By Eiler R. Cook and Bernard Levine

Mr. Eiler R. Cook of North Carolina is a distinguished world traveler and collector of exotic knives. He provided illustrations and descriptions for nearly two-thirds of the knives shown in this section.

Introduction

IN THIS SECTION, Mr. Cook and I describe the basic types of fixed blade knives used in the four corners of the world. We illustrate at least one example of each type and provide an estimate of that example's current value on the American collector market. We also give plus or minus adjustment factors to enable you to estimate the value of similar knives with different features.

The knives are arranged geographically by region:

A: **Latin American**
B: **Scandinavia**
C: **Europe**
D: **Africa**
E: **Middle East and Indian Sub-Continent**
F: **East and Southeast Asia**
G: **Malaysia, Indonesia, and the Philippines**
H: **Australia**

At the end of this section is a brief chapter on modern high-grade reproductions of some more interesting foreign and exotic edged weapons.

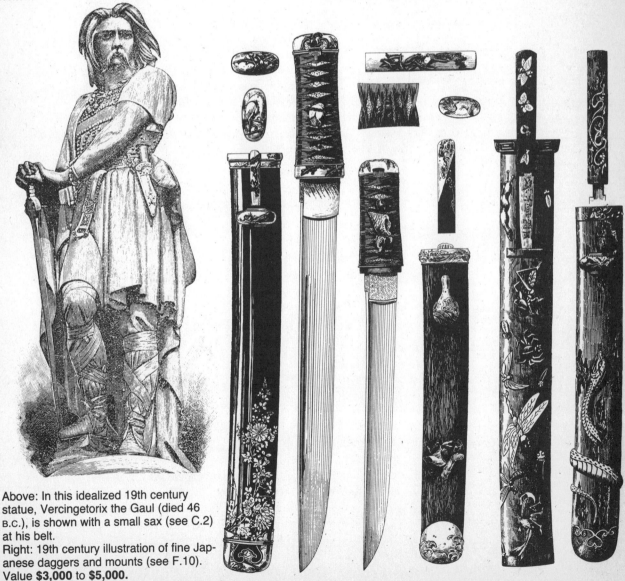

Above: In this idealized 19th century statue, Vercingetorix the Gaul (died 46 B.C.), is shown with a small sax (see C.2) at his belt.
Right: 19th century illustration of fine Japanese daggers and mounts (see F.10).
Value $3,000 to $5,000.

Area A: Latin America

A.1. Mexico. Hunting knife.

About 14 inches overall. Both sides of blade etched with scenes or slogans. Handle stag, sometimes snake skin, with white metal fittings. Hand tooled leather sheath. 19th–20th centuries. Example shown made in Oaxaca in 1966. Value **$75**. Silver mounts **add 50%**. Lower quality examples with aluminum or brass and horn handle, cruder etching, **subtract 75%**.

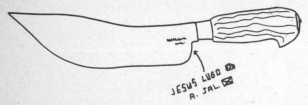

A.2. Mexico. Utility knife.

About 12 inches overall. Horn or wood handle with brass mounts. Crude workmanship. 20th century. Example shown made in Jalisco circa 1970. Value **$5**. Courtesy *Knife World*.

A.3. Guatemala. Highland Indian knife.

About 10 inches overall. Carved horn handle. Leather sheath. 19th–20th centuries. Examples shown circa 1960. Value **$5–10**.

Crude handcrafted knives sold in highland markets.

A.4. Argentina (also Uruguay). PUNAL or gaucho knife.

About 10 inches overall. Sheath and scabbard usually metal, rarely wood handle and leather sheath. 17th–20th centuries.

The gauchos are the cowboys of the pampas or prairies of southern South America. The CUCHILLO or knife in its various forms (PUNAL, FACON, DAGA) is a central part of their life and lore.

A.4.1. Modern Argentine PUNALES have relatively crude decoration and are poorly fitted. Nice ones are still made in Germany (e.g. by Carl Linder). Example shown: PUNAL with plated mounts made in Argentina circa 1940. Value **$45**. Silver mounts **add 100%**.

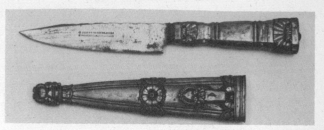

A.4.2. 19th century PUNALES with finer engraving, often have gold rosettes on silver mounts. Blades (often whole knives) made in England, Germany, or France. Old fine silver handles sometimes fitted with recent poor quality Argentine-made replacement blades (**subtract 75%**). Example shown: 19th century PUNAL with silver mounts and original blade. Blade made by Joseph Rodgers & Sons of Sheffield. Mounts marked L.COSTA. Value **$200**. Courtesy California Academy of Sciences, Rietz Collection.

A.4.3. 17th–18th century PUNALES were made in Spain, look similar to Mediterranean daggers but with all silver mounts. Usually have ornate steel bolster, silver overlaid ricasso, and chasing on blade. Pictorial touchmarks on back side of blade. Example shown: 18th century PUNAL made in Spain. Value **$250**.

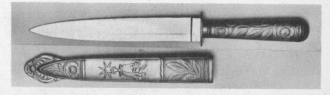

A.5. Brazil (also Argentina). FACON.

About 10 inches overall. Metal mounts. 19th–20th centuries. Example shown has aluminum mounts, from Rio Grande do Sul, Brazil, circa 1970. Value **$35**.

Spear point gaucho knife. More modern design than PUNAL. Doubled-edged version called DAGA in Argentina.

Foreign Exotic, Primitive and Historical Fixed Blade Knives

A.6. South America. CUCHILLA (utility knife).

About 12 inches overall. Blade often Sheffield made, marked in English. Pressed horn handles with cast bolsters. May have leather sheath. 19th–20th centuries. Example shown marked WARRANTED CAST STEEL/SHEFFIELD, circa 1900. Value **$35.**

This type of Sheffield knife was probably traded in Africa and Asia as well as South America.

A.7. Venezuela. LANZA.

About 15 inches overall. Steel lance head with long socket which serves as handle when LANZA is used as a dagger. Unmounted LANZA carried in belt sheath, while its pole is carried by a servant. 17th–19th centuries. Example shown 19th century. Value **$200.**

A.8. Central America. Spanish Colonial dirk.

About 16 inches overall. Hardwood handle, sometimes of wood disks separated by brass spacers. 18th–19th centuries. Value **$40–100,** depending on age and quality. Example shown early 19th century.

A.9. Central America. MACHETE.

About 25 inches overall. Handles of horn, wood, or plastic. Leather sheath. 19th–20th centuries. Example shown made in West Germany, 1967, sheath made for it in El Salvador. Value **$35.** Stainless blade and deluxe scabbard, **add 100%.** Plain local blade and sheath, **subtract 50–75%.**

Hundreds of different shapes of machetes have been made, each for a specific region, crop, or type of vegetation. Until the mid-1960s, the best known in Latin America were made by the Collins Company of Connecticut, who also made U.S. military machetes. The Collins brand name is still used in Central America. Machetes made in England and Germany were used in Asia and Africa.

For more on machetes, see *U.S. Military Fixed Blade Knives.*

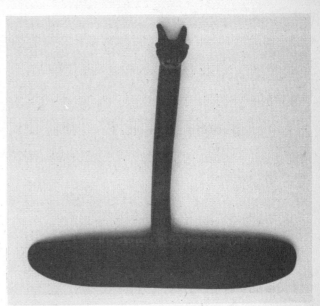

A.10. Peru. TUMI.

About 6 inches wide. Solid wrought copper. Llama-head finial. Pre-Columbian Inca sacrificial knife. Example shown, early 20th century reproduction. All known authentic examples in museums. Value of good reproduction **$100–150.**

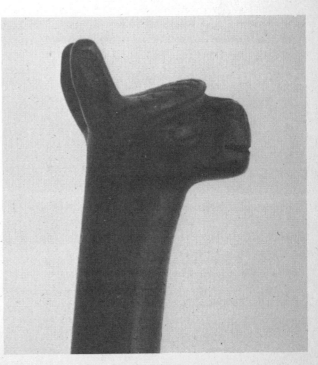

B.1. Lapland. Hand-made Lapp hunting knife.

About 10 inches overall. Wood handle. Carved reindeer horn sheath with reindeer hide throat. Example shown late 19th century. Value **$200**.

Modern hand-made examples with fancier carving sell for up to **$500**.

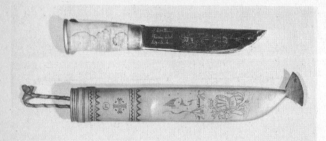

B.2. Finland. Standard PUUKKO or Finnish sheath knife.

About 8 inches overall. Wood handle (usually birch) with white metal mounts. Ornamented leather sheath. 19th–20th centuries. Example shown circa 1950s, value **$30**.

Larger size, about 12 inches, called LAPINLEUKU (Lapland knife) **add 50%**. Miniatures, about 4 inches, **subtract 50%**. Russo-Finnish War commemorative inscription, **add 50%**. Puukkos are sold world wide. Puukkos by J. Marttini, Rovaniemi, the foremost maker, are sold in U.S.

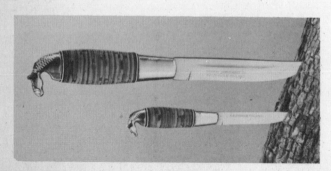

B.3. Finland. Horsehead PUUKKO.

About 6 inches overall. Plastic or pressed bark handle, brass or white metal mounts. Horsehead-shaped pommel. Leather sheath. 20th century. Value **$15**. Courtesy Gutmann Cutlery.

Made in Kauhava, exported to the U.S. since 1930s.

B.4. Finland. Modern style PUUKKO.

About 8 inches overall. Dark plastic or wood handle with brass or silver mounts. Leather sheath. 20th century. Example shown circa 1970, value **$50**.

This knife designed by Tapio Wirkkala.

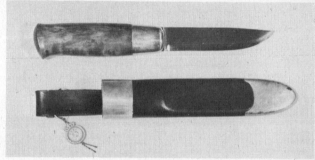

B.5. Norway. TOLLEKNIV or Norwegian sheath knife.

About 8 inches overall. Standard types have hardwood handles with white metal, pewter, or silver mounts. Leather sheath with matching fittings. 19th–20th centuries. Value **$40**. Silver or pewter **add 50%**. Example shown is David-Andersen's "Peer Gynt" knife with silver mounts, circa 1963. Value **$60**.

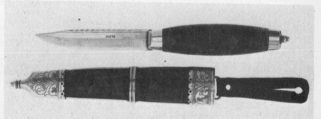

B.6. Norway. Deluxe TOLLEKNIV.

Fancier types have carved wood, bone, or ivory (walrus) handles with metal mounts and matching sheaths of the *same* material. Some have cross-guard. Mainly 19th century. Value **$80** (wood or bone), **$150** (ivory). Example shown has maple handle and sheath, engraved nickel silver mounts. Made by Jean Mette of Kristiania (now Oslo). Courtesy Bill Spivey.

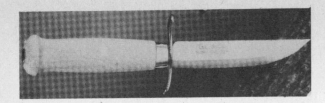

B.7. Sweden. Hunting knife.

About 9 inches overall. Three-part laminated steel blade. Birch handle with steel fittings. Leather sheath. 20th century. Example shown made in Mora currently, value **$8.** Courtesy Gutmann Cutlery.

SLOYD KNIVES

No. 2   Sloyd Knives. Oval Cocobolo Handles. 2⅝ in. Sabre Through Tang Blades.
No. 52 Sloyd Knives. Same as No. 2 except Handles are Varnished Beech.
Weight per dozen 1¼ lbs.

B.8. Sweden. SLOYD (manual training) knife.

About 5 inches overall. Wooden handle with iron or brass mounts. Fiber sheath, or none. 19th–20th centuries. Value **$4** (small and plain) to **$20** (large and decorated).

A simple whittling and utility knife. Identical knives made in U.S.A. Example shown American, c1930. Courtesy Jim Emerson.

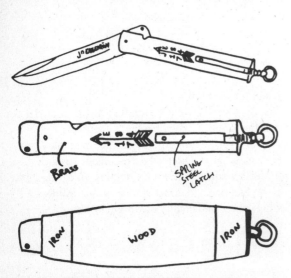

B.9. Sweden. Barrel knife (folding SLOYD).

About 6 inches long overall. Narrow straight blade. Barrel-shaped maple handle with steel fittings. Brass liners. Mid-19th-century to circa 1920s. Example shown circa 1900. Value **$40.**

This is a fixed blade that takes apart to fold up. Made in Eskilstuna by several firms, including John Engstrom (marked JE/1874 on liners) and Erik A. Berg. Courtesy *Knife World*.

C.1. Western Europe. Bronze Age daggers.

About 8–15 inches overall. Bronze blades. Riveted or integral bronze hilts. Circa 500 B.C. and earlier. European bronze daggers are rare and valued in the **$1,000s.** Virtually all known examples were found in excavations. Most are in museums.

C.2. Northwestern Europe. SAX (SCRAMASAX).

About 10 inches overall up to short sword length. Straight single-edged blade. Flat rounded pommel. Flat wood or horn grips. No guard. Leather or wood scabbard. Migration period to circa 15th century.

The Sax was the belt knife and short sword of the Germanic tribes in the Dark Ages, and later of the Vikings. All known Saxes are from excavations and are in relic condition. I have never heard of one for sale, but if there were one, its value would be several thousand dollars.

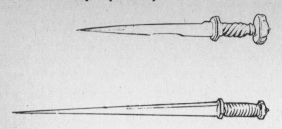

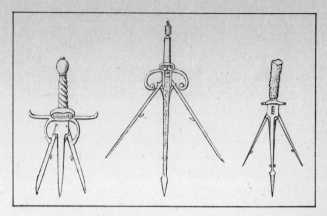

C.3. Western and Central Europe. Rondel dagger.

About 12 inches overall. Narrow straight blade. Disc shaped guard and pommel. An aristocratic dagger of the 14th to 16th centuries. Authentic example valued at **$750** up, depending on quality and condition.

C.5.3. Three-bladed parrying dagger. About 20 inches long. A combined dagger and sword catcher. 17th–18th centuries. Value **$400** and up.

C.4. Western Europe. Ballock or kidney dagger.

About 12 inches overall. Straight blade. Carved one-piece phalliform hilt with integral ballock shaped guard. 14th–17th centuries. Predecessor of the Scottish DIRK. Value **$500** and up.

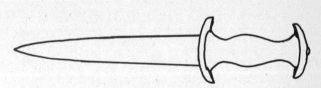

C.6. Western Europe. BASELARD.

About 15 inches overall. Sharp pointed double-edged blade. Hilt shaped like capital "I." 14th–16th centuries (revived by German Nazi party in 1930s). Early baselards are very rare outside of museums. Value in the **$1000s.** Nazi baselards valued about **$250**; later reproductions about **$40**.

A popular dagger in the late Middle Ages, it came originally from Basel, Switzerland.

C.5. Western Europe. Parrying daggers.

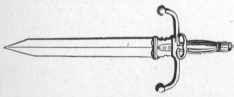

C.5.1. Quillon dagger. About 12 inches overall. A simple dagger with forward projecting crossguard. 13th–16th centuries. Value of original examples **$400** and up.

C.7. Scotland. DIRK

Usually about 19 inches overall. 19th–20th century dress dirks have wood or horn handle, often with Celtic weave carving and thistle-shaped butt. Earlier examples may have bone or metal grip. Often silver mounted. Leather scabbard with metal mounts, sometimes holding an eating knife and fork. Middle Ages to 20th century. Value **$200–1,000** depending on age and quality of workmanship.

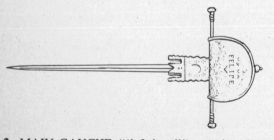

C.5.2. MAIN GAUCHE ("left hand") parrying dagger. About 20 inches long. A long slender dagger with guard and hilt like a sword. A "modern" refinement of the medieval Quillon Dagger. Used in combination with a sword. 16th–18th centuries. Value **$300** and up.

C.7.1. Early DIRK. Example shown circa 17th–18th centuries (excavated). Bone (?) handle with wrought iron mounts. Value **$500.** Courtesy California Academy of Sciences, Rietz collection.

C.7.2. DIRK. Example shown early 19th century flat dirk for concealment. Made by Boog of Edinburgh. Checkered boxwood handle, silver mounts. Value **$250.**

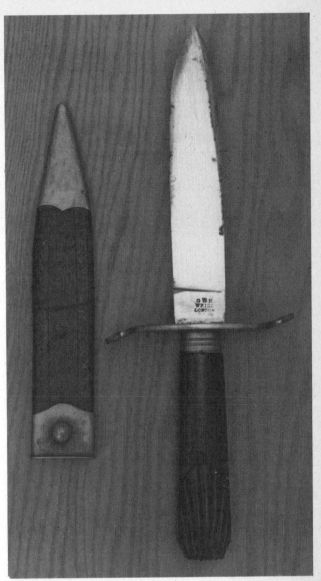

C.7.3. Dress DIRK. Example shown current replica, made in India. Value: dirk, **$125;** sgian dubh, **$35;** both with sheath. Courtesy A-C Enterprises. (Weyer photo)

C.8. Scotland. SGIAN DUBH ("black knife").

Up to 8 inches overall. Black wood or horn handle with carved weave design, silver (or plated) mounts, pommel usually set with large cairngorm (smoky yellow quartz). Black leather sheath with matching mounts. Mid-18th–20th centuries. Example shown circa 1930. Value **$100.** Older or with regimental crest, **add 50–100%**, modern, **subtract 50%**.

Pronounced "skene-dhu." Worn in top of right stocking as part of Highland dress. Each Highland regiment had its own model with distinctive crest.

C.9. England. London hunting knife.

At least 12 inches overall. Spear point blade. Massive stag, boxwood, ebony, or ivory handle with iron, nickel silver, or sterling mounts. Brown or black leather sheath, usually with matching mounts. 19th century. Value **$750** in excellent condition. Example shown by John Weiss (1787–present) made circa 1815–1830, ebony and nickel silver. Courtesy Walter Moreau.

This was the English gentleman adventurer's counterpart to the American bowie knife. Those marked LONDON were made there, usually by surgical instrument makers and of the highest quality, with very stout blades. Those with just a London street address were made in Sheffield for a London retailer (**subtract 50%**).

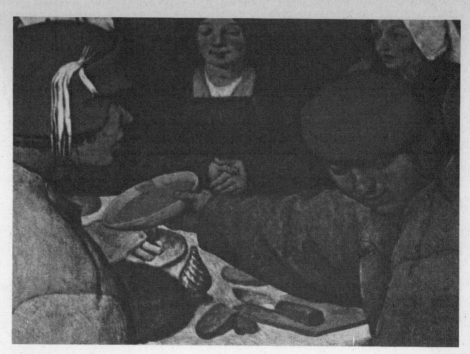

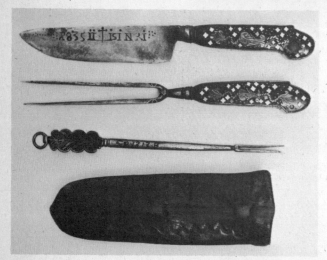

C.11. Bavaria (southern Germany). TROUSSE (hunting set).

Up to 8 inches overall. Pewter brass or silver handles with inlaid horn (usually) or stag panels and decorative rivets. Leather sheath holding matching knife and fork and, often, a sharpening steel. Steel often hollow, unscrews to reveal skewer, marrow fork, or corkscrew. Late 18th–early 20th centuries. Value **$100–250** depending on quality. Silver mounts **add 50%**. Factory-made **subtract 50%**. I have been offered $1,000 for a good quality trousse with a steel that contains a corkscrew, but I have yet to see one. Example shown dated on blade 1835. Value **$200**. Courtesy Smithsonian Institution, Wiebusch Collection.

This type of trousse was derived from the larger trousses of the 15th and 16th century nobility. There is often a date on handle, blade, or sheath. Earliest I have seen is 1799. Most trousses are hand-made and look much older than they are. Late ones are factory-made and highly finished, but of inferior quality.

C.10. Northern Europe. HAUSWEHRE ("home defense").

About 14 inches overall. Wood, stag, bone, or horn handle. Drop-in leather or cloth sheath worn hung from belt or girdle. Middle Ages to 18th century.

Common peasant's and workingman's all-purpose belt knife. Older examples appear similar to older Mediterranean daggers, though wider. Both are ancestors of most modern sheath knife styles. Known mainly from art-work. Few *proven* original examples are known. Example shown in a 16th century painting.

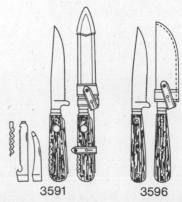

3591   3596

C.12. Germany and Austria. JAGDNICKER or WEIDMESSER ("hunting knife"). Also called TRACHTENMESSER ("dress knife").

About 8 inches overall. Handle usually stag (one-piece with ferrule and cap, or two-piece riveted), also chamois horn and deer-foot. Leather sheath with metal throat and tip, but no belt attachment. Worn in Lederhosen pocket. 18th–20th centuries. Value **$25** for little-known brands up to **$100** for well-known makes such as Puma, Henckels, Boker, Linder. Examples shown current Puma. Silver mounts, **add 50%**. Folding blades in handle, **add 50%**.

C.13. Germany, Austria, Czechoslovakia. Deerfoot knife.

About 9 inches overall. Handle made from deer's foot with the hair on. Leather sheath with nickel silver fittings. 19th–20th centuries. Example shown from a 1983 American catalog. Value **$30.** Courtesy Gutmann Cutlery.

Many of these were and are made for export to the United States (on these the markings are in English). Folding versions also made.

C.14. Germany. Hanger or hunting sword.

12 inches long up to short sword size. Usually stag handled, with crossguard and counter-guard like a sword. Often with etched blade and deerfoot shaped quillons. Heavy leather sheath with metal fittings. 18th–20th centuries. Example shown late 19th century. Value **$175.** Courtesy California Academy of Sciences.

These big knives were used for killing wounded animals, for disjointing game, and as personal defense weapons. They were derived from the large blunt-ended hunter's choppers of the Middle Ages. In turn, they were an important forerunner of the bowie knife.

C.15. Germany. Export Daggers and Knives.

Several standard styles distributed around the world. Late 19th century to present. Value range **$15–150,** depending on finish, condition, and handle material.

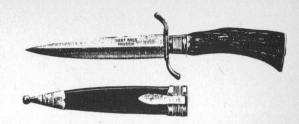

C.15.1. Export Dagger. 10 inches overall. Stag handle, black leather sheath. Nickel silver mounts. Example shown from a 1903 American hardware catalog. Value **$30.**

C.15.2. Export Dagger. 11 inches overall. Ebony handle, black leather sheath. Nickel silver mounts. Example shown from a 1903 American hardware catalog. Value **$60.**

C.15.3. Export Knife. About 11 inches overall. Leather and aluminum handle. Current. Value **$25.** Courtesy Gutmann Cutlery.

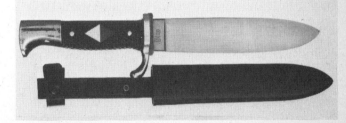

C.15.4. Youth Knife. About 10 inches overall. Plastic handles. Plated mounts. Metal and leather sheath. Current example by Wingen. Value **$25.** Courtesy Gutmann Cutlery.

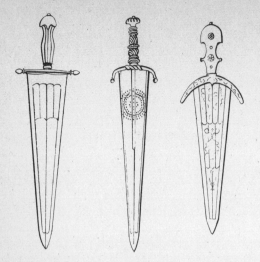

C.16. Southern Europe, mainly Italy. CINQUEDEA.

Up to 18 inches overall. Wide heavy triangular blade, often fullered and pierced. Ornate hilt. 15th–16th centuries. Value **$500** and up.

C.17. Southwestern Europe. Mediterranean dagger.

8–18 inches overall. Every possible handle and sheath material from wood to gold and jewels. Middle Ages to 19th century.

For centuries this was the standard belt knife of southern Europe, and of Spanish areas of the New World. The earliest bowie knives of the 1830s looked similar. The South American gaucho's PUNAL is still made in this shape, though with all metal mounts.

C.17.1. Plain example, circa 19th century, Spanish style, probably Moroccan. Horn handle partly wrapped with wire, copper inlaid mark in blade. Value **$50.** Finer quality large examples in excellent condition valued into the **$1,000s.**

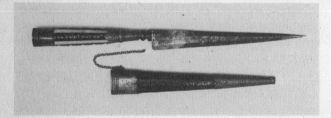

C.17.2. Mediterranean dagger, small fancy example. Probably 18th century from Sardinia. Double-edged triangular blade. Pearl and tortoise handle mounted in silver. Silver-mounted green Morocco sheath. Value **$350.** Courtesy California Academy of Sciences, Rietz collection.

C.18. France. Dagger.

About 7 inches overall. Hollow blued steel handle, gilt brass mounts. Etched blade and scabbard. 19th century. Value **$85.**

C.19. Italy. STILETTO.

About 12 inches overall. Slender blade with two, three, or four edges. Often all steel. 17th–20th centuries. Example shown probably 19th century. Value **$60.** Older finer examples rare and worth much more.

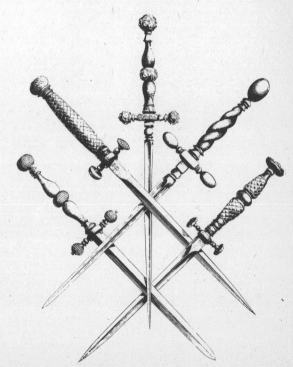

19th century engraving of a group of fine old stilettos. Value **$250** and up.

C.20. Eastern Europe. Fancy dagger.

About 16 inches overall. Ornate metal hilt. Wood sheath with matching metal fittings. 19th century. Example shown circa 1825. Value **$90**.

C.21. Russia (Caucasus). KAMA or KINDJAL.

About 20 inches overall. Semi-circular pommel with narrow grip, usually of wood, horn, ivory, or silver embellished with niello work. Wood sheath covered with velvet, leather, or matching silver. 18th to early 20th centuries.

The word "Kindjal" is the Russian version of the Arabic word "Khanjar." Both simply mean "knife." The KAMA is the traditional knife of the Cossacks. A similar knife may have been used in Persia.

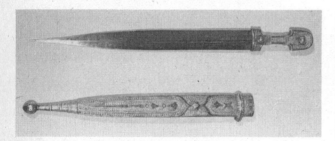

C.21.1 Example shown silver mounted, circa 1900. Value **$300**. Plain horn handle, **subtract 50%**. Fine ivory mounts, **add 30–50%**.

C.21.2. KAMA reportedly collected in Persia in the 19th century. Value **$200**.

C.22. Greece. KOPIS.

Ancient Greek bronze fighting knife with curved blade and concave cutting edge. Known mainly from artwork and literature.

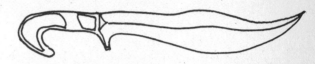

C.23. Greece. MACHAIRA.

Ancient Greek bronze fighting knife with curved blade and convex cutting edge. Known mainly from artwork and literature.

The KOPIS and the MACHAIRA seem to be the ancestors of many more modern knives, including the Kama, Khanjar, Kukri, and Jambiya.

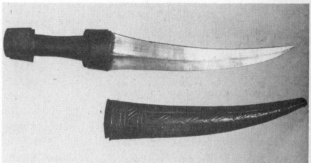

C.24. Balkans (Albania). Eastern European JAMBIYA.

About 15 inches overall. Handle of horn, wood, or metal. Leather, wood, or metal sheath. 18th century or earlier through early 20th century. Example shown late 19th century, value **$75**. Full silver mounts, **add at least 200%**.

The Jambiya is of Arab origin. It spread throughout Moslem-ruled lands from Eastern Europe through the Middle East to India in the period of the Ottoman Empire. Shape and decoration vary from region to region.

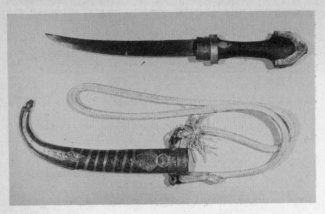

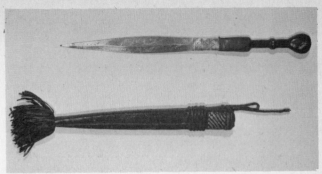

D.1. Morocco (Mokhazni tribe). KOUMMYA.

About 15 inches overall. Curved single edged blade, usually European made. Wood handle with flared pommel trimmed with brass or silver. Wood sheath with two suspension rings, matching trim. 18th–20th centuries. Example shown brass trimmed, circa 1950. Value **$50.** Fine silver mounts, **add 200%.**

D.4. North Africa (Tunisia, possibly Senegal). Dagger.

About 14 inches overall. Leather covered wood handle with rounded knob pommel. Tooled Morocco leather sheath with tassel. 19th–20th centuries. Example shown early 20th century. Value **$60.**

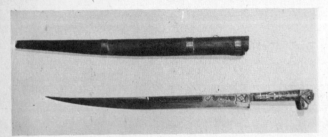

D.2. Morocco. FLYSSA.

Around 18 inches overall. Brass inlaid iron hilt integral with blade. Blade may be brass-inlaid as well. Mythic animal head pommel. Wooden sheath with brass bands. 18th–19th centuries. Example shown late 19th century. Value **$60.**

This is the national dagger of the Kabyle people, a fiercely independent branch of the Berbers.

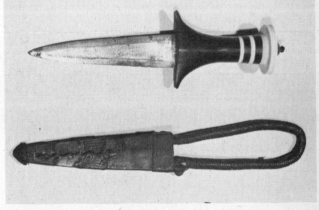

D.5. Sudan. Arm dagger.

About 9 inches overall. Wood and ivory hilt with circular pommel and flaring self-guard. Leather sheath with armband for wear on upper arm. 19th century. Example shown, late 19th century. Value **$75.**

A very good quality primitive African knife.

D.3. North Africa. TELEK (Tuareg arm dagger).

About 18 inches overall. Cross-shaped hilt with leather and brass binding. Worked leather sheath with typical arm loop. 18th–19th centuries. Example shown mid-19th century. Value **$130.**

Used by the nomadic Tuareg warriors of the Sahara desert region. Worn upside down on the left arm for quick draw with right hand.

D.6. Sudan. Arm Knife.

About 12 inches overall. Similar to above except for pommel and blade shape. Ebony handle. Light well-tempered double-edged blade. 19th century. Value **$75.**

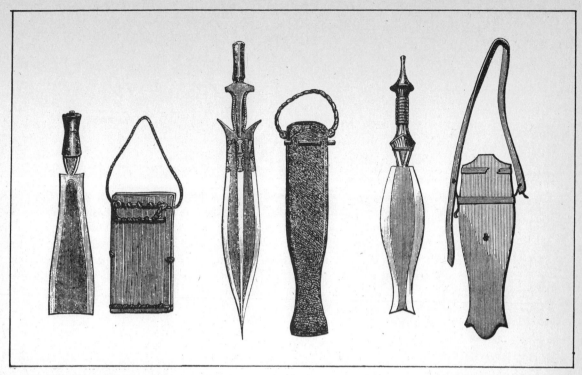

D.9. Southern Africa. Knives and dagger.

Illustrations from a 19th century book. Value **$75** to **$100** each.

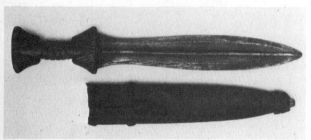

D.7. Central Africa. Dagger.

About 15 inches overall. Leaf-shaped blade with median ridge. Carved wood handle, leather sheath. Example shown probably early 20th century. Value **$75.** Courtesy California Academy of Sciences, Rietz collection.

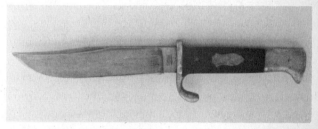

D.10. South Africa. Hunting knife.

11 inches overall. Nickel silver handle with horn scales. Blade etched BUSHMAN'S FRIEND. Made by William Rodgers of Sheffield, England, circa 1930s. Copied from a German design. Value **$60.** Other styles of hunting knives with this same blade etching were made for sale in Africa, and also, I believe, Australia.

"Bushman" is a British colonial term, common both in Africa and Australia. It is roughly equivalent to such American terms as "woodsman" and "frontiersman."

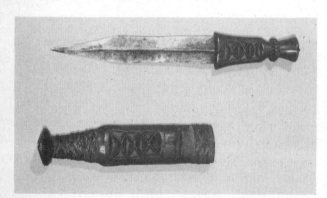

D.8. Southwest Africa (Ovamboland, Namibia). Dagger.

About 10 inches overall. Carved wood handle and sheath, often bound with brass wire. 18th–19th centuries. Example shown 19th century. Value **$40.**

Spear shaped blade tapers to almost a needle point, as on certain bronze age swords.

E.1. Western Persia (ancient Luristan). Bronze dagger.

About 14 inches overall. Solid cast bronze with edges of blade hammered to work-harden. Originally had inlaid bone, wood, or hardstone handle scales. Example shown, before 700 B.C. Value **$300.** With original handles, **add 50%.**

These daggers were grave goods and have survived in relatively large numbers. There are several variants, particularly with larger pommels.

The Jambiya or Arab dagger was the free man's belt knife wherever Moslems ruled. Eastern Europe, North Africa, Turkey, Persia, and India all had variations of the Jambiya. Contemporary hand-made examples in Yemen and Oman cost from **$300** for plain ones, to **$800** for a nice silver-mounted one, on up to **$3,000** for one with a rhinoceros horn handle and silver trim.

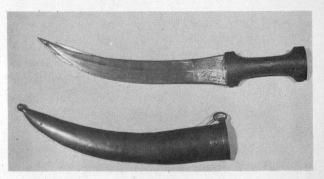

E.3. Persia (Iran). JAMBIYA.

About 16 inches overall. Metal hilt with gold inlay designs and flat-topped Indo-Persian style pommel. Metal sheath. 18th–19th centuries. Value **$100.** Example shown mid-19th century, has unusual blade tip that divides into five points for added shocking power when stabbing. Value **$200.** More ornate examples with jeweled hilts, **add 100%** and more.

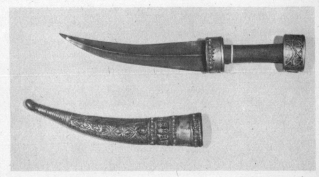

E.2. Arabian Peninsula. JAMBIYA.

About 14 inches overall. Curved double-edged blade with median ridge or groove. Wood, horn, ivory, or metal self-guard handle. Curved or L-shaped scabbard of leather or wood covered with leather, cloth, or metal. Middle ages to present. Example shown silver mounted, probably 19th century. Value **$400.** Courtesy California Academy of Sciences.

E.4. Iraq. JAMBIYA.

About 15 inches overall. Wood grip with embossed silver covered guard and pommel. Silver covered wood sheath. Silver sometimes inset with turquoise or coral. 18th–20th centuries. Example shown 20th century. Value **$90.** More ornate examples are more valuable.

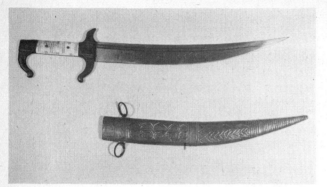

E.5. Turkey. Dagger.

About 15 inches overall. Curved blade with Arabic inscription. Ivory grips. Hook-like pommel and guard of ebony. Brass sheath. 19th–20th centuries. Example shown early 20th century. Value **$45.**

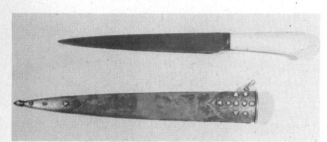

E.6. Afghanistan (also Persia, northern India, Central Asia, Armenia, Turkey). KARD.

About 14 inches overall. Forged bolster. Thick blade, usually straight, sometimes curved. Ivory, jade, or metal handle. Sheath of velvet covered wood with ornate metal throat and tip. Middle ages to 19th century. Example shown circa 1800, sheath fittings embellished with turquoise. Value **$175.** Blade damascened in gold or silver, **add 25%.** Blade of damascus steel, **add 100%.** Jade handle, **add 50%.** Metal handle, **subtract 75%.**

The Kard was Persian in origin, brought to Afghanistan and northern India by the Mughals in the 16th century. A larger version was used in Central Asia. Kards sometimes were concealed in canes or riding crops.

E.7. Afghanistan. SALWAR YATAGHAN (Khyber knife).

14 inches up to sword size. Triangular blade with T-shaped cross-section. Leather sheath covers entire knife. Horn, bone, or ivory (usually walrus) handle. 17th–20th centuries. Example shown probably 19th century, ivory handle. Value **$350.** Courtesy California Academy of Sciences, Rietz Collection.

I once saw a superb 19th century Khyber knife made by Joseph Rodgers & Sons of Sheffield. Value **$500.**

E.8. Northern India (also Persia). PESH-KABZ.

Up to 18 inches overall. Narrow straight bolstered blade, usually T-backed like a Khyber knife, but narrow and stiff for piercing chain mail armor. Handle often walrus ivory. Sheath of metal or leather over wood. 17th–19th centuries. Example shown probably 18th century. Value **$250.** Courtesy California Academy of Sciences, Rietz collection.

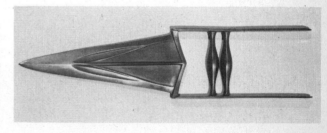

E.9. India. KATAR.

About 15 inches overall. All steel. Hilt may be damascened in gold. Some have two additional blades that spring out to the sides when the two handles are squeezed together. 16th–19th centuries. Example shown probably 19th century. Value **$200.** Ornate damascening, **add 100%.** Triple-bladed, **add 100%.**

Like the Moslem PESH-KABZ, the Hindu KATAR was designed for piercing chain mail. It was used with a punching blow. The side rails were used for parrying.

E.10. Southern India (Madras). Bowie-type knife. (Not illustrated)

About 14 inches overall. Heavy single edged clip or spear point blade. Crossguard. Hilt often of ivory. Looks similar to American or English bowie knives, but marked ARNACHELLUM/SALEM or AUSTIN/TRICHINOPOLY. 19th century. Value **$250.**

E.12. Southern India. PICHANGATTI ("hand knife").

About 13 inches overall. Heavy straight clip point blade. Round-end pistol grip handle with horn or silver scales. Wood sheath with silver or brass mounts. 18th–20th centuries. Value **$75.** Silver mounts, **add 100%.** A similar shaped blade was also used on a pole-arm.

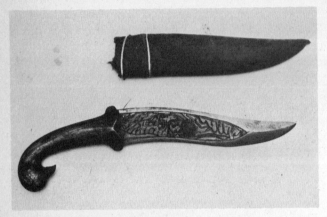

E.11. S.W. Asia, from Arabia through N. India. KHANJAR.

About 14 inches overall. Slightly recurved double-edged blade. Indian examples often have blade decorations. Pistol-grip hilts range from plain metal to finest jade. Sheath of velvet covered wood. 17th century to present. Example shown 20th century. Value **$40.** Ornate examples with jewelled or jade hilts worth up to **$1,000** or more.

Smaller knives of this shape with multi-piece hard stone handles are made in Assam and Burma. Value **$50.** An Indian version with a fan-shaped pommel is called a KHANJARLI.

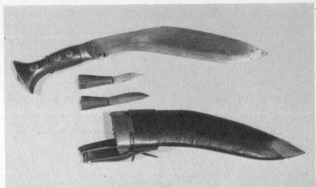

E.13. Nepal. Gurkha KUKRI.

About 16 inches overall. Heavy forward curved blade. Plain wood or ivory hilt with ridge around middle. Wood sheath covered with leather or velvet, often holds two miniature KUKRIES. Ancient times to present. Example shown 1950s. Value **$75.** Chrome plated blade with black handle, marked INDIA, **subtract 75%.** Ivory handle, **add 200%.**

In addition to being the national knife of Nepal, used as both jungle brush knife and weapon, the KUKRI is an issue arm of the Nepalese Gurkha troops serving in the British Army.

E.11.1. KHANJAR by Joseph Rodgers & Sons from a 1912 catalog. Value **$500.**

E.14. Sri Lanka (Ceylon). PIHA-KAETTA.
About 12 inches overall. Narrow heavy blade inlaid and overlaid with engraved silver or brass panels. Ornate handle of wood, horn, or ivory, often trimmed with metal. Equally ornate wood sheath with metal mounts. 17th–20th centuries.

E.14.1. Example shown mounted in ivory and brass, 19th century. Sheath missing. Value **$250**. Plainer example, **subtract 50%**. Fine ivory and silver mounts, **add 50%**. Courtesy California Academy of Sciences, Rietz collection.

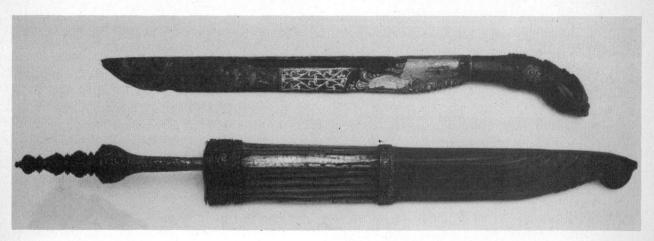

E.14.2. PIHA-KAETTA. Example shown mounted in horn, silver, and brass. Wood sheath mounted in silver and brass also contains an ornate skewer. Probably 19th century. Value **$300**. Courtesy California Academy of Sciences, Rietz collection.

Area F: East and Southeast Asia

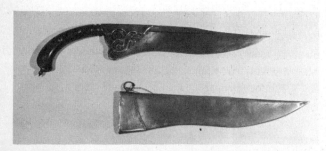

F.1. Southeast Asia (Burma south to Malaya). Knife.
About 16 inches overall. Kopis-shaped blade with carved metal side plates. Pistol-shaped horn or wood grips. 19th century. Example shown value **$100**.

F.2. Tibet. PHURBU.
6–20 inches overall. Short triangular pyramidal blade. Heavy elaborate hilt. All brass, or else iron blade with brass or wood hilt. Tibetan Buddhist ritual knife. Example shown all brass, 18th–19th century. Value **$550**. Courtesy Museum of Historical Arms, Miami Beach, Florida.

F.3. Bhutan, Tibet. Bhutan Dagger.

About 15 inches overall. Straight blade. Wood grip wrapped with silver wire. Wrought silver pommel. Silver mounted leather sheath. 18th–19th century. Example shown circa 1880. Value **$140.** For mounts of low silver content alloy, **subtract 30%.**

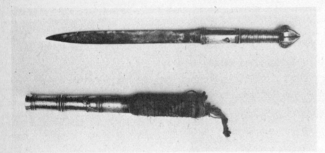

F.4. Burma and Thailand (Mountain regions). DHA.

About 15 inches overall, up to sword length. Plain slender blade. Hilt of silver over wood (usually) or of ivory, with onion-shaped pommel. Sheath of silver over wood with flat bottom. Red carrying cord. 18th–19th centuries. Example shown late 19th century. Value **$110.** Exceptional silver work, **add 100%.**

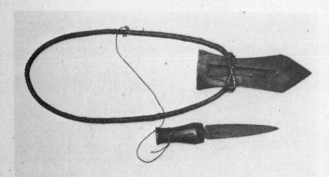

F.5. Taiwan. Formosan aboriginal dagger.

About 14 inches overall. Wooden hilt and sheath with braided shoulder loop. 17th–18th centuries. Example shown 20th century replica. Value **$35.**

F.6. China. Fighting knife (Chinese ''bowie'').

About 13 inches overall. Sharp pointed diamond-shaped single-edged blade. Fluted handle of red wood or ivory with brass ferrules, heavy oval guard, and faceted pommel. Flat wooden sheath. 19th century. Unmarked examples made both in China and in California. Example shown value **$250.** Example made by Will & Finck of San Francisco mounted in ivory and silver with silver-plated sheath, value **$2,500.**

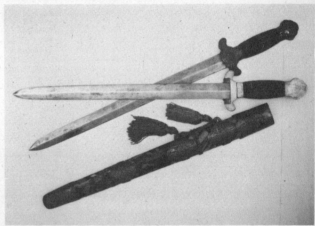

F.7. China. Double dagger.

Up to about 24 inches overall. A pair of matching knives with handles and mounts flat on one side so they nest together in one sheath. Blades may be sword style as in example shown, or may be fighting knife style, or have broad triangular blades with knuckle-bows (called ''butterfly knives''). Wooden handles. Brass or iron mounts. Wooden sheath with metal fittings. 19th–20th centuries.

Example shown has engraved brass fittings and tortoise shell veneer on scabbard, circa 1900. Value **$350.** Courtesy John Crain.

A fine quality undecorated pair of iron-mounted butterfly knives would be worth about **$600.**

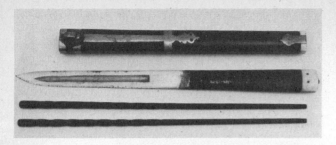

F.8. China, Mongolia, and Tibet. Trousse.

Up to about 12 inches overall. Stiff slender food preparation knife with forged bolster. Handle scales of wood or horn with ivory or bone ends. Wooden sheath with metal and ivory mounts, usually wrapped in ray skin or metal. Holds pair of chopsticks of ivory, bone, or wood. 18th to early 20th centuries. Example shown has sheath wrapped in black lacquered ray skin, ebony chopsticks. Value **$200.** Courtesy California Academy of Sciences, Rietz collection.

Miniature trousse, handle and sheath covered in tortoiseshell, silver chopsticks, value **$150.**

F.9. China. Western style dagger.

Light straight double-edged blade. Brass mounts. Steel scabbard with brass mounts. Late 19th and 20th centuries. Example shown has designs of crossed U.S. and Nationalist flags, U.S. Marine Corps emblem, dragons. Value **$125.** Strictly Chinese decoration, **subtract 50%.**

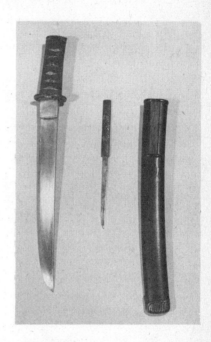

F.8.1. Some larger examples include a similarly shaped dagger along with the knife. A fine example of this type with laminated blades and matching mounts would be worth up to about **$1,500.**

Example shown, Chinese trousse with iron mounts, wood handles and bone ends on dagger and knife, bone chopsticks. Dagger blade marked "59" in Chinese. Value **$250.**

F.10. Japan. TANTO.

Up to 18 inches overall. Stout single-edged laminated blade, polished to reveal grain. Tang may be signed. Copper or silver blade collar (*habaki*). Small iron or copper alloy guard (*tsuba*). Wood handle (*tsuka*) covered with ray skin (*sa-me*) and usually wrapped with braid, secured by single peg (*mekugi*). Matching decorated butt cap (*fuchi*), ferrule (*kashira*), and grip ornaments (*menuki*). Lacquered wood scabbard may also have metal mounts. As in example shown, sheath may hold auxiliary knife (*kogatana*, handle called *kodzuka*). 14th century to present. Example shown dated February 2, 1855. Value **$1,000.**

The tanto was originally meant to be worn with armor, its main function being to cut the wearer out of his armor if he fell in the water. A similar dagger without a guard is sometimes called an *aikuchi*.

Value of a Japanese weapon depends on quality of blade, fame of maker, quality of mounts, and condition. DO NOT polish or oil a tanto. Consult an expert. Kodzuka alone may be worth **$50–300** depending on quality and condition.

F.8.2. Some Mongol trousses have metal covered sheaths often inset with large colorful uncut stones. Example shown has plated mounts, early 20th century. Value **$150.**

Best quality Mongol trousses have heavy silver mounts with flat flaring bottoms, inset orange and blue stones, fine quality blades. Value of these **$500.**

Area F: East and Southeast Asia (cont.)

F.11. Japan. KAIKEN or KWAIKEN.

About 12 inches overall. Slender single-edged blade, usually laminated. Blade collar (*habaki*). One-piece hilt of wood or metal over wood. Matching sheath. Mounts may look like fan or other harmless object. 15th–19th centuries. Example shown 19th century. Value **$250.** Courtesy California Academy of Sciences, Rietz collection.

This is the traditional woman's dagger, worn concealed in the kimono. Its primary function was self-defense.

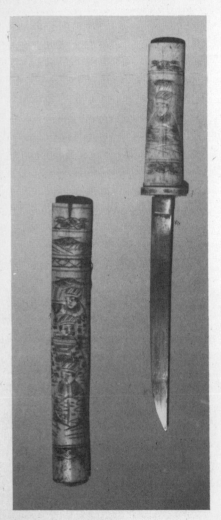

F.12. Japan. Souvenir knife.

About 1–2 feet long. Inferior blade and collar (*habaki*). Carved bone or (rarely) ivory mounts. 19th–20th centuries. Example shown value **$60.**

Exceptionally fine carving will increase the value.

Foreign Exotic, Primitive and Historical Fixed Blade Knives

Area G: Malaysia, Indonesia and the Philippines

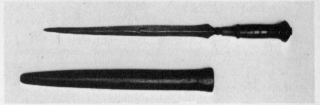

G.1. Malaya. LADING TERUS.

About 18 inches long overall. Narrow stout double-edged blade resembling a lance head. Turned wood hilt and rounded wooden sheath. 18th–19th centuries. Example shown 19th century. Value **$40.**

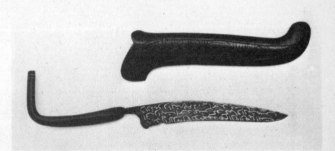

G.2. Malayan Archipelago. BADE BADE (RENTJONG).

About 11 inches long overall. Slightly curved single-edged blade. Hardwood hilt with right angle bend to facilitate quick draw. Wooden sheath. 19th century to present. Example shown has blade etched with Arabic writing, 1970s. Value **$20.**

G.3. North Borneo. BARONG.

About 20 inches overall. Broad single-edged leaf-shaped blade. Wood handle, rarely ivory. Wooden sheath. 19th century or earlier to present. Example shown late 19th century, well made with ornamental carving. Value **$125.** Plainer modern example, **subtract 50%.** Ivory handle, **add 50%.**

The Moro jungle and combat knife, it was the inspiration for the various U.S. Army bolos.

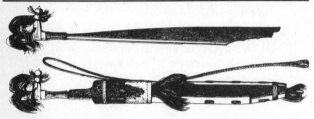

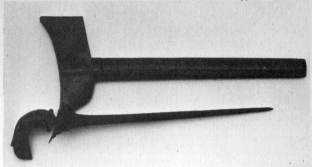

G.5.2. KRIS. Example shown from Malaya, 19th century. Note rectangular sheath throat. Value **$100.**

G.4. Sarawak, Malaysian Borneo. MANDAU (PARANG-ILANG).

About 25 inches overall. Stag tine handle decorated with paint and cord. Wooden sheath decorated with paint, cord, fur, teeth, and beads, also holds small 6-inch knife. 18th–20th centuries. Example shown 20th century. Value **$130.** Older or better decorated example, **add 50%.**

The traditional knife of the Dyak headhunters of central Borneo.

G.5.3. KRIS. Example shown from Malaya or southern Thailand. Note unusual ''barbs'' on blade and decorated sheath. Probably 19th century. Value **$200.**

G.5. Malaysia and Indonesia. KRIS.

About 18 inches overall. Slim delicate double-edged blade with elaborately wrought pointed self-guard. Blade usually ''pamur'' (welded damascus), may be straight or wavy. Carved wood or, rarely, ivory hilt with worked metal ferrule or ring. Streamlined wooden scabbard with boat-shaped throat. Throat may be ivory to match hilt. 14th–20th centuries.

Krisses vary widely in quality and value. Many small and badly worn old krisses were dumped in the U.S in the 1970s at under **$10 each.** These are not worth over **$25** now. However, a very fine kris in superb condition is worth perhaps **$400–800.**

G.5.1. KRIS. Example shown from Java, circa 1800. Wooden mounts. Value **$130.**

G.5.4. KRIS (KERIS MAJAPAHIT). Example shown from Java. Sheath and figural hilt wrapped with metal and set with stones. Believed to be the earliest style of kris. 19th century blade in 20th century mounts. Value **$250.**

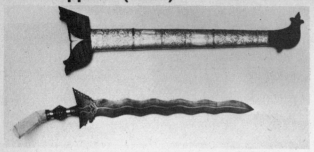

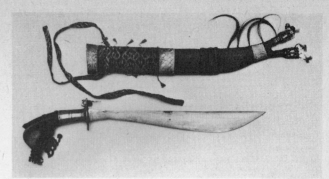

G.6. Philippines (Mindanao or Jolo). Moro KRIS.

About 24 inches overall. Shaped like Malay kris but larger and sturdier. Wood or ivory handle. Wood scabbard usually wrapped with metal. 15th–20th centuries. Example shown has ivory hilt and silver wrapped scabbard. Early 20th century. Value **$250**. Plain example, **subtract 60%**.

This is the short sword of the Muslim Moros of the southern Philippines. The example shown is one of a pair given by a hadji, a Moslem who has been to Mecca, to his favorite son.

G.9. Philippines (Davao del Sur, Mindanao). BOLO.

About 14 inches long overall. Wood handle and scabbard with metal trim and woven decorations. From the non-Muslim Bagobo tribe. 18th–20th centuries. Example shown early 20th century. Value **$90**.

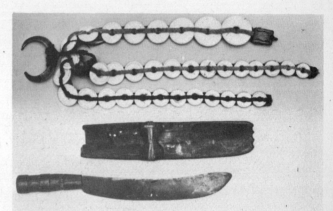

G.7. Philippines (Jolo). PUNAL.

About 13 inches overall. Double-edged blade. Curved wood hilt with metal mounts. Metal covered wooden scabbard. 15th–20th centuries. Example shown has silver mounts, late 19th century. Value **$150**. Plain example, **subtract 75%** or more.

"Punal" is Spanish for "dagger;" the same word is used for the gaucho knife. This type of "punal" is a dagger of the Moros. The example shown is one of a pair that belonged to a chieftain (*datu*) on Jolo Island.

G.10. Philippines (Northern Luzon). Ifugao knife.

About 16 inches overall. Crude wooden hilt and sheath. 18th–20th centuries. Example shown circa 1900, with belt of fish bone discs and boar's teeth attached to circa 1898 U.S. Army web belt. Value **$80**.

The Ifugao were headhunters in the mountains of northern Luzon.

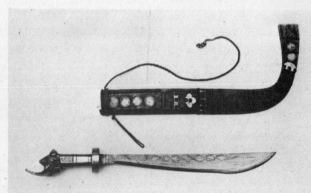

G.8. Philippines (Northern Mindanao). Moro dagger.
About 23 inches long overall. Double edged blade with fuller. Elaborate bird-head (*sarimanuk*) hilt of a silver-copper alloy. 18th–20th centuries. Example shown 19th century blade in 20th century mounts. Value **$130**. A Maranao Muslim weapon.

G.11. Philippines (Panay). SANDUKO BOLO.
About 30 inches long overall. Elaborate hilt wrapped in silver and gold. Wood sheath decorated with old Spanish coins (earliest on example shown: 1777). 18th–19th centuries. Example shown late 19th century. Value **$200**.

A rare weapon used by the Mondo tribe of Panay Island.

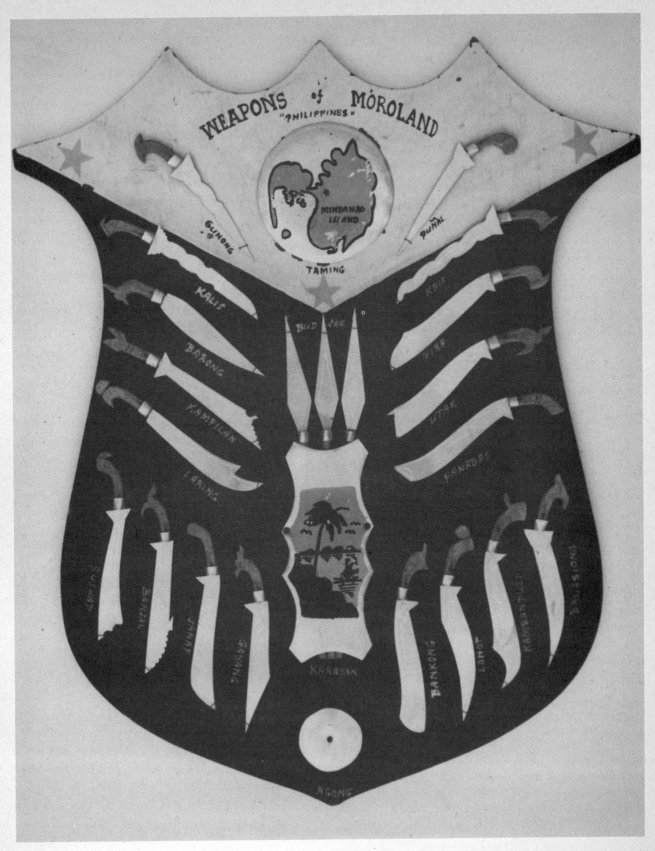

G.12. Philippines.
 Souvenir plaque, made of painted wood and tin, showing the names and shapes of regional edged weapons. 20th century. Value $35.

Area H: Australia

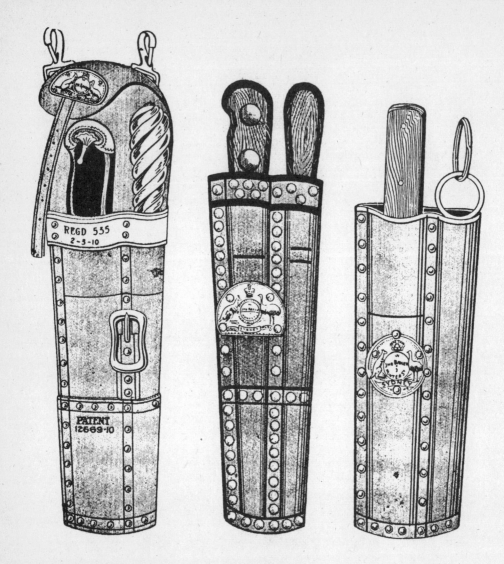

H.1. Australia. Sheath knives and sets.

About 10 inches overall. Wood handles. Knives made in
England. Fancy leather sheaths made in Australia. Early 20th
century. Examples shown from W. Jno. Baker, Sydney,
1924 catalog. Value range: plain knife **$20**; with sheath **$50**;
"Oriental Design" knife **$50**; with sheath **$80**; complete
sets **$100–200**.

In Australia, a "Boundary Rider" is a skilled hand on a
sheep station (a "station" is what we call a ranch) who
patrols and maintains the vast networks of fences that keep
the sheep from straying. W. Jno. Baker, a retailer, was established in 1888. The firm is now on Pitt Street in Sydney.

GIRTH STRAP

W. JNO BAKER NEW DESIGN DAGGING AND SKINNING OUTFIT.

Outfit consists of Red Tang Doublé Hollow-ground Dagging Shears, Boundary Rider's Skinning Knife, and Steel for sharpening same. The Sheath is of the Very Best Leather. The whole riveted throughout for lasting wear, with Loops to attach to saddle, and double-hand girth strap.

No. 24—Outfit, with Plain Beech Handle Knife and Steel, complete, **27/6.**

No. 26—With Strong Rosewood Handle, Knife and Steel, complete, **30/-.**

No. 27—With Oriental Design Knife (No. 1) and Horn Steel, as illustrated, complete, **35/-.**

Any of the above posted, 1/3 extra. Flaps fitted over Knife and Steel, as in No. 17, 2/- extra per outfit.

W. JNO. BAKER DAGGING BOTTLE AND SKINNING OUTFIT.

Outfit consists of Red Tang Double Hollow-ground Dagging Shears, Boundary Rider's Skinning Knife, and Steel for Sharpening, and ¾-pt. Tin Bottle. The Sheath is of the very best leather, riveted throughout for lasting wear, with Loops to attach to saddle, and double-hand girth strap.

No. 17—Outfit, with Plain Beech Handle Knife and Steel, complete, **35/-.**

No. 19—With Strong Rosewood Handle Knife and Steel, complete, **37/6.**

No. 20—With Oriental Design Knife (No. 1) and Horn Steel, as illustrated, complete, **42/-.** Any of the above posted, 1/6 extra.

The Sign of Good Cutlery
AT
THE HOUSE OF STEEL
FOUNDED A·D·1888

430—W. JNO. BAKER BUSH KNIFE, specially designed by W. Jno. Baker for Australian Use; Extra Strong Good Steel Blade, Good Grip Rosewood Handle, **6/9** each. W. Jno. Baker Registered Collar Cap Sheath, No. 436, **2/-** extra. Plain Sheaths, without Cap and Collar, **1/6** extra.

111—W. JNO. BAKER CAMP KNIFE, Good Grip Rosewood Handle, Extra Fine Steel 5in. Blade, **5/-**; 5½in. Blade, **5/6** each. W. Jno. Baker Patent Collar Cap Sheath, No. 436, **2/-** extra. Plain Sheath, without Cap and Collar, **1/6** extra.

109—W. JNO. BAKER SPEAR KNIFE, Rosewood Handle, Extra Good Steel, 5in. Blade, **4/3**; 5½in. Blade, **4/9** each. W. Jno. Baker Patent Collar Cap Sheath, No. 436, **2/-** extra. Plain Sheath, without Cap and Collar, **1/6** extra.

114—W. JNO. BAKER BOAT KNIFE, Good Grip Rosewood Handle, Extra Fine Steel ,5in. Blade, **5/6** each. W. Jno. Baker Registered Collar Cap Sheath, No. 436, **2/-** extra. Plain Sheath, without Cap and Collar, **1/6** extra.

70—W. JNO. BAKER STAINLESS STEEL SHEATH KNIFE— "Sportsman's Friend," with Sturdy Rosewood Haft, 6½in. Blade, **7/6.** W. Jno. Baker Registered Collar Cap Sheath, No. 436, **2/-** extra.

W. JNO. BAKER BOUNDARY RIDER'S SHEATH KNIVES—
No. 1 Oriental Design (as illustration), knife only . . . . **9/6** each
No. 3 Quite Plain, Rosewood Handle, knife only . . . . **4/6** each
No. 4 Quite Plain Beech Handle . . . . **4/-** each
Post free

W. Jno. Baker Registered Collar Cap Sheath, No. 436, fitted to above for **2/-** each extra.

4—W. JNO. BAKER BOUNDARY RIDER'S SHEATH KNIFE, specially designed by W. Jno. Baker for Australian use; Good Steel Blades, Good Grip, Plain Rosewood Handle, **4/6** each; Plain Beech Handle, **4/-** each. Plain Sheath, **1/6** extra; Collar Cap Sheath, **2/-** extra.

W. JNO. BAKER BOUNDARY RIDER'S STEELS ONLY—
No. 1 Fluted Horn Haft . . . . **6/6** each
No. 2 Smooth Horn Haft . . . . **5/6** each
No. 3 Plain Rosewood Haft . . . . **5/-** each
No. 4 Plain Beechwood Haft . . . . **4/-** each

Post free.

436 — COLLAR CAP LEATHER SHEATH, designed by W. Jno. Baker for the Australian Bush. The Sheath is rivetted right round, a collar on the top protects and strengthens the top, a cap of double leather prevents the point from piercing the bottom. An ideal Sheath for rough wear.

SHEATHS MADE AT 3 HUNTER STREET, SYDNEY.

SHEFFIELD MADE HAFT AND BLADE.

34—W. Jno. Baker Extra Good Double Shear Steel Sticking Knives, Beech Handles, 6½in. Blades **3/9** each. Post free With Rosewood Handles, **4/3** each. Post free.

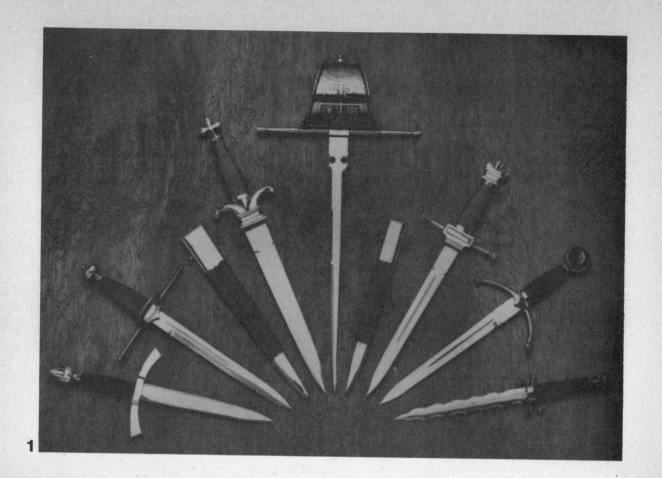

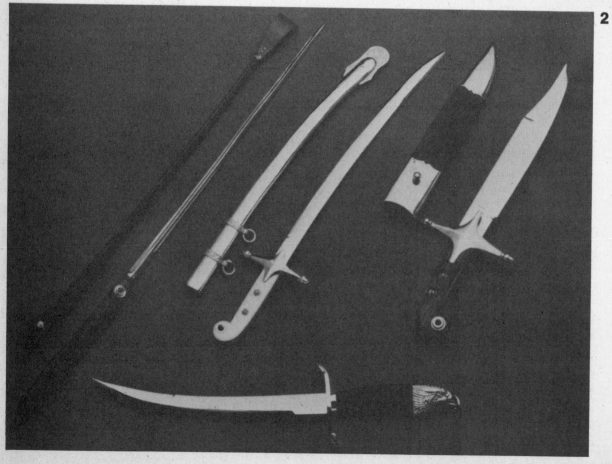

Historical Reproductions of European Edged Weapons

In Spain today, the tradition of fine blade forging is still carried on. Though the *Artilleria Fabrica de Toledo* no longer turns out its renowned presentation daggers, other workshops in the old city of Toledo carry on the local tradition of quality.

One of the leading edged weapons producers in Toledo is an American. He is Oscar Kolombatovich, an international fencing master who has worked with such diverse organizations as the U. S. Military Academy at West Point, and New York's Metropolitan Opera.

Mr. Kolombatovich moved to Toledo in 1974. Since then, his workshops there have specialized in the production of reproduction historical swords. More recently he has added historical bowie knives, fighting knives, and daggers to their output.

His knives and swords are carefully researched for authentic design. What is more, they are functional, with blades of forged and tempered steel, unlike most of the lower-priced Spanish reproduction swords sold in this country today.

Among his most important customers are opera and movie companies that wish to be sure that their edged weapon props are authentic in design. Besides standard swords and daggers, he offers theatrical customers a line of telescoping "stage daggers" that can be driven in to the hilt without danger of injury to the actors.

Oscar Kolombatovich

Here are some examples of Kolombatovich knives and daggers, with their current retail prices.

PICTURE 1 (Left to Right):

No. 1343	Man-at-Arms **$83.**
No. 1356	Anneau Parrying Dagger **$77.**
No. 1349	Doge Venetian Dagger **$97.**
No. 1364	Aguirre Main Gauche **$119.**
No. 1350	Condottiere Renaissance Dagger **$96.**
No. 1341	Quillon Crusader Dagger **$75.**
No. 1393	Skull & Bones Pirate Dirk **$49.**

PICTURE 2 (Left to Right):

No. 1768	Gen. Patton Swagger Stick **$74.**
No. 1376	Marine Corps Dirk **$190.**
No. 1397	Marine Mameluke Hilt Bowie **$175.**
No. 1380	Eagle Naval Dirk **$75.**

These are all available from his United States agent: Mr. Eiler R. Cook, P.O. Box 188, Etowah, North Carolina 28729.

In addition, these other swords and daggers are sometimes available. Call to check on availability.

Roman Short Swords from **$124.**
Broadswords from **$132.**
Claymores from **$189.**
Cavalry Sabers from **$153.**
Viking Swords under **$200.**
Rapiers under **$200.**
Renaissance Swords under **$200.**
Bonapartist Sword Cane **$85.**
Deluxe Cinquedea **$179.**
Lancelot Knight's Dagger **$55.**
Telescoping Stage Daggers from **$87.**
Presentation Military Dirk **$119.**
Presentation Naval Dirk **$89.**
Civil War Bowie **$270.**
Covasi Boar Hunting Knife **$219.**
"Sevillana" Navaja (folder) **$87.**
Cossack Kindjal **$120.**
Brass Knuckle Bowie **$150.**
Arab Jambiya **$49.**

Kitchen and Butcher Knives

This pattern is our own original design and on account of its peculiar and convenient shape, combining a Butcher, Sticking, Skinning and Bread Knife, it has been imitated in cheap quality. The original and only genuine bears our "AAA1" trade mark. Take no other.

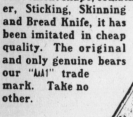

We designate them Melon Knives and they are handy for Butchering, Sticking, Skinning or for any service.

PRICE EACH
6 inch........$1 00
7 inch........ 1 25

A SPLENDID HOTEL COOKS' KNIFE
Ground very thin.   Flexible point.

This Boxwood Handle will outlast Ebony and the steel is "AAA1."

PRICE EACH
5 inch	$0 75
6 inch	1 00
7 inch	1 25
8 inch	1 50
9 inch	1 75
10 inch	2 00
12 inch	3 50
14 inch	4 50

INDIVIDUAL CARVER OR CHOP KNIVES

Made of our finest steel into thin flexible Carver Blades, Boxwood Handles, IN THREE SHAPES.

PRICE EACH
5 inch	$0 75
6 inch	1 00
7 inch	1 25
8 inch	1 50
9 inch	1 75
10 inch	2 00

HOUSEHOLD KNIFE

Another new style of our own. Very popular because it's so handy around the house and meat shop. It makes an Elegant Boning Knife.

HOUSE KNIFE
one size only
6 inch........$0 80

Ask any Butcher if this is not the correct shape for a convenient Boning Knife.

PRICE EACH
5 inch	$0 70
6 inch	80
7 inch	1 00

NOTE THE CORRECT SHAPE FOR SKINNING

Our Boxwood Handle Skinning Knives are sold by many of the largest Butcher Supply Houses in America, East as well as West.

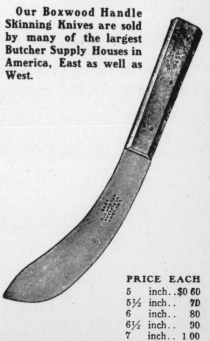

PRICE EACH
5 inch	$0 60
5½ inch	70
6 inch	80
6½ inch	90
7 inch	1 00

KITCHEN KNIVES are so much a part of daily life for most of us that it may be hard to picture them as collector's items. However, when you include people who collect knives as tools to use, I believe that there are more people who collect kitchen knives than who collect all other types of knives combined. The first knife collectors I ever met collected kitchen knives, and kitchen knives were my own first interest in the world of cutlery.

Just about all of the people who collect kitchen knives collect them to use. Therefore, unlike in other areas of knife collecting, mint or unused examples do not command much of a premium in price over knives in excellent condition, at least not at the present time.

Knives in excellent original condition are of course worth more than worn or restored pieces, though an artistically rehandled kitchen knife can be worth almost as much as an all original one. People who collect kitchen knives to use generally take good care of them, so that even years of use do not significantly reduce their value.

Historically Interesting Brands

There is, at present, one class of kitchen and butcher knives that is worth more to collectors who won't use them than to ones who will. This is knives by prominent early-to-mid-19th century American cutlery factories and individual cutlers. Lists of these firms and makers are included in the chapters on *American Bowie Knives*, *Indian Trade Knives*, *Table Knives* and *Carving Sets*. Early knives with these old names are worth two to five times as much as the very best using knives.

European and American kitchen knives made before 1800 are even rarer than early 19th century ones. In this country they are so rare that they are less valuable than many later knives. However, they are still worth a good deal more as keepers than as users, especially since their blade quality is not very high.

Facing page: A.J. Jordan knives from a 1912 catalog (courtesy Dave Jordan). Values in excellent condition: Chef knives: **$50–75**; Small slicing or boning knives: **$35–45**; Skinning knives: **$60**; Large carving or butcher knives (not shown): **$40**.

Blade Steel

I have owned about 10,000 antique kitchen and butcher knives, and examined perhaps 20 times that number. I have found that good quality modern stainless knives, *when properly sharpened*, are superior in use to *all* older knives, even the very best. Stainless knives can be made at least as sharp as carbon steel ones, they stay sharp many times longer, and, of course, they do not stain. Also, modern synthetic handles will not rot, split, or fall off.

The president of a major knife company put it very well when he said to me that preferring carbon steel knives over stainless types is like preferring vacuum tube radios over transistor ones. Tube radios and carbon steel knives were fine in their day, and now they can be fun to collect and use, but anyone who thinks they are better than their modern successors in any practical sense is simply fooling himself.

Carbon steel knives do win out over stainless steel knives in one respect. They are a lot more interesting to collect.

Stainless knives have been made for about 65 years, and the best ones have been of superior quality for about 30. In most of this recent period, design and workmanship have not been paramount concerns, and decoration has been almost nonexistent.

Carbon steel knives have been around for many centuries. The variety of their designs is almost endless. The workmanship on the better quality older knives is astounding. Some of them even have exquisite decoration.

Brands

People who collect kitchen knives are concerned primarily with quality. They look at brand names, not so much for their historical significance, the way other collectors do, but as indications of quality. Several old brands have a dedicated following based, in most cases, on the consistent high quality of the products of those manufacturers.

I have found that older professional-style knives by any of the reputable makers are almost always of excellent quality. The differences *in use* between the best and the ordinary are, in my experience, relatively slight. However, differences in use *are* there, and the differences in fit, finish, and choice of materials are often obvious. If you want to own the best, here are some names for you to look for.

A. J. JORDAN

There are several older kitchen knife brands that are consistently superb. In my experience, the very best of all seems to be A. J. Jordan.

A. J. Jordan kitchen and butcher knives are something of an anomaly. Jordan was an American firm based in St. Louis. Its kitchen knives were made in Sheffield, in a plant

SHEFFIELD, ENGLAND.

called the East India Works on Furnival Street that Andrew Jordan must have owned or controlled, because no other knives look anything like them. The only other Sheffield kitchen knives that compare to Jordan in quality are older Joseph Rodgers.

In addition to kitchen and butcher knives, Jordan also distributed other types of cutlery. However their carving sets and table knives, their pocketknives and razors, all appear to be contract goods, and are not of as high quality as the kitchen knives.

In their catalogs, Jordan modestly called their kitchen and butcher knives **THE BEST ON EARTH**. Though theirs was an era of grossly exaggerated advertising claims, this claim, as far as I can tell, was true.

All Jordan kitchen and butcher knives have ''seasoned Persian boxwood handles.'' This costly wood is a light golden color, takes a high polish, and wears almost like iron. Many of their handle and blade shapes are original and distinctive. All their knives are light in weight, and they do not have bolsters.

For their blades, Jordan used a special formula of double shear steel. Jordan acknowledged that cast steel was usually superior to shear steel, but they asserted that *their* shear steel was better than any other steel, and their knives seem to prove their point.

Shear steel was made by case-hardening thin wrought iron bars in charcoal, breaking them up, and forge welding them into a solid mass. If shear steel is hardened, broken up, and re-welded, it becomes double shear steel. Cast steel was made by melting wrought iron in a sealed crucible with charcoal and flux. Neither technique has been used since about 1940.

Jordan was in business from about 1870 to about 1926.

They distributed their knives all over the United States. However, based on a selection of testimonial letters that they published in 1912, 95% of their business was from Virginia south and from Indiana west. Of the 71 letters:

12 were from California; 6 each were from Illinios and Minnesota; 5 were from Tennessee; 4 each were from Alabama, Georgia, and Colorado; 3 were from Louisiana; 2 each were from Arizona, Kentucky, Mississippi, Oregon, Pennsylvania, Texas, Virginia, and Washington; and 1 each from Florida, Iowa, Indiana, Kansas, Massachusetts, Missouri, Montana, North Dakota, New Mexico, Ohio, and South Carolina.

Other Premium Brands

SHEFFIELD

Let me repeat that from the viewpoint of quality in use, most older professional-style knives are a good deal more than adequate. Even the majority of older household-style knives work very well, assuming, of course, that they are ground thin enough at the edge, correctly honed, and steeled regularly.

For those who want the very best, and who are willing to spend time and money to find it, Jordan is not the only brand that will satisfy. I already mentioned that knives by Joseph Rodgers & Sons, of Sheffield, are superb. This applies mainly to their 19th century knives, which can be identified by the V (crown) R royal cypher in the mark. All of Rodgers' many types of cutlery made in the Victorian era are of the same high standard.

Joseph Rodgers c1900 butcher knife. Value **$40.** Not shown: Chef's knife: **$60;** Slicer: **$35.**

Another English brand that was very good, at least in the 19th century, was John Wilson (I. Wilson). This firm made only butcher knives. Though Wilson blades were good, their handles and tangs were inferior to Jordan's, and usually need repair.

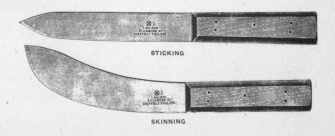

I. Wilson c1914 sticking knife (**$30**) and skinning knife (**$35**). Butcher knives (not shown): **$25–35.**

As far as other Sheffield brands are concerned, cutlers there stuck to hand methods for so long that quality varies widely. One knife with a certain name may be first rate, while another with the same name may have a flagrant defect. When the English finally got around to standardizing their product after World War I, they set the standard very low. Old Sheffield knives are historically interesting, but as users most of them are chancy at best.

Germany

In this country in the 19th century, ''Made in Germany'' was nearly synonymous with ''inferior quality.'' Most German cutlery manufacturers had decided that there were only two ways for them to compete in the American market: low prices and misrepresentation. Either they sold shoddy mass-produced knives at prices so low that no one in the world could compete with them, or they sold barely adequate goods marked with American or British sounding brand names.

J. A. HENCKELS

A few German pocketknife firms did go against this trend by selling good knives in America under their own names. The first German kitchen and butcher knife firm to try this positive approach here was J. A. Henckels, Twinworks, of Solingen. Thanks largely to the promotional efforts of Henckels, and to the superb quality of their merchandise (especially between the two World Wars), ''Made in Solingen'' now has a very positive meaning for American consumers.

Henckels entered the American market in 1883, when the firm was already 152 years old. They opened a retail store in New York City and arranged for wholesale distribution by a firm called Graef & Schmidt, succeeded 65 years later by Iversen & Albrecht. Since 1960, Henckels has managed its own distribution.

Like Rodgers of Sheffield, Henckels made almost every type of cutlery, most of it first-rate. They made thousands upon thousands of patterns. They also published very nice catalogs, and many of the illustrations in this chapter are from their 1930s American line catalog.

Thanks both to their earlier promotional efforts and to their current advertising campaigns, the Henckels brand is the best known and most sought after among collectors and users of older kitchen knives. Today, Henckels limits its production almost entirely to kitchen and butcher knives, but in this area it is still one of the most popular brands in this country.

(Continued on page 472)

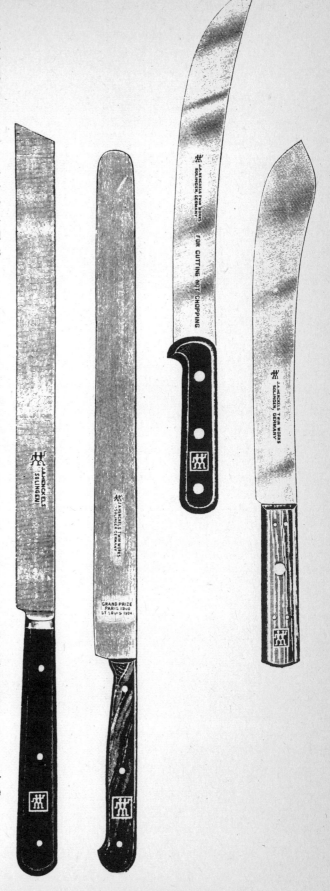

Henckels 1930s carving and butcher knives: Ham slicer (square point), Beef slicer (round point), Scimitar steak knife (curved blade), Butcher knife (clip point).
Values: Large sizes: **$35–50**; Small sizes: **$20–35**.
(Values of other top brands are **50–75%** of these.)

COOK'S KNIVES

No. 108 — Cook's Knife, 9", 10", 11", 12", 13" and 14". Sabatier shape, glazed blade with heavy heel, polished black wood handle, German silver tubular rivets, scale tang.

No. 102 — Cook's Knife, 8", 9", 10", 11", 12" and 13". Sabatier shape, glazed blade, polished black wood handle, two German silver rivets, one German silver tubular rivet, scale tang.

No. 225 — Cook's Knife, 9", 10", 11" and 12". Sabatier shape, glazed blade, polished black wood handle, two German silver rivets, one German silver tubular rivet, scale tang.

No. 100 — Cook's Knife, 7", 8", 9", 10", 11" and 12". Sabatier shape, glazed blade, polished black wood handle, polished steel ferrule, through tang.

No. 101 — Cook's Knife, 3", 3⅞", 5", 6", 7", 8" 9", 10" and 12" narrow glazed flexible blade, polished black wood handle, German silver ferrule, through tang.

Facing page: Much sought-after Henckels chef's knives from the 1930s. Note GRAND PRIZE markings. Most also stamped with model number and length. Values: 108 (heavy, with flexible point): **$75–100;** 102 (standard): **$60–75;** 225 (no bolster): **$25–35;** 100 (one-piece handle): **$45–65;** 101 (narrow): 3"– 5": **$30;** 6"–8": **$40;** 9"–12": **$30.** (Values of other top brands are **75–100%** of these.)

Henckels 1930s household cleaver (**$35**), lobster splitter (**$75**), and boning knife (**$20–30**).

Henckels 1930s bread knife (**$30**), forged bolster utility knife (**$40;** same style by Village Blacksmith **$30**), French pattern slicer (**$12**), and forged bolster slicer (**$25**).

Henckels 1930s paring knives. Values: **$10–15.** Decorating knife: **$25.**

F. DICK

Although Henckels has been a leader in butcher and kitchen knives in the American market for over a century now, it has never been a serious contender in the specialized area of sharpening steels. Henckels makes them and sells them, but few professionals buy their brand.

In the 19th century, the leading sharpening steels sold here

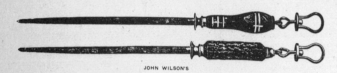

JOHN WILSON'S

were the I. Wilson brand from Sheffield. Beginning almost a century ago, however, F. Dick steels were made available in this country. They were so good and so good looking that, despite their relatively high cost, no other maker could offer them serious competition.

Friedrich Dick of Esslingen, Germany, was established in 1788. Unlike Henckels, Dick's cutlery production has always been limited to professional cutlery: cook's knives, butcher knives, and steels. They have also manufactured machine tools.

F. Dick knives are first-class, as good as anything made in Solingen. However, their sharpening steels are what the firm is best known for here.

In their earlier days, F. Dick offered a bewildering variety of steels. The plainest have turned wooden handles. Next up the ladder have stag or fancy metal handles. The top of the line have elaborately turned and machined cow horn handles, often inlaid with panels of nickel silver, or even mother-of-pearl. A nice looking example of these in excellent condition is worth **$150** to **$200**. Stag or metal handled ones are worth **$50 to $75,** wood handled, **$25 to $30.** Wilson steels are worth about two-thirds of these prices, other good brands in excellent condition about one-half.

The business end of a Dick steel can be round, oval, square, or flat in cross-section. The very best, called slicks, are as smooth and nearly as hard as glass. Slicks are used by packing house butchers, and by anyone who requires a *really* sharp edge. They cost more than fine-cuts, which are made for ordinary use. Dick never sold coarse steels.

I have met several people who collect fancy old Dick steels, and many people who use them. To determine if an old steel is still usable, examine it for cross-wise nicks. Even one nick is liable to chip your knife blades, and is enough reason to reject a steel for use.

Then, try the steel out with a sharp but expendable knife. Old steels sometimes got used as fire pokers which drew

their temper, spoiling them. If the knife bites into the steel, the steel's temper has been drawn and it is useless. However, if the handle looks nice, even a ruined steel has some value as a wall decoration.

TRIDENT

A first-class brand of German kitchen and butcher knives widely sold in this country today is Trident, made by Eduard Wusthof of Solingen. Although Wusthof is an old firm, founded in 1814, it did not enter the American market until 1959. Therefore there are hardly any older Trident knives in this country to attract the interest of collectors.

French Sabatiers

Both to the trained chef and to the knowledgeable amateur cook, the most basic kitchen knife is the "French chef's knife." The modern form of this knife dates to the latter part of the 19th century and is attributed to a Frenchman named Sabatier. John Goins reports that this was a cutler named Jean Augustin Sabatier who first worked in 1846. I have also seen it alleged that Sabatier was a master chef.

COOKS' KNIVES

GENUINE FRENCH SABATIER

Original *La Trompette* sabatier from c1914. Value in excellent condition: 6″–8″: **$30**; 10″–12″: **$40.**

To this day, most French-made chef's knives are called sabatiers. The sabatier design is a refinement of the traditional French butcher knife, an example of which is shown in *Indian Trade Knives*.

In the United States, up through World War I, the standard French-made sabatier chef knife was the Trumpet Brand, *La Trompette*. Trumpet sabatiers have high quality light weight blades, but their one-piece ebony handles are weak and brittle. American and German firms copied the original Sabatier design, defects and all. They also made improved versions with full tangs and riveted slab handles. French firms make both types today.

American Kitchen and Butcher Knives

As I mentioned earlier, most early to mid-19th century American brands of butcher and kitchen knives are even more valuable as historical artifacts than they would be as tools. Several more recent American brands are equal in quality to the better imports, but since they are less well known, they are often less expensive.

HARRINGTON

Henry Harrington was one of the first American manufacturing cutlers. He worked from 1818 to 1876. Any knife with his mark is a valuable artifact. Knives by his son, Dexter Harrington, and their successors, are of excellent quality for use, but they are not old enough to interest the historical collector.

Pre-Second World War professional knives by the Harrington firm are very neatly stamped HARRINGTON CUTLERY CO. (curved) /DEXTER/SOUTHBRIDGE, MASS.

Pre-War Dexter skinning knife with guard: **$20.**

They usually have rosewood handles which are often marked DEXTER as well. Current Dexter professional knives still have the handle stamping, but the blade markings are electro-etched.

Older Dexter Harrington industrial knives and some kitchen knives are marked D. HARRINGTON & SON/ SOUTHBRIDGE, MASS. The most interesting ones are marked D. HARRINGTON & SON/CUTLERS TO THE PEOPLE/SOUTHBRIDGE, MASS., a dig at Joseph Rodgers' haughty CUTLERS TO HER MAJESTY.

RUSSELL

John Russell opened his Green River Works in Greenfield, Massachusetts, in 1834. In 1870, his successors moved the firm to Turners Falls, to what was then the largest single cutlery factory in the world.

Since 1933, Russell knives and Dexter knives have been made in the same factory in Southbridge, Massachusetts. Dexter is the premium brand. Older Russell butcher and kitchen knives have a historical value to collectors quite out of proportion to their quality, which is good but not outstanding. The chapter on *Indian Trade Knives* includes information on dating Russell marks.

LANDERS FRARY & CLARK

Landers Frary & Clark of New Britain, Connecticut, was founded in 1862 or 1863 and incorporated in 1865. George Landers was a hardware manufacturer, James Frary was an inventor and maker of scales and cutlery, and Clark was an attorney.

Their firm first made hardware and scales, but in 1866 they built a new building and began to make table cutlery. Within a few years, they added butcher and kitchen knives to their line. By 1903, Landers Frary & Clark was the biggest cutlery firm in the world. Pocket cutlery was not added until 1912, and was dropped in about 1933. L. F. & C. went out of business in 1954.

L. F. & C. sold butcher and kitchen knives under a multitude of brand names over the years. In addition to the full name, they used Landers, Aetna Works, and Universal. They used the names Samuel Lee on cleavers and Lee's on sharpening steels. They acquired the names Putnam and Old Put when they bought the Putnam Cutlery Company in 1909. They used BLUE in a diamond on the handles of professional knives in the 1930s. They used Meriden after 1916.

Landers Frary & Clark made some absolutely first-rate knives. L. F. & C. professional knives marked DOUBLE SHEAR STEEL or GRAND PRIZE/ST. LOUIS 1904 are usually of this caliber. They also made some low cost lines of adequate but not extraordinary quality.

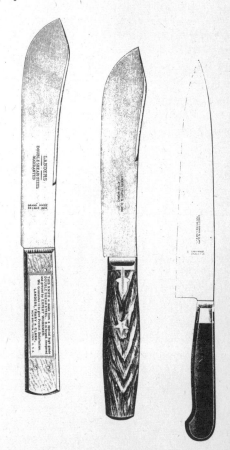

L. F. & C. butcher knives (**$15** plain, **$25** fancy) and cast-bolstered chef knife (**$25**).

Other American Brands

Several high quality American makers of kitchen and butcher knives have almost been forgotten today. Any of their knives would be a valuable find to a collector who likes to use fine old cutlery.

Nichols Brothers of Massachusetts, in business from about the 1880s to the 1920s, made professional knives, cleavers,

Nichols Bros. c1900 ripping knife: **$20.**

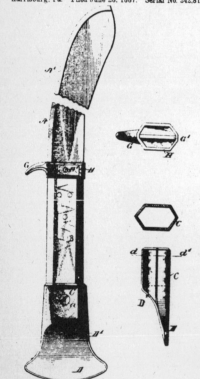

:369,314. SKINNING-KNIFE ATTACHMENT. DAVID J. BROUGHER. Harrisburg, Pa. Filed June 28, 1887. Serial No. 242,813. (Model.)

Claim.—1. In combination with the handle of a skinning-knife, the parting-bit D, formed with blunt edge and arranged on the side of the handle B, as and for the purpose set forth.

2. In combination with a butcher's skinning-knife, the parting-bit D, formed with the inclined shoulder D' and the socket C, and secured upon the knife-handle B, substantially as and for the purpose set forth.

3. The combination, with a butcher's skinning-knife, of a parting-bit, D, attached to the rear end of the knife-handle, and the guard G, attached to the front end of said handle, substantially as and for the purposes set forth.

Brougher 1887 patent skinning knife made by Nichols Bros.: **$35.**

and steels. Some of their knives are marked W. R. NICHOLS, and they also made private brands, such as GLOEKLER of Pittsburgh. Eager to compete with Wilson and Jordan, Nichols advertised that their knives were also made from English double shear steel.

BEATTY BUTCHERS' CLEAVERS
Polished Cast Steel Blades. Varnished Hickory Turned Handles.

Beatty cleaver c1914: **$25–40.**

William Beatty & Son of Chester, Pennsylvania, made meat cleavers in about the same period. Their cleavers have turned one-piece wooden handles and a distinctive blade profile.

The Washington Cutlery Company of Watertown, Wisconsin, made Village Blacksmith brand crucible steel butcher and household knives from 1898 to 1940. Their forged bolster household slicer was copied by Henckels.

The Old File Cutlery Company of Havana, Illinois, made Old File brand butcher and kitchen knives from 1906 to 1966. They were not really made from files.

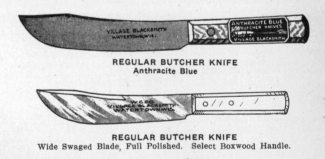

REGULAR BUTCHER KNIFE
Anthracite Blue

REGULAR BUTCHER KNIFE
Wide Swaged Blade, Full Polished. Select Boxwood Handle.

Village Blacksmith c1914 butcher knives: **$20.**

Small Firms

All of the American firms named so far were relatively sizable commercial undertakings. A multitude of smaller firms, often only one or two men, also made butcher and kitchen knives for regular but local sale. Despite (or because of) the fact that they were hand-made, knives by these little firms vary widely in quality.

Knives by small manufacturers are very rare and documentation of these firms' existence and operation is even rarer. The principal appeal of their knives is as artifacts of local history. Research is usually required to distinguish locally made butcher knives from contract knives made by large national firms and stamped with the name of a local dealer.

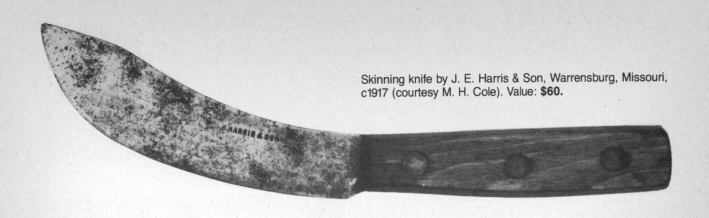

Skinning knife by J. E. Harris & Son, Warrensburg, Missouri, c1917 (courtesy M. H. Cole). Value: **$60.**

Packing House Pork Cleaver.

Solid Iron Hand, wrapped with tarred marline.
Fully warranted.

20 in.	$5.00
22 in.	6.00
24 in.	7.00

Beef Splitter, Flat Handle.

A trial will convince the most skeptical that this Beef Splitter will give better satisfaction than any style heretofore on the market. Furnished also with tarred marline handle.

12 in. ———— $3.00   13 in. ———— $3.50   14 in. ———— $4.00

Market Cleaver.

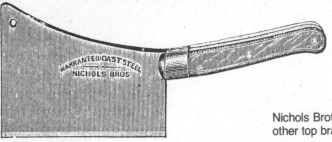

Nichols Brothers cleavers, c1900. Values **$35–75.** (Values of other top brands similar.)

Lamb Cleaver.

CLEAVER PRICE LIST.

Size.	Market.	Lamb.	Choppers.
6 in.	$ .75	$	$ .75
7 in.	1.00	.60	.80
8 in.	1.25	.80	1.00
9 in.	1.50	1.00	1.25
10 in.	2.00	1.25	1.50
12 in.	3.00	1.50	1.75

Round Handle Choppers.

Table Knives and Forks

MOST people own a couple of dozen table knives and forks, and never give them a second thought. Yet table cutlery has an interesting history. Indeed, because they are so universal, and because they have been around for so long, it is in table knives and forks that one can most readily trace the technological, cultural, and artistic evolution of cutlery.

In the Middle Ages, an ordinary person would likely own just one knife, which he carried with him and used for eating, and every other cutting chore. A wealthy woman might carry a matched pair of knives, so she could eat without soiling her fingers.

In the 16th century, the Italians began to use scaled down carving forks for eating. The fashion of eating with forks spread to Germany and France, and then after the Restoration (1660), to England.

Medieval English eating knives had riveted bolsters. About 1555, Richard Matthews of Sheffield introduced the forged wrought iron bolster welded to a steel blade (see below, center). This became standard practice in Sheffield until the late 19th century. American inventors re-introduced cast and riveted bolsters on inexpensive knives in the late 1860s.

The American table cutlery industry began in 1834. See *Bowie Knives* for names and dates of the important 19th century American table cutlery manufacturers.

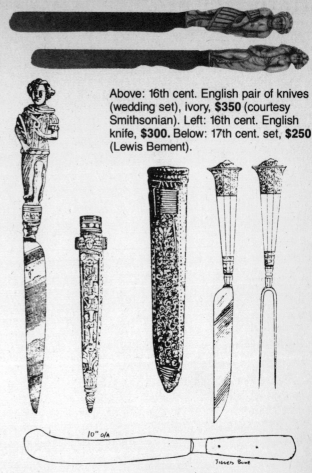

Above: 16th cent. English pair of knives (wedding set), ivory, **$350** (courtesy Smithsonian). Left: 16th cent. English knife, **$300**. Below: 17th cent. set, **$250** (Lewis Bement).

Early 18th cent. English table knife, jigged bone, **$25**.

19th cent. children's set, English, **$25**.

One-armed man's knife. Example by L.F.&C., stainless (post–1921), **$10**.

L.F.&C. take-apart picnic set, c1912, wood and pewter mounts, **$15**.

Small dessert pairs by the American "big three:" Pratt Ropes, Lamson Goodnow, and Russell. Marks and bolsters indicate c1850. **$20/pair**.

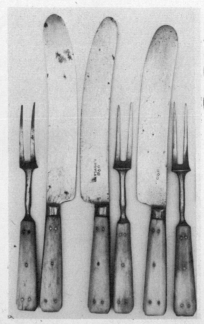

Late 18th cent. Sheffield knives and forks, bone. Back of knife blade shows typical "puddled" weld between iron bolster and steel blade. **$25/pair**.

Carving Sets

THE carving set, consisting of knife, fork, and sharpening steel, was a fixture of every well-dressed dinner table until a generation or two ago. Deluxe sets might include two to five different knives, each with its fork, a steel, corkscrew, bone holder, skewer puller, marrow scoop, cheese scoop, and poultry shears. From the 16th to the mid–19th century, the carving set and table knives and forks usually matched.

The most celebrated American carving sets were made by the San Francisco makers Will & Finck, Michael Price, and the others. See *Bowie Knives* for list.

A carving knife alone is worth 50% of the value of a set. Forks and steels alone are worth about 10%. An original fitted case adds about 20%.

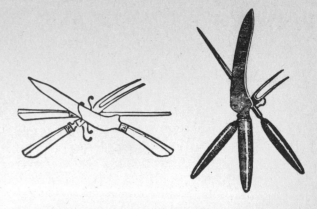

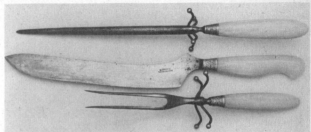

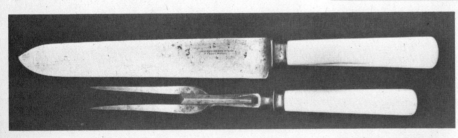

Above: San Francisco sets, walrus ivory, **$250 each.** Left top: bread knife, carved boxwood, **$25.** Left: Lamson & Goodnow classic New England pair, c1860, **$50.**

Below left: carving knife styles, prices for 3-piece sets: two 19th cent. English styles (note iron caps), **$50;** four c1900 American (also German) styles, **$35.**

No. 329—Genuine Stag Handles, Especially Selected. Solid Forged Octagon Steel Bolsters. German Silver End Plates. 8 inch Swaged Spanish Slicer Blade. Full Crocus Polished..Per Set,

No. 298—Genuine Stag Handles, Especially Selected. Fancy German Silver Ferrules and End Plates. 8 inch Fancy Swaged Turkish Cimeter Blade. Full Crocus Polished..Per Set,

No. 309—Genuine Stag Handles, Carefully Selected and Finely Finished. Fancy German Silver Ferrules and End Plates. 8 inch Swaged French Slicer Blade. Full Crocus Polished..Per Dozen,

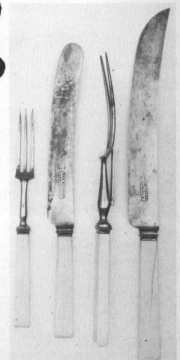

Right: W. & S. Butcher matched carving and table pairs, ivory, c1840, **$100.**

Industrial Knives

"INDUSTRIAL KNIVES" are knives made for use by artisans, craftsmen, and production workers. Some of them are general purpose, such as "shoe knives," but the most intriguing ones are highly specialized.

At present, collecting industrial knives is not very popular, so most prices are very low. The only high prices now are for knives made by the American firms that made 19th century bowies and Indian trade knives. See those chapters for more information. The examples shown are a sampling of the many varieties.

Some typical prices: pen machine: **$60;** ink eraser: plain: **$5;** bone or advertising: **$15;** ivory, pearl, or picture handle: **$30;** oilcloth knife: San Francisco maker: **$200;** other heavy weight: **$25;** light weight: **$4;** furrier's knife (all metal): **$20–50;** cigar knife: **$10;** oyster knife: plain: **$4;** San Francisco: **$40** (with ivory, **$100**); feather curling: plain: **$20;** San Francisco: **$75;** plain "push-tang" knives (e.g. banana, paper hanger's, shoe): **$2–5;** farrier's (horse shoer's): bone or iron: **$20;** iron changeable blade: **$25.** Check the blade shapes in *Special Purpose Jack Knives* for more clues to identifying odd-looking knives.

P . 513.
PEN MACHINE.

OILCLOTH KNIVES.

Will & Finck's buckhorn handle

Will & Finck furrier's knife.

CIGAR KNIVES

Cigar Knife — "DEXTER"

Wide Cincinnati — Maple Handle

OYSTER KNIVES.

CELLULOID HANDLE

MILLINER'S FEATHER CURLING KNIFE

BANANA KNIFE

PAPER HANGER'S KNIFE

SHOE KNIVES

TUBB'S

FARRIERS' KNIVES

WOSTENHOLM'S I X L
Bone Handle. Extra Quality Crucible Steel Blade, Highly Tempered; Glazed Finish. Assorted Width

IV: APPENDIX

Some Specialist Dealers in Collectible Knives

I AM ACQUAINTED with most but not all of these dealers. They know their business and try to be fair. However, I cannot guarantee anyone's performance. Common sense plus good manners should keep you out of trouble. Think about time zones before telephoning. SASE means self-addressed stamped envelope.

For exact show dates and locations, consult the Show Calendar in *Knife World* magazine. Current issue $1.50 from Knife World, Box 3395, Knoxville TN 37927.

A & J Enterprises (Stephen Dlack), Box 1343 S.S.S., Springfield MO 65805. (414)887-7345. Custom knives. Mail order. SASE for list.

American Historical Foundation, 1022 West Franklin St., Richmond VA 23220. (804)353-1812. Limited edition military knife reproductions and commemoratives. Write for current offerings.

American Manor House (R.C. Hogensen), 6433 Frederick Road, Baltimore MD 21228. (301)788-2344. South African custom and military knifes. Mail order catalog (2/year) $1. Displays at New York Custom and Blade Super Shows, Soldier of Fortune Convention, many eastern gun and knife shows.

Atlanta Cutlery Corp. (Bill Adams), 911 Center Street, Box 839, Conyers GA 30207. (800)241-3595 toll free. Military knives, foreign and exotic knives, factory close-outs from England and Germany, supplies. Mail order catalog (4/year) $1.50. Displays at larger shows in the Southeast. Established 1971.

Roger Baker, Box 620417, Woodside CA 94062. (415)851-7188. Old pocketknives, bowies, and folding dirks. Mail order. Send want list.

Boggess Knife Works, Rt. 2, Box 218, Eldorado IL 62930. (618)273-5294. Fight'n Rooster and NKCA Club Knives. List: SASE and 5 stamps.

Lawrence Byars and Associates, Custom Knife Brokers, Box 33154, Fort Worth TX 76133. (817)921-6756. Represent several custom makers. SASE for list and show schedule.

Collectors Ltd.:
Steven Weiss, 2201 Chestnut Street, San Francisco CA 94123. (415)921-6461.
Mal Mele, 3212 7th Street, Metairie LA 70010, (504)837-1281.
Paul Resnick, Box 8013, Redwood City CA 94063. (415)367-0200.
Custom knives by top makers: Horn, Lake, Frank, Henry, Hayes, etc. By mail, send want list. Display at Guild and New York shows. Custom knife consignment auction (write for schedule and location).

Columbus Cutlery, 358 Columbus Avenue, San Francisco CA 94133. (415)362-1342. Folding and fixed. Wide range of imported and domestic brands. Retail store only.

Eiler R. Cook (agent for Oscar Kolombatovich of Toledo, Spain), Box 188, Etowah NC 28729. (704)692-0323. High quality modern reproductions of historical knives and swords. Scandinavian knives. Write for current list and show plans.

Larry A. Cook, Box 3215, Coos Bay OR 97420. (503)888-5284. Old pocketknives. Mail order, shows. Write for list.

Cutlery World Stores, "In a mall near you." Many branches of this nationwide chain stock a selection of custom and limited edition knives for the collector. See listings in Ken Warner's *Knives* annual, or check your Yellow Pages. Headquarters: 380 Civic Drive, Pleasant Hill CA 94523. (415)676-4200.

Paul Davis, Box 9354, Chattanooga TN 37421. (404)866-1310. Old pocketknives. Mail order and some shows. SASE for one list, $3 for one year.

Charlie Dorton (imports Bulldog Brand Knives) P.O. Box 4125, Johnson City TN 37601. (606)928-4922. Large inventory of old pocketknives, sold only at shows: Blade Show, Louisville and Cincinnati NKCA shows, Fort Worth show, Columbus Ohio gun show.

Kurt Ehrlich Co., 517 S. Washington, Royal Oak MI 45067. (313)547-5699. Custom knives. Mail order, SASE for list.

Happy Jack Knives (Jack Bromley), 15623 East Scorpion Drive, Fountain Hills AZ 85268. (602)837-9298. Old, new, limited edition, and custom knives. Mail order, write for list (3/year). Displays at Guild, California Custom, Solvang, and Glendale knife shows; February Las Vegas and all Arizona gun shows.

Hardin Wholesale (George P. Smith), 514 14th St., Kenova WV 25530. (304)453-3498. Wholesale and retail of major brands; imports Flying Crown brand from Germany. Special order advertising knives. Displays at most southeastern knife shows.

Knife Nook (Jim Schleyer), Box 243, Burke VA 22015. (703)569-6665 (evenings). Co-author and publisher of definitive Case book. Older Case knives, especially trappers. Mail order and some shows. Lists (3–4/year) for SASE.

Matthews Cutlery, 3845 E N. Druid Hills Rd., Decatur GA 30033. (404)636-3970. Imports and distributes many German brands. Specializes in old stock.

Bob Murray, Million Dollar Hwy., St. Marys PA 15857. (814)834-4758. Older folding and fixed blade knives. Mail order. SASE for list (6/year), or send want list.

The Museum of Historical Arms (Col. Marvin E. Hoffman), 1038 Alton Road, Miami Beach FL 33139. (305)672-7480. Antique swords, daggers, guns, and accoutrements from around the world. Established 1952. Mail order. Catalog (2/year) $7 each.

Nordic Knives (Bob Gaddis), 1634 C Copenhagen Drive, Solvang CA 93463. (805)688-3612. Custom knives. Full stock of Randall knives. Retail store, mail order, and some shows. Sponsors Solvang show. Custom list (4–5/year) and Randall list $2 each, both for $3.

Nubbin Ridge Knives (Willard Beshires), Firetower Road, Silerton TN 38377. (901)658-2747. New, limited edition, club, and discontinued folding knives. Mail order, write for list (12/year), also wholesale list (2/year). Displays at shows in middle and west Tennessee.

Plaza Cutlery (Dan Delavan), South Coast Plaza, Costa Mesa CA 92626. (714)549-3932. Branch at Palm Desert Town Center, Palm Desert CA 92260. (619)341-3691. Custom knives, limited editions, complete factory knife lines. Retail stores. Mail order, free monthly custom knife and Case old lists. Sponsors California Custom Knife Show and Hawaiian Knife Show. Displays at Guild show; Great Western and winter Las Vegas gun shows.

Pumphreys Knives, 1500 N. High, Wichita KS 67203. (316)942-3512. Old and new pocketknives. Mail order and some shows. SASE for list.

R. & C. Knives (Ray and Carol Clark), Box 32631, San Jose CA 95152. (408)923-5728. Custom knives. Mail order, catalog (3/year) $2. Display at Guild, California Custom, and San Jose knife shows; Vallejo, Sacramento, Cow Palace, Great Western, and spring Las Vegas gun shows; S.F. Boat Show.

Cindy Rabb, Box 304, Newton MA 02161. (617)244-7187. Old factory folding knives, mainly U.S. made, also fixed blades, razors, and cutlery ephemera. Mail order and shows. List free with SASE (7/year). Displays at most NKCA shows (Chattanooga, Knoxville, Nashville, Louisville, Cincinnati, Tampa, Fort Worth, Birmingham, Orlando, Lexington), also at Eugene knife show and at Oklahoma City, Tulsa, Houston, and most New England gun shows.

Ramrod Gun & Knife (Steve and Lea Alexander, Mike Dale), R.R.5, ST.RD.#3 N., New Castle IN 47362. (317)529-0882. Custom knives. Retail store, mail order. SASE for list.

Michael R. Reape, Box 927, Woodstock NY 12498. (914)679-8083. Custom knives. "Purveyor of the finest hand forged high carbon and damascus blades." Mail order (current list $1) and some shows (Guild Show, Blade Show, New York, Tulsa).

Remington Cutlery, 60 Main St., Bridgeport CT 06602. (203)367-4400. The headquarters office of this national retail chain carries a large inventory of Buck commemorative and limited edition knives. (See Ken Warner's *Knives* annual for a list of Remington stores.)

Romex International, Inc. (Morris Gruenberg) Box 597, Polson MT 59860. (406)883-2481. World fighting knives and daggers, American and English bowie knives, American Indian knives. Mainly mail order. Catalog $6/year (3 issues). Sells only to subscribers. Usually displays at Las Vegas, Denver, Kalispell, and Missoula gun shows.

A.G. Russell Co., 1705 Hiway 71 North, Springdale AR 72764. (501)751-7341. Since 1970. Custom knives and a few antiques. Mainly consignments. By mail and phone. Lists (approx. 3–4/year) $5/year ($10 foreign). 25% commission on consignments. Mr. Russell is honorary president of the Knifemakers Guild. He is also president of the "Knife Collectors Club," which offers limited production knives.

San Francisco Gun Exchange (Nate Posner), 124 Second Street, San Francisco CA 94105. (415)982-6097. Custom knives, large selection. Full stock of Randall knives. Many factory brands. Retail store only.

Sargent Cutlery (Jim Sargent), 1403 Chisholm Road, Florence AL 35630. (205)766-8099. Shows and mail order. Lists (4/year) SASE. Old pocketknives, emphasis on Case, Remington, Winchester, Schrade. Wholesale of major current brands. Displays at most NKCA shows, southeastern gun shows. Co-author of definitive Case book.

Joe Seale, 11711 Buckingham Rd., Austin TX 78759. (512)258-3925 6:30–9:30PM CST. Old American pocketknives. Mail order and some shows. $3 and SASE for lists (3–4/year).

Tommy Shouse, 1231 Bunny Trail, Winston-Salem NC 27105. (919)924-4755. Old pocketknives, especially Case. SASE for list.

Jerry and Carolyn Skelton, Route 1, Alamo TN 38001. (901)656-2443. NKCA and Case club knives, old pocketknives. List: SASE with two stamps.

Smokey Mountain Knife Works, 204 Parkway, Sevierville TN 37863. (615)453-5871. Largest selection of current brands I have ever seen. Retail store and mail order.

Larry P. Thomas, Sr., 2705 Tennyson Avenue, Sinking Springs PA 19608. (215)678-6132. U.S. military knives. Mail order and some shows. Send want list or write for show plans.

Neil Wayne (The Razor Man), Old Chapel, Bridge Street, Belper, Derby DE5 1AZ, England. Tel. 44-77382-7910 or 44-77382-7020. Telex: 377106 ATT: DUSTFORD. Antique and rare Sheffield, London, and Continental knives, razors, and related cutlery items. Special emphasis on fancy fruit knives, quill knives, multiblades, figurals, medical knives, and cased sets. Mail and phone orders, and some shows. Free catalog (4–6/year). Free shipping on orders over $100. Usually displays at Louisville, Eugene, and San Jose knife shows, Pasadena antiques shows.

Many other knife dealers can be found at knife shows, gun shows, and swap-meets around the country. Also check the knife magazines for dealer ads.

If you are a dealer in collectible knives and would like to be listed in the next edition of this book, write to Bernard Levine, Box 40336, San Francisco CA 94140. Send your latest list and your show schedule.